GERMAN NAVAL GUNS
1939-1945

GERMAN NAVAL GUNS 1939-1945

MIROSŁAW SKWIOT

Seaforth PUBLISHING

Frontispiece: Forward superstructure of *Deutschland* photographed during her stay in Hamburg, in late May and early June 1934. This photo shows the turret roofs which had been painted dark grey earlier in the year. 'A' turret also has a large white circle on the top – an identification sign for the Luftwaffe. *(S Breyer collection)*

First published in Poland by AJ-Press, Gdańsk as *Niemiecka Artyleria Okrętowa, Volumes I-IV*, 2004-2010.

This edition first published in Great Britain in 2011 by
Seaforth Publishing
An imprint of Pen & Sword Books Ltd
47 Church Street, Barnsley
S Yorkshire S70 2AS

www.seaforthpublishing.com
Email info@seaforthpublishing.com

British Library Cataloguing in Publication Data
A CIP data record for this book is available from the British Library

ISBN 978 1 84832 080 2

Typeset and designed by Stephen Dent
Printed and bound in China by Imago

Contents

Introduction 7

Heavy Guns

2. The 40cm SK C/34 Guns of Battleships 'H', 'J', 'K', 'L', 'M' and 'N' 19
3. The 38cm SK C/34 Guns of the Battleships *Bismarck* and *Tirpitz* 20
4. The 28cm SK C/28 Guns of the *Deutschland* class 'Pocket Battleships' 32
5. The 28cm SK C/34 Guns of the *Scharnhorst* class Battleships 73

Medium Guns

6. The 20.3cm SK C/34 Guns of the *Admiral Hipper* class Heavy Cruisers 85
7. The 15cm SK L/45 Guns of the Cruiser *Emden* 96
8. The 15cm SK C/25 Gun:
   Aboard 'K' class Cruisers 103
   Aboard the Cruiser *Leipzig* 115
   Aboard the Cruiser *Nürnberg* 117
9. The 15cm SK C/28 Gun:
   Aboard *Deutschland* class 'Pocket Battleships' 119
   Aboard *Scharnhorst* class Battleships 126
   Aboard the Aircraft Carrier *Graf Zeppelin* 129
   In DrhL C/34 Turrets aboard *Scharnhorst* and *Gneisenau* 130
   In DrhL C/34 Turrets aboard *Bismarck* and *Tirpitz* 133
10. The 15cm Tbts K C/26 gun aboard Destroyers 161
11. The 12.7cm SK C/34 Gun aboard Destroyers 175

105mm and 88mm Guns

12. Introduction 185
13. 105mm Guns:
    Single Mounts 189
    Twin Mounts 205
14. 88mm Guns:
    The 8.8cm SK C/31 Gun 216
    The 8.8cm SK C/30 Gun in Single Pedestal Mounts 249
    The 8.8cm SK C/30 Gun in Twin Pedestal Mounts 258
    The 8.8cm SK L/45 Gun in MPL C/13 Single Pedestal Mounts 265

Light Anti-Aircraft Guns

15. Introduction 267
16. The 4cm Flak 28 Bofors Gun 269
17. 3.7cm Guns 305
18. 2cm U-Boat Turrets 344
19. 2cm Guns 347

Index 396

Left: Supplies and ammunition being loaded aboard the 'pocket battleship' *Deutschland* during her stay in Spanish waters. *(M Skwiot collection)*

Below, left: Stern of the battleship *Admiral Scheer* during her stay in Gotenhafen (occupied Polish Gdynia) in the autumn of 1939. *(A Jarski collection)*

Above: *Deutschland* photographed in the Deutsche Werke shipyard at Kiel during final fitting-out. *(M Skwiot collection)*

Left: 'B' turret of *Deutschland* with the coat of arms and nameplate – 'Hindenburg' – clearly visible. *(M Skwiot collection)*

1

INTRODUCTION

The development of German naval ordnance both before and during the Second World War is closely bound up with the terms of the Versailles Treaty of 1919. From the outset, most Germans regarded the peace treaty enforced upon them by the victorious Allies as unacceptable. Almost from the day after the treaty was signed, ways were found to circumvent it – the best example is the development of anti-aircraft artillery in other countries. Many foreign companies were more than eager to cooperate with Germany in research and development of these weapons, absorbing German expertise and know-how accumulated during long years of experimentation, but not actually producing such weapons for the Weimar Republic. The Germans were convinced that sooner or later the Treaty restrictions would be lifted one way or another, and modern artillery designs for both land and sea service would then be vital. Waiting for that day, and craving an opportunity to battle-test their new hardware, the Germans kept up the appearance of abiding by the Treaty in order to avoid political friction with the victorious powers, whilst secretly working feverishly in design bureaus and laboratories.

It was relatively easy to develop and even clandestinely manufacture light artillery, but heavy naval and coast-defence guns were quite another matter. The history of the dispute over the main armament for the *Deutschland* class 'pocket battleships' is a good example of what kind of hurdles they had to negotiate. In 1923, one of the initial designs called for 380mm guns as the main armament for the class. It was possible to design a capital ship with guns of that size because at that time the Allies had not set a permitted maximum calibre for such weapons. But then, suddenly, they changed their mind, and almost as an afterthought, forbade the manufacture of new guns over 305mm calibre. The Germans complied and in early 1925 305mm guns replaced the 380mm guns on the drawing boards. The 305mm guns were perfectly adequate for the time and Krupp's was able to design and manufacture them. But only up until early 1925, because in May that year French troops occupied the Ruhr Valley – ostensibly in retaliation for unpaid war reparations. As of May 1925 Krupp's were forbidden to produce more than one gun over 300mm in calibre per year! It would take almost a decade, therefore, to manufacture the guns for just one capital ship. The calibre had to be changed to 280mm – the only alternative was to replace the new weapons with four reserve coast-defence ones of inferior performance per ship. This would have crippled the ships from the outset and made them inferior to all foreign battleships. The situation would be even worse for Battleship 'D', for which no guns were available in reserve. Faced with this dilemma like this, the Germans were forced to postpone the calibre issue for Battleships 'D' and 'E' to a later date, while concentrating on smaller units, such as cruisers and torpedo-boats.

The 1933 naval budget provided 1.4 million Reichsmarks for designing the new 330mm naval guns, earmarked for Battleships 'D' and 'E'. The political situation was still unfavourable, and it was decided that a reduction to 305mm calibre would be a good idea. The Ordnance Bureau estimated that the

ERSATZ PREUSSEN

1:500

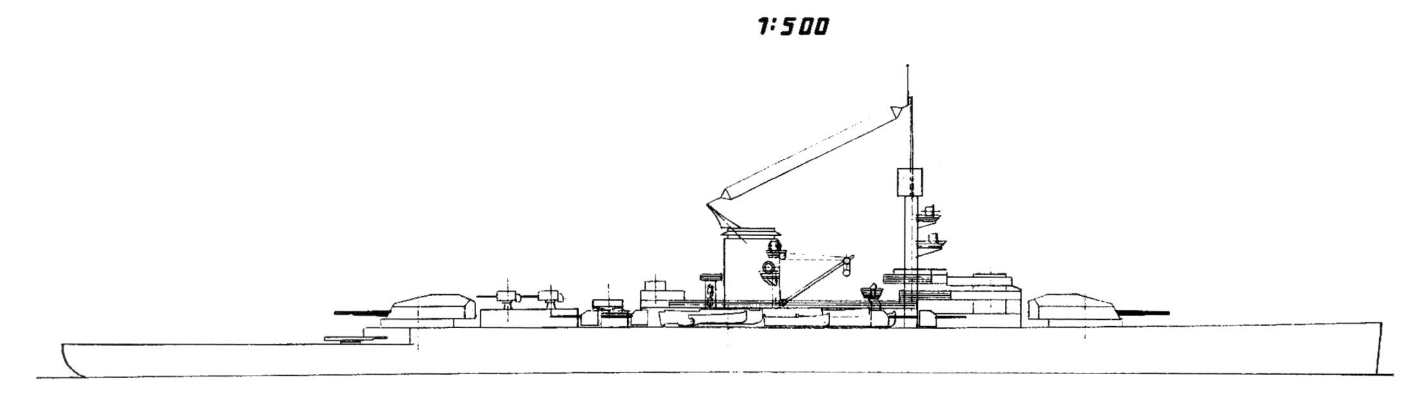

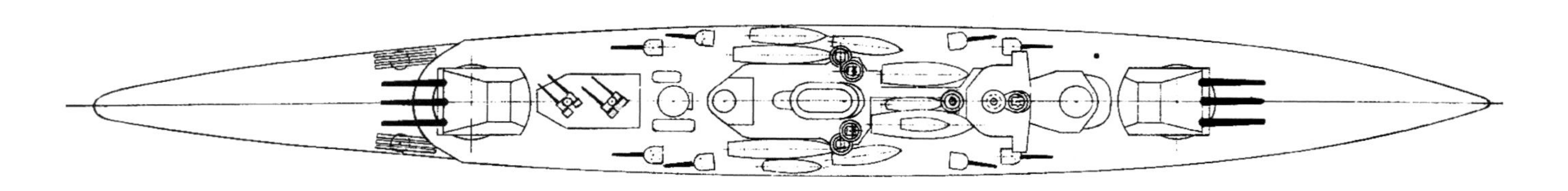

Below: Variant of the battleship Ersatz *Preussen* drawn to 1:500th scale, sent for approval to the Naval High Command. The resulting 'pocket battleship' *Deutschland* was built more or less according to these plans. *(CAW collection)*

Above: *Deutschland* during sea trials, on 18 and 19 January 1933, still without her after torpedo tubes. *(Photo Drüppel, A Jarski collection)*

Below: *Deutschland* in the Wilhelmshaven roadstead, preparing to man her rails. *(CAW collection)*

Above: Many drawbacks and faults discovered during the first years of *Deutschland*'s commission were rectified in later ships of her class, but the number and calibre of the guns remained unchanged. This photograph, taken on 5 July 1942 from (probably) *Admiral Hipper*, shows *Admiral Scheer* during the Convoy PQ17 operation. *(CAW collection)*

Below: *Admiral Graf Spee* by the A9 buoy in Kiel, in early May 1936. She had the same main armament as the *Deutschland*.
(Photo Klein, T Klimczyk collection)

Above: *Prinz Eugen* in Kiel after commissioning, during preparations for her redeployment to the Baltic. This photo shows the aerial recognition signs being painted on the roofs and top slopes of the main turrets. *(Photo Drüppel, A Jarski collection)*

Left: The ice-covered forward turrets of *Admiral Hipper* while in Norwegian waters. This photograph, retouched for propaganda purposes, shows the difficulties of operating in Arctic waters. Main turrets were able to function, but smaller guns were put out of action. *(A Jarski collection)*

Above: 'A' turret of *Deutschland* photographed from the mainmast during the Spanish Civil War, as shown by the aircraft recognition symbol painted on the top of the turret. *(M Skwiot collection)*

Above: Interior of a 28cm turret. *(M Skwiot collection)*

Right: Medium and light anti-aircraft guns aboard the battleship *Tirpitz*, photographed during her sea trials in the Baltic in 1941. *(M Skwiot collection)*

Above and right: Damaged 15cm turrets aboard *Deutschland*, photographed undergoing temporary repairs on her return voyage to Germany. *(M Skwiot collection)*

Above: Changes in gun calibre could only be contemplated in the subsequent battleship design, Battleships 'D' and 'E'. But despite these initial plans, these were eventually also armed with 280mm guns. Here, *Scharnhorst* is off Wilhelmshaven in the summer of 1939, just after the reconstruction of her bows had been completed. *(M Skwiot collection)*

Below: *Scharnhorst*'s sister-ship *Gneisenau* also had 280mm guns. Here she is moored in the Heikendorf roadstead, Kiel, in the spring of 1939. *(Polish Naval Museum collection)*

Above: *Gneisenau* in the Hjelte fjord, outside Bergen. *(CAW collection)*

design time for a new turret would be about a year, with another three-and-a-half years to build a prototype ship. Should the programme be given the go-ahead, the construction of the 25,000-ton battleships armed with six 305mm guns could only have begun in late 1935 or early 1936 at the earliest. Taking into consideration that the first naval armaments treaty would expire in 1936, this would gain Germany one year in building time, if hull construction began in 1935. Contrary to what one might believe, after all the paperwork was done, all the 'I's dotted and 'T's crossed in the design, construction did not begin immediately. The issue of the calibre of the main armament came back with a vengeance. In March 1935, five design variants were prepared. The first three proposed a 34,000–37,000-ton ship armed with nine 305mm guns in triple turrets. However, it transpired that it would take eighteen months to design a turret of that type, which, combined with three-and-a-half years to build and fit-out the ship, meant that it would be five years between laying the ships down and commissioning them – i.e. the 1935 ships would not enter service until 1940. Another downside was the cost: nine 305mm guns would be the best armament scheme for a new ship at that time – but that would mean that the 11 million Reichsmarks already invested in the 280mm guns and their turrets would be wasted, and Germany at that time could not afford such a waste. As is now obvious, the choice of main battery calibre was not a decision to be taken lightly! Each option had its advantages, but at the same time some disadvantages as well, not least the considerable costs. In the end, the choice of calibre for the main battery of Battleships 'D' and 'E' became a compromise between the political and the economic situation of the Reich. It was decided to arm the new ships with three triple 280mm turrets – but with a proviso that 305mm guns would replace them should the situation change. As we all know, it did not.

In early 1935 a profound political change occurred in Germany. On 16 March, Reich Chancellor Adolf Hitler unilaterally abrogated the military terms of the Treaty of Versailles. Quick diplomatic action brought about the naval treaty with Great Britain on 13 June, according to which Germany was allowed to built up to 35 per cent of the Royal Navy's displacement of ship of all types – including submarines. In terms of battleships that meant a limit of 184,000 tons. The three *Deutschland* class 'pocket battleships' already built and the two ships of the *Scharnhorst* class under construction totalled only 83,000 tons, leaving 101,000 tons for new construction, including the recently-designed Battleships 'F' (Ersatz *Hannover*) and 'G' (Ersatz *Schleswig-Holstein*). The Washington Treaty of 1922 and the First London Naval Disarmament Conference had set the upper limit for this type of ship at 35,000 tons, and Germany intended to build their new battleships up to this limit, using all their remaining battleship displacement allowance. At first the Naval General Staff insisted that Battleship 'F' kept to the 35,000-ton limit. The planned armament was a main battery of eight 330mm guns and a secondary battery of a dozen 150mm guns in triple turrets, as well as sixteen 105mm guns.

At the same time a dispute was raging between the supporters of the 330mm and 350mm guns as to which would make up the main battery of the future

Above: Increased-calibre main armament was finally introduced in the *Bismarck*-class battleships, armed with the 380mm gun. *Bismarck* in the Kieler Bay between 18 and 23 September 1940. *(Photo Schäffer, M Skwiot collection)*

Below: *Bismarck*, assisted by tugboats, negotiating the Elbe River on 15 September 1940. This voyage started badly – at 1658hrs the mighty battleship collided with the tug *Atlantik*. *(Photo Urbahns, M Skwiot collection)*

Above: *Bismarck* during fleet exercises in the Baltic sea. This is one of the rare photos showing the roof and slopes of 'A' turret painted a different colour – probably maroon – from the other turrets. *(M Skwiot collection)*

battleships. Increasing the calibre from 330mm to 350mm would bring about a corresponding increase in displacement. Experiments proved that the performance of the 350mm gun was indeed superior, but the 330mm gun was perfectly adequate for penetrating the armour of foreign battleships. Range, time of flight, angle of elevation etc., were also comparable for both guns, but the 350mm suffered from a short barrel life, a mere 180 rounds.

After 16 March 1935, a third option was introduced: 380mm guns. It was now obvious that the Versailles Treaty would no longer restrict the development of the German Navy. On the other hand, mounting 380mm guns would increase the ships' displacement by 1,500 tons, resulting in a final figure somewhere between 42,000 and 42,500 tons. With a displacement like this, German naval bases would be too shallow for them. The Design Bureau therefore beat a hasty retreat to the 350mm concept. A battleship with 350mm guns would displace 41,000 tons with a draught of 9.25m, which would allow the ship to fit into the largest lock at Wilhelmshaven. The same ship with 380mm guns would draw 9.40m, which would have precluded negotiating the locks. On the other hand, the reduction in calibre would be to the detriment of performance against the French *Dunkerque* class battleships. Another suggestion was to mount the 380mm guns in triple turrets, but this also rejected because the ship's draught would again have been too great.

On 1 April 1935 Grand Admiral Raeder consulted the main department heads on the final choice of calibre, and decided that the future battleship would sport eight 350mm guns in four twin turrets. The first unit of the new class, Battleship 'F', was ordered from the Blohm & Voss shipyard in Hamburg on 1 April 1936. The general consensus was that the recent conferences and the treaties yet to be signed between the main sea powers would soon allow the rearmament of the new battleships with 380mm guns. The design was handed over to the Ordnance Bureau so that whenever the opportunity arose, the re-arming could be effected on six months' notice. On 9 May 1935, Raeder officially approved the 380mm guns for the new battleships.

German foreign policy at that time required that the scheduled flag-hoisting date of 1 December 1939 be brought forward to 1 October that year instead. Both ships were to be launched by mid-March 1939, with the ships to be completed in the spring of 1940. The fitting-out was to be finalised within the next year and a half. The crucial factor for finishing the ships on schedule was the delivery of machinery. All contracts signed to date had a scheduled delivery date of December 1939.

In spring 1940 Hitler demanded that the construction of Battleship 'F' be speeded up and wanted to have her commissioned by 1 December that year. The same date was demanded for Battleship 'G', whose scheduled commissioning date of 1 January 1941 had recently been put back to 1 April 1941. After many further conferences the head of the Design Bureau stated that both ships were very much alike and so the crucial factor in their delivery date was the

Above: *Tirpitz*, the second *Bismarck*-class battleship, returning to Kieler Bay during a lull in sea trials, early July 1941. *(M Skwiot collection)*

delivery of the engine-room machinery. Unexpectedly though, delivery of the main turrets became a problem. The head of the Ordnance Bureau reported that the sub-contractors had postponed their delivery dates by four to five months, threatening the whole schedule.

The prototype 380mm turret was ready by December 1938. The head of the Ordnance Bureau reported that the turret construction could be speeded up, if the unit price was increased. Increasing the budget would allow Krupp's to hire more workers and change to three shifts a day, which would save the Battleship 'F' and 'G' schedules by speeding-up the delivery of the turrets. Eventually, both the shipyards and all the component manufacturers drew on their last hidden reserves and both ships were finished ahead of the shortened schedule, and within the planned budget.

Left: The roof and top slopes of *Tirpitz*'s 'C' turret being painted over during the Baltenflotte battle group operations in the Baltic in September 1941. Note the *Admiral Scheer* in the background. *(CAW collection)*

Opposite: *Tirpitz*, seen from *Admiral Hipper*, returning from manoeuvres held between 20 and 29 August 1942. The light cruiser *Köln*, following the battleship, also participated. *(CAW collection)*

Above: In the foreground, *Tirpitz*'s 'B' turret with a quadruple 2cm Flakvierling 38 anti-aircraft gun fitted on top of it. *(S Breyer collection)*

German naval artillery nomenclature after 1918

All German naval guns were named according to a standard system. It consisted of several parts, the first of which was the calibre measurement, traditionally given in centimetres, which distinguished the German system from all other metric ones. After the calibre came the class designation: all deck-mounted naval guns produced after the end of the First World War were classified as 'ship's cannon' (Schiffskanone), abbreviated to SK. Older guns were still designated 'quick-firing gun' (Schnelladekanone), with the same abbreviation. In the older system, the class was followed by the nominal length of the barrel measured in calibres: e.g. the 28cm SK L/50 meant a 280mm naval gun with a barrel 50 calibres long (50 x 280mm = 14m). During the inter-war period, the barrel length was replaced by the model designation, based on the year of introduction. The Navy was the only one of the armed services to retain the old imperial designation system with the letter C and the year of introduction after the slash. Note that this derived from the word 'Konstruktionsjahr' or 'design year', but written as 'Construktionsjahr', which was an old grammatical form used prior to the reform of German grammar in the late 1890s. And so the 28cm SK C/34 means the 'Gun, naval, 280mm, Model 1934'. The same nomenclature was used throughout this period, and not only for guns but also for all other related equipment – turrets, propellant charges and projectiles.

Some types of German naval artillery had additional designators, indicating their specific purpose. So, guns mounted on submarines were additionally designated 'Ubts' (U-bootskanone), e.g. the 8.8cm SK C/35 Ubts L C/35 – 'Cannon, naval, 88mm, Model 1935, on mount, single, submarines, Model 1935'. A similar designation – 'Tbts K' (Torpedobootskanone) – was used for the torpedo-boat guns. Some naval anti-aircraft artillery was designated 'Flak' (Fliegerabwehrkanone), just like their land-service counterparts, but this was often omitted from ships' guns.

New guns introduced into the Kriegsmarine inventory from mid-1940 on were designated according to a slightly differing system. It still began with the calibre in centimetres, but after that 'SK' was replaced by 'KM' (Kanone Marine), for naval gun or 'Flak M' (Flak Marine), for naval anti-aircraft gun, e.g. 10.5cm KM 44 – the 'Gun, naval, 105mm, Model 1944'. The coastal defence guns, sometimes used on board naval vessels, retained their land-service designations (mostly Flak), while experimental weapons sometimes combat-tested aboard ships were designated 'Gerät' (Device) with their appropriate number, e.g. Gerät 055.

Gun mounts were classified in two groups: turrets ('DrhL', Drehscheiben-lafette) and pedestal mounts ('MPL', Mittelpivot-lafette). The latter, used for the most part with lighter guns, sometimes had an additional designation attesting to their special application: 'Tbts L' (Torpedoboots-lafette – torpedo-boat mount), 'Ubts L' (U-boots-lafette – submarine mount), 'Flak L' (Fliegerabwehr-lafette – anti-aircraft mount), or dual-purpose 'ML' (Marine-lafette – naval mount).[1]

1 Most coastal artillery guns were installed on *Bettungschiess-gerüst* (BSG) mounts.

2

THE 40cm SK C/34 GUNS

OF BATTLESHIPS 'H', 'J', 'K', 'L', 'M' AND 'N'

The 40cm SK C/34 gun was intended to arm the proposed Battleships 'H', 'J', 'K', 'L', 'M' and 'N', construction of which was approved by Hitler on 18 January 1939. There were only four shipyards in Germany capable of building ships of that size: the Blohm & Voss yard in Hamburg, which was to build Battleships 'H' and 'M'; Deschimag in Bremen which received 'J' and 'N'; Kriegsmarine Werft in Wilhelmshaven which was to build 'L'; and Deutsche Werk in Kiel which was to build 'K'.

The early stages of the design work on these ships had seen serious controversy, with Hitler insisting on their being armed with the heaviest guns that German industry could produce. The monster 406mm gun had been in development since 1934, but despite all the time and money that had been spent, only one prototype gun for test firing had been completed, because of the higher priority given to the development of other weapons, such as the 380mm guns of the *Bismarck* class and the 280mm guns of the *Scharnhorst* class.

When construction of Battleship 'H' was due to begin at Blohm & Voss, Krupp's had completed seven guns (six for the ship and one spare). In 1940, Hitler had ordered that the 406mm gun project be designated high priority, but these guns would never be mounted on this or any other ship. Construction of Battleship 'H' was suspended in September 1939 and abandoned on 25 November 1941, the assembled materials being diverted to other ships under construction in the shipyard. The contracts for the ship were finally cancelled on 29 and 31 August 1942. The seven existing guns were assigned to the coastal artillery. Four were sent to Norway, to be emplaced near Narvik, but one was lost in transit. The Norwegians retained this battery in service after the war until 1954, and the guns were not finally stricken from the reserve inventory until 1968. The other three guns were fitted on railway mounts. Two were originally intended to be deployed on the Hel Peninsula in Poland, covering the approaches to Danzig, but in the end all three were sent to France in the autumn of 1941 and positioned around Blanc Nez to interdict Allied shipping in the English Channel.

Above: The hull of the uncompleted Battleship 'H' was built at the Blohm & Voss shipyard in Hamburg. *(Blohm & Voss)*

Krupp's built three versions of the SK C/34 gun. The first was the prototype, used for development and test-firing. The second was the three railway guns, which used the standard naval barrels and chambers. The third was the four coastal artillery guns, which were fitted with extended chambers to take larger propellant charges, to give greater range.

40cm SK C/34 naval gun

Calibre:	406.4mm
Weight of gun:	159,900kg
Overall length:	21,130mm
Length bore:	19,750mm
Length chamber:	2,481mm
Volume chamber:	420dm^3
Length rifling:	17,066mm
Grooves:	90 (4.8mm x 7.98mm)
Weight projectile:	1,030kg
Propellant charge:	262kg of RP C/38 (22/11)
Muzzle velocity:	810m/s
Working pressure:	3,200kg/cm^2
Approximate service life:	180-210 effective rounds
Maximum range:	36,400m at 30°

Left: Guns for Battleship 'H' were handed over to the coastal artillery and mounted in Battery Lindemann in France. *(S Breyer collection)*

3

THE 38cm SK C/34 GUNS

OF THE BATTLESHIPS *BISMARCK* AND *TIRPITZ*

The design of this gun was based on the 38cm SK C/13 of the First World War. The old design was thoroughly revised, and following the necessary field tests and trials, the new gun was approved for series production as the 38cm SK C/34. Although it was the same calibre as the guns that had armed the *Baden*-class battleships, the barrel was 6.03 calibres longer, at 48.43 calibres. This, together with other modifications to both the gun and its mounts, gave improved accuracy and greater range. The increased muzzle velocity imparted by the longer barrel improved the trajectory of the shell, making the gun perfectly suited to the type of naval engagement fought in the North Sea. Elevation was limited to 30°, which was considered more than sufficient at the time the ships were designed. It was believed that future actions would take place at ranges where only 20° of elevation would be required, although an extra 10° was allowed for to accommodate the rolling of the ship in the stormy North Atlantic.

Below: Fitting-out of the after compartments on *Bismarck*, 1938. The third armoured bulkhead in the foreground, with the barbettes for 'C' and 'D' turrets behind it. *(Blohm & Voss via Jörg Schmiedeskamp)*

38cm SK C/34 gun

Calibre:	380mm
Weight of gun:	111,000kg
Overall length:	19,630mm
Length bore:	18,405mm
Length chamber:	2,230mm
Volume chamber:	319dm^3
Length rifling:	15,982mm
Grooves:	90 (4.5mm x 7.76mm)
Weight projectile:	800kg
Propellant charge:	212kg of RP C/38 (17/7)
Muzzle velocity:	820mps
Working pressure:	3,200kg/cm^2
Approximate service life:	250 effective rounds
Maximum range:	35,550m at 30°

Range and ballistic data for 800kg projectiles

Range	Elevation	Angle of descent	Flight time	Velocity
5,000m	2.2°	2.4°	6.5 sec	727mps
10,000m	4.9°	5.8°	13.9 sec	641mps
15,000m	8.1°	10.4°	22.3 sec	568mps
20,000m	12.1°	16.4°	32.0 sec	511mps
25,000m	16.8°	23.8°	43.0 sec	473mps
30,000m	22.4°	31.9°	55.5 sec	457mps
35,000m	29.1°	40.3°	69.9 sec	462mps

The guns of Battleships 'F' and 'G' (as *Bismarck* and *Tirpitz* were originally designated) were mounted in four twin turrets, a layout which gave a more efficient broadside. The guns, their mounts and the turrets were all designed and built by Krupp's. After consultations with the Kriegsmarine and once the details of the project had been approved, Krupp's designer decided to build the turrets with the armour plates bolted on to the framework.

The gun

The Krupp 38cm SK C/34 had a vertical sliding breech block. The main propellant charge was contained in a 420mm-diameter brass case – larger than the diameter of the projectile – and, once removed from the ammunition hoist, it was chambered by a single stroke of the hydraulic rammer. The complete firing cycle – chambering the shell and charges, firing and ejecting the empty case – took eighteen seconds.

The Drehscheiben-lafette C/34 (DrhL C/34) turret

The main turrets of German capital ships were – with a few exceptions – hydraulically trained, the system being powered by electrically-driven pumps. The complete loading procedure was governed by the Siemens-designed remote power control (RPC) apparatus, based on a tacho-generator/thyratron operating the four main valves, which was fitted to all turrets with guns of 203mm calibre and above. However, its performance was considered far from satisfactory, control being non-linear and depending on acceleration and on the pressure-drop in the accumulator, and attempts to improve it were largely unsuccessful. A new system designed by Askania and fitted in the

Above: The battleship *Bayern*, whose main armament was the starting-point for that of *Bismarck* and *Tirpitz*. *(A Jarski collection)*

Above: Forward turrets of the *Bismarck* during final fitting-out in the spring of 1940. Note that the armoured rangefinder covers on 'A' turret are still empty. *(Blohm & Voss via Jörg Schmiedeskamp)*

Below: *Bismarck* steaming along the River Elbe, towards the Kiel Canal, on 15 September 1940. Note that 'A' turret still has its 10m optical rangefinder, which was later removed. *(S Breyer collection)*

Above: *Bismarck*'s 'A' and 'B' turrets during final fitting-out in the spring of 1940. *(Blohm & Voss via Jörg Schmiedeskamp)*

Admiral Hipper class cruisers gave better results.

Each turret had six working levels – (a) the gun platform with the main turret; (b) the training platform; (c) the machinery platform; (d) the intermediate level; (e) the magazine platform; and (f) the shell room platform – although the superfiring 'B' and 'C' turrets had an extra intermediate level. Each gun had its own independent optical sight, mounted on the respective sides of the turret. Mounted at the rear of the turret were electric fans for the rapid evacuation of smoke and fumes, and in the floor were two ejection ports, covered by flaps, for spent propellant cases.

DrhL C/34 turret

Revolving weight:	1,064 tons
Ball track diameter:	8,750mm
Barbette internal diameter:	10,000mm
Distance between gun axes:	3,750mm
Recoil distance:	1,050mm
Maximum elevating speed:	6°/sec
Maximum training speed:	5.4°/sec
Turret 'A' and 'B' arcs of fire:	215° – 0° – 145°
Turret 'C' and 'D' arcs of fire:	35° – 180° – 325°
Firing cycle (minimum):	1 shot every 26 sec. at +4° elevation
Turret armour:	Face 360mm; side 220mm; rear 320mm; front and rear slopes 180mm; side slopes 150mm; flat part of roof 130mm

The barbettes

The barbettes consisted of two conical cylinders, superimposed one upon the other. The lower cylinder, constructed of 220mm-thick KC n/A steel, reached from the armoured deck to the main deck level. The upper cylinder was thicker, at 320mm. However, the US Navy Technical Mission in Europe Report No 224-45 gives different thicknesses, the lower cylinder at only 221mm but the upper one thicker at 342.9mm.

The detailed drawings of 'A' and 'D' barbettes, dated 16 November 1936 (drawing S No 38, Turret A and D, 1/10th scale) show that the barbettes were connected to the armoured deck by steel formers. The upper cylinder was similarly connected to the main deck. The sets of drawings that survive for the forward and after barbettes of Battleship 'F', though very incomplete, show that their layout and that of the adjacent compartments was much the same. There were armoured access doors at the armoured deck (Panzerdeck) level for barbettes 'A' and 'D' and at

Right: The ventilation ducts placed on the port side of the barbettes were similarly redesigned. This is the left side of 'B' turret barbette during final fitting-out, in the summer of 1940. *(S Breyer collection)*

Left: 'B' turret barbette aboard *Bismarck* – note the ventilation ducts in the foreground. In the floor of turret there is an ejection port for spent cases with a two-part cover. Note the escape hatch, with its separate cover. *(S Breyer collection)*

battery deck (Batteriendeck) level, on the opposite side, for the superfiring 'B' and 'C' barbettes.

Below the armoured deck was the internal structure supporting the revolving platform of the turret mounting. The internal diameters were chosen so that they did not interfere with the revolving and operation of the working levels of the turret, and therefore they differed at different levels. Projectiles from the shell rooms at the foot of the turrets were moved up to the guns on hoists. The revolving weights of the turrets (including the turret bearing ring and the gun mountings but excluding ammunition and hoists) was 1,082 tons for 'A' and 'D' turrets and 1,097 tons for 'B' and 'C' turrets.

Below: 38cm gun cradle aboard *Bismarck*. *(M Skwiot collection)*

Left: Starboard bows of the *Bismarck*, during final fitting-out at the Blohm & Voss shipyard in the summer of 1940. This photo shows the ventilation ducts on the right side of 'B' turret barbette. These were frequently swamped by waves during sea trials, so it was decided to redesign them, by lengthening the air inlets and turning them to face astern. *(S Breyer collection)*

Right: 'A' and 'B' turrets of *Tirpitz*. Faults detected in the early phases of the *Bismarck*'s commission were immediately rectified on her sister-ship. The large ventilation ducts on *Tirpitz*'s 'B' barbette were replaced with much smaller ones while she was still on the slipway. *(S Breyer collection)*

Right: *Tirpitz* in the Baltic Sea, September 1941. 'A' turret has already had its 10m rangefinder removed – note the armoured plate covering the objective ports. *(S Breyer collection)*

Below: 'C' and 'D' turrets of *Bismarck* during the commissioning ceremony on 24 August 1940. As can be seen in this photo, the ship was still far from being battle-ready: the after main fire director and the 105mm anti-aircraft guns are yet to be fitted. *(S Breyer collection)*

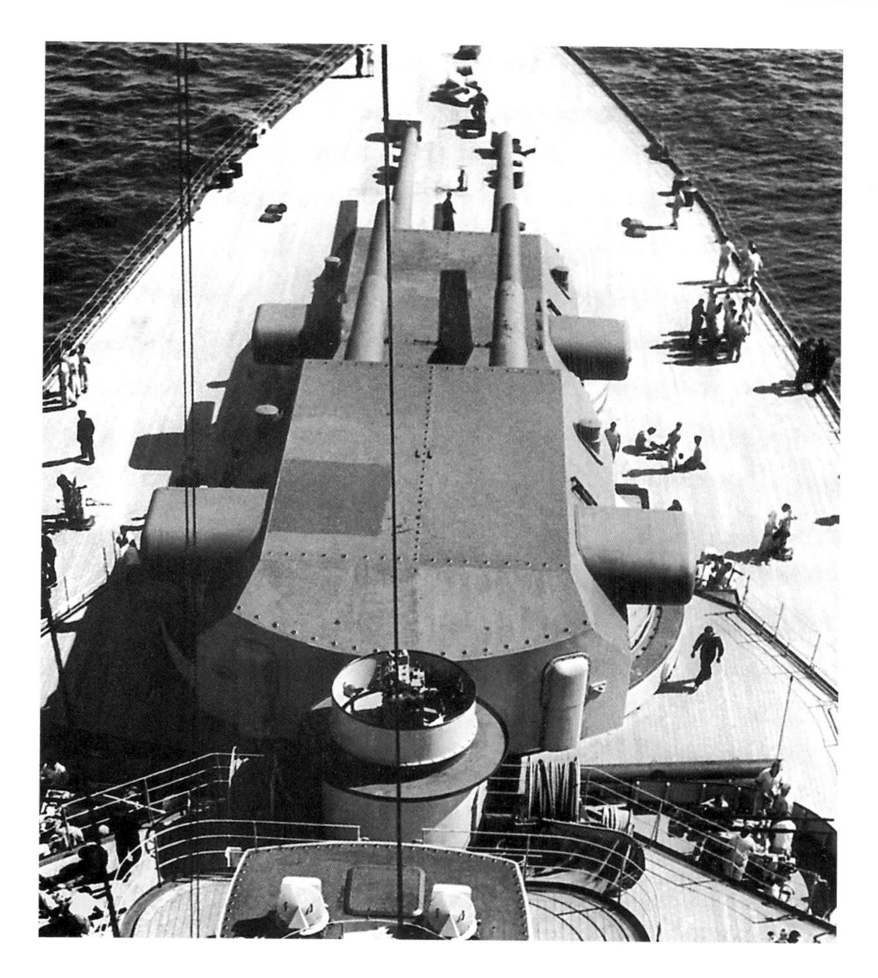

Left: *Tirpitz*'s stern as seen from the mainmast platform. The EM II rangefinder mounted on the after fire control tower is in the foreground, with 'C' and 'D' turrets behind it. 'B' and 'C' barbettes aboard *Tirpitz*, the ones reaching above than the main deck, were peculiar in having lockers fitted to their sides. This photo was taken in June 1941, during a break in sea trials in the Baltic. *(M Skwiot collection)*

Ammunition

According to German sources, all 380mm shells could be used both in the guns of the existing ships and of those yet to be built. They were manufactured by Krupp's, the main supplier of all German artillery ammunition over 150mm calibre.

380mm shells

(a) Armour-piercing shell L/4.5, weight 800kg, length 1,672mm, Bdz 38 base fused.
(b) High-explosive shell L/4.5, weight 800kg, ength 1,710mm, Bdz 38 base fused.
(c) High-explosive shell L/4.6, weight 800kg, length 1,748mm, Kz 27 nose fused.

380mm charges

Two types with RP C/38 propellant:
(a) Main charge (in brass case) – 182.5kg
(b) Fore charge (in silk bag) – 99.5kg

Right: The guns of *Tirpitz*'s 'B' turret being pulled through after gunnery practice. *(M Skwiot collection)*

Below: The forward superstructure and 'B' turret of *Tirpitz*, Baltic Sea, late September 1941. *(M Skwiot collection)*

Above: *Tirpitz*'s first main battery firing trials did not take place until the latter part of September 1941, owing to the late delivery of her fire-control equipment. *(S Breyer collection)*

Above: During *Tirpitz*'s stay at the Deutsche Werke shipyard in September 1941, the after fire control tower was finally topped with a 10m rangefinder and the FuMO 23 gunnery radar aerial. It was only then that the battleship was able to start the second series of main armament exercises, including the calibration of the after director and the synchronisation of 'C' and 'D' turrets with the rest of the fire-control system. *(CAW collection)*

Right: After turrets of the *Tirpitz* as seen from the roof of the after director. Note the port quadruple 20mm Flakvierling 38 anti-aircraft gun, with the elevated barrels of 'C' and 'D' turrets in the background. This photograph was taken during her trials in the Baltic in June 1941. *(CAW collection)*

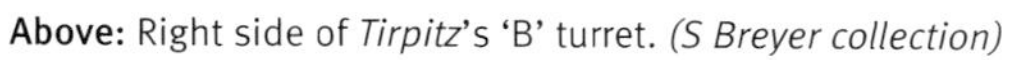

Above: Right side of *Tirpitz*'s 'B' turret. *(S Breyer collection)*

Above: *Tirpitz* anchored in the Kaafjord, winter of 1942. 'A' and 'B' turrets in the foreground. *(S Breyer collection)*

Below: The crew of the *Tirpitz* were kept busy during her long stays in the Norwegian fjords by constantly changing and improving her camouflage against aerial reconnaissance. This photograph shows her appearance being changed again, with tarpaulins and locally-felled fir and spruce branches.

Right: The tarpaulin spread between the barrels of 'D' turret, as well as hiding the ship's silhouette, here also served as an awning for the 'stage' this dance troupe is performing for the crew on. *(NHC collection)*

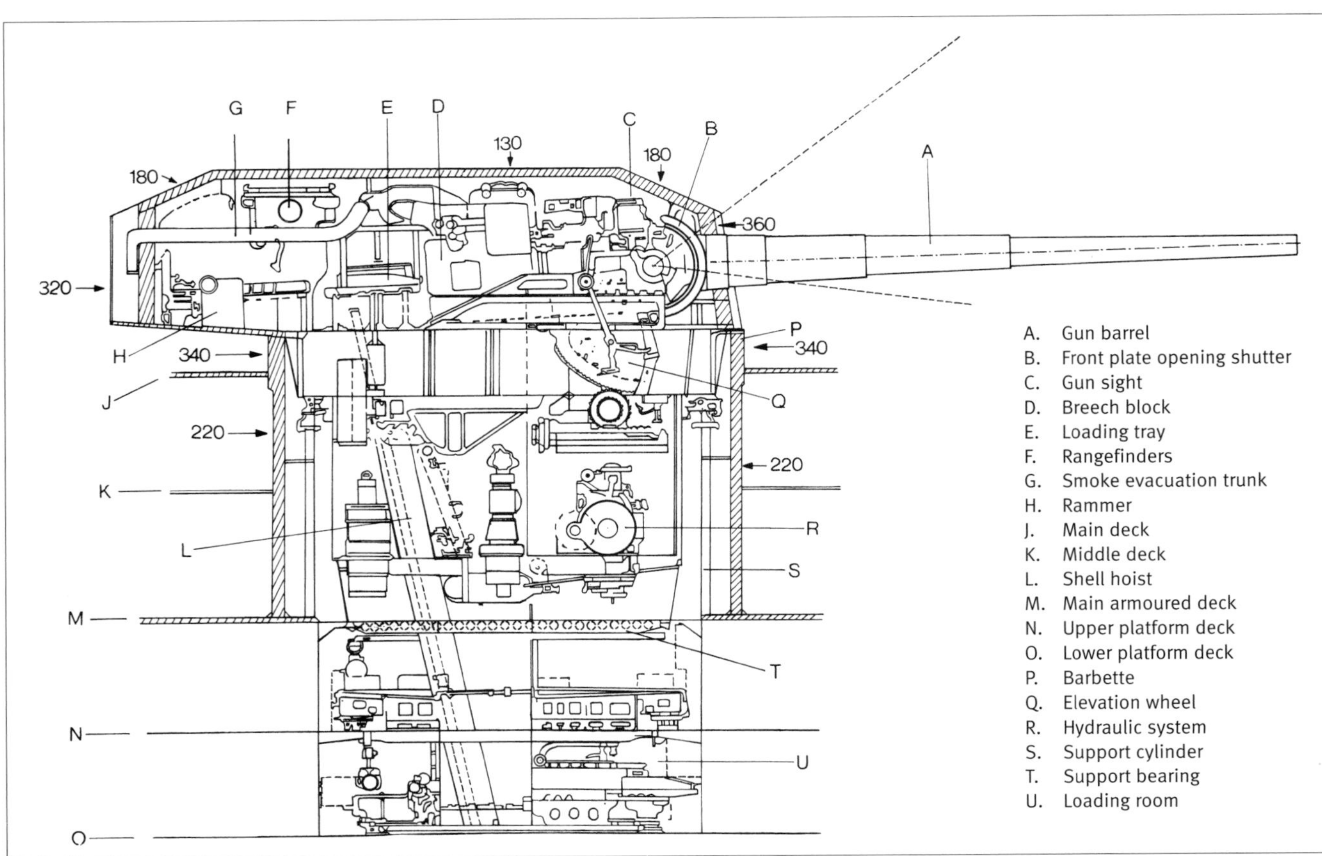

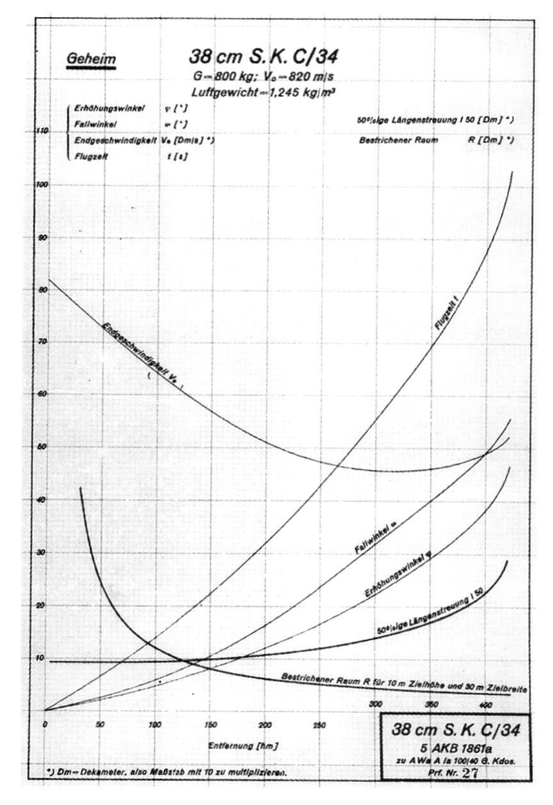

Above: Ballistic curves for the 38cm SK C/34 gun. *(J Rico collection)*

Right: The crew of the *Tirpitz* drawn upon the forecastle after the Norwegian deployment in 1942. Note the canvas blast bags on 'B' turret's guns. *(NHC collection)*

Cross-sections of the 380mm turret

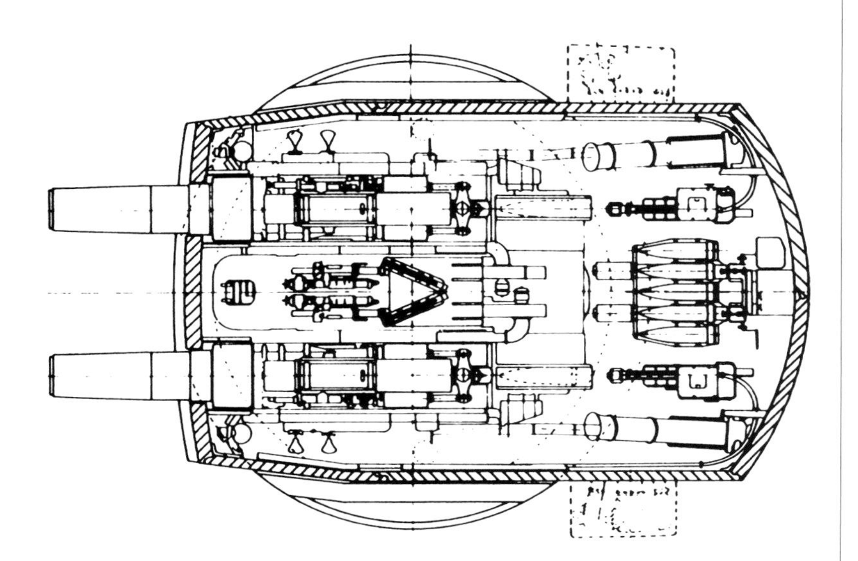

Depression/elevation:
–5.5° to +30°

Horizontal field of fire:
– 'A' and 'D' turrets: 290°
– 'B' and 'C' turrets: 270°

Bismarck and *Tirpitz*'s ammunition stores

The shell rooms and magazines were grouped around the barbettes with the armoured citadel, in compartments III, IV, V, VI VII, XV, XVI, XVII, XVIII and XIX, thus minimising the distance between them and the ammunition hoists. The propellant charge magazines were at the upper platform deck (oberes Platformdeck) level, while the shell rooms were immediately below them at intermediate platform deck (mittleres Platformdeck) level. Nearby there was a compartment housing the cooling system for the magazines and shell rooms. The ammunition stores were designed to hold a total of approximately 1,000 rounds – 125 per gun.

Turret designations and names

In all Kriegsmarine warships, the main turrets were designated by alphabetical letter-flag codenames: the foremost turret was thus always 'Anton', the forward superfiring turret 'Bruno', the after superfiring turret 'Caesar' and the aftermost turret 'Dora'. This system had been retained from the Kaiser's navy and indeed is still in use aboard German warships today. However, the pre-war Kriegsmarine had also given individual names to their ships' turrets, usually accompanied by a coat of arms of some kind, fitted to the front or side of the turret. It is therefore likely that the turrets of Battleships 'F' and 'G' were originally intended to receive such names, but before they could be assigned war broke out and the practice was abol-

Above and left: *Tirpitz* on her speed trials in the Baltic, early 1941. *(S Breyer collection)*

Right: *Tirpitz* in May 1941, during her first gunnery practice in Kiel Bay. *(S Breyer collection)*

Bezeichnung u. Lage d. Munitionskammern 4				Geschosse 38cm				Zündungen/Zink Kstf.		Kasten f.			
Blatt Nr.	Leckraum zeichen	Deck	Spant	Psgr. L/4,4	Spgr. L/4,5 Bdz (m Hb)	Spgr L/4,6 KZ		BdZ 38	KZ 27	kl u. gr Zdl 98 u. Zdl 08m Zdl A		lg Zdl 08 m Zdl B	
								zu 10 Stck		zu 40 Stck			
38cm Granatkammer:													
2	XIX 7a29	M.Plfd.	196,9-202,7 m	12	21	21		4	3			2	
				12	21	21		4	3			2	
4	XVIII 7a30	" "	182,3-188,186 m	56	50	50		12	5			4	
				56	50	50		12	5			4	
6	XVIII 7a29	" "	178,7-182,3 m	24	24	32		6	4			2	
				24	24	32		6	4			2	
9	XVI 7a3	" "	169,986-178,7 Stb	18	18			4				1	
				18	18			4				1	
10	XVI 7a4	" "	169,986-178,7 Bb	18	18			4				1	
				18	18			4				1	
12	XV 7a29	" "	166,4-169,986 m	31	31	56		6	6			4	
				31	31	56		6	6			4	
45	VII 7a29	" "	68,714-72,3 m	28	28	52		5	5			3	
				28	28	52		5	5			3	
48	VI 7a3	" "	60-68,714 Stb	18	18			4				1	
				18	18			4				1	
49	VI 7a4	" "	60-68,714 Bb	18	18			4				1	
				18	18			4				1	
51	V 7a30	" "	56,4-60 m	44	28	18		5	4			3	
				44	28	18		5	4			3	
53	V 7a29	" "	50,514-56,4 m	52	62	62		12	7			5	
				52	62	62		12	7			5	
59	III 7a30	" "	36-41,8 m	34	22	22		6	2			2	
				34	22	22		6	2			2	
Es sind an Bord zu geben:				353	338	373		72	36			29	
Staueinrichtg. sind vorh. für:				353	338	373		72	36			29	

Kriegssoll

Bezeichnung u. Lage d. Munitionskammern 5				Kartuschen 38cm					
Blatt Nr.	Leckraum zeichen	Deck	Spant	Hüls Kart. 34 -Gef Ldg-		Kartb 34	Vor-Kart. 34 -Gef Ldg-		Vor-Kartb 34
38cm Pulverkammer:									
1	XIX 8.29	O.Plfd.	196,9-202,7 m	52		52	46		46
				52		52	46		46
3	XVIII 8.30	" "	182,3-188,186 m	106		106	110		110
				106		106	110		110
5	XVIII 8.29	" "	178,7-182,3 m	92		92	78		78
				92		92	78		78
7	XVI 8.3	" "	169,986-178,7 Stb	31		31	52		52
				31		31	52		52
8	XVI 8.4	" "	169,986-178,7 Bb.	32		32	52		52
				32		32	52		52
11	XV 8.30	" "	166,4-169,986 m	130		130	106		106
				130		130	106		106
44	VII 8.29	" "	68,714-72,3 m	114		114	114		114
				114		114	114		114
46	VI 8.3	" "	60-68,714 Stb	44		44	46		46
				44		44	46		46
47	VI 8.4	" "	60-68,714 Bb	44		44	46		46
				44		44	46		46
50	V 8.30	" "	56,4-60 m	102		102	98		98
				102		102	98		98
52	V 8.29	" "	50,514-56,4 m	136		136	122		122
				136		136	122		122
54	IV 8.1	" "	41,8-50,514 Stb				29		29
							29		29
55	IV 8.2	" "	41,8-50,514 Bb	24		24			
				24		24			
56	IV 7a3	M.Plfd.	41,8-50,514 Stb	12		12	13		13
				12		12	13		13
57	IV 7a4	M.Plfd.	41,8-50,514 Bb	72		72	13		13
				72		72	13		13
58	III 8.30	O.Plfd.	36-41,8 m	74		74	76		76
				74		74	76		76
Es sind an Bord zu geben:				1005		1005	1001		1001
Staueinrichtg. sind vorh. für:				1005		1005	1001		1001

Kriegssoll.

Above: A detailed listing of the ammunition stores aboard the *Bismarck*. (*J Rico collection*)

ished. All turret names and coats of arms were ordered to be removed to prevent the enemy being able to identify individual ships. As both battleships were commissioned after the outbreak of war, their turrets never carried individual names – or at least I have never seen such names on any photographs of the ships during construction, fitting-out, sea trials or commissioning.

380mm guns in other ships and shore batteries

Apart from the *Bismarck* class, the planned Battlecruisers 'O', 'P' and 'Q', to be built by the Deutsche Werke and Germania Werft yards in Kiel and the Kriegsmarinewerft in Wilhelmshaven, were also to be armed with 380mm guns. Hitler and Admiral Raeder had approved the plans for these ships in 1940, but they were cancelled soon after.

Two of the 380mm turrets being built by Krupp's were ordered by the Soviet Union, under the military co-operation clauses of the Nazi-Soviet Pact signed in August 1939, along with the complete engineering specifications of the *Bismarck* class. But delivery of these orders was repeated delayed, under a variety of pretexts, as the Soviet Union was going to be the Germans' next target and the last thing they wanted to do was to give it vital technical know-how. The Soviets had ordered sixteen 380mm guns, to equip their planned battleships *Sevastopol* and *Kronstadt*.

Four guns were sent to France to arm the Atlantic Wall. Construction of the Siegfried Battery had begun as early as August 1940 on the d'Harinzelles plateau, 3km east of Cap Gris-Nez, was completed in November 1941 and the battery commissioned on 10 January 1942. The guns arming the battery were modified for shore service with a longer chamber to accommodate a larger propellant charge for greater range, along with other minor changes. Shortly afterwards, the battery was renamed 'Batterie Todt' in honour of the Armaments Minister Dr Fritz Todt who had been killed in a plane crash.

It was also intended to re-arm the *Gneisenau*, commissioned in 1938, with 380mm guns, and a preliminary design for this was approved by the Oberkommando der Marine (OKM) on 21 July 1942. This would not have been an easy job, as the ship would require extensive refitting to accommodate the heavier guns. For one thing, the electrical system would have to have been overhauled, necessitating the complete re-wiring of the ship. The hull structure supporting the barbettes would have to be strengthened – particularly for 'Bruno' turret – and the ammunition hoists, magazines and shell rooms would all have to be altered for the larger and heavier projectiles and charges. All this, plus the added weight of the new guns themselves, would have increased the ship's displacement and therefore her trim and stability coefficients, requiring a complete re-calibration of the fire-control system. The main concern, however, was how the refitted hull would stand up to the greater recoil and blast effects of the new guns.

Despite all this, the project was approved and Krupp's began work on the new turrets for the *Gneisenau*. Only one of these, with its armour plate, was completed by the time the project was cancelled, and it was shipped to Gotenhafen (now Gdynia) to serve as a shore battery.

4

THE 28cm SK C/28 GUNS

OF THE *DEUTSCHLAND* CLASS 'POCKET BATTLESHIPS'

Opposite, top: Cross-section and top view of a main turret of the *Deutschland* class 'pocket battleships'. *(S Breyer collection)*

Opposite, bottom: *Deutschland* fitting out at the Deutsche Werke shipyard in Kiel. 'B' turret in the foreground. *(CAW collection)*

Below: An armoured plate being fitted to the roof of 'A' turret of *Deutschland*. *(M Skwiot collection)*

When Admiral Behncke took command of the newly-created Reichsmarine on 23 March 1921, his most pressing priority was the replacement of the obsolete warships which were all that had been left to Germany under the terms of the Treaty of Versailles. This would be easier said than done, however, as the same treaty banned Germany from building ships over 10,000 tons, and it would be difficult to build a fast and powerful capital ship within this restricted displacement. After several years of discussions and the evolution of a series of designs, it was decided that Germany's new battleship would be armed with 280mm guns in triple turrets.

The design of the gun was based on that of the excellent 28cm SK L/50, which the battlecruisers *Moltke*, *Goeben* and *Seydlitz* had used to such great effect against Allied warships during the First World War. The new gun differed from its predecessor in barrel length, chamber capacity, weight of projectile, range and angle of elevation. For the first time in a German capital ship, the main battery was to be in two triple turrets, mounted fore and aft on the centreline.

The guns

The 28cm SK C/28 was built by Krupp's and was specifically designed for the DrhL C/28 turrets built for the three new battleships, later to be named *Deutschland*, *Admiral Scheer* and *Admiral Graf Spee*. The gun had the standard German vertical sliding breech block and fired a 189.5kg main charge in a 71kg brass case. The loading system enabled a round to be fired every 17 seconds.

28cm SK C/28 gun

Calibre:	283mm
Weight of gun:	48,200kg
Overall length:	14,815mm
Length bore:	13,905mm
Length chamber:	2,333mm
Volume chamber:	160dm^3
Length rifling:	11,411mm
Grooves:	80 (3.25mm x 6.72mm)
Weight projectile:	300kg
Propellant charge:	107kg of RP C/38 (16/7.2)
Muzzle velocity:	910mps
Working pressure:	3,200kg/cm^2
Approximate service life:	340 effective rounds
Maximum range:	36,470m at 40°

The DrhL C/28 turret

In order to keep the *Deutschland* class within the Treaty displacement limit while still ensuring a combat-effective ship, the main armament had to be fitted in triple turrets. Krupp's accepted this challenge as an opportunity to design a modern turret.

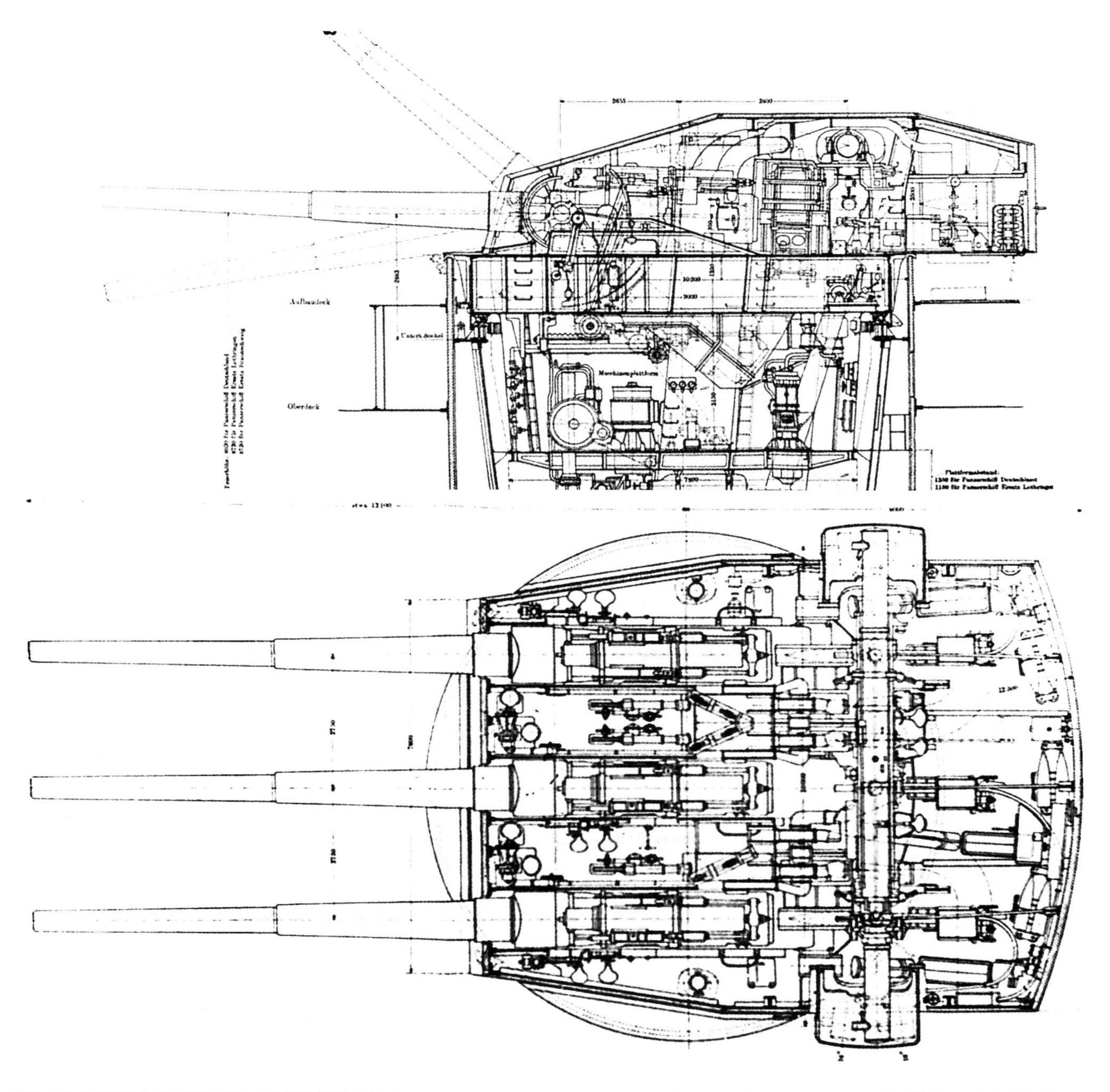
Aufbaudeck
Oberdeck

Range and ballistic data for 300kg projectiles

Range	Elevation	Angle of descent	Velocity
5,000m	1.9°	2.4°	752mps
10,000m	4.5°	6.0°	611mps
15,000m	8.0°	11.8°	493mps
20,000m	12.5°	21.4°	407mps
25,000m	18.6°	34.2°	360mps
30,000m	26.3°	46.4°	353mps
35,000m	36.4°	56.0°	380mps

Below: *Deutschland* moored at Wilhelmshaven several days before her commissioning ceremony. Note there is still no coat of arms on 'B' turret. *(A Jarski collection)*

Bottom: Both of *Deutschland*'s main turrets were given individual names and coats of arms. 'A' turret was christened 'Adolf Hitler' and carried a name plate as well as the NSDAP crest on the sides. *(T Klimczyk collection)*

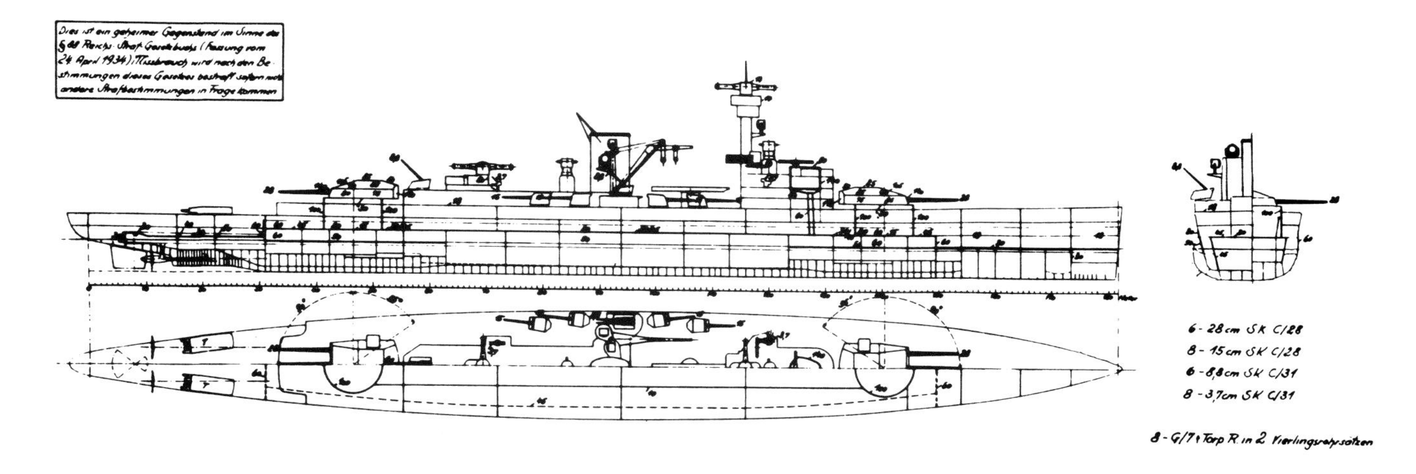

Name (Baubezeichnung)	Etatsjahr I. Rate	Bauwerft	Bauauftrag	Kiellegung	Stapellauf	Voraussichtliche Fertigstellung zu Probefahrten	Länge über Alles m	Länge in der C.W.L. m	Grösste Breite m	Konstr. Tiefe m	Deplacement etwa t	Maschinen Zahl der Wellen	Masch. Leistung Entwurf W.P.S.	Masch. Leistung Probef. W.P.S.	Geschwindigkeit Entwurf Kn.	Geschwindigkeit Probef. Kn.	Kessel	Brennmaterial bei C.W.L. t	Brennmaterial voll m³	Besatzung
Deutschland		Deutsche Werke Kiel		9.2.1929	19.5.1931	1.4.1933	186,00	181,70	20,64 in der C.W.L.	5,786	11900	2×4 Hauptölmotoren	54000	48390	26	28	2 Hilfskessel	1680	3200	781

Above: Diagram of *Deutschland*'s armour protection. *(S Breyer collection)*

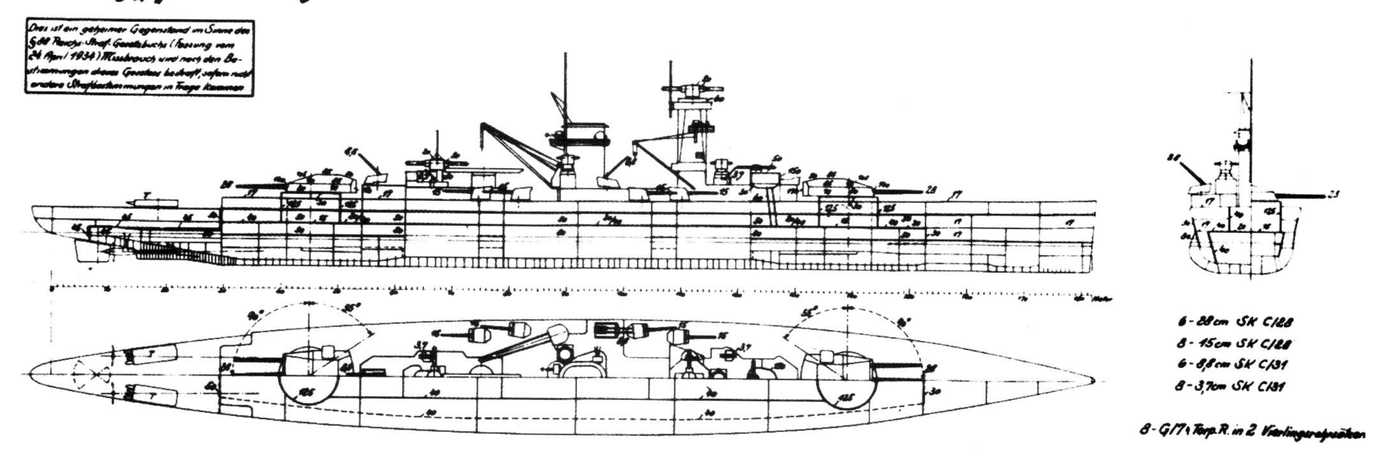

Name (Baubezeichnung)	Etatsjahr I. Rate	Bauwerft	Bauauftrag	Kiellegung	Stapellauf	Voraussichtliche Fertigstellung zu Probefahrten	Länge über Alles m	Länge in der C.W.L. m	Grösste Breite m	Konstr. Tiefe m	Deplacement etwa t	Maschinen Zahl der Wellen	Masch. Leistung Entwurf W.P.S.	Masch. Leistung Probef. W.P.S.	Geschwindigkeit Entwurf Kn.	Geschwindigkeit Probef. Kn.	Kessel	Brennmaterial bei C.W.L. t	Brennmaterial voll m³	Besatzung
Admiral Scheer		Mar. Werft		25.6.1931	1.4.1933	12.11.1934	186,00	181,70	20,64 in der C.W.L.	5,786	11960 12109	2×4 Hauptölmotoren	54000	52050	26	28,3	2 Hilfskessel	1680	2900	726

Above: Diagram of *Admiral Scheer*'s armour protection. *(S Breyer collection)*

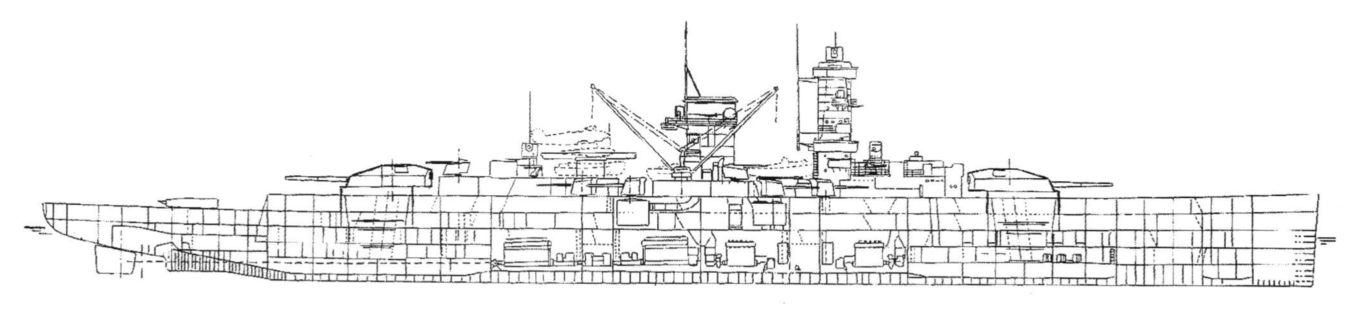

Above: Longitudinal section of *Admiral Graf Spee*. *(Drawn by S Breyer)*

Above: The crew of the *Deutschland* off duty during their first deployment to Spanish waters, between 26 July and 25 August 1936. On 31 July *Deutschland* was ordered to paint the national colours on top of the main turrets for better identification by friendly air forces. These were painted across the front top slopes. *(M Krzyżan collection)*

Left: *Deutschland*'s 'A' turret. The roof and top slopes were painted dark grey as an identification sign for the Luftwaffe. *(CAW collection)*

Opposite: *Deutschland*'s 'A' turret painted light grey. It was painted this colour in April 1934, during Hitler's visit. This photo shows her steaming across the Songe fjord. *(CAW collection)*

Above: *Deutschland* moored at the Gazelebrücke. Coffins with fallen sailors are laid at the foot of 'B' turret, awaiting transfer to the trucks waiting on the quay. This shot shows many details of 'B' turret, which bore the name 'Hindenburg' as well as the Hindenburg family's coat of arms on the sides. *(CAW collection)*

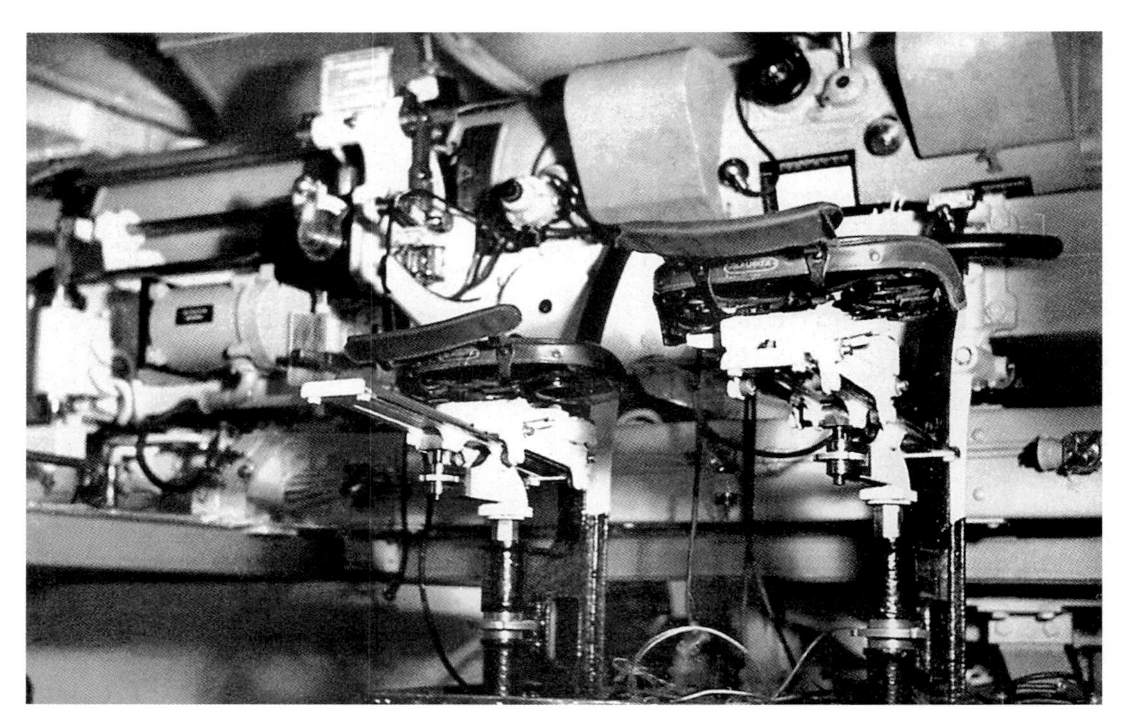

Right: Interior views of one of *Deutschland*'s main turrets. *(A Jarski collection)*

The turret had six working levels. The armoured gun platform was level with the upper rim of the barbette, superimposed on the training platform. Below that was the machinery platform, then the intermediate platform, the magazine platform and finally the shell room platform at the bottom of the turret.

The gun platform was protected by armour plates fixed to the internal framework of the turret and inside the gunhouse the guns themselves were separated from each other by splinter shields. The turret turntable was shaped to absorb the shock of recoil after firing. The arc of training was 290°, with the fields of fire of the individual turrets as follows:

'Anton' turret: 0° to 145° on each side
(215° – 0° – 145°),

'Bruno' turret: 0° to 145° on each side
(35° – 0° – 325°).

The DrhL C/28 turret

Revolving weight:	750 tons
Ball track diameter:	9,000mm
Barbette internal diameter:	10,200mm
Distance between gun axes:	2,750mm
Recoil distance:	1,200mm
Maximum elevating speed:	8°/sec
Maximum training speed:	7.2°/sec
Rangefinder:	10.5m optical
Turret armour:	Face 360mm; sides 200mm; upper slope 150mm

Above: *Deutschland*'s 'B' turret with awning eyelets visible on the forward slope. *(CAW collection)*

Below: The *Lützow* (ex-*Deutschland*) had bad luck during Operation 'Weserübung' (the invasion of Norway). She was hit several times by the shore batteries along the Oslofjord, when forcing entry into it, and then, at 0129hrs on 11 April 1940, she was torpedoed by the British submarine HMS *Spearfish*. It took two days to get the damaged battleship back to Kiel, and on 13 April she was towed into the Deutsche Werke dock. This photo shows the damaged stern of the ship before the water was pumped out. Note that 'B' turret in the background has had its nameplates etc, removed. *(Photo Drüppel, S Breyer collection)*

Right: *Admiral Scheer*'s conning tower during her modernisation at the Deutsche Werke in Kiel between late December 1936 and late February 1937. 'A' turret in the foreground. *(M Krzyżan collection)*

Left: Main battery practice aboard *Admiral Graf Spee*. *(CAW collection)*

Barbettes

Each barbette was a conical cylinder formed of ten segments of 125mm-thick rolled Wh/Na steel, each with an external diameter of 10,200mm, 5,560mm high and weighing about 17.5 tons, the entire barbette thus totalling 175 tons. The lower rim of the barbette was bolted to the armoured deck using steel formers, while the upper rim extended 500mm above the main deck.

Above: Heinkel He 60 floatplane 60 + D91 being launched from *Admiral Scheer*. This photo shows the crest on 'A' turret. *(Polish Navy Museum collection)*

Below: 'B' turret of *Admiral Scheer* after the outbreak of war. Prior to that it was christened Friedrich der Große and carried its namesake's coat of arms. After the war broke out, all such emblems were removed from Kriegsmarine ships. *(CAW collection)*

Above: *Admiral Scheer* had her conning tower modernised at the Kriegsmarinewerft in Wilhelmshaven during the winter of 1938/39. 'A' turret in the foreground. *(S Breyer collection)*

Ammunition

Propellant charges

Two types with RP C/38 propellant
(a) Main charge in brass case – 189.5kg
(b) Fore charge in silk bag – 36kg

280mm shells

(a) Armour-piercing shell L/3.7, weight 300kg, length 1,047mm.
(b) High-explosive shell L/4.2, weight 300kg, length 1,188mm, Bdz base fused.
(c) High-explosive shell L/4.2, weight 300kg, length 1,748mm, Kz nose fused.

Above: *Admiral Scheer* steaming out of Swinemünde (Świnoujście) along with *Deutschland* (in the background) for another patrol in Spanish waters in 1937. 'A' and 'B' turrets of both battleships have the German national colours painted on them. *(M Skwiot collection)*

Above and below: *Admiral Scheer* moored at the French Pier at the naval base at Gotenhafen (occupied Polish Gdynia). Note the 20mm anti-aircraft gun mounted on 'A' turret. *(A Jarski collection)*

Above: *Admiral Graf Spee* after the modernisation of her conning tower, which took place at the Deutsche Werke in Kiel, between March and May 1938. *(Photo Klein, T Klimczyk collection)*

Ammunition stores aboard the *Deutschland* class

The main battery magazines and shell rooms were placed around the barbette within the armoured citadel, in compartment XIII for 'Anton' turret and compartment IV for 'Bruno' turret. The magazines were at the lower platform deck level, inside the barbettes, while the shell rooms were immediately below the barbettes, just above the double bottom. These were capable of holding a maximum of 720 rounds, that is between 315 and 360 rounds per turret, the ammunition load varying according to specific operational requirements.

Above: Stern of the battleship *Admiral Scheer* during her stay in Gotenhafen (occupied Polish Gdynia) in the autumn of 1939. *(A Jarski collection)*

Turret names and markings

Before the outbreak of the Second World War, the turrets of the *Deutschland* class ships had carried individual names and their associated coats of arms. Aboard *Deutschland*, 'Anton' turret was named 'Hitler' and had the Nazi Party crest on the side, while 'Bruno' turret was 'Hindenburg' with that family's arms on it. (Some pre-war sources state that 'Anton' turret was called 'Anna'.) *Admiral Scheer*'s 'Anton' turret bore the name and arms of 'Lützow', and 'Bruno' turret those of 'Friedrich der Große'. The turrets of *Admiral Graf Spee* were named after two of Admiral Maximilian Graf von Spee's armoured cruisers sunk at the battle of the Falkland Islands in December 1914: 'Anton' turret was 'SMS *Scharnhorst*' and 'Bruno' 'SMS *Gneisenau*'.

While serving in the international neutrality patrols off Spain in 1936 and 1937, the main turrets of the *Deutschland* class ships were painted with recognition stripes in the three German national colours of black, white and red. On *Deutschland* and *Admiral Scheer*, these were painted across the front of the turrets, while on *Admiral Graf Spee* they were across the rear of the roof.

Right: 280mm shells and cased propellant charges temporarily stacked on the bank of a Norwegian fjord. *(CAW collection)*

Above: *Admiral Graf Spee* at sea. This photo was probably taken in mid-1937, just after she took part in the naval review at Spithead. *(T Klimczyk collection)*

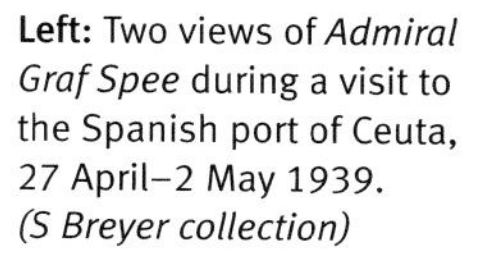

Left: Two views of *Admiral Graf Spee* during a visit to the Spanish port of Ceuta, 27 April–2 May 1939. *(S Breyer collection)*

Opposite: *Admiral Graf Spee* and *Deutschland* on 1 April 1939, during the fleet review at Wilhelmshaven. The main turrets were painted light grey at that time. *(CAW collection)*

Above: *Admiral Graf Spee* in Kiel Bay, late 1938 or early 1939. *(CAW collection)*

Right: Scuttling the *Admiral Graf Spee* was easier said than done – there were insufficient explosives left on board, so six torpedo warheads were used as improvised demolition charges. The ship then sank in 9m of water. *(Imperial War Museum)*

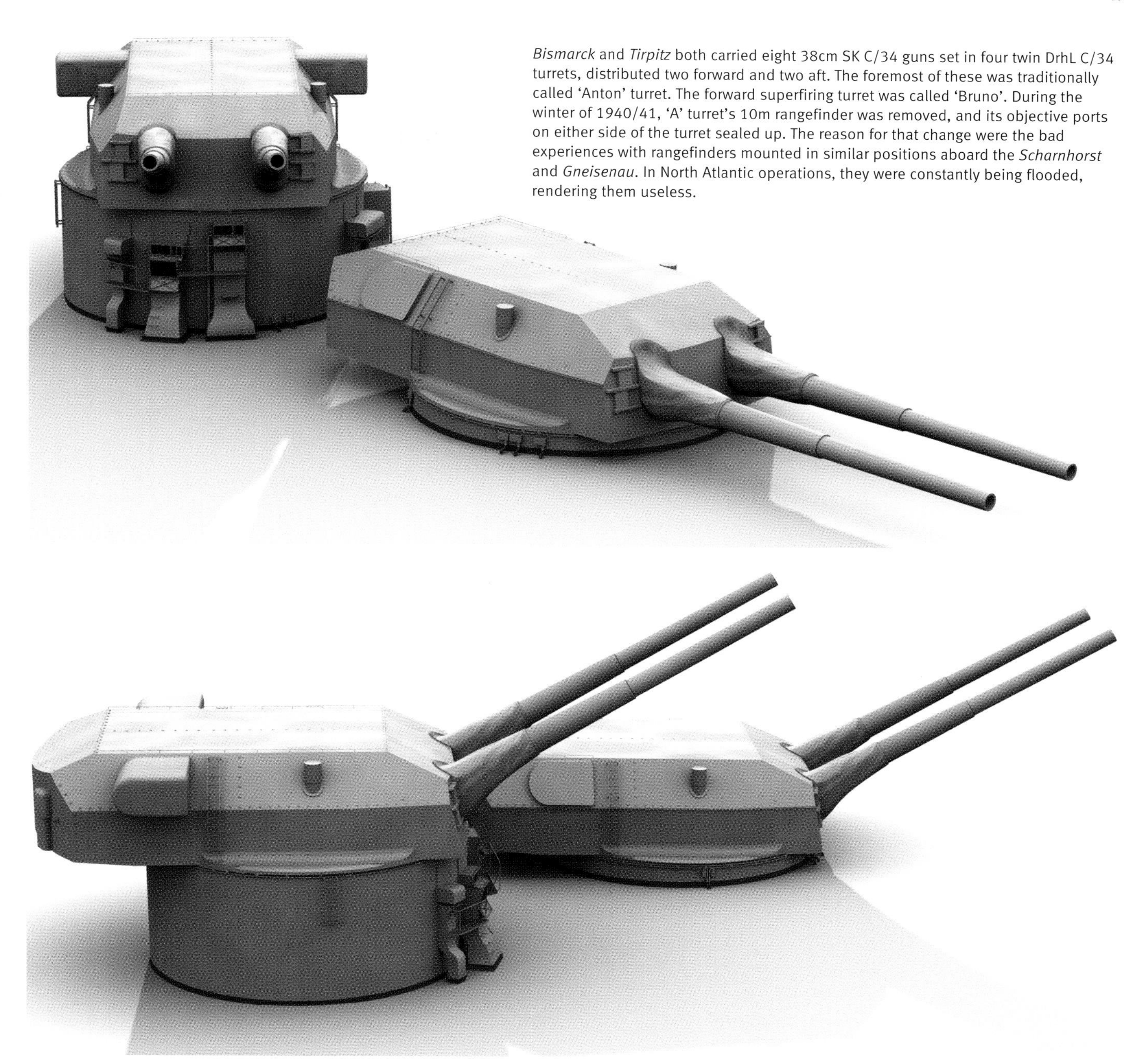

Bismarck and *Tirpitz* both carried eight 38cm SK C/34 guns set in four twin DrhL C/34 turrets, distributed two forward and two aft. The foremost of these was traditionally called 'Anton' turret. The forward superfiring turret was called 'Bruno'. During the winter of 1940/41, 'A' turret's 10m rangefinder was removed, and its objective ports on either side of the turret sealed up. The reason for that change were the bad experiences with rangefinders mounted in similar positions aboard the *Scharnhorst* and *Gneisenau*. In North Atlantic operations, they were constantly being flooded, rendering them useless.

Bismarck, the first of her class to be built, was also the first to be modernised. As the Kiel Canal and bays froze-up, the battleship spent the winter moored at Blohm & Voss. During this three-month forced break from her preparations for active service, the most important changes were introduced. The ventilation ducts on both sides of 'B' turret were set higher and fitted with splash covers to protect them against flooding. Also the after ventilator on the left side of 'B' barbette was turned to face astern.

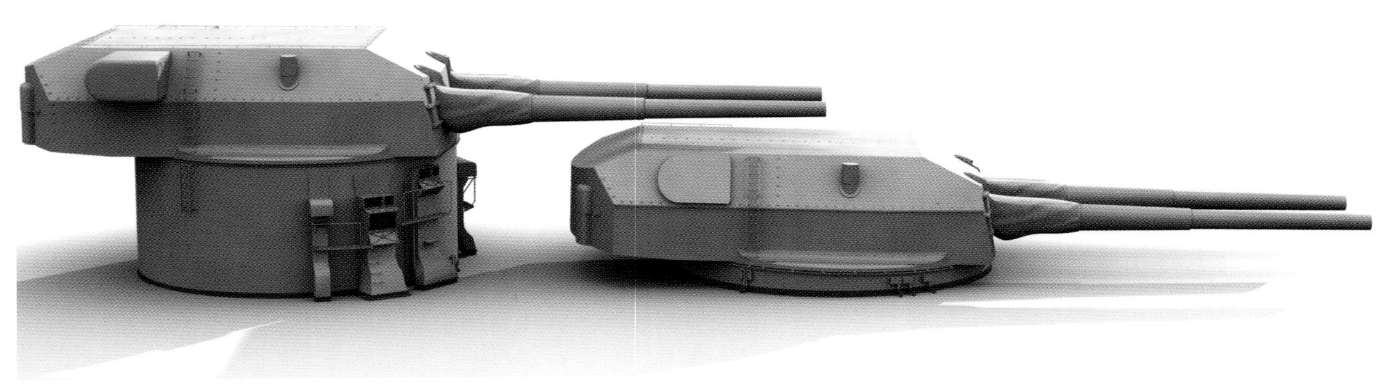

Right and left sides of *Bismarck*'s main turrets and barbettes after the January 1941 modernisation.

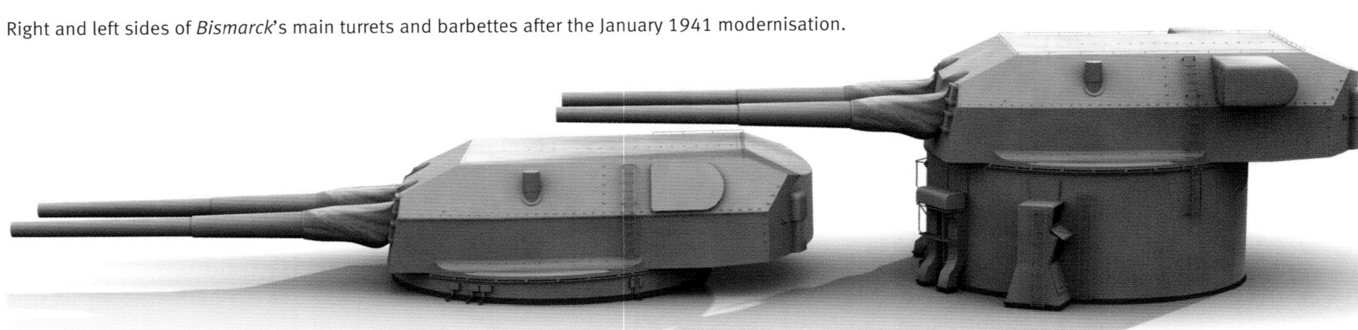

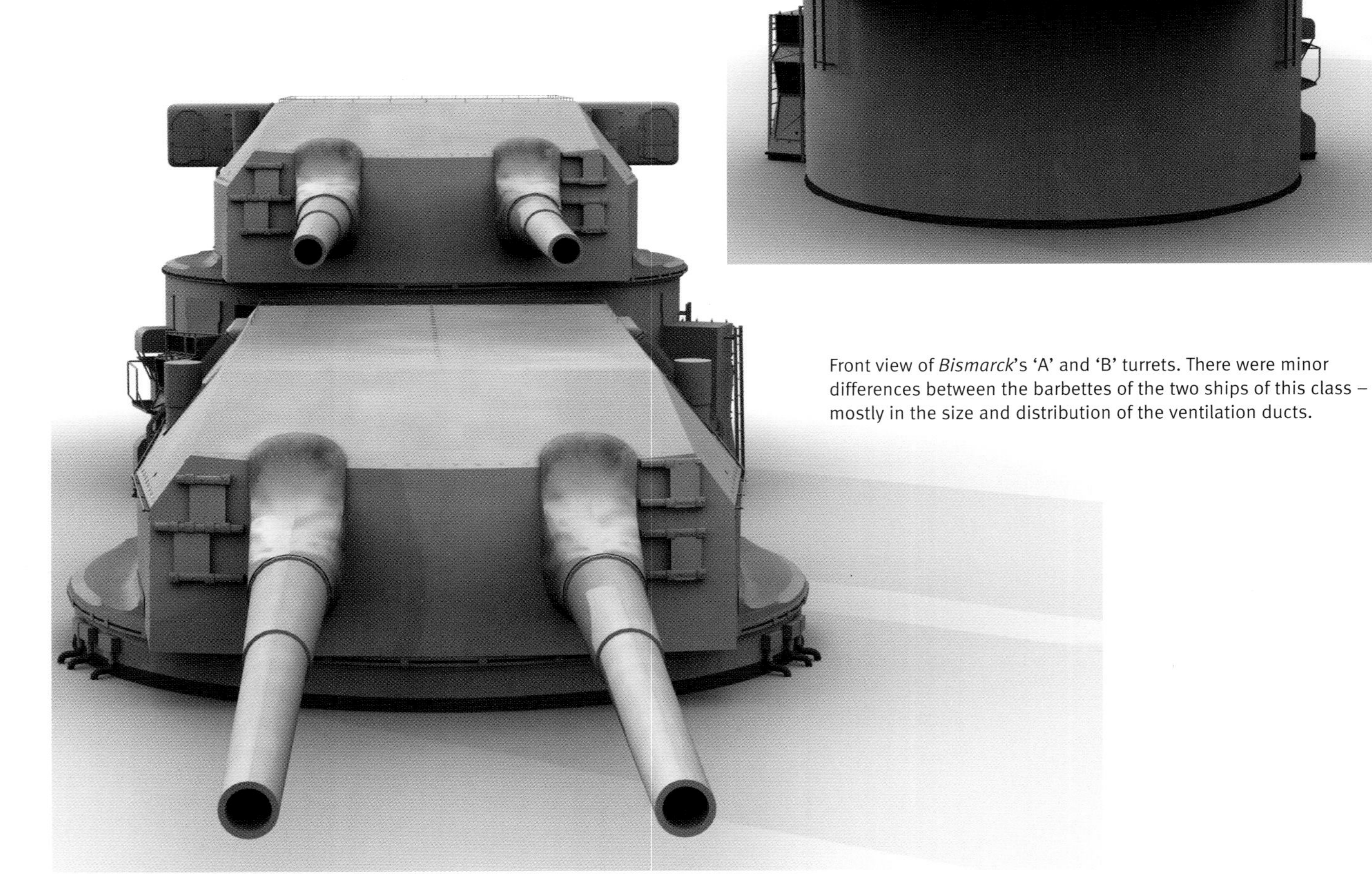

Rear view of *Bismarck*'s 'B' turret.

Front view of *Bismarck*'s 'A' and 'B' turrets. There were minor differences between the barbettes of the two ships of this class – mostly in the size and distribution of the ventilation ducts.

Bismarck's 'A' and 'B' turrets from above.

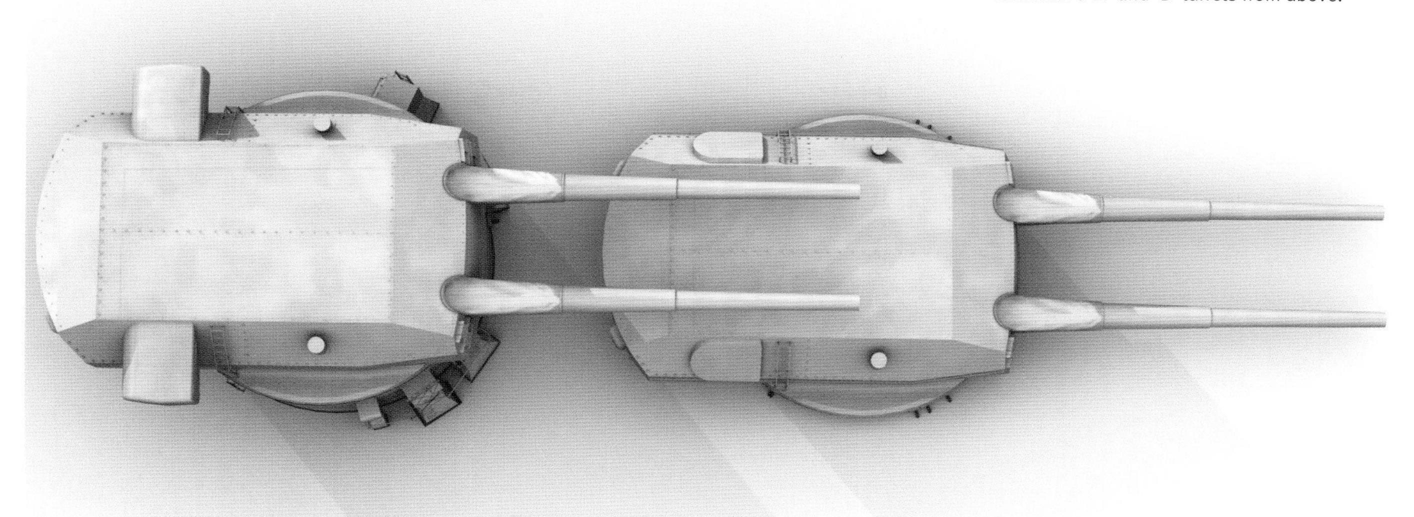

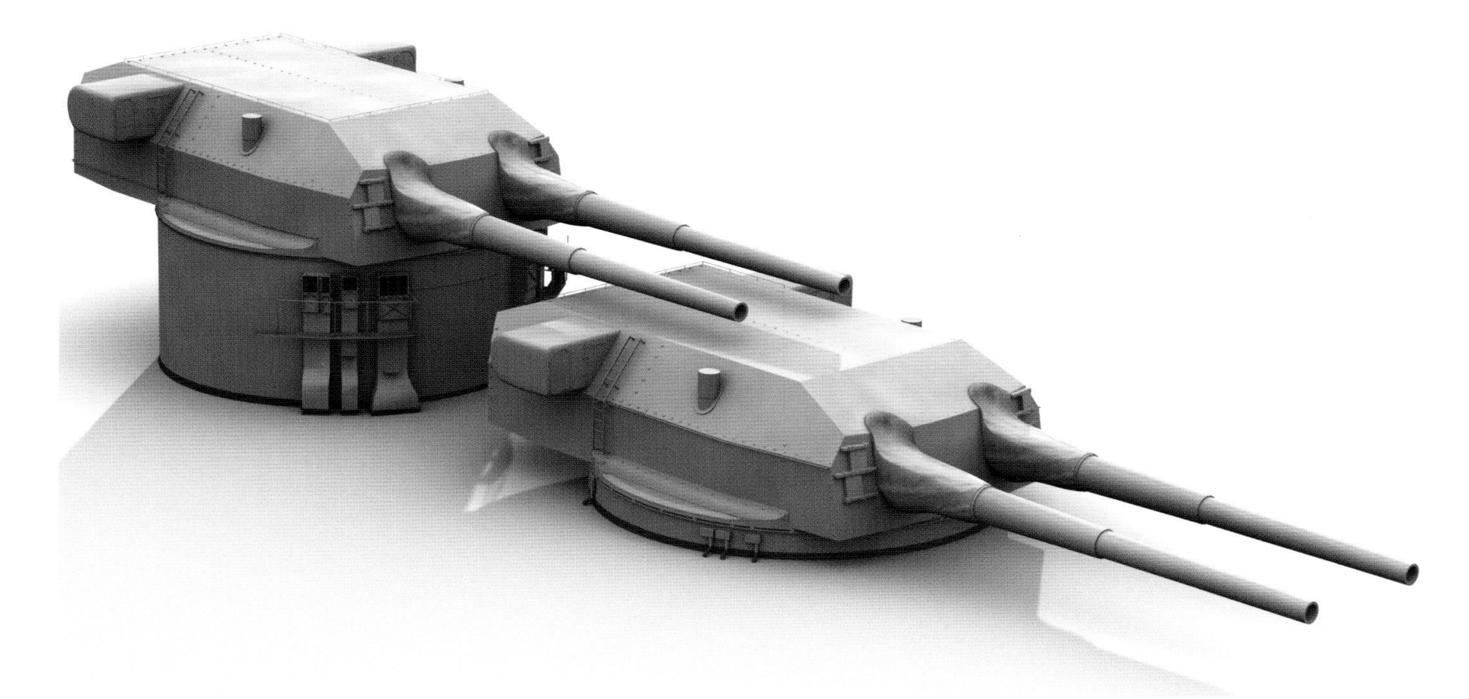

Bismarck's after turrets. Both 'C' and 'D' turrets retained their rangefinders.

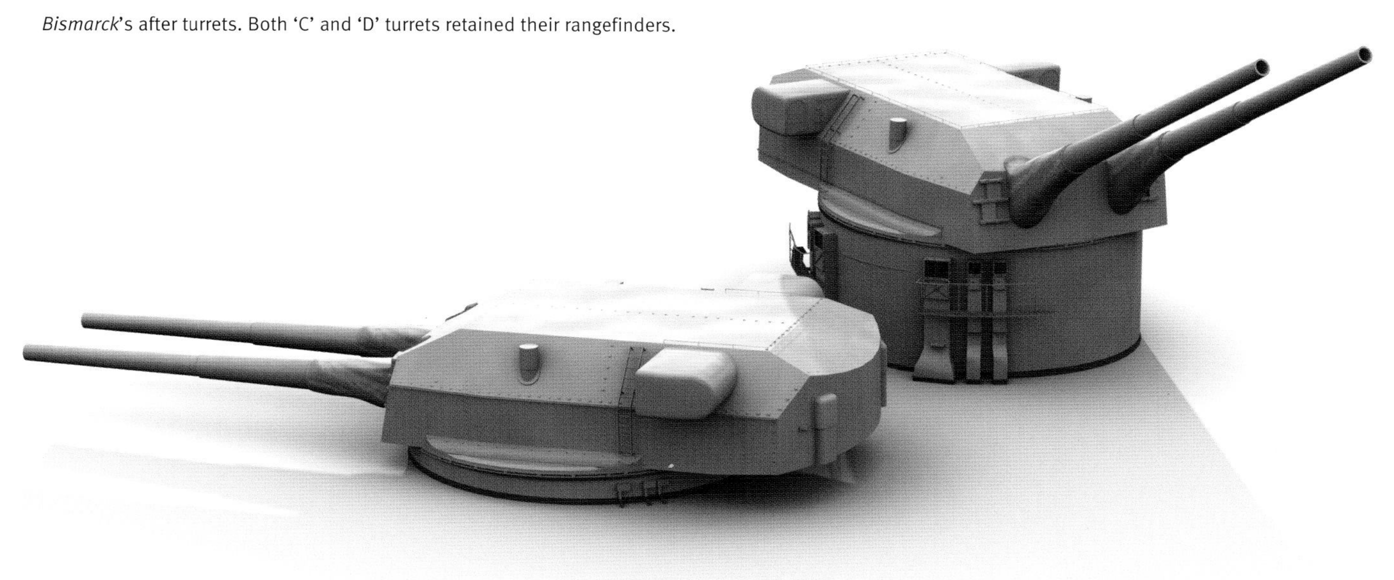

Electric fans were installed in the rear of the DrhL C/34 turret to rapidly extract fumes from the turret after firing. This drawing shows the two ducts leading these fumes out of the turret. There were two ports in the floor of the turret through which spent cases were ejected.

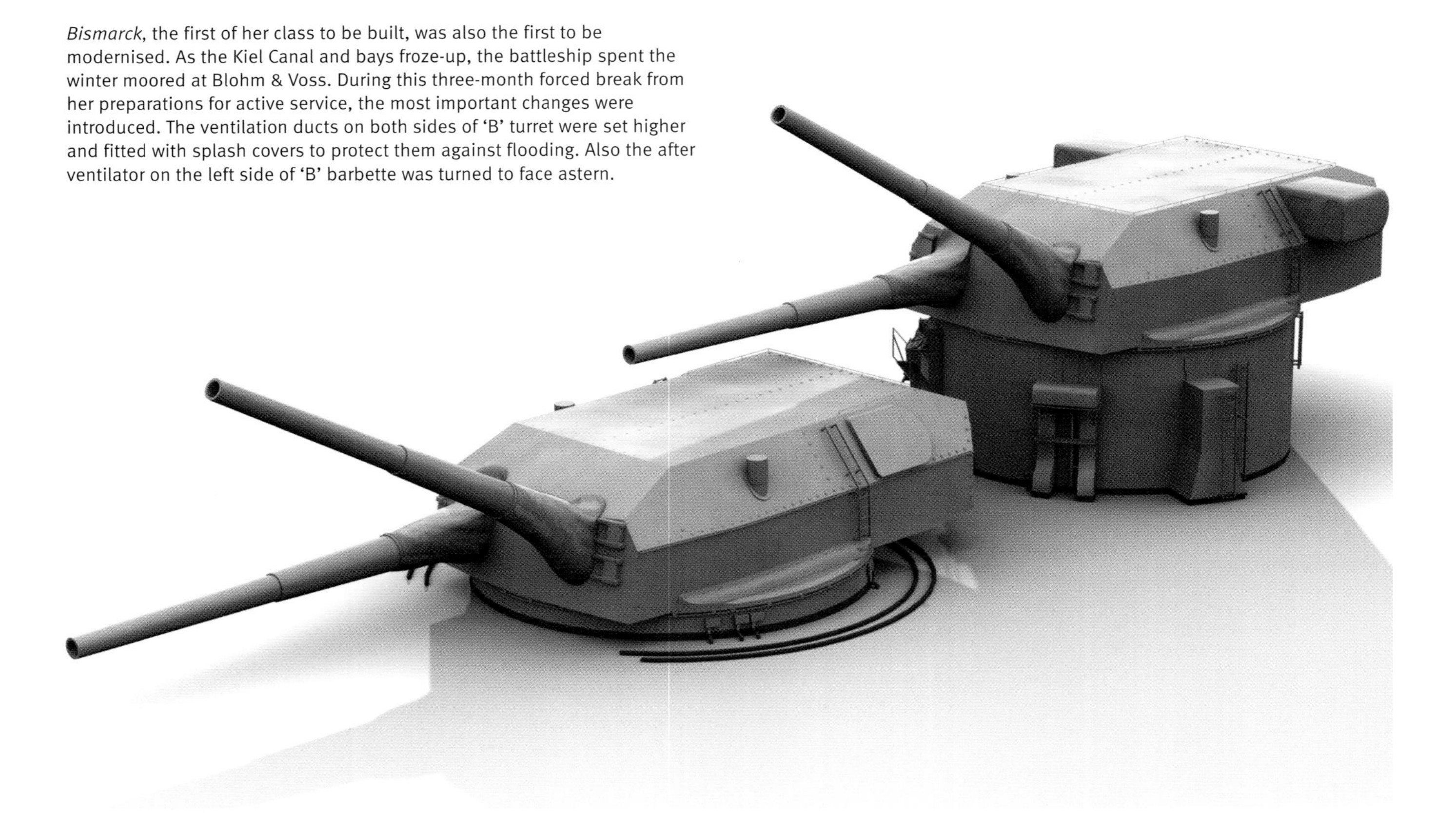

Bismarck, the first of her class to be built, was also the first to be modernised. As the Kiel Canal and bays froze-up, the battleship spent the winter moored at Blohm & Voss. During this three-month forced break from her preparations for active service, the most important changes were introduced. The ventilation ducts on both sides of 'B' turret were set higher and fitted with splash covers to protect them against flooding. Also the after ventilator on the left side of 'B' barbette was turned to face astern.

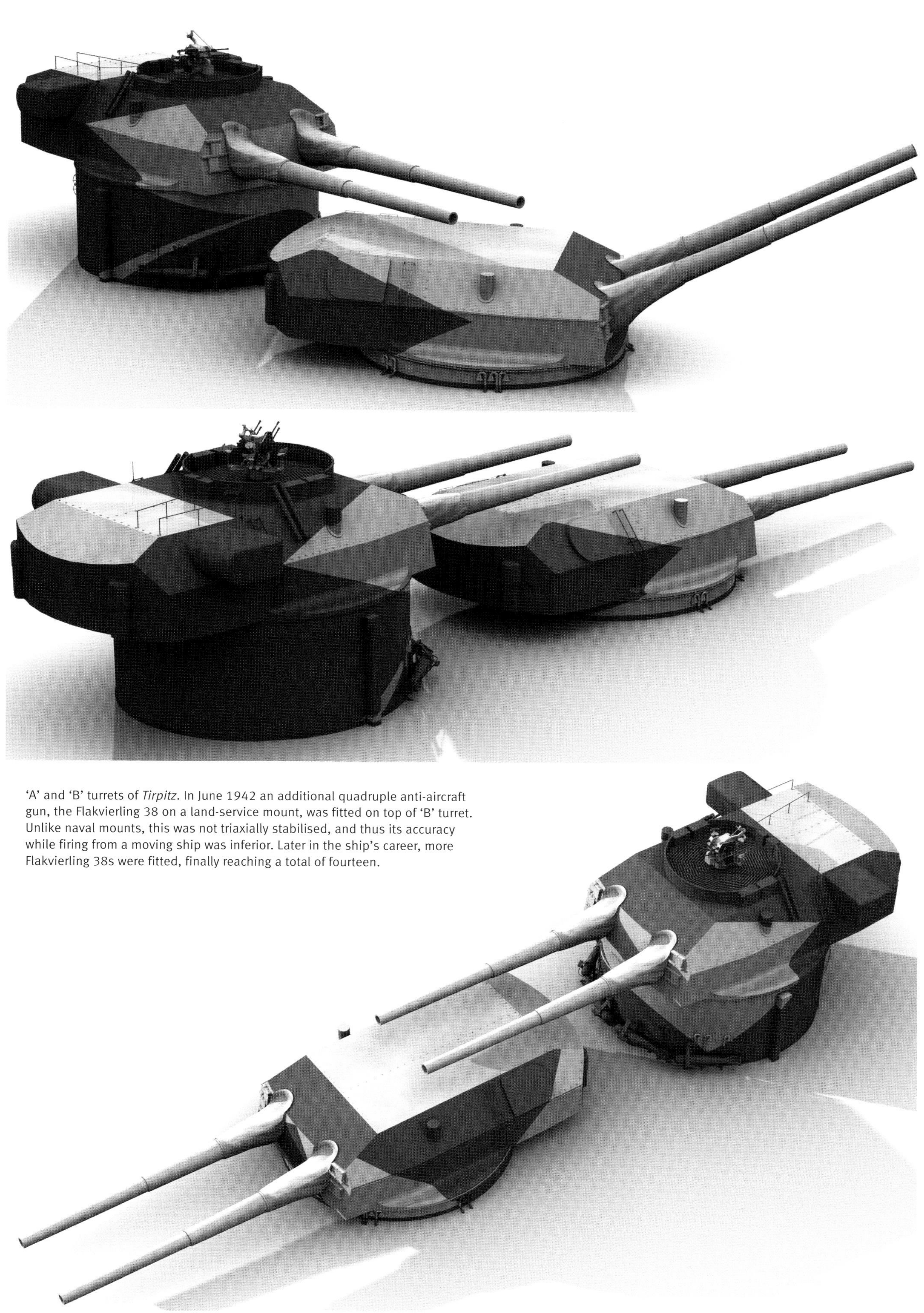

'A' and 'B' turrets of *Tirpitz*. In June 1942 an additional quadruple anti-aircraft gun, the Flakvierling 38 on a land-service mount, was fitted on top of 'B' turret. Unlike naval mounts, this was not triaxially stabilised, and thus its accuracy while firing from a moving ship was inferior. Later in the ship's career, more Flakvierling 38s were fitted, finally reaching a total of fourteen.

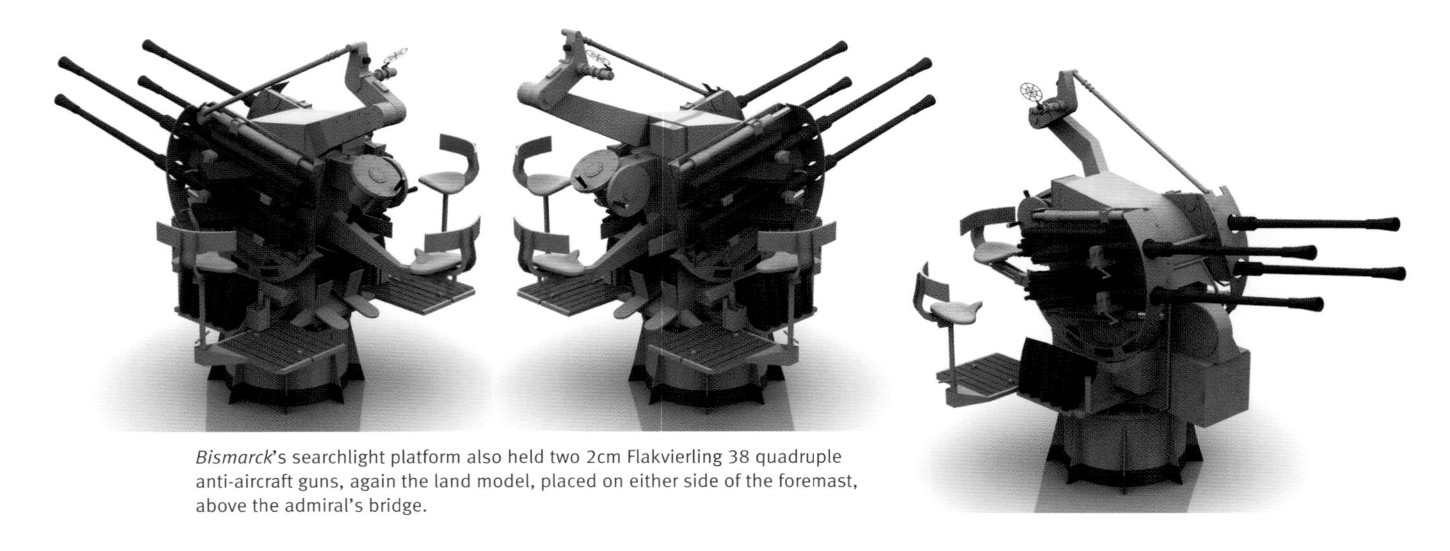

Bismarck's searchlight platform also held two 2cm Flakvierling 38 quadruple anti-aircraft guns, again the land model, placed on either side of the foremast, above the admiral's bridge.

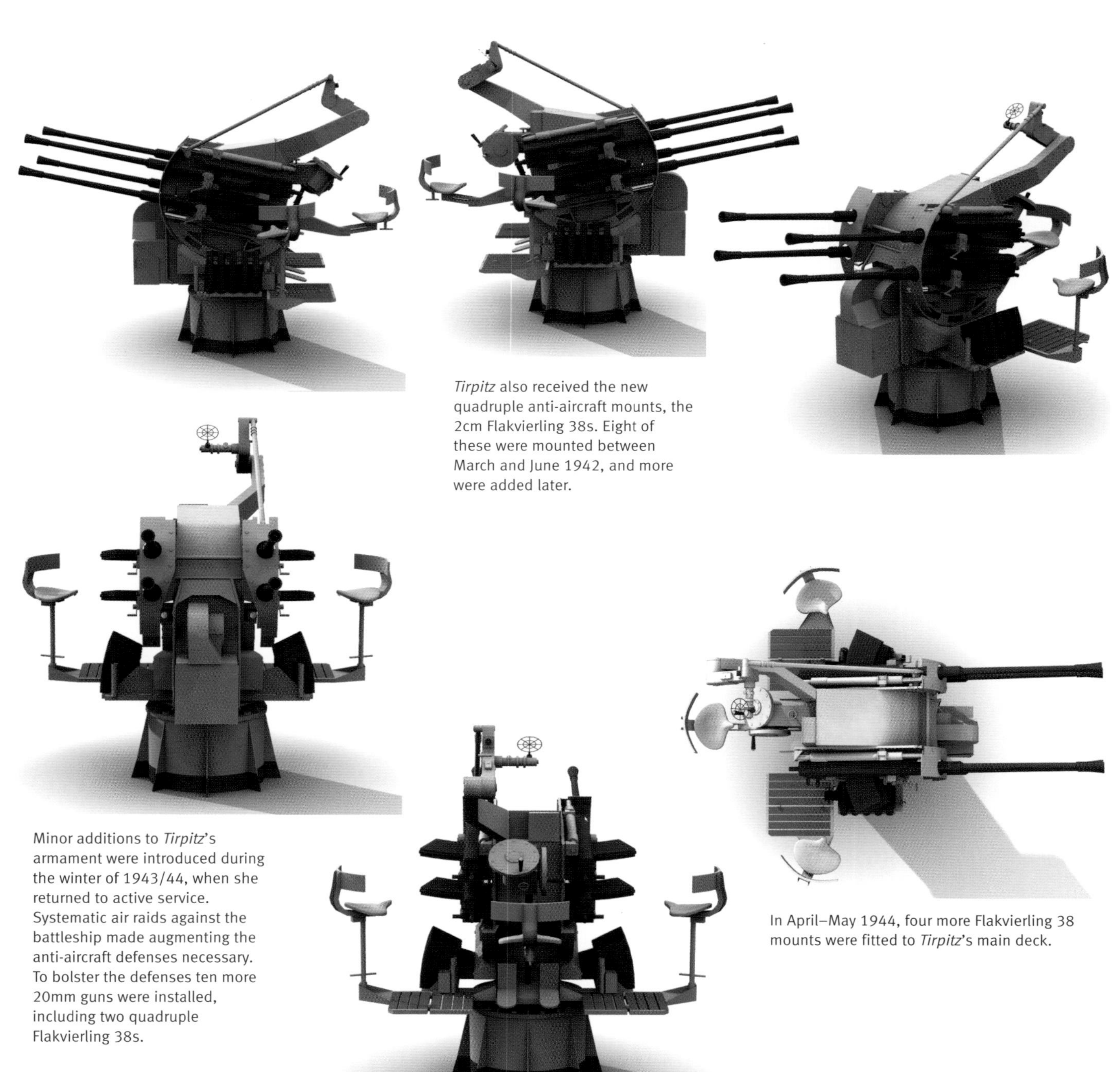

Tirpitz also received the new quadruple anti-aircraft mounts, the 2cm Flakvierling 38s. Eight of these were mounted between March and June 1942, and more were added later.

Minor additions to *Tirpitz*'s armament were introduced during the winter of 1943/44, when she returned to active service. Systematic air raids against the battleship made augmenting the anti-aircraft defenses necessary. To bolster the defenses ten more 20mm guns were installed, including two quadruple Flakvierling 38s.

In April–May 1944, four more Flakvierling 38 mounts were fitted to *Tirpitz*'s main deck.

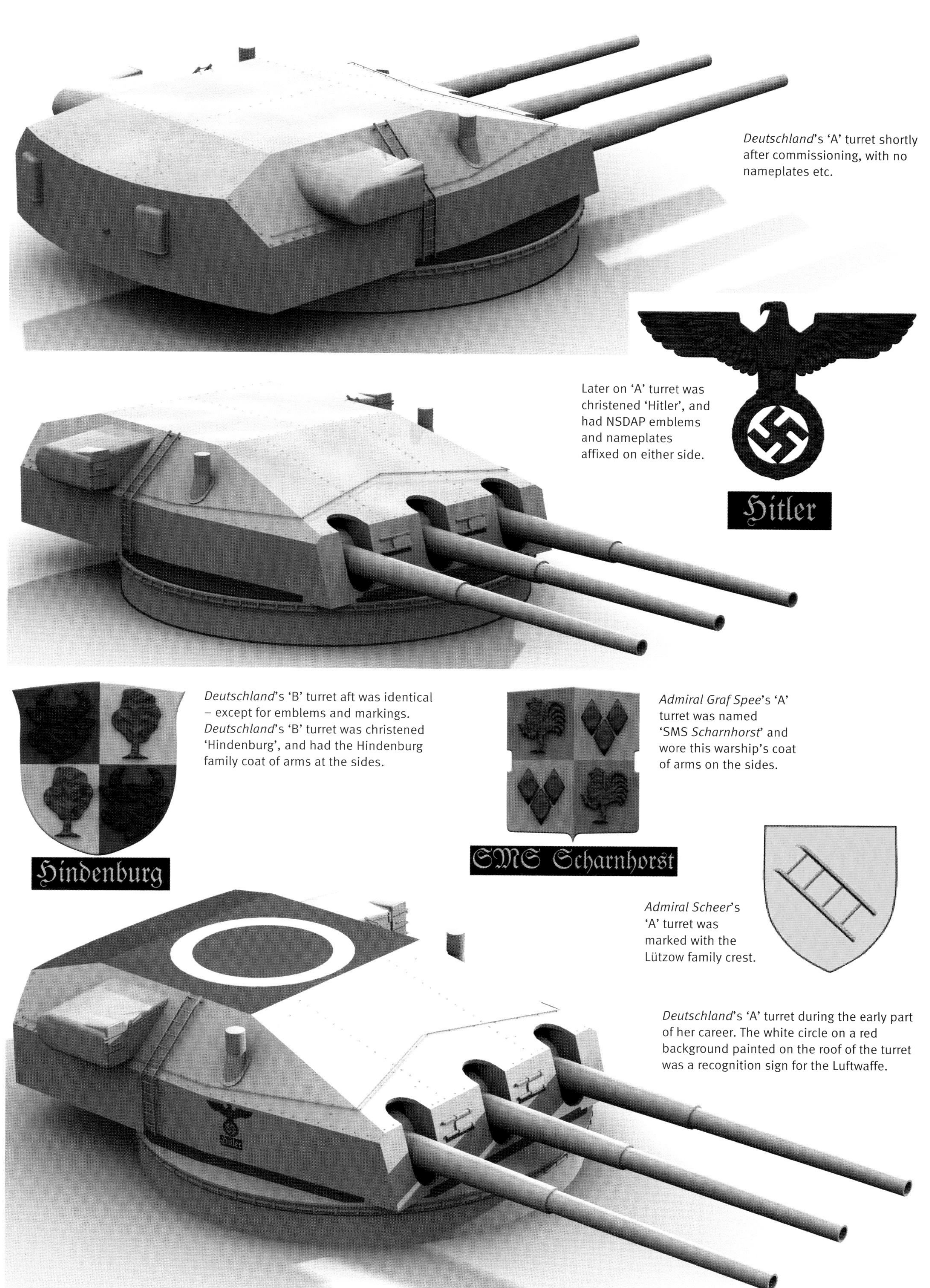

Deutschland's 'A' turret shortly after commissioning, with no nameplates etc.

Later on 'A' turret was christened 'Hitler', and had NSDAP emblems and nameplates affixed on either side.

Deutschland's 'B' turret aft was identical – except for emblems and markings. *Deutschland*'s 'B' turret was christened 'Hindenburg', and had the Hindenburg family coat of arms at the sides.

Admiral Graf Spee's 'A' turret was named 'SMS *Scharnhorst*' and wore this warship's coat of arms on the sides.

Admiral Scheer's 'A' turret was marked with the Lützow family crest.

Deutschland's 'A' turret during the early part of her career. The white circle on a red background painted on the roof of the turret was a recognition sign for the Luftwaffe.

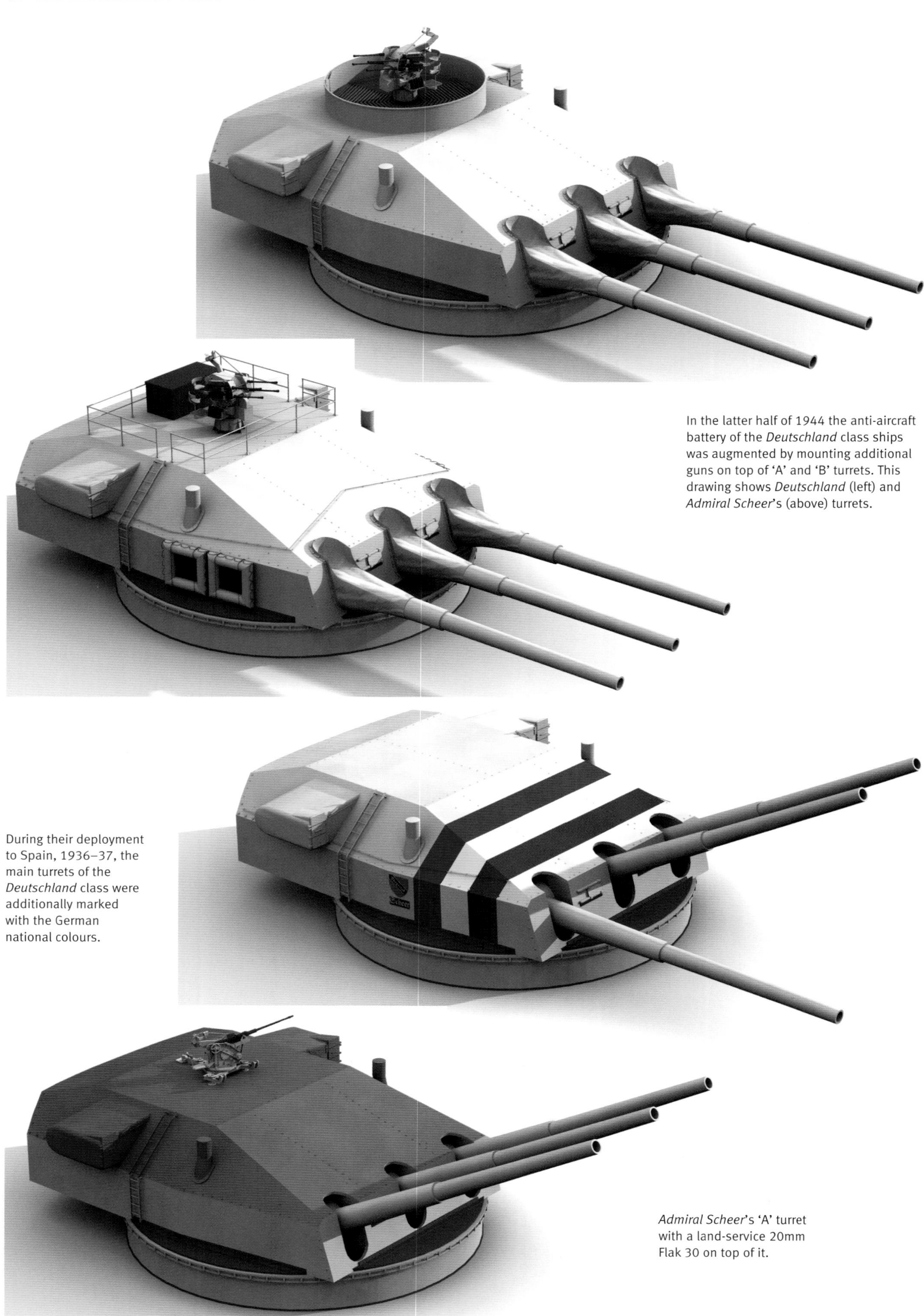

In the latter half of 1944 the anti-aircraft battery of the *Deutschland* class ships was augmented by mounting additional guns on top of 'A' and 'B' turrets. This drawing shows *Deutschland* (left) and *Admiral Scheer*'s (above) turrets.

During their deployment to Spain, 1936–37, the main turrets of the *Deutschland* class were additionally marked with the German national colours.

Admiral Scheer's 'A' turret with a land-service 20mm Flak 30 on top of it.

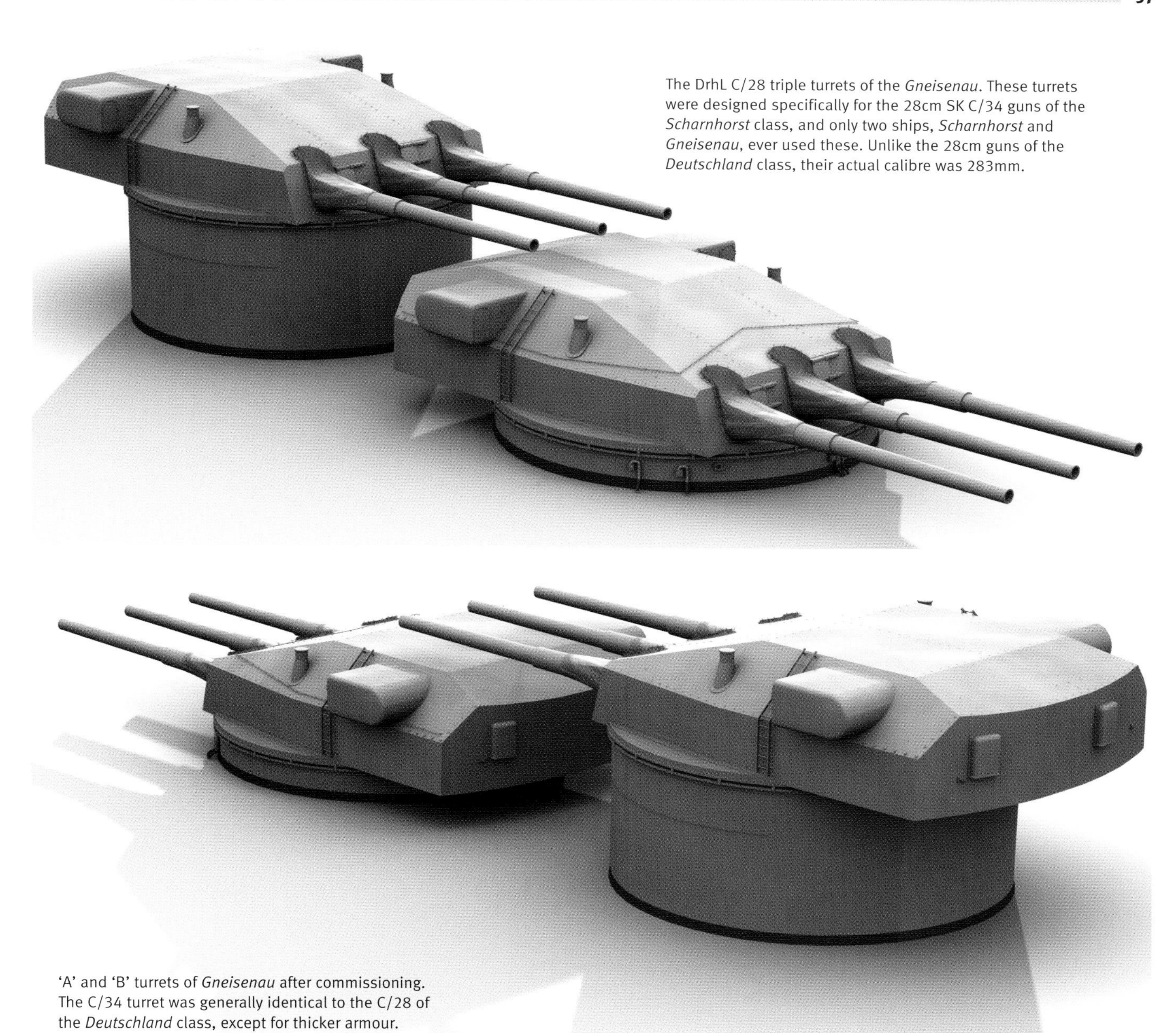

The DrhL C/28 triple turrets of the *Gneisenau*. These turrets were designed specifically for the 28cm SK C/34 guns of the *Scharnhorst* class, and only two ships, *Scharnhorst* and *Gneisenau*, ever used these. Unlike the 28cm guns of the *Deutschland* class, their actual calibre was 283mm.

'A' and 'B' turrets of *Gneisenau* after commissioning. The C/34 turret was generally identical to the C/28 of the *Deutschland* class, except for thicker armour.

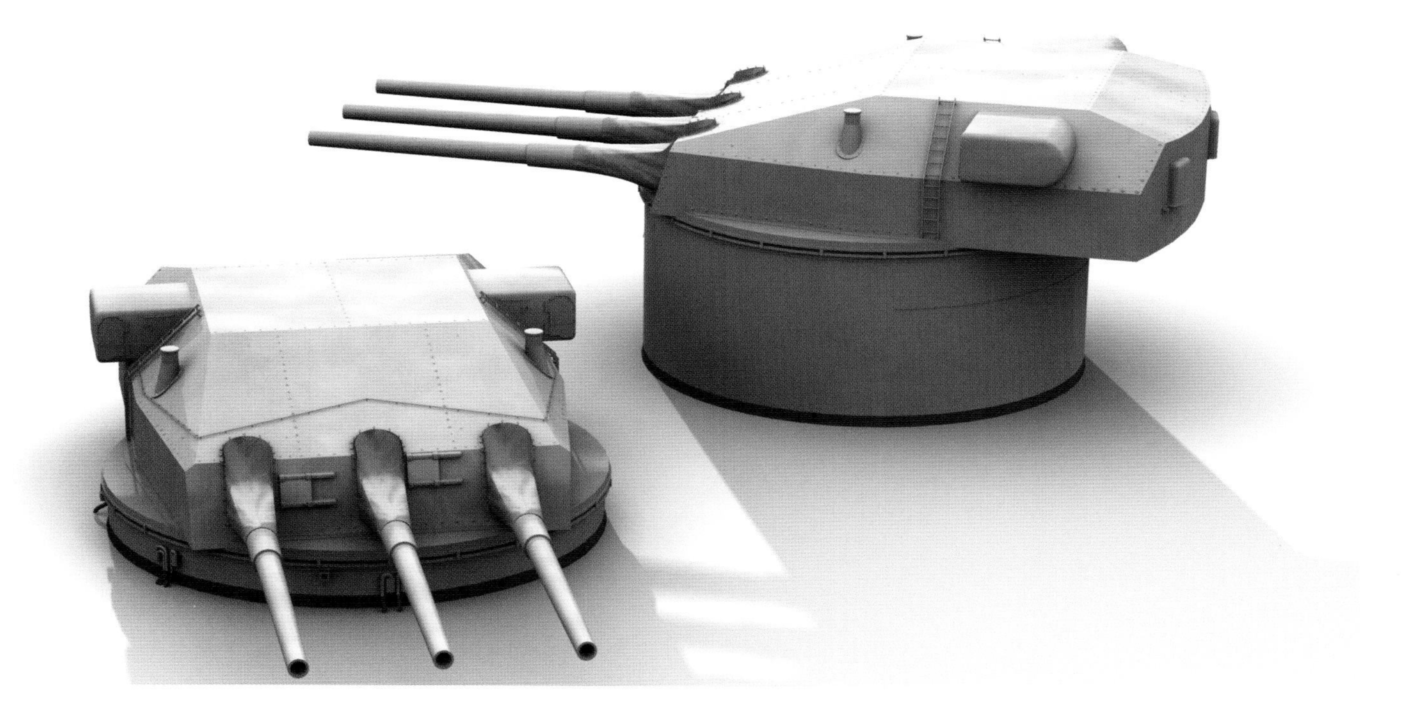

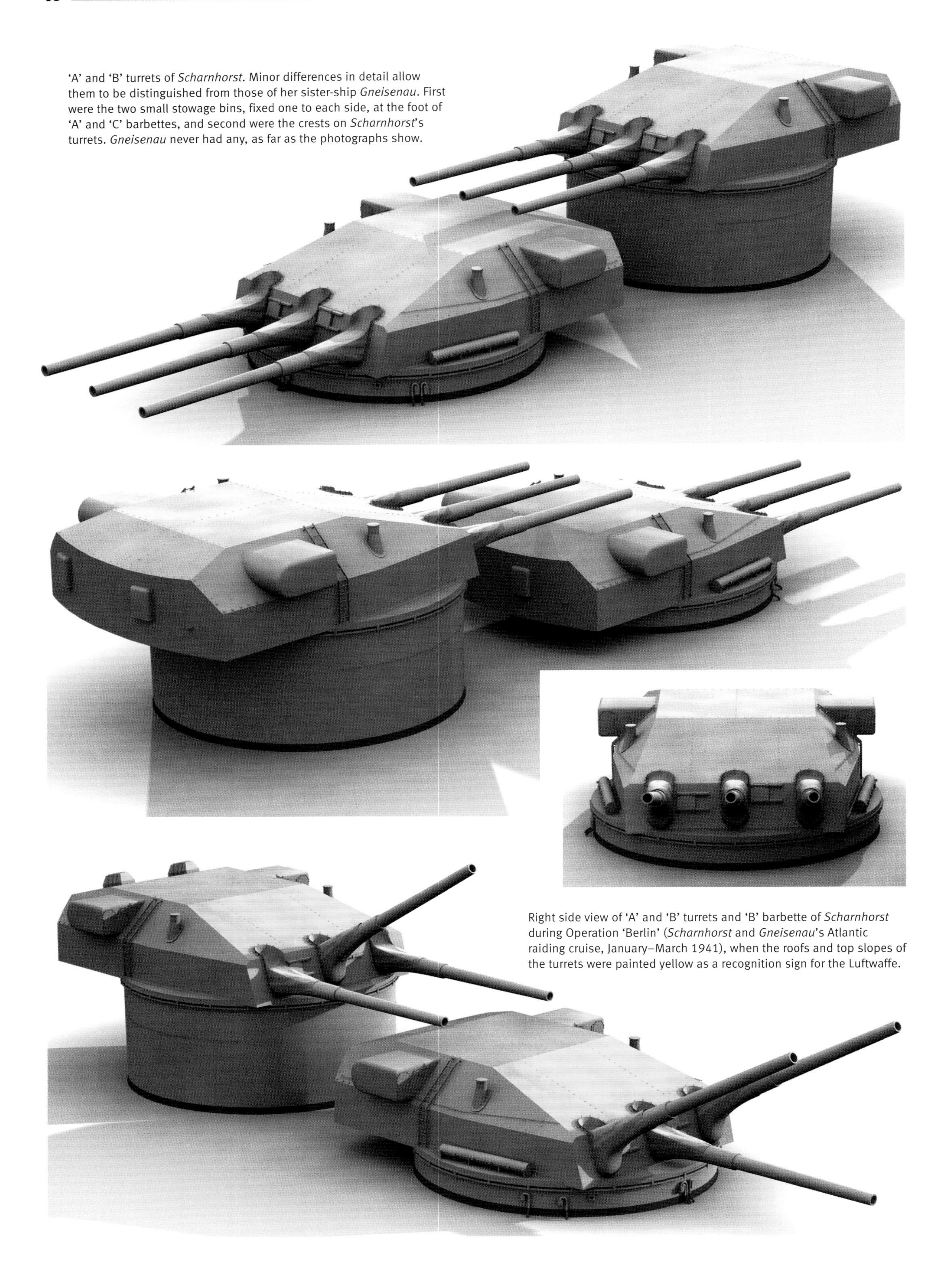

'A' and 'B' turrets of *Scharnhorst*. Minor differences in detail allow them to be distinguished from those of her sister-ship *Gneisenau*. First were the two small stowage bins, fixed one to each side, at the foot of 'A' and 'C' barbettes, and second were the crests on *Scharnhorst*'s turrets. *Gneisenau* never had any, as far as the photographs show.

Right side view of 'A' and 'B' turrets and 'B' barbette of *Scharnhorst* during Operation 'Berlin' (*Scharnhorst* and *Gneisenau*'s Atlantic raiding cruise, January–March 1941), when the roofs and top slopes of the turrets were painted yellow as a recognition sign for the Luftwaffe.

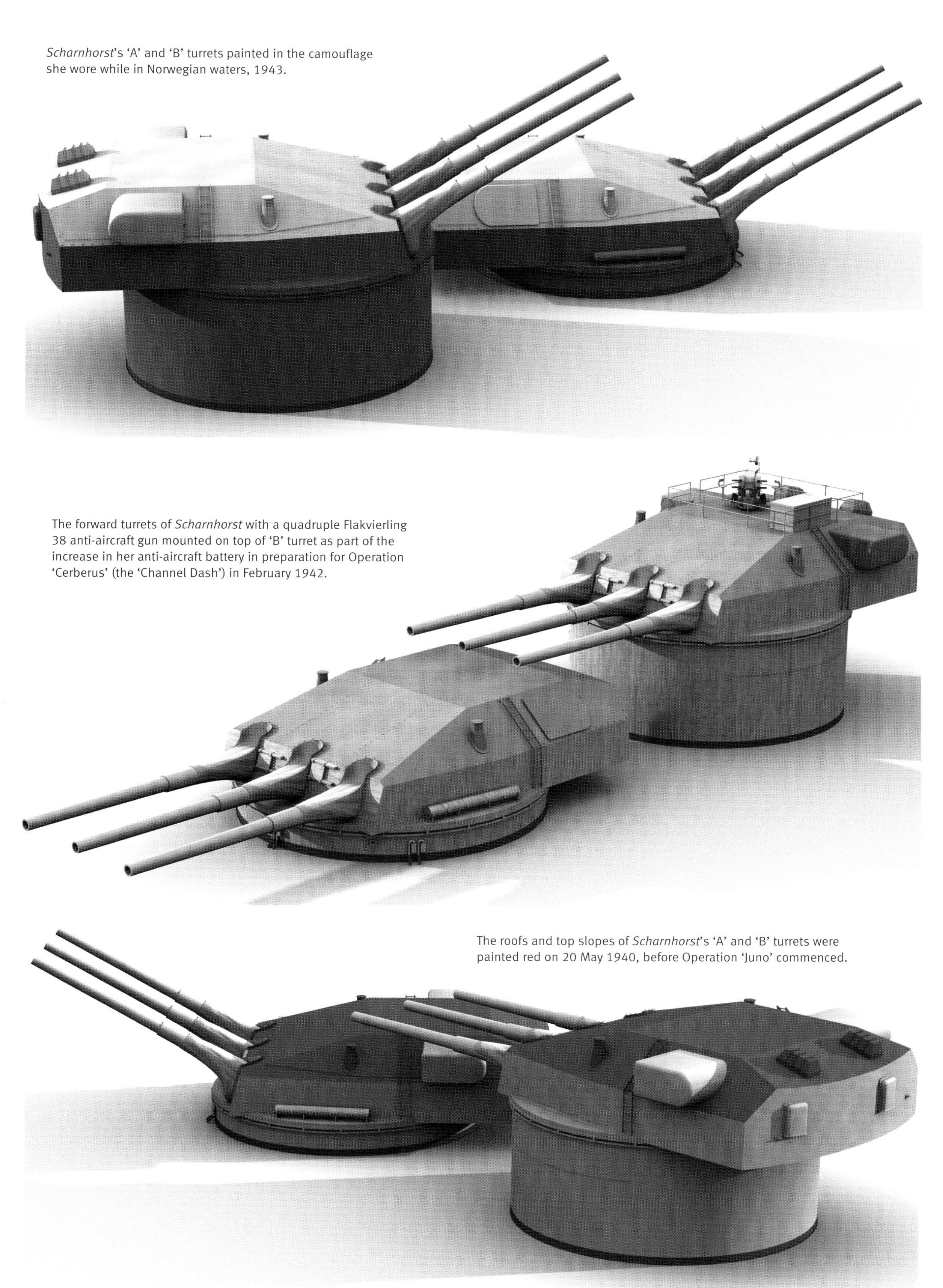

Scharnhorst's 'A' and 'B' turrets painted in the camouflage she wore while in Norwegian waters, 1943.

The forward turrets of *Scharnhorst* with a quadruple Flakvierling 38 anti-aircraft gun mounted on top of 'B' turret as part of the increase in her anti-aircraft battery in preparation for Operation 'Cerberus' (the 'Channel Dash') in February 1942.

The roofs and top slopes of *Scharnhorst*'s 'A' and 'B' turrets were painted red on 20 May 1940, before Operation 'Juno' commenced.

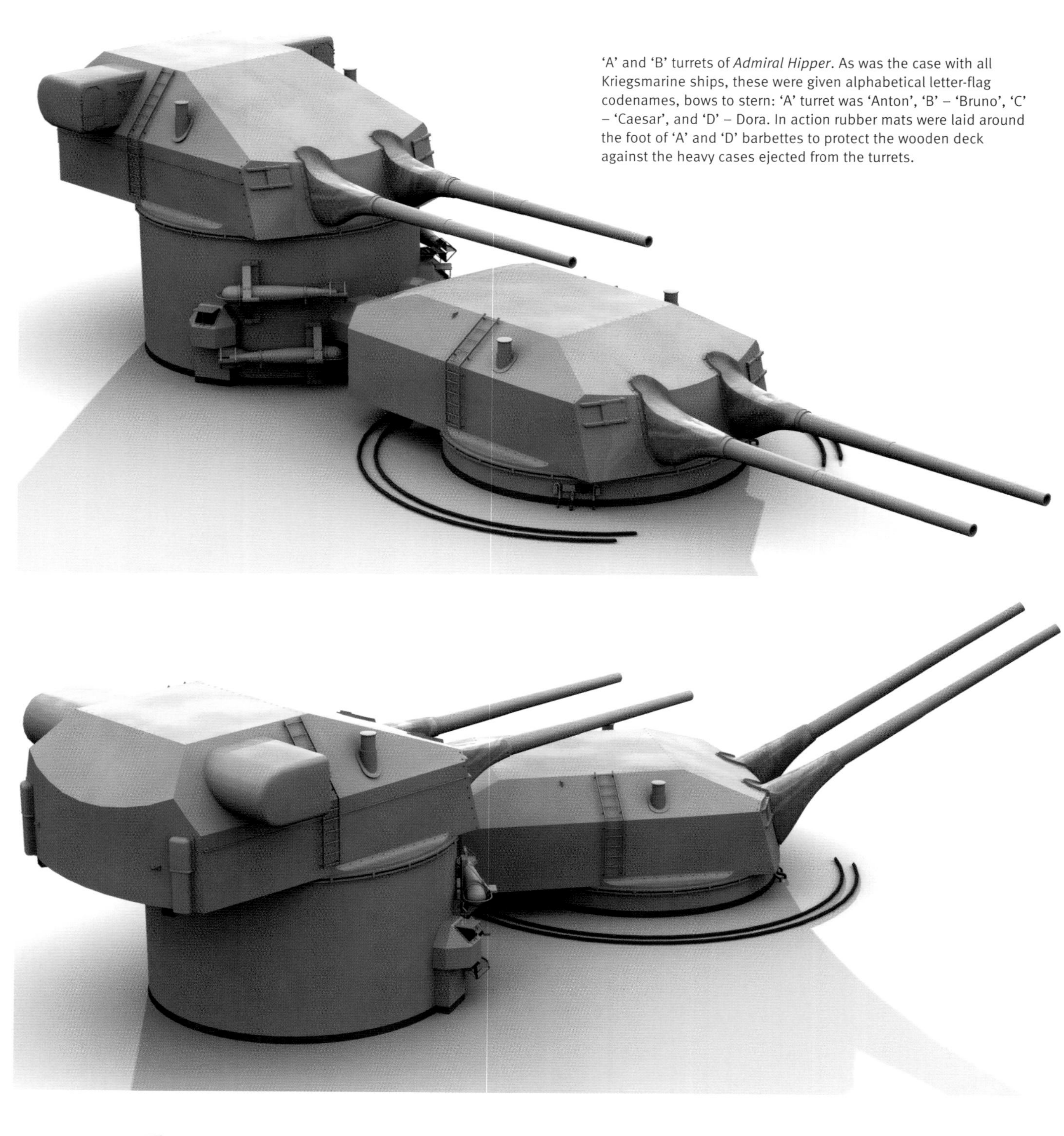

'A' and 'B' turrets of *Admiral Hipper*. As was the case with all Kriegsmarine ships, these were given alphabetical letter-flag codenames, bows to stern: 'A' turret was 'Anton', 'B' – 'Bruno', 'C' – 'Caesar', and 'D' – Dora. In action rubber mats were laid around the foot of 'A' and 'D' barbettes to protect the wooden deck against the heavy cases ejected from the turrets.

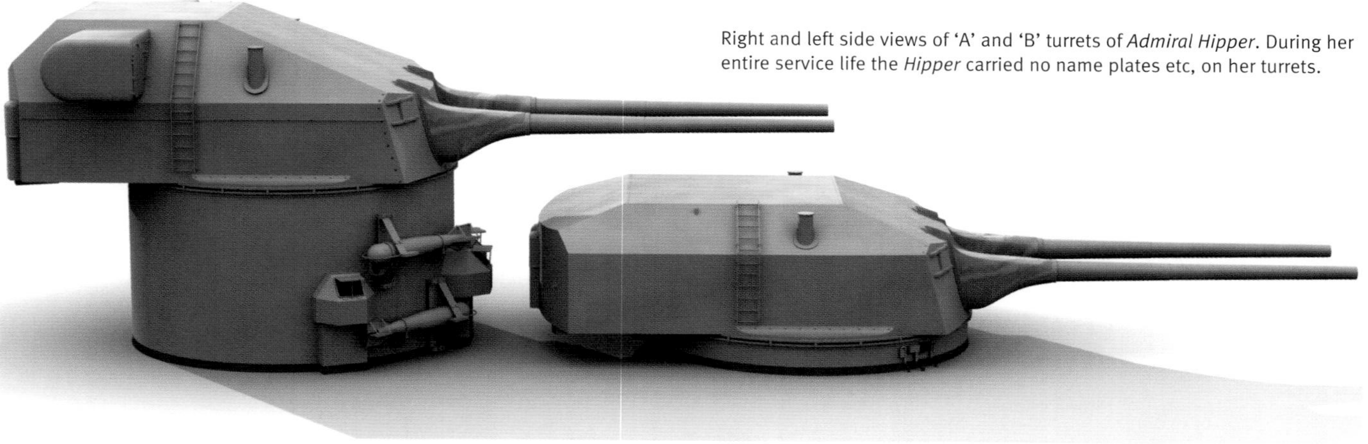

Right and left side views of 'A' and 'B' turrets of *Admiral Hipper*. During her entire service life the *Hipper* carried no name plates etc, on her turrets.

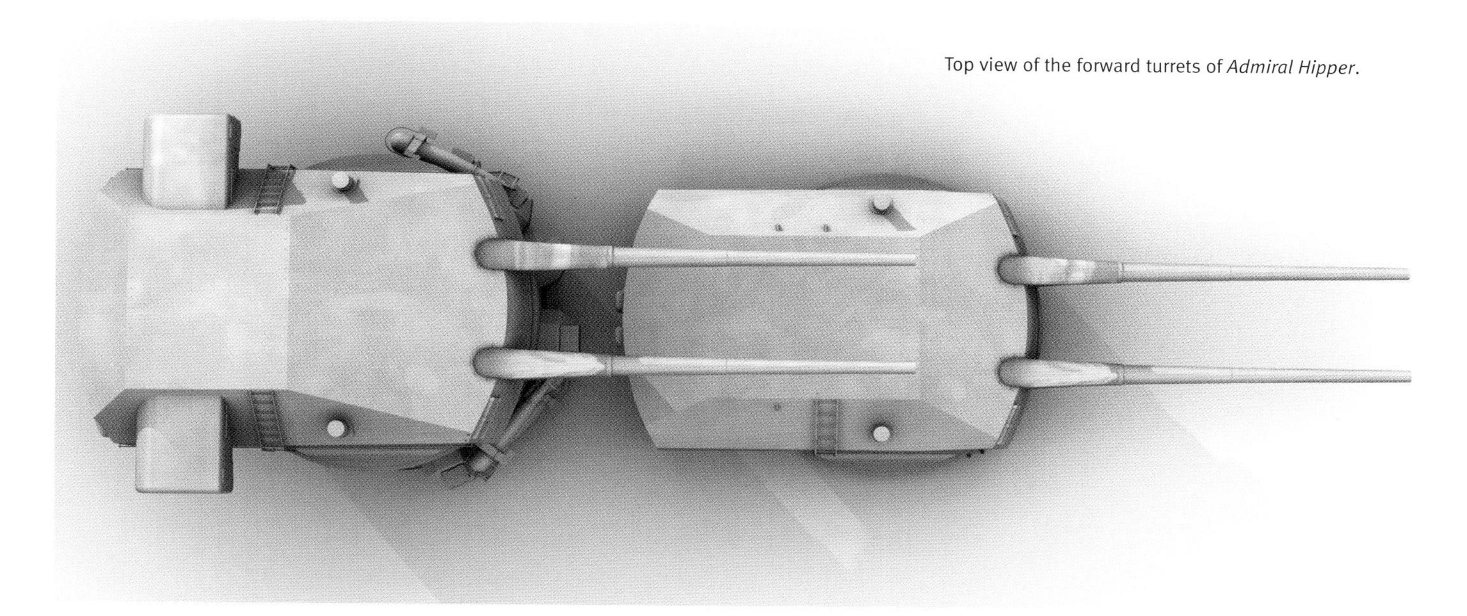
Top view of the forward turrets of *Admiral Hipper*.

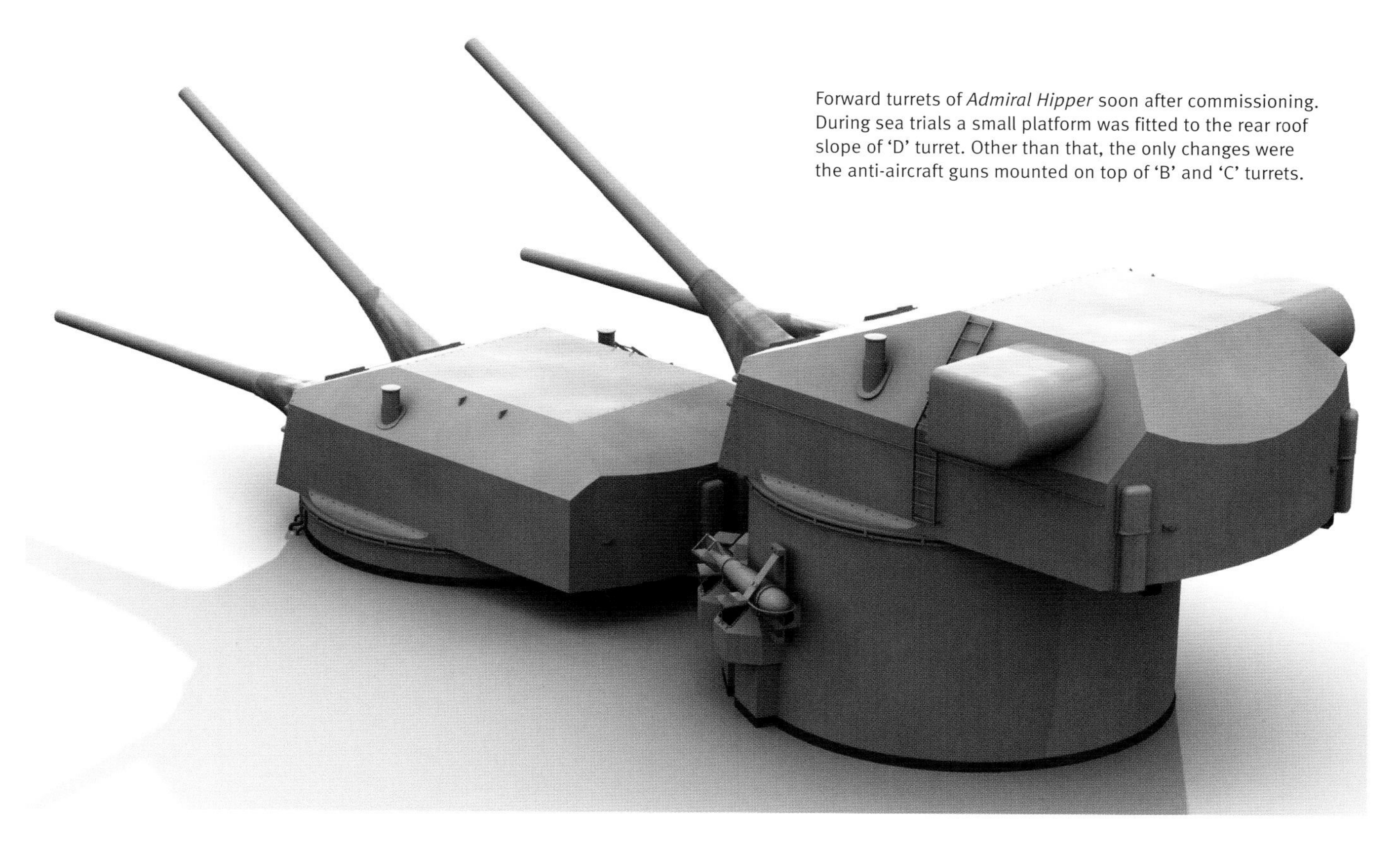
Forward turrets of *Admiral Hipper* soon after commissioning. During sea trials a small platform was fitted to the rear roof slope of 'D' turret. Other than that, the only changes were the anti-aircraft guns mounted on top of 'B' and 'C' turrets.

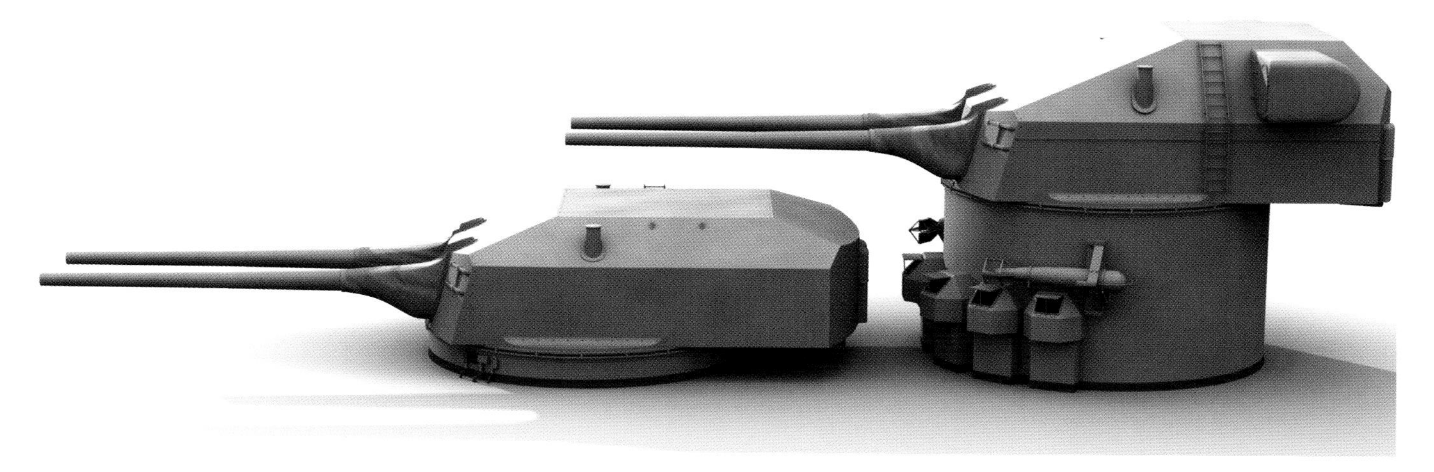

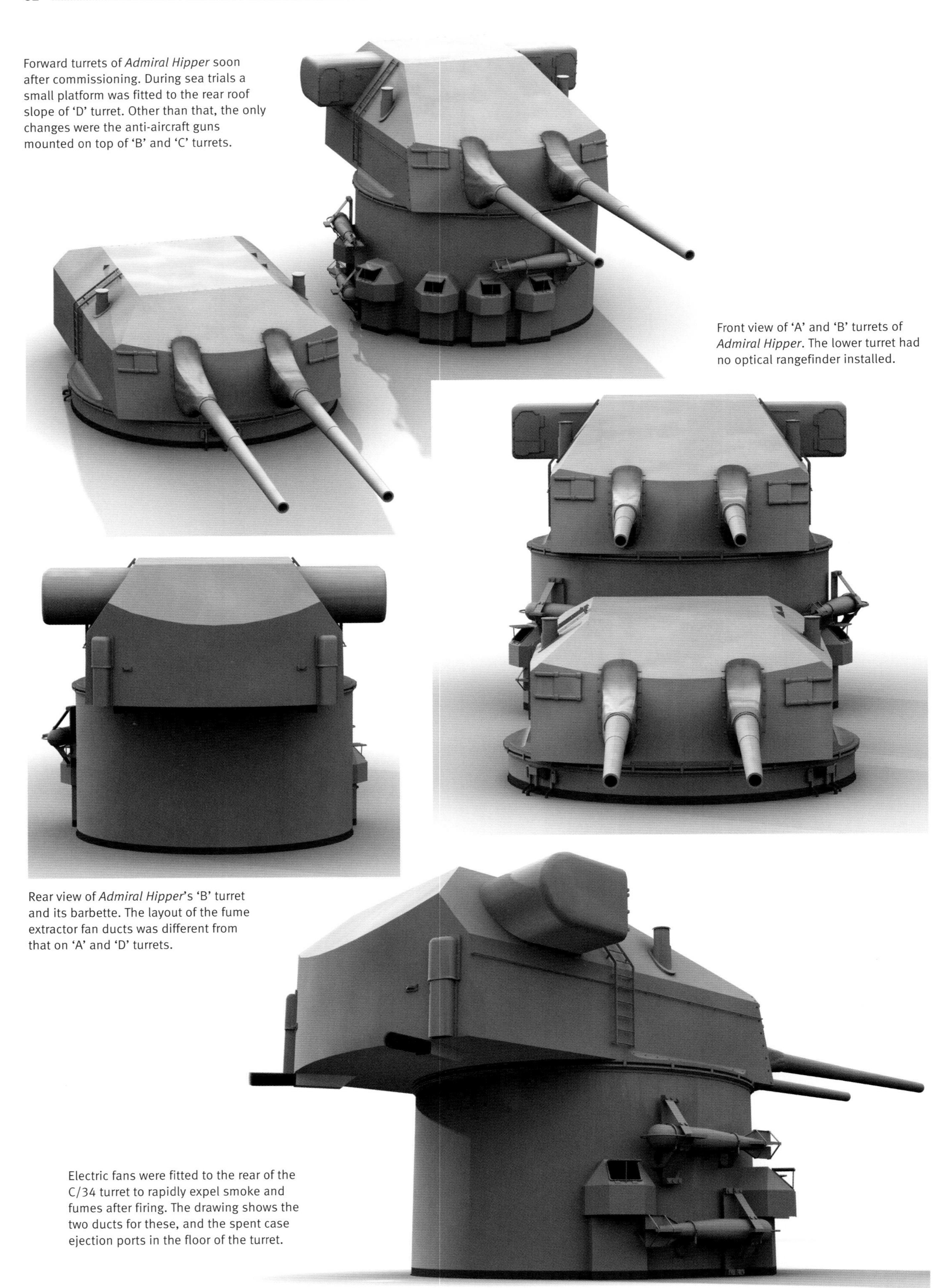

Forward turrets of *Admiral Hipper* soon after commissioning. During sea trials a small platform was fitted to the rear roof slope of 'D' turret. Other than that, the only changes were the anti-aircraft guns mounted on top of 'B' and 'C' turrets.

Front view of 'A' and 'B' turrets of *Admiral Hipper*. The lower turret had no optical rangefinder installed.

Rear view of *Admiral Hipper*'s 'B' turret and its barbette. The layout of the fume extractor fan ducts was different from that on 'A' and 'D' turrets.

Electric fans were fitted to the rear of the C/34 turret to rapidly expel smoke and fumes after firing. The drawing shows the two ducts for these, and the spent case ejection ports in the floor of the turret.

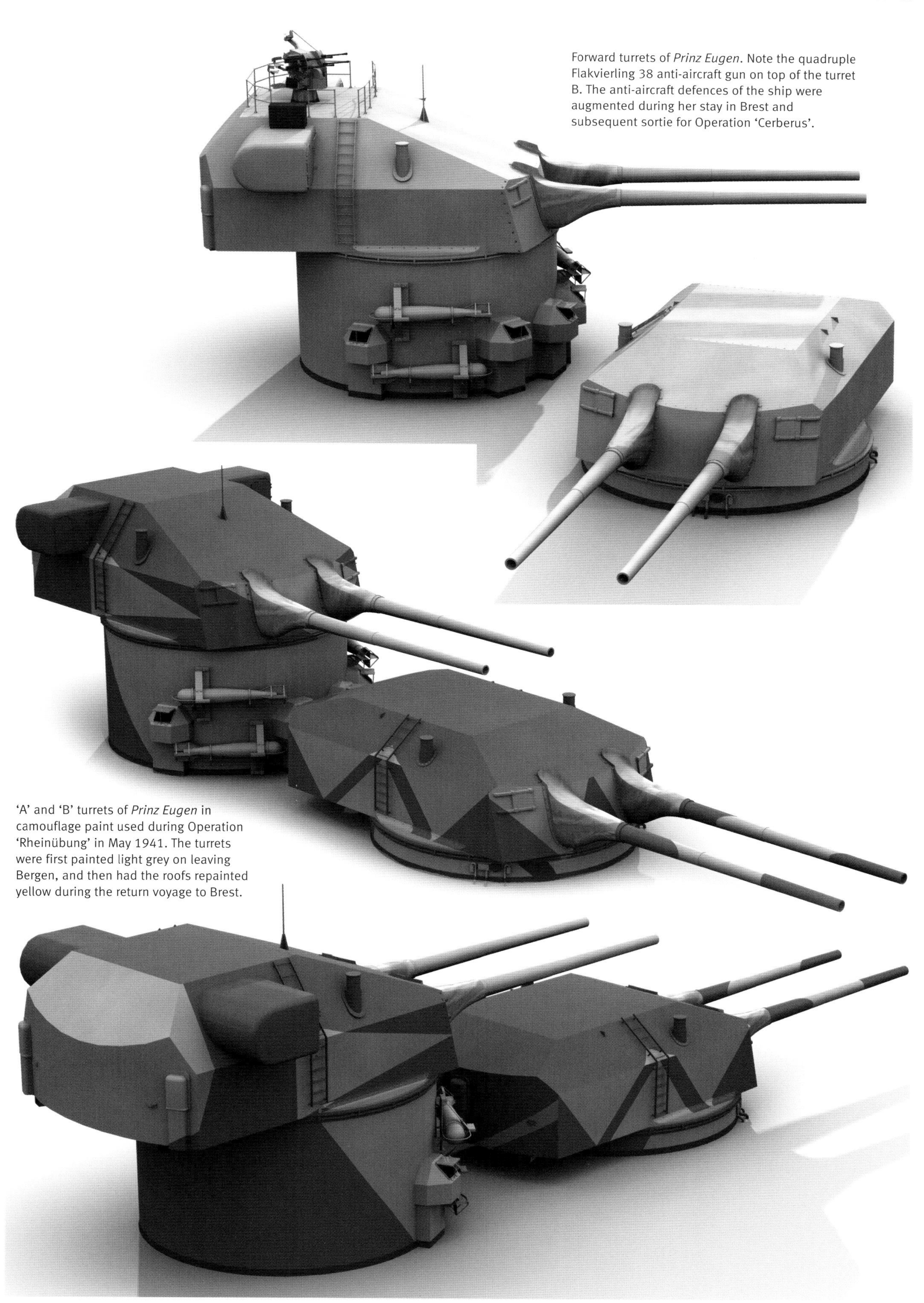

Forward turrets of *Prinz Eugen*. Note the quadruple Flakvierling 38 anti-aircraft gun on top of the turret B. The anti-aircraft defences of the ship were augmented during her stay in Brest and subsequent sortie for Operation 'Cerberus'.

'A' and 'B' turrets of *Prinz Eugen* in camouflage paint used during Operation 'Rheinübung' in May 1941. The turrets were first painted light grey on leaving Bergen, and then had the roofs repainted yellow during the return voyage to Brest.

The main turrets of the heavy cruiser *Prinz Eugen*, soon after commissioning, when individual turrets had their names painted on the sides. These were painted over soon afterwards, when she started her fire-control calibration in the western Baltic.

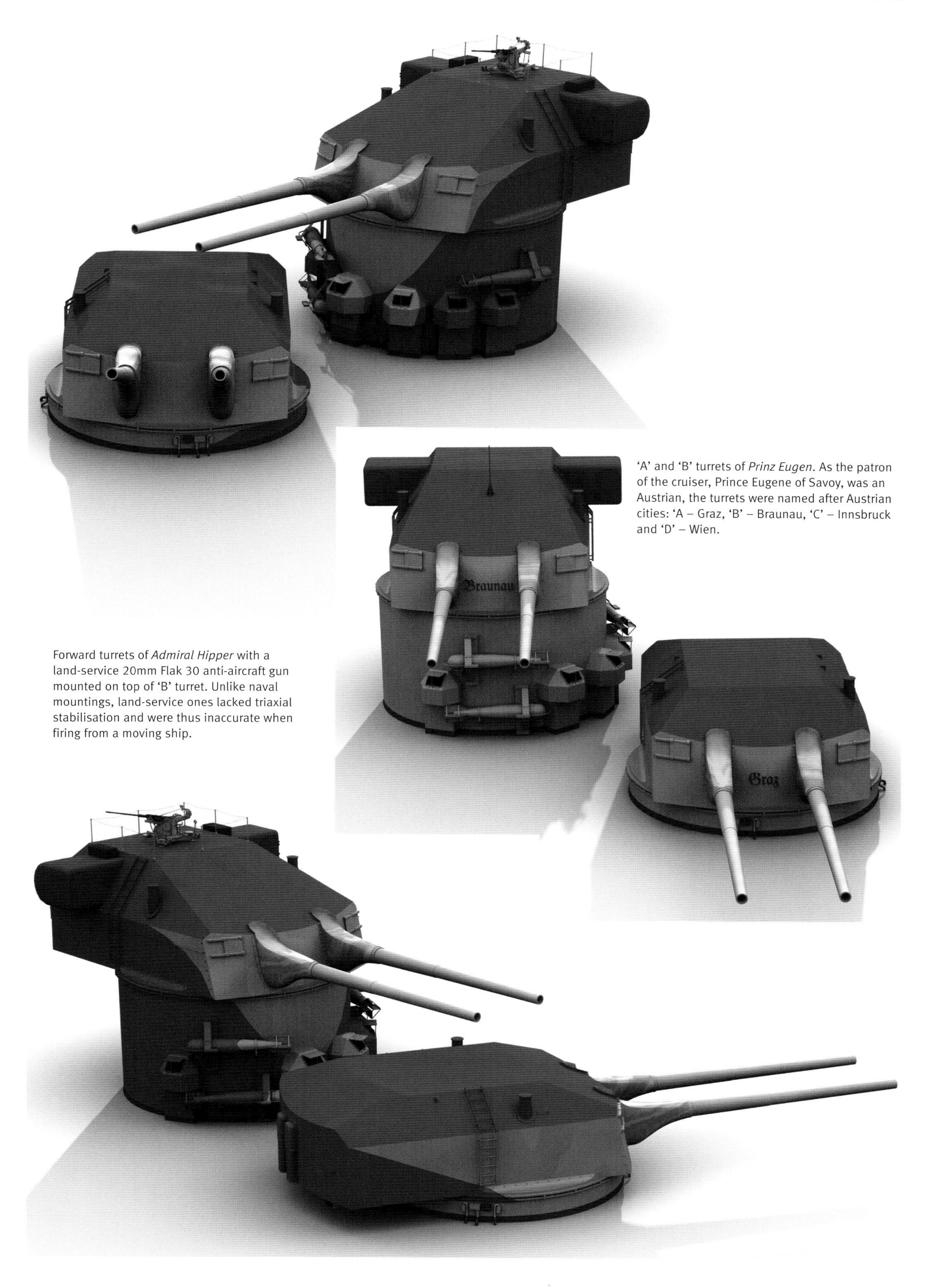

'A' and 'B' turrets of *Prinz Eugen*. As the patron of the cruiser, Prince Eugene of Savoy, was an Austrian, the turrets were named after Austrian cities: 'A – Graz, 'B' – Braunau, 'C' – Innsbruck and 'D' – Wien.

Forward turrets of *Admiral Hipper* with a land-service 20mm Flak 30 anti-aircraft gun mounted on top of 'B' turret. Unlike naval mountings, land-service ones lacked triaxial stabilisation and were thus inaccurate when firing from a moving ship.

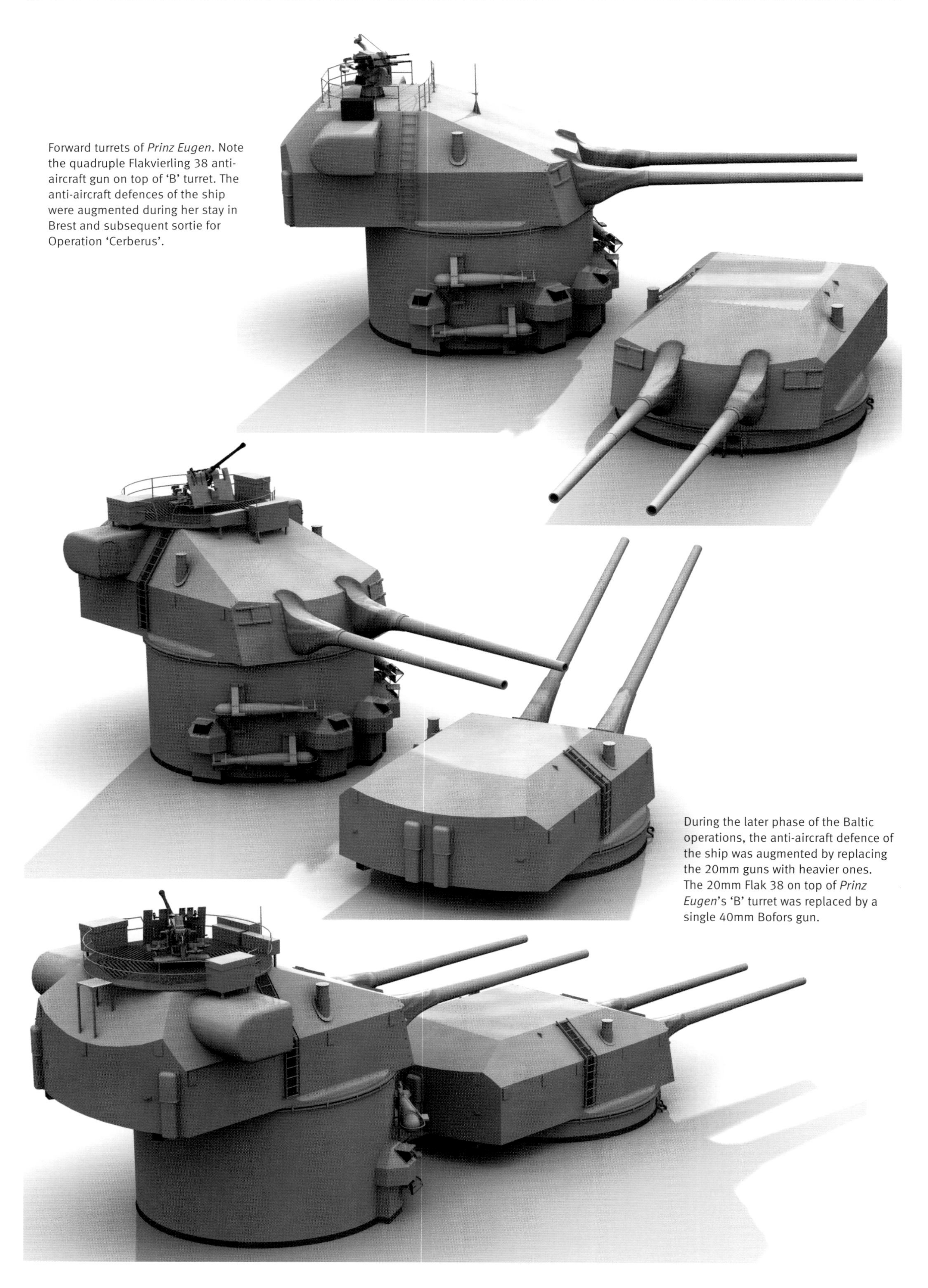

Forward turrets of *Prinz Eugen*. Note the quadruple Flakvierling 38 anti-aircraft gun on top of 'B' turret. The anti-aircraft defences of the ship were augmented during her stay in Brest and subsequent sortie for Operation 'Cerberus'.

During the later phase of the Baltic operations, the anti-aircraft defence of the ship was augmented by replacing the 20mm guns with heavier ones. The 20mm Flak 38 on top of *Prinz Eugen*'s 'B' turret was replaced by a single 40mm Bofors gun.

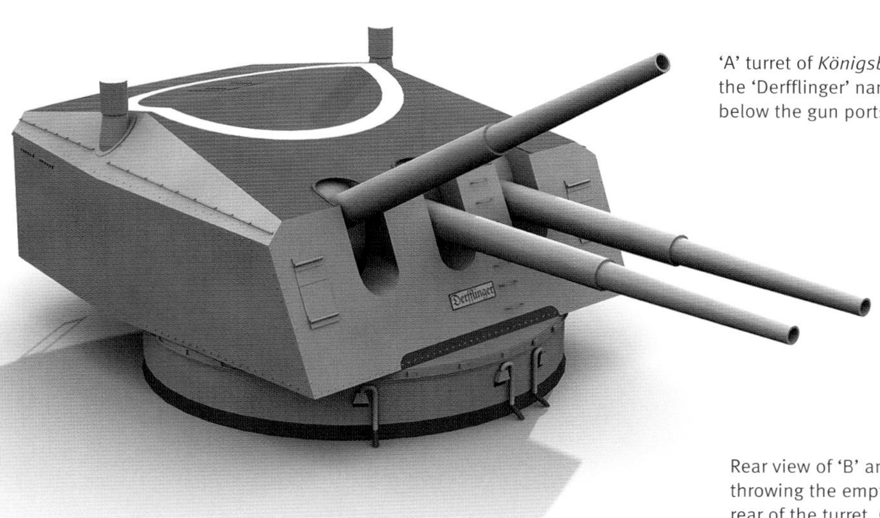

'A' turret of *Königsberg*. Note the 'Derfflinger' nameplate below the gun ports.

SMS *Derfflinger*'s coat of arms on the back of 'A' turret.

Rear view of 'B' and 'C' turrets of *Königsberg*. Note the ejection ports for throwing the empty cases out of the turret into the baskets hung from the rear of the turret. Coats of arms are fixed over the hatches of each turret.

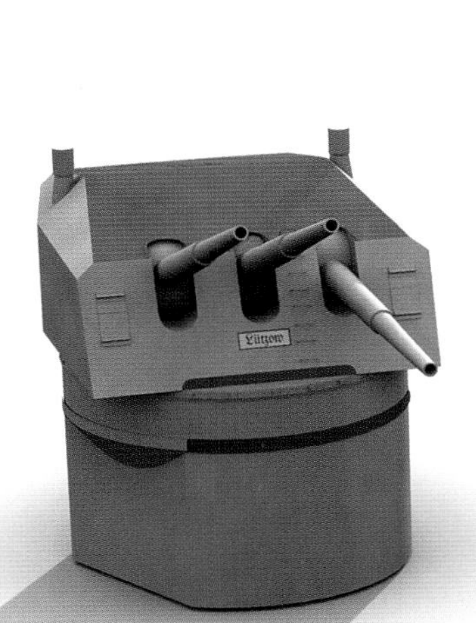

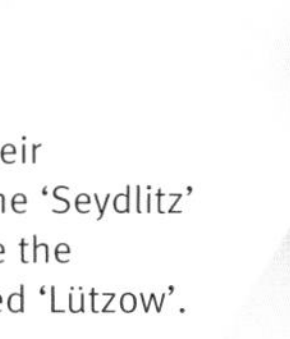

After turrets of *Königsberg* with their nameplates. 'C' turret has the name 'Seydlitz' and the motto 'Allen voran!', while the superimposed 'B' turret was named 'Lützow'.

Lützow coat of arms on the back of 'B' turret.

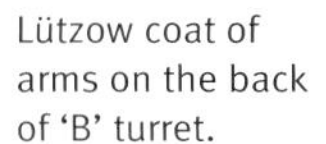

Seydlitz coat of arms on the back of 'C' turret.

Slight differences between the turrets of the 'K' class cruisers aid in identifying them. In this case, *Köln*'s 'B' and 'C' turrets had two rows of awning attachment points at the sides.

Helgoland coat of arms on 'A' turret.

After turrets of *Karlsruhe*. They carried brass nameplates affixed to their glacis, commemorating SMS *Breslau* on 'B' turret and SMS *Goeben* on 'C' turret.

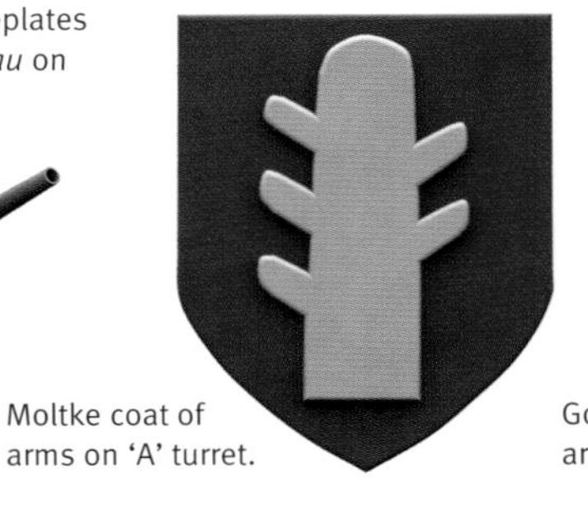

Moltke coat of arms on 'A' turret.

Goeben coat of arms on 'C' turret.

Brass nameplates on the glacis of the three turrets.

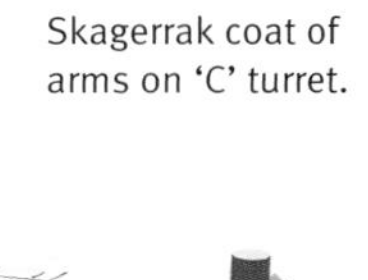

'B' and 'C' turrets of *Köln* with nameplates commemorating naval battles: 'Doggerbank' on 'B' turret and 'Skagerrak' on 'C' turret.

Skagerrak coat of arms on 'C' turret.

Doggerbank coat of arms on 'B' turret.

Rear view of 'B' and 'C' turrets of *Köln* showing flaps at the rear, covering the ejection ports. Baskets were secured below these, to catch the spent cases thrown by hand from the turrets. After the outbreak of war, all identifying markings were removed from the cruisers, including the turret nameplates and emblems.

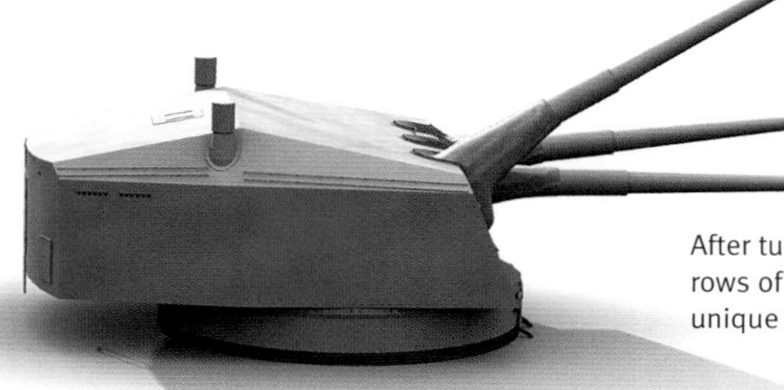

After turrets of *Köln* with the two rows of awning attaching points unique to that ship.

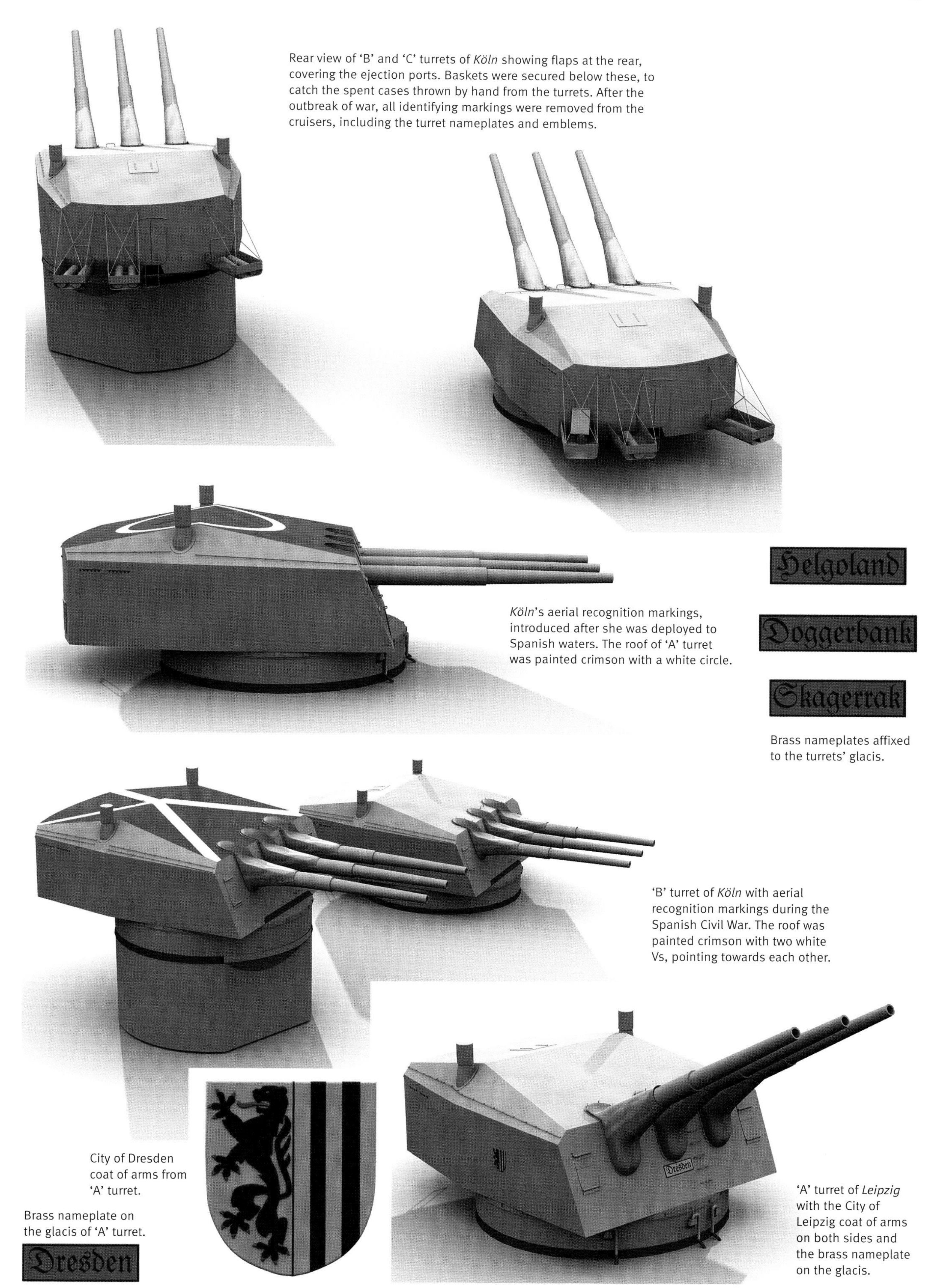

Rear view of 'B' and 'C' turrets of *Köln* showing flaps at the rear, covering the ejection ports. Baskets were secured below these, to catch the spent cases thrown by hand from the turrets. After the outbreak of war, all identifying markings were removed from the cruisers, including the turret nameplates and emblems.

Köln's aerial recognition markings, introduced after she was deployed to Spanish waters. The roof of 'A' turret was painted crimson with a white circle.

Brass nameplates affixed to the turrets' glacis.

'B' turret of *Köln* with aerial recognition markings during the Spanish Civil War. The roof was painted crimson with two white Vs, pointing towards each other.

City of Dresden coat of arms from 'A' turret.

Brass nameplate on the glacis of 'A' turret.

'A' turret of *Leipzig* with the City of Leipzig coat of arms on both sides and the brass nameplate on the glacis.

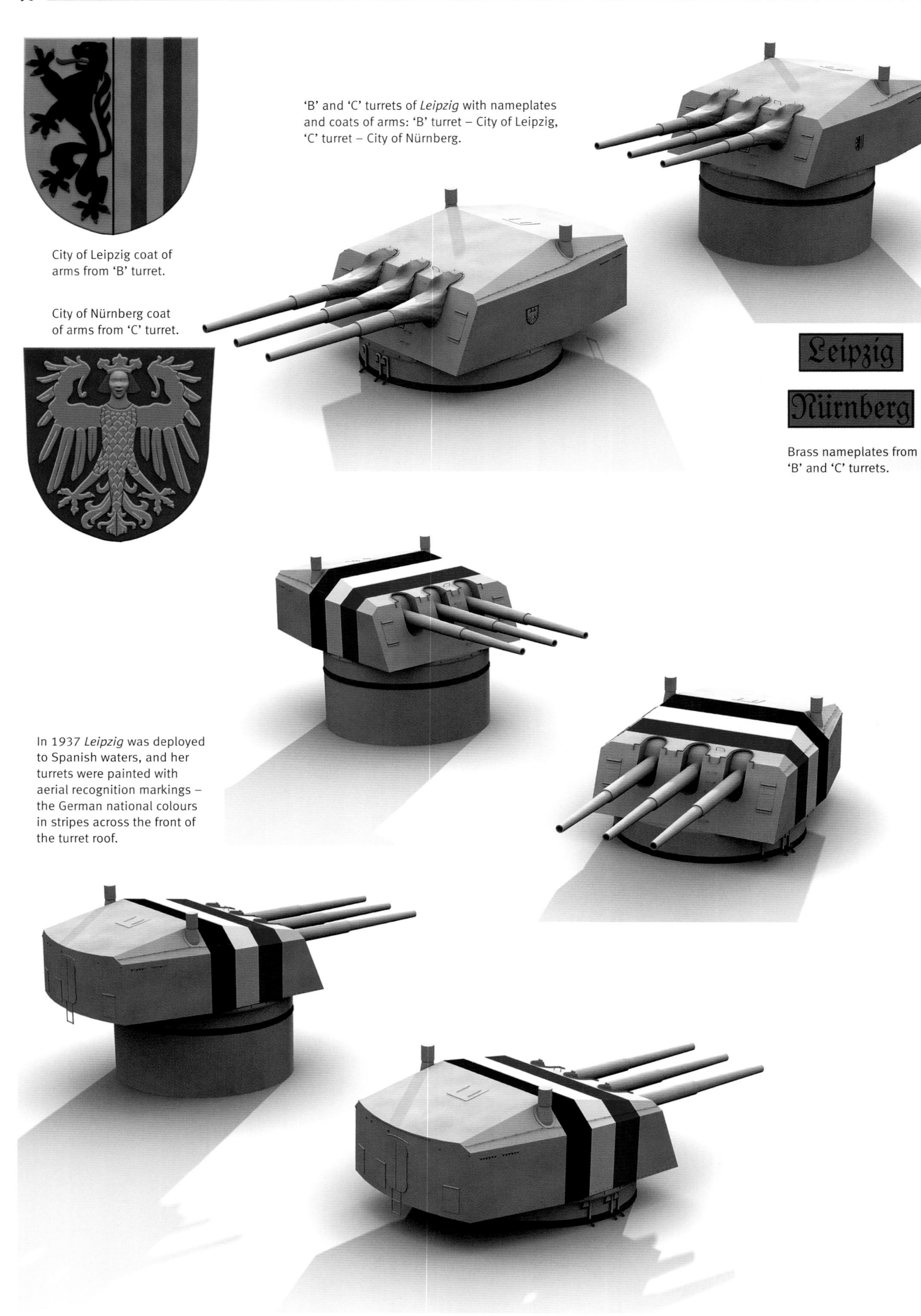

'B' and 'C' turrets of *Leipzig* with nameplates and coats of arms: 'B' turret – City of Leipzig, 'C' turret – City of Nürnberg.

City of Leipzig coat of arms from 'B' turret.

City of Nürnberg coat of arms from 'C' turret.

Brass nameplates from 'B' and 'C' turrets.

In 1937 *Leipzig* was deployed to Spanish waters, and her turrets were painted with aerial recognition markings – the German national colours in stripes across the front of the turret roof.

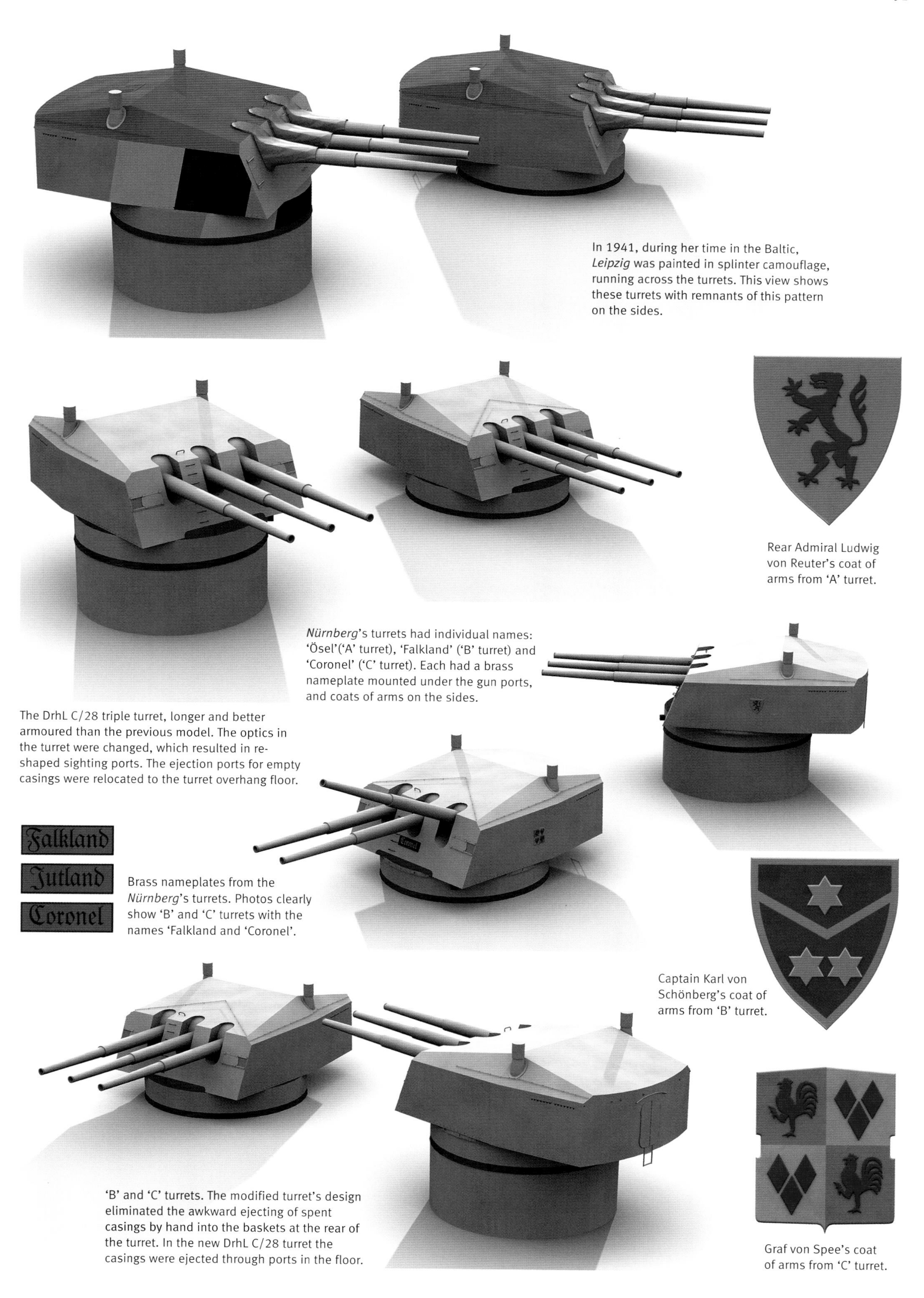

In 1941, during her time in the Baltic, *Leipzig* was painted in splinter camouflage, running across the turrets. This view shows these turrets with remnants of this pattern on the sides.

Rear Admiral Ludwig von Reuter's coat of arms from 'A' turret.

Nürnberg's turrets had individual names: 'Ösel'('A' turret), 'Falkland' ('B' turret) and 'Coronel' ('C' turret). Each had a brass nameplate mounted under the gun ports, and coats of arms on the sides.

The DrhL C/28 triple turret, longer and better armoured than the previous model. The optics in the turret were changed, which resulted in re-shaped sighting ports. The ejection ports for empty casings were relocated to the turret overhang floor.

Brass nameplates from the *Nürnberg*'s turrets. Photos clearly show 'B' and 'C' turrets with the names 'Falkland and 'Coronel'.

Captain Karl von Schönberg's coat of arms from 'B' turret.

'B' and 'C' turrets. The modified turret's design eliminated the awkward ejecting of spent casings by hand into the baskets at the rear of the turret. In the new DrhL C/28 turret the casings were ejected through ports in the floor.

Graf von Spee's coat of arms from 'C' turret.

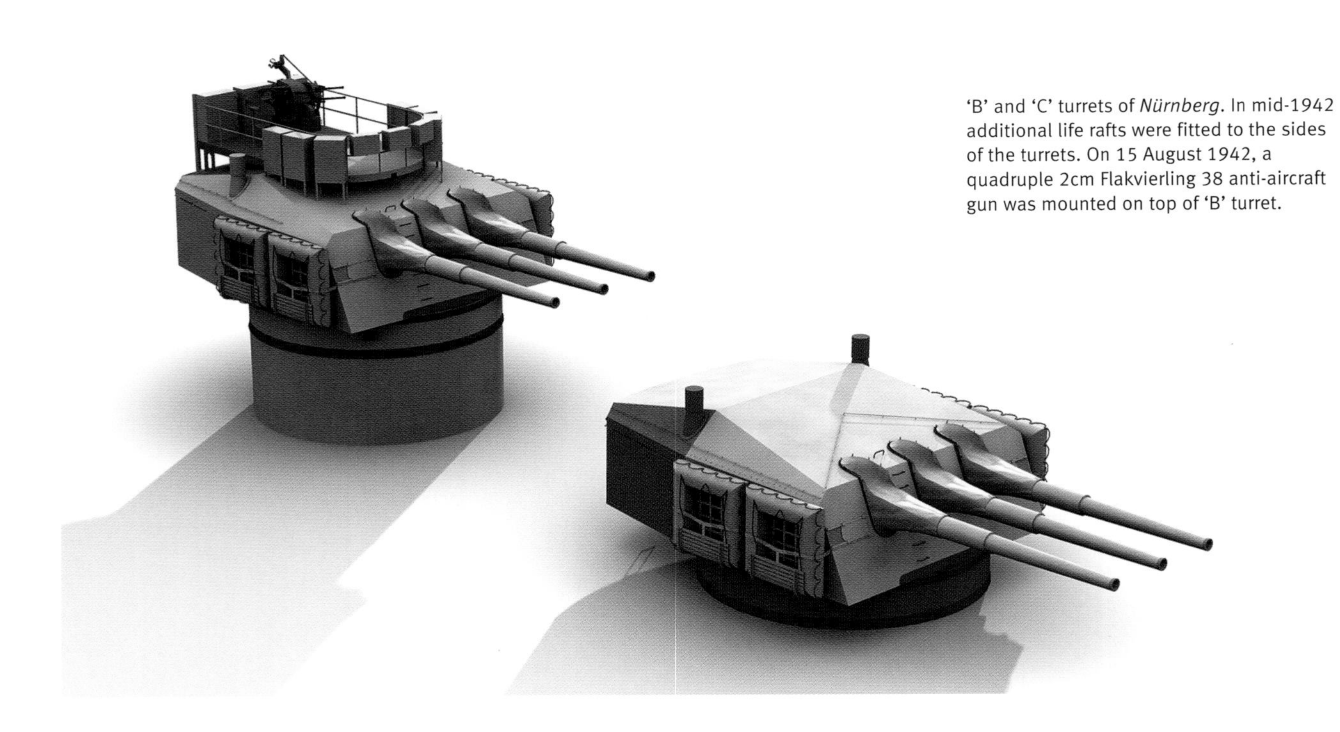

'B' and 'C' turrets of *Nürnberg*. In mid-1942 additional life rafts were fitted to the sides of the turrets. On 15 August 1942, a quadruple 2cm Flakvierling 38 anti-aircraft gun was mounted on top of 'B' turret.

5

THE 28cm SK C/34 GUNS
OF THE *SCHARNHORST* CLASS BATTLESHIPS

On 11 October 1933, at a meeting concerning Battleship 'D', it was decided to arm her with the 280mm guns already proved in the *Deutschland* class, and her first main turrets were ordered in November of the same year. But a month later the subject was reconsidered. At a meeting with Hitler, Admiral Raeder proposed increasing the combat effectiveness of the new battleship by adding a third 280mm turret, but Hitler rejected this. Raeder was far from satisfied with the design of the new ship, believing that it had been compromised by political factors and that she was thus inferior to her likely opponents, the French *Dunkerque* class. Adding the third turret would at least make a start in closing the gap between them. On 5 June 1934 Hitler finally agreed to the third turret, but was still resolutely opposed to any increase in gun calibre. Of course, the decision to add the extra turret brought an immediate halt to construction work on

Left: *Scharnhorst*'s commissioning ceremony was held on 7 January 1939, in Wilhelmshaven. Captain Otto Ciliax – the officer saluting on the podium erected on the 'C' turret catapult – had just taken command of the new ship. *(CAW collection)*

Above: *Scharnhorst* fitting-out in the summer of 1937. 'A' turret, covered by a tarpaulin, in the foreground. Behind it the first level of the forward superstructure and the conning tower have just been built. 'B' barbette can be seen in the centre of the photograph. *(S Breyer collection)*

Above: A 28cm gun mount for the *Scharnhorst*. *(M Skwiot collection)*

Below: 'B' turret of *Scharnhorst*. Note the welding seam joining the armour slabs making up the barbette. 'A' turret is in the background, with the tell-tale stowage bin. *(Photo Dr Wehlau, A Jarski collection)*

Below: 'A' turret with armoured covers protecting the optical rangefinder. The absence of a crest dates the photo to after the outbreak of war. *(Photo Dr Wehlau, A Jarski collection)*

Left: Forward turrets of *Scharnhorst*, late November 1939. Note that the military censor has obliterated the naval base scenery from the photo, giving a maritime background instead. *(M Skwiot collection)*

Below: The forward turrets of the battleship *Scharnhorst*. Minor differences in detail allow them to be distinguished from those of her sister-ship *Gneisenau*. First were the two small stowage bins, fixed one to each side, at the foot of 'A' barbette, and second were the crests on *Scharnhorst*'s turrets. *(M Skwiot collection)*

Left: Forward superstructure of *Scharnhorst*, April 1940, off Wilhelmshaven. The battleship has recognition signs for the Luftwaffe, consisting of the national flags painted on the forecastle and fantail, as well as the roofs and roof slopes of the main and secondary turrets painted red. *(Photo Dr Wehlau, A Jarski collection)*

Left: Main turrets of *Scharnhorst* seen from the forecastle. The turret roofs and slopes are painted red. This photo was taken off Wilhelmshaven in April 1940, during the preparations for Operation 'Weserübung'. *(Photo Dr Wehlau, A Jarski collection)*

Above: Cleaning 'A' turret's guns. To make this a bit easier, the guns were set at maximum depression. Note that 'B' turret, trained to port, has a small stowage bin (barely visible in this photo) on the rear slope, which *Gneisenau* did not have. *(Photo Dr Wehlau, A Jarski collection)*

Below: Main turrets of *Scharnhorst* seen from the forecastle. The turret roofs and slopes are painted red. This photo was taken off Wilhelmshaven in April 1940, during the preparations for Operation 'Weserübung'. *(Photo Dr Wehlau, A Jarski collection)*

Battleship 'D', as serious redesign of the hull was now needed. A later proposal to arm the ship with 330mm guns in twin turrets was rejected because the changes necessary would have delayed the commissioning of the ship until mid-1939!

The subject of her armament was still far from closed, however. The design had been accepted on the proviso that, should the need arise, the ship could be re-armed with heavier guns at nine month's notice. In March 1935 new proposals for re-armament were in the air, and 305mm, 330mm, 350mm and 380mm guns were all considered. The decisive factor seems to have been ammunition supply: with 280mm guns, the ship could hold up to 150 rounds per gun, but only 130 rounds per gun with a 380mm main battery. On the other hand, bigger guns meant a heavier shell and longer range, allowing effective fire to be opened at greater distances, but at extreme ranges the chance of penetrating the armour of the *Dunkerque* class had to be sufficient to warrant all the trouble of fitting the heavier guns. So, the choice of main armament calibre was not a decision to be taken lightly. Each option had as many disadvantages as advantages. Once again, the final outcome was a compromise between operational requirements on the one hand and Germany's economic and political situation on the other. The ships were to be provisionally armed with 280mm guns pending rearmament with a new 350mm gun once it was perfected. But after a while it became clear that the 350mm was only marginally superior in performance to the 330mm gun, and after another round of arguments, the subject was finally shelved for good.

The gun

Scharnhorst and *Gneisenau*'s 28cm SK C/34 guns were in fact of 283mm calibre. The only difference between this weapon and its predecessor aboard the *Deutschland* class was that it fired a shell with a

Right: *Scharnhorst*'s 'C' turret, with the crew assembled in the background. *(Photo Dr Wehlau, A Jarski collection)*

Below: *Scharnhorst*'s 'C' turret with a floatplane catapult, in the Wilhelmshaven roadstead, November 1939. *(S Breyer collection)*

Above: *Scharnhorst* moored at the H1 quay in Hipper Basin, Wilhelmshaven. The photo, taken probably in early March 1940, shows new engineering ratings being trained at the pier. Note the battleship's floatplane catapult suspended from the Lange Heinrich floating crane in the background. Experience showed that having the catapult on top of 'C' turret was not a good idea and it was soon removed. *(S Breyer collection)*

different aspect ratio – even the propellant charge was the same. The new armour-piercing shell was heavier due to its redesigned core, intended to provide superior penetration.

The guns were mounted in triple DrhL C/34 turrets. The ammunition hoists were placed between the guns, a double one between the right and centre gun, and a single one between the centre and left guns. Each hoist carriage had three trays for (bottom to top) the projectile, the fore charge and the main charge, which mirrored the layout of the magazines and shell rooms. The shell room was at the deepest level of all, with the magazine above it. The projectiles were first fed onto the revolving shell ring at the base of the turret, and then over rollers to the hoist carriage. At the same time, one deck up, the propellant charges were being loaded into the hoist carriage. The door to the hoist trunk in the magazine had two shelves on it, the upper one for the main charge and the lower for the fore charge. The cased main charges were passed in cartridge-ring cars while the bagged fore charges were passed manually. The charges were placed on their respective shelves on the door, which was then closed, automatically transferring them to the corresponding trays in the hoist carriage. After the carriage had been raised to the gun platform level, the shell slid back onto a loading tray, where it was chambered by a single stroke of a hydraulic rammer. At the same time, the charges were placed in the appropriate parts of the loading tray. The fore charge was chambered by hand while the rammer was retracting, ready to chamber the main charge with its second stroke. The gun was now loaded and the breech block closed. All the hoists and ramming gear were manually controlled.

Should the main ammunition hoist malfunction, there was an auxiliary electrically-powered hoist behind the centre gun, which in the course of normal operations was used to return ammunition components to the magazines. Even if the electric hoist failed, ammunition could still reach the guns via a manually-operated back-up hoist.

After the gun had fired, the empty case slid down a chute to the ejection port in the turret floor, which was covered by a manually-operated flap. The breech was sealed with a special cover which funnelled the smoke and powder fumes towards the electric extractor fans at the rear which expelled them from the turret. Three other extractor fans were fitted in other parts of the turret, and fresh air was drawn in through three flap-covered inlets in the floor.

The 28cm SK C/34 gun

Calibre:	283mm
Weight of gun:	53,250kg
Overall length:	15,415mm
Length bore:	14,505mm
Length chamber:	2,619mm
Volume chamber:	180dm^3
Length rifling:	11,725mm
Grooves:	80 (3.25mm x 6.72mm)
Weight projectile:	330kg
Propellant charge:	119kg of RP C/38 (15/4.9)
Muzzle velocity:	890mps
Working pressure:	3,200kg/cm^2
Approximate service life:	300 effective rounds
Maximum range:	40,930m at 40°

Range and ballistic data for 300kg projectiles

Range	Angle of elevation	Angle of descent	Velocity
5,000m	2.0°	2.5°	766mps
10,000m	4.3°	5.7°	652mps
15,000m	7.4°	10.3°	556mps
20,000m	11.3°	17.2°	481mps
25,000m	16.2°	25.7°	436mps
30,000m	22.0°	35.3°	418mps
35,000m	29.2°	44.0°	428mps
40,000m	38.2°	52.0°	460mps

The DrhL C/34 turret

Each turret had three 280mm guns in C/28 mounts. Apart from their increased armour protection, they were virtually identical to those mounted on the *Deutschland* class.

The two lower turrets had six working levels:

1. The armoured gun platform (above the barbette).
2. The training platform (turntable) (inside the barbette).
3. The machinery platform.

Above: The forward turrets of *Gneisenau* in the summer of 1938. Note what are probably awning eyelets on the forward slope of the turret. *(Photo Urbahns, T Klimczyk collection)*

Right: Tarpaulin covers being put over the barrels of 'A' turret, to shield the turret from the waves. *(Photo Krasemann, CAW collection)*

Left: *Gneisenau*'s forecastle and forward turrets photographed off Wilhelmshaven. *(Photo Dr Wehlau, A Jarski collection*

4. The intermediate platform.
5. The magazine platform.
6. The shell room platform.

The single superfiring turret differed in having an additional intermediate platform. The gun platform housed three individually-mounted guns in separate cradles, with crank-actuated horizontally-sliding breech blocks. The breech-block cranks were hydraulically powered, but could be manually operated in an emergency. The firing system was electro-magnetic, with a manual back-up. Each gun had two hydraulic recoil

Below: *Gneisenau* after the review in honour of the visiting Hungarian regent, Admiral Miklos Horthy. Note that the turret has no name plaques or crests whatsoever. Sorting through the photographs of the battleship, I have never seen one showing her with any devices of that type on her turrets. *(Photo Urbahns, T Klimczyk collection)*

Above: During her stay in Wilhelmshaven the ship's anti-aircraft battery was augmented by mounting this Flak 38 gun on its land-service mount, here being uncovered by its crew, on top of 'A' turret. Later on it was removed.
(S Breyer collection)

Opposite, above: *Gneisenau*'s quarterdeck being readied for Admiral Lütjens' inspection on 14 April 1941. Note that 'C' turret, in the background, also had awning attachment points like the forward turrets.
(S Breyer collection)

Opposite, below: Forward guns of the *Gneisenau* during her stay at Wilhelmshaven in the winter of 1940/41.
(S Breyer collection)

absorbers and a pneumatic recuperator.

There were two sighting positions between the guns, the right-hand one having an optical sight and a direction indicator. On either side of each gun were the elevation controls, and there were periscope visors for the turret commander outside of the left- and right-hand guns. The ammunition hoists were between the guns, and at the rear of the turret were the extractor

The DrhL C/34 turret

Revolving weight:	750 tons
Ball track diameter:	9,000mm
Barbette internal diameter:	10,200mm
Distance between gun axes:	2,750mm
Recoil distance:	1,200mm
Maximum elevating speed:	8°/sec.
Maximum training speed:	7.2°/sec.
Fields of fire:	
Turrets 'A' and 'C':	290°; 0° thro' 145° on each side (215° – 0° – 145°)
Turret 'B':	290°; 0° thro' 145° on each side (215° – 0° – 145°)
Rangefinder:	10.5m optical fitted in Turrets 'A', 'B' and 'C' (only 'B' and 'C' from 1942)
Turret armour:	Face 360mm; sides 180mm; slopes 150mm; roof 180mm
Rate of fire:	1 shot every 17 sec. at +4° elevation (reloading gear operated at +2° elevation)
Depression/elevation	
Turrets 'A' and 'C':	–8°/+40°
Turret 'B':	–9°/+40°

fans and the spent-case ejection ports, as well as a 12-round ready-use ammunition supply.

The gun platform was protected by an armoured shield resting on the turret turntable, the side and top plates being bolted to the turret framework. The rangefinder optics were shielded by armoured caps, and inside the turret the guns were separated by splinter shields. The whole structure was designed to dissipate the force of the recoil.

The lower part of the gun platform rested on ball bearings, with the electric motors and training gear suspended beneath it. Theoretically the turret could rotate 360°, but the actual arcs of fire were as follows:

Turrets 'A' and 'C': 290° – 0° thro' 145° on each side
(215° – 0° – 145°)
Turret 'B': 290° – 0° thro' 145° on each side
(215° – 0° – 145°)

The hydraulic elevating gear (with an electric back-up system for emergencies) was also suspended beneath the gun platform. Maximum elevation was +40° and maximum depression -8° (-9° for the single super-firing turret). All other systems – hoists, rammers, etc – were hydraulically operated.

The turret's hydraulic system was powered by two paired electric motors and compressors on the machinery platform level. The control panel for the valves for all the motors was on the forward wall of the machinery space, which also accommodated a 220V petrol-driven DC electric generator, with a control panel on the rear wall. Steel cylinders for compressed air for the pneumatic systems were beneath the machinery platform.

The barbettes

Battleship 'D's barbettes consisted of a single conical cylinder, reaching from the armoured deck to just above the main deck, made of 350mm-thick KC n/A steel. The lower rim of 'B' turret's barbette was rivetted to the 95mm armour deck with steel formers, while that of 'A' turret was rivetted to the 110mm armour and that of 'C' turret to the 105mm armour. The magazines and shell rooms under the barbette were within the armoured citadel.

Ammunition

As with all German heavy-calibre ammunition, that for the *Scharnhorst* class ships was supplied by Krupp's.

28cm SK C/34 shells

(a) Armour-piercing shell L/4.4 weighing 300kg, 1,245mm long, with Bdz C/38 base fuse.
(b) High-explosive shell L/4.4 weighing 315kg, 1,245mm long, with Bdz C/38 base fuse.
(c) High-explosive shell L/4.4 weighing 315kg, 1,273mm long, with Kz C/27 nose fuse.

Propellant charges

Two types with RP C/32 propellant
(a) Main charge (cased) of 74.8kg or 77.2kg
(b) Fore charge (cotton bag) of 41.1kg or 42.4kg.

For ease of identification the different types of shell were painted different colours: armour-piercing were blue, high explosive yellow and inert training rounds red.

Left: Details of *Gneisenau*'s 'B' turret and barbette. *(Photo Dr Wehlau, A Jarski collection)*

Magazines and shell rooms

These were positioned within the armoured citadel, in compartments XVII and XVIII for 'A' turret, XV and XVI for 'B' turret and III and IV for 'C' turret. This minimised the distance ammunition had to travel to the hoists, thus speeding up the loading process and thus also the rate of fire. The propellant charge magazines were at the platform deck level, directly above the shell rooms on the intermediate platform deck (mittleres Platformdeck) level.

Turret designations, names and markings

As with all Kriegsmarine ships, the turrets of *Scharnhorst* and *Gneisenau* were designated with alphabetical letter-flag codenames: the forward turret was thus 'A for Anton', the superfiring turret 'B for Bruno' and the after turret 'C for Caesar'. Neither ship is known to have had individual names given to their turrets, but photographs taken between April and May 1939 show that *Scharnhorst* had her coat of arms on the front or sides of her forward turrets. As with all identifying badges etc, aboard German ships, these were removed at the outbreak of war.

28cm SK C/34 guns in shore batteries

When the *Gneisenau* was disarmed in 1943, 'B' and 'C' turrets were sent to Norway to become shore batteries. 'B' became Batterie Fjell on the island of Sotra off Bergen and 'C' became Batterie Ørland at the entrance to the Trondheim fjord. The three guns removed from the burnt-out 'Anton' turret were mounted in single C/37 turrets, destined for a shore battery near Rotterdam in the Netherlands.

Left and below: The forward turrets of *Scharnhorst* engage enemy shipping. The absence of awning mounting points confirms the identity of the ship. *(CAW collection)*

6

THE 20.3cm SK C/34 GUNS

OF THE *ADMIRAL HIPPER* CLASS HEAVY CRUISERS

The first plans for German heavy cruisers were drawn up in February 1934. They had to meet three requirements: they had to be comparable to the French *Algerie* class, they had to be faster than the *Dunkerque*, and they had to have sufficient range for commerce-raiding in the Atlantic. The decision on their main armament was postponed, the choice being between a battery of eight 203mm guns or twelve 150mm guns. In April 1934, Admiral Raeder chose the 203mm gun, but this was not the end of the matter. In May 1935 there was a proposal to arm these ships with 190mm guns, the point being that with these only marginally lighter weapons a considerable saving in overall displacement could be made. However, detailed investigation found that the weight saving achieved was insufficient to justify the cost of the change and the loss in combat power, so the 190mm project was abandoned.

Construction of the first two units of the class began in secret, as the political situation was unfavourable to a German heavy cruiser programme, but all secrecy was abandoned in March 1936, when Germany finally repudiated the Treaty of Versailles. These ships, Cruisers 'K' and 'L', had been laid down as light cruisers armed with 150mm guns, but in order to meet their required speed and level of

Left: The heavy cruiser *Admiral Hipper* moored at buoy A9 in the Heikendorf roadstead, Kiel, soon after commissioning. *(M Skwiot collection)*

Above: *Admiral Hipper* putting out of Kiel. Note that she still has a straight prow, dating the photo to the period before her modernisation. An interesting point in this photo is 'A' turret with a white circle painted on the roof as a recognition sign for the Luftwaffe – such signs were not used prior to the outbreak of war. *(Photo Drüppel, A Jarski collection)*

armour protection, their displacement had almost doubled from their planned 10,000 tons, so they were reclassified as heavy cruisers and armed with 203mm guns.

The guns

The 20.3cm SK C/34 guns were mounted in two types of turret (see below) in the *Admiral Hipper* class cruisers. As with all German naval guns of this period, they were of modern design with sliding breech blocks and hydraulic loading gear, giving them a theoretical rate of fire of 4-4.5 rounds per minute, or one shot every 13-15 seconds. However, the need to depress the guns to +3° for reloading meant that in practice the rate of fire was one salvo per turret every 21-22 seconds.

A unique feature of this gun was the design of its multi-layered barrel. The inner liner was loose inside the two-layer outer barrel, and could fit any variant of the gun. It could be easily replaced when worn by unscrewing the breech piece and withdrawing the liner from the rear end of the barrel, thus greatly facilitating barrel replacement by making it unnecessary to dismantle the gun completely.

Above: *Admiral Hipper* putting into Brest in 1941. She is painted in one of the early Norwegian 'splinter' camouflage schemes. *(Photo Drüppel, M Skwiot collection)*

Right: *Admiral Hipper* being docked in Brest. 'C' and 'D' turrets in the foreground. *(Photo Drüppel, M Skwiot collection)*

The 20.3cm SK C/34 gun

Calibre:	203mm
Weight of gun:	20,700kg
Overall length:	12,150mm
Length bore:	11,518mm
Length chamber:	1,873mm
Volume chamber:	70dm^3
Length rifling:	9,527mm
Grooves:	64 (2.4mm x 5.76mm)
Weight projectile:	122kg
Propellant charge:	50.8 kg of RP C/38 (11/4.3)
Muzzle velocity:	925mps
Working pressure:	3,200kg/cm^2
Approximate service life:	510 effective rounds
Maximum range:	33,540m at 37°

Range and ballistic data for 122kg projectiles

Range	Elevation	Angle of descent	Time of flight	Velocity
5,000m	1.9°	2.1°	6.0 sec	744mps
10,000m	4.4°	6.1°	13.6 sec	587mps
15,000m	8.1°	12.8°	23.4 sec	463mps
20,000m	13.3°	23.6°	35.9 sec	382mps
25,000m	20.3°	36.8°	51.1 sec	353mps
30,000m	29.1°	48.8°	69.0 sec	363mps

The DrhL C/34 turret

Apart from their different dimensions, these hydraulically-trained twin turrets were very similar in layout to those for the 380mm gun. Early on in their design process, it was decided to remove the rangefinders

Left: After turrets of *Admiral Hipper* returning from gunnery practice held between 20 and 29 August 1942. Note the rubber mats placed around 'D' barbette: these were to protect the wooden deck from the heavy cases ejected from the turret. Note *Tirpitz* in the background of the upper photo. *(CAW collection)*

Above: *Admiral Hipper* during her stay in Loofjord. Note the quadruple Flakvierling 38 anti-aircraft gun on top of 'C' turret. *(Photo Drüppel, M Skwiot collection)*

from 'A' and 'D' turrets, which accounts for their being lower and lighter than the superfiring ones, which retained the rangefinders.

The turrets had five working levels:

1. Gun platform level.
2. Machinery platform level.
3. Intermediate platform level.
4. Magazine level.
5. Shell room level.

The superfiring turrets had an extra intermediate level. Electric extractor fans were fitted to the rear of the turrets: on the lower turrets they were in the middle of the rear wall, while on the superfiring ones they were positioned at either end of the rear wall. As in the turrets of *Bismarck* and *Tirpitz*, there were two spent-case ejection ports in the rear floor plate.

Right: *Blücher* fitting-out in the Deutsche Werke shipyard, Kiel, in late 1938. *(S Breyer collection)*

Above: The heavy cruiser *Admiral Hipper* in the Deutsche Werke shipyard basin. She was covered with camouflage netting to conceal her from British aircraft – the extent of the damage she suffered in air raids shows that this was far from successful. 'C' and 'D' turrets in the foreground. *(Imperial War Museum)*

Left: Hoisting the flag aboard the newly-commissioned heavy cruiser *Admiral Hipper*. *(CAW collection)*

Above: *Blücher* off Kiel, soon after she had been commissioned. *(M Skwiot collection)*

Above: *Blücher* steaming out of Kiel for sea trials, late September or early October 1939. The background has been doctored by the military censor to prevent the location being identified. *(M Skwiot collection)*

Below: *Prinz Eugen* in Kiel after commissioning, during preparations for her redeployment to the Baltic. This photo shows the aerial recognition signs being painted on the roofs and top slopes of the main turrets. *(Photo Drüppel, A Jarski collection)*

Left: Forward turrets of *Prinz Eugen* during gunnery practice prior to Operation 'Rheinübung'. *(CAW collection)*

The DrhL C/34 turret

Revolving weight:	248 tons
Ball track diameter:	5,330mm
Barbette internal diameter:	6,400mm
Distance between gun axes:	2,160mm
Recoil distance:	625mm
Maximum elevating speed:	8°/sec
Maximum training speed:	8°/sec
Fields of fire:	
Turrets 'A' and 'D':	290°; 0° thro' 145° on each side (215° – 0° – 145°)
Turrets 'B' and 'C':	290°; 0° thro' 145° on each side (215° – 0° – 145°)
Rate of fire:	1 shot every 12 sec (or 5 rpm) at +4o elevation
Turret armour:	
Turrets 'A' and 'D':	Face 160mm; sides 70mm; rear 90mm; turret slopes – front 105mm, rear 80mm, sides 80mm, roof 70mm.
Turrets 'B' and 'C':	Face 160mm; sides 70mm; rear 60mm; turret slopes – front 105mm, rear 70mm, sides 80mm, roof 70mm
Elevation/depression:	
'B', 'C' and 'D' turrets:	–10°/ +37°
'A' turret:	–9°/+37°
Loading elevation:	+3°

The crews of 'A' and 'D' turrets numbered 72 men each, with 'B' and 'C' having four extra men each for their rangefinders. Differences in armour protection, plus the rangefinders, meant that 'A' and 'D' turrets each weighed 249 tons each, while 'B' and 'C' each weighed 262 tons.

The barbettes

The barbettes of 'A' and 'D' turrets consisted of a single cylinder of 80mm-thick KC armoured steel, 5,700mm high, which reached from the armoured deck to about 1m above the level of the main deck. The superfiring barbettes were similar, both in construction and arrangement.

Ammunition

20.3cm SK C/34 shells

(a) Armour-piercing shell L/4.4, weight 122kg, length 895mm, Bdz C/38 base fused.
(b) High-explosive shell L/4.7, weight 122kg, length 956mm, Bdz C/38 base fused.
(c) High-explosive shell L/4.7, weight 122kg, length 953mm, Kz nose fused.

Propellant charges

Two types with RP C/38 propellant
(a) 21.1kg fore charge, 900mm long.
(b) 29.7 kg main charge, 875mm long in an 18.2kg case.

Ammunition stores aboard *Admiral Hipper* class cruisers

Magazines and shell rooms were housed close to the main barbettes within the armoured citadel, in compartment IX for 'A' and 'B' turrets and compartment II for 'C' and 'D' turrets. Initially the 203mm ammunition load for these ships was 320 armour-piercing shells, 320 based-fused high explosive and 320 nose-fused high explosive, with 960 propellant charge sets (fore charge and main charge). 'B' and 'C' turrets were also supplied with 40 rounds of star shell each. Later the ammunition load was increased to 1,280 rounds, i.e. 160 per gun. However, the actual supply loaded in fact depended on the operation requirements of the ship's mission. For example, for her Atlantic raid in 1941 *Admiral Hipper* took on board 1,470 rounds of main-gun ammunition, as well as 40 rounds of star shell.

Right: 20.3cm ammunition for *Admiral Hipper* class heavy cruisers temporarily stacked beside a Norwegian fjord. *(CAW collection)*

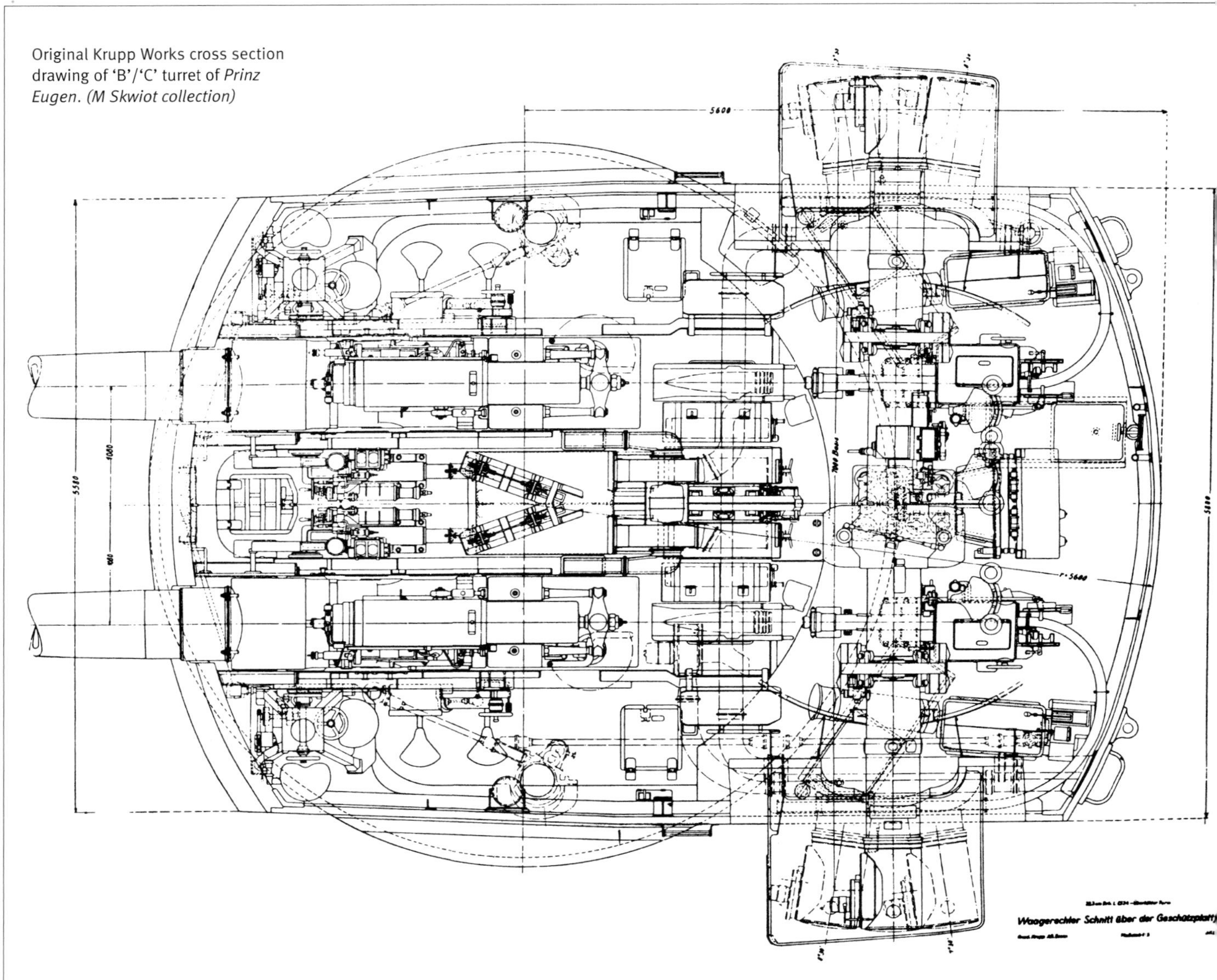

Original Krupp Works cross section drawing of 'B'/'C' turret of *Prinz Eugen*. *(M Skwiot collection)*

Above: Forward turrets *Prinz Eugen* approaching Brest in May 1941. Note the turret roofs are painted yellow, an aerial recognition sign for the Luftwaffe. *(S Breyer collection)*

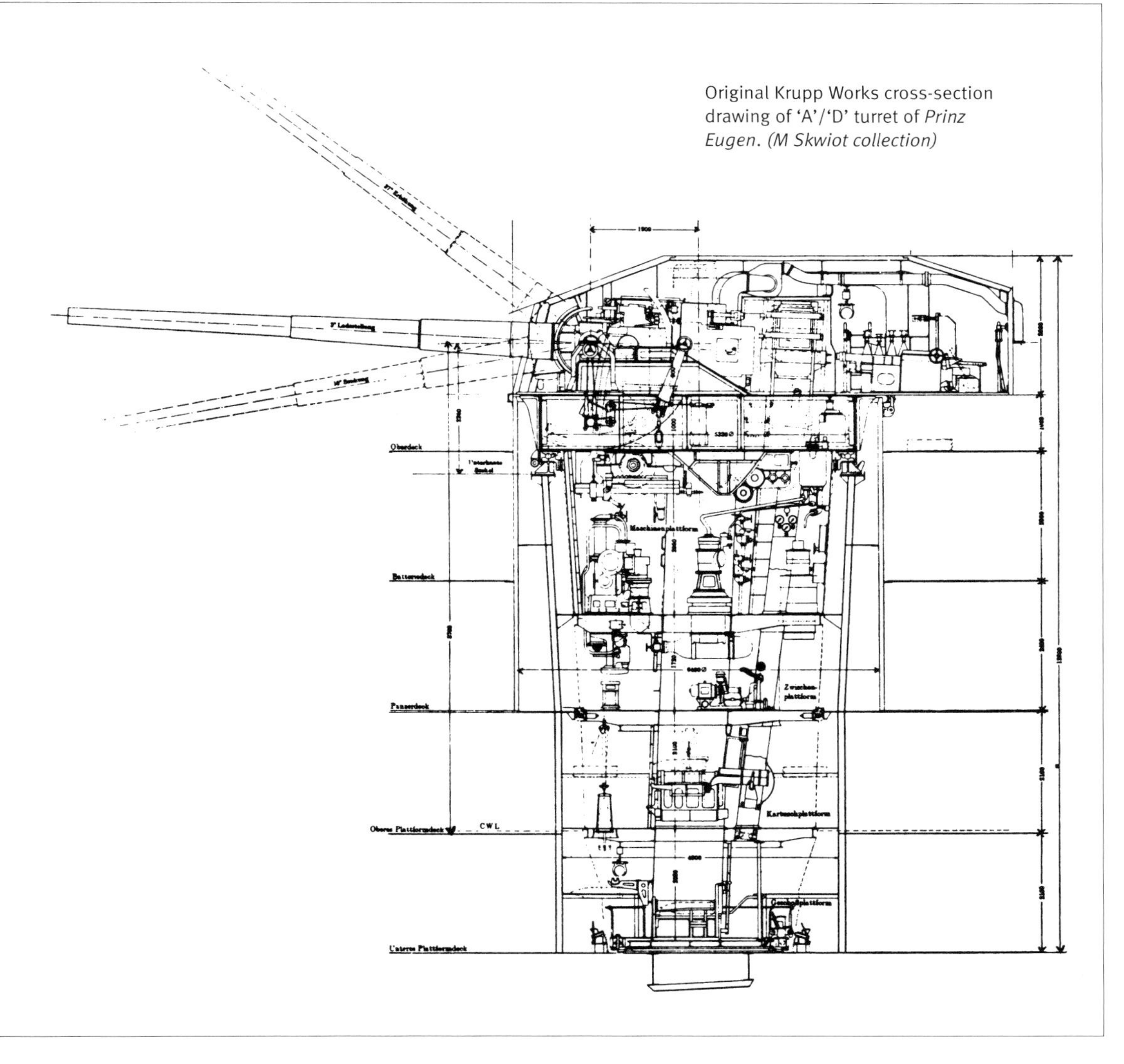

Original Krupp Works cross-section drawing of 'A'/'D' turret of *Prinz Eugen*. *(M Skwiot collection)*

Above and below: *Prinz Eugen* entering the Grimstadtfjord on 22 February 1942. *(CAW collection)*

Left: After turrets of *Prinz Eugen*. *(M Skwiot collection)*

20.3cm SK C/34 guns in shore batteries

When the cruiser *Seydlitz* was ordered to be completed as an aircraft carrier in 1942, her guns and turrets were transferred to the coastal artillery. Two turrets were installed on the Île de Croix off Lorient and the other two were intended for the Île de Re off La Pallice. Other spare guns were converted into railway guns as part of the 'Sofortprogramme' – a crash programme to reinforce coastal batteries with railway guns in preparation for the imminent Allied invasion. The eight 68-ton 20cm Kanone (E) L/59 that were completed were manned by Kriegsmarine fleet personnel, a departure from normal practice for such weapons. In 1944 all these guns were in France and soon six were captured, either directly by Allied forces or when the German fortresses on the Atlantic coast finally surrendered.

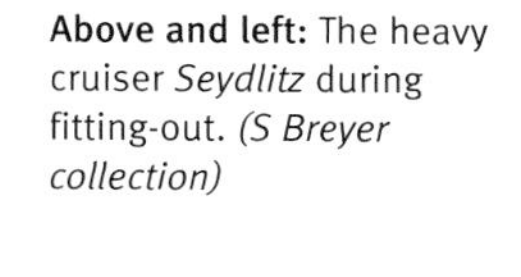

Above and left: The heavy cruiser *Seydlitz* during fitting-out. *(S Breyer collection)*

7

THE 15cm SK L/45 GUNS
OF THE CRUISER *EMDEN*

After defeat in the First World War, little of Germany's once enormous fleet was left to her. With her modern ships either lost in action or seized by the Allies, all that remained were some ageing and long-obsolete pre-war vessels. Although the Treaty of Versailles permitted the new Kriegsmarine to replace these ships once they were twenty years old, Germany's political and financial situation meant that this could only happen piecemeal. The first ship to come due for replacement was the cruiser *Ariadne*. The design for 'Ersatz *Ariadne*', as the ship was first known, was based on that of the wartime-built cruisers, restricted to a displacement of 6,000 tons, and included an armament of 150mm guns in newly-designed twin turrets. However, a severe shortage of materials at Rheinmetall meant that these new turrets were never built. Instead, the new ship was to be armed with surplus 15cm SK L/45 guns in single mounts. These weapons had formed the secondary armament of battleships and battlecruisers, and were cheap and readily available. Once these casemate guns had been fitted with new shields, they could be mounted on the deck of the new cruiser.

In 1929, a plan to re-arm the *Emden* with twin 150mm turrets, as originally intended, was considered but it was shelved because the turret design team was busy with work on the *Königsberg*, the first of the 'K' class cruisers armed with brand new triple turrets, which were necessary if German ships were to be able to compete with their foreign counterparts whilst remaining within the Treaty-imposed limits on displacement.

The 15cm SK L/45 gun

Calibre:	149.1mm
Weight of gun:	5,730kg without shield, 6,102kg with shield
Overall length:	6,710mm
Length bore:	6,326mm
Length chamber:	1,150mm
Volume chamber:	21.7dm^3
Grooves:	48
Weight projectile:	45.3kg
Propellant charge:	14.35kg
Muzzle velocity:	835m/s
Approximate service life:	1,400 effective rounds
Maximum range:	19,400m at 30°
Depression/elevation:	−10°/+27°
Rate of fire:	4-5 rounds per minute

Below and opposite: The *Emden*'s guns had previously been mounted in casemates aboard capital ships, so for use as deck guns they had to be fitted with armoured shields to protect their crews. *(Photo Renard from A Jarski collection [below], CAW collection [opposite])*

Above: The cruiser *Emden* in the Kiel roadstead. She was armed with single-mounted 15cm SK L/45 guns, which had been taken from the secondary batteries of decommissioned First World War battleships and battlecruisers. *(Photo Drüppel, A Jarski collection)*

The 15cm SK L/45 gun on the MPL C/16 mount

This gun had entered service with the Imperial German Navy in 1908, after two years of trials. After the First World War, it survived as the secondary armament of the ageing pre-dreadnought battleships *Schliesen* and *Schleswig-Holstein*, while others were taken from decommissioned ships and used to arm auxiliary cruisers during the Second World War.

The *Emden*, the first post-war German warship, was commissioned on 15 October 1925. She was armed with eight 15cm SK L/45 guns in single MPL C/16 mounts. 'A' gun was forward, at frame no. 94. 5 with 'B' gun at frame no. 84 superimposed, both with training arcs of 210°–0°–150°. On the starboard side forward, at frame no. 73.7, was 'C' gun with an arc of 10°–165° and further aft at frame no. 43.5 was 'D' gun with an arc of 15°–80°. Astern were superimposed 'E' gun at frame no. 20 and 'F' gun at frame no. 9, both with arcs of 30°–180°–330°. 'G' gun was on

Right: *Emden* entering the naval base at Wilhelmshaven. *(CAW collection)*

Below: Many civilians were able to see the *Emden*'s powerful armament during her frequent visits to various ports, where she was open to the public. Allied observers frequently mingled with the visitors on board to keep a watchful eye on Germany's observance of the terms of the peace. These photos show *Emden* during her stay at Wilhelmshaven. *(CAW collection)*

the port side aft, at frame no. 43.5 with an arc of 180°–345° and forward of that at frame no. 73.7 was 'H' gun with an arc of 195°–360°

Ammunition

15cm SK L/45 shells

(a) 45.3kg high-explosive nose-fused shell, 612mm long.
(b) 45.3kg high-explosive nose-fused shell, 609mm long.

The propellant charge was 14.35kg of RPC/38 in a 22.7kg brass case.

Ammunition stores aboard *Emden*

According to the original construction drawings of the ship dated November 1940, amended February 1941 and signed by the builder Krug, the magazines and shell rooms were housed in the following compartments: gun 'A' – XIX and XX; gun 'B' – XVII; guns 'C' and 'H' – XV; guns 'D' and 'E' – X; gun 'E' – V; and gun 'F' – II. The amendments do not include a proposal to re-arm *Emden* with single 15cm Tbts K C/36 guns in single Tbts L C/36 mounts. The ammunition supply carried equated to 120 rounds per gun.

Gun designations and names

Apart from the standard Kriegsmarine alphabetical letter-code designations for gun mounts, there is no evidence that *Emden*'s guns ever had individual names or badges of any kind.

Above: *Emden* leaving the naval base at Wilhelmshaven. *(CAW collection)*

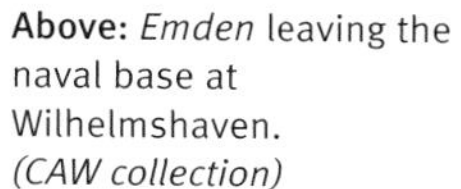

Left: Plans were drawn up for *Emden* to be re-armed with new 15cm Tbts K C/36 guns in single C/36 mounts, of the type designed for destroyers and torpedo boats, but in the end it never happened. *(Photo Drüppel, A Jarski collection)*

Below: *Emden*'s captain addressing his crew. Note the gun house of the forward 'A for Anton' gun. Superimposed above that was 'B for Bruno'. All main turrets were given alphabetical signal-flag names. *(CAW collection)*

Above: *Emden* at the pier in Kiel. *(CAW collection)*

Left: The pre-dreadnought *Schleswig-Holstein* passing under the Levensau bridge on the outskirts of Kiel, en route to Wilhelmshaven. Her secondary battery casemate guns were the same as *Emden*'s main battery. *(CAW collection)*

Below: *Schlesien*, *Schleswig-Holstein*'s sister-ship, was also armed with 15cm SK L/45 guns in casemates. *(CAW collection)*

Above: *Schlesien* at sea. Note the 15cm SK L/45 guns in casemates. *(M Skwiot collection)*

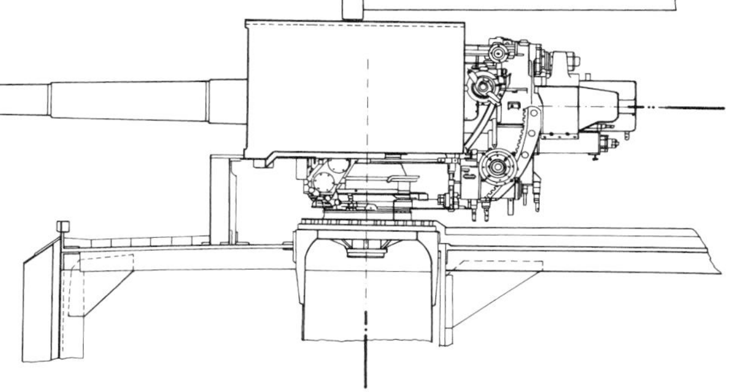

Above: Single-mounted 15cm SK L/45 gun.

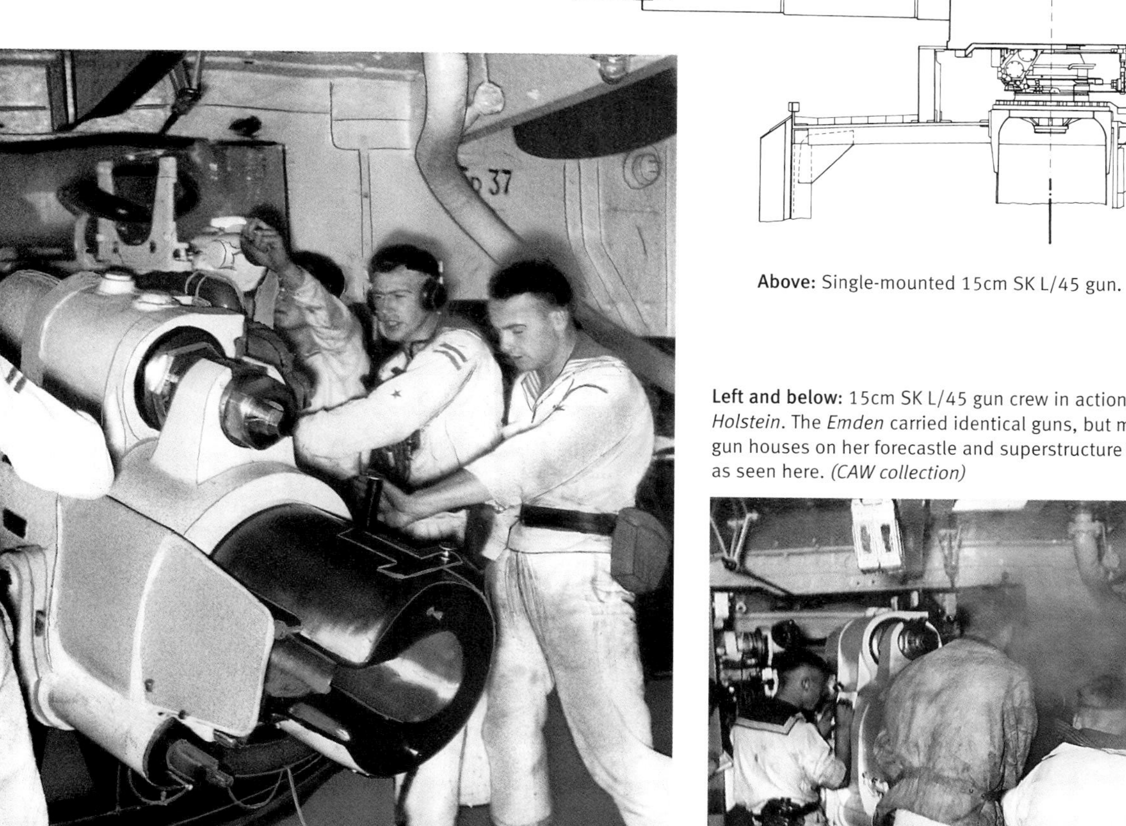

Left and below: 15cm SK L/45 gun crew in action, on board the *Schleswig-Holstein*. The *Emden* carried identical guns, but mounted in semi-enclosed gun houses on her forecastle and superstructure instead of in casemates, as seen here. *(CAW collection)*

Above and below: *Schleswig-Holstein* steaming down the Kiel Canal. Upper photo shows her broadside view before modernisation. *(CAW collection)*

8

THE 15cm SK C/25 GUN

ABOARD 'K' CLASS CRUISERS

At the same time as the *Emden*, a new class of 6,000-ton light cruisers was being designed, also to be armed with 150mm guns. Initially these were to be fitted in single shielded open mounts, but as all other contemporary cruisers had their main armament in enclosed turrets it was decided to adopt this arrangement as well. Two variants of the design were prepared, the first with four twin turrets as had originally been planned for the *Emden*. These mounts were to be thoroughly trialled first in this ship, so any changes needed could be incorporated before they were fitted to the new cruisers. The second version, which was the one adopted, had three new DrhL C/25 triple turrets with guns firing the heavier 45.5kg shell.

After the first of class, *Königsberg*, was launched in mid-1926, there was a proposal to arm the ship with 190mm guns in triple turrets. Although an attractive option, the fact that such turrets would not be available until February 1929 and the ship was due to commission in the autumn of 1928 meant that it was dropped.

Königsberg was commissioned on 17 April 1929, followed by *Karlsruhe* on 6 November and *Köln* on 15 January 1930. They completed with nine 150mm guns in three DrhL C/25 triple turrets, one forward and two aft. 'A' turret was mounted at main deck level, but the after turrets, uniquely, were mounted offset from the centreline in order to increase their arc of fire. The superimposed 'B' turret was offset 2,250mm to port, while 'C' turret was offset 1,950mm to starboard. This configuration was not repeated on any future ships.

The guns

The 'K' class were armed with quick-firing 15cm SK C/25 guns with 60-calibre barrels, mounted in DrhL C/25 triple turrets designed and built by Rheinmetall of Düsseldorf.

The 15cm SK C/25 gun

Calibre:	149.1mm
Weight of gun:	11,970kg
Overall length:	9,080mm
Length bore:	8,570mm
Length chamber:	1,396mm
Volume chamber:	27.7dm^3
Length rifling:	7,067mm
Grooves:	44 (1.75mm x 6.14mm)
Weight projectile:	45.5kg
Propellant charge:	20.4kg of RPC/38 (10/4.4)
Muzzle velocity:	960mps
Working pressure:	3,000 kg/cm^2
Approximate service life:	500 effective rounds
Maximum range:	25,700m at 40°, 14,100m at 10°

Below: *Königsberg* was the first 'K' class cruiser, commissioned on 17 April 1929. Her main battery consisted of nine quick-firing 15cm SK C/25 guns mounted in C/25 turrets. *(CAW collection)*

Range and ballistic data with 45.5kg projectiles

Range	Elevation	Angle of drop	Velocity
5,000m	1.7°	2.2°	673mps
10,000m	5.3°	8.8°	445mps
15,000m	11.5°	23.5°	318mps
20,000m	21.4°	42.0°	314mps
25,000m	36.3°	59.5°	332mps

Above: Calibration shooting by the fore and aft main turrets aboard *Königsberg*, 1937. Note that the medium-calibre anti-aircraft guns are still yet to be mounted. *(A Jarski collection)*

The DrhL C/25 turret

The three turrets of these ships were outwardly identical except for the position of the ladder on the front of the turret: on 'A' turret it was between the right and centre guns, while on 'B' and 'C' turrets, it was between the left and centre guns. Because the guns were mounted at different levels within the turret, each had its own cradle, with each one having

Right: The C/25 turrets were the first such design in the German Navy, and had certain drawbacks. One of these was having to eject the spent cases by hand through ports in the rear of the turret, below which baskets were fitted to catch them. *(A Jarski collection)*

Above and left: 'B' and 'C' turrets were mounted in a rather unusual way on board the 'K' class cruisers. To increase their arcs of fire, they were offset from the centerline of the ship. 'B' turret was offset 2,250mm to port, and 'C' turret 1,950mm to starboard. This novel arrangement did not prove advantageous and was never used again. *(CAW collection)*

Top left: *Königsberg*'s rear turrets with a nameplate clearly visible. *(CAW collection)*

Below: 'C' turret with an engraved brass nameplate commemorating SMS *Seydlitz* bolted to the glacis, just below the line of the gun ports. This photo was taken during her visit to the Polish naval base at Gdynia. *(CAW collection)*

separate ammunition supply arrangements.

There were two main hydraulic ammunition hoists and one emergency back-up electric hoist. The right-hand hoist served the right and centre guns, while the remaining gun had its own hoist on the left-hand side of the turret. The projectiles and cased charges came up on the hoist together, separating at the gun platform level and being moved to the breech on two trays. Loading was by hand, and the guns had semi-automatic vertical sliding breech blocks. The rate of fire for one gun was one round every 7.5 seconds.

Training and elevation were by electric motors, though this could be done manually in an emergency. The DrhL C/25 was the first German triple turret for light cruisers, and there were numerous teething problems. One of these involved the ejection of spent charge cases from the turret. These were ejected by hand through flap-covered ports at the back of the turret, outside which a canvas net was fixed to catch

Left: 'A' turret of *Königsberg* soon after she was commissioned. Note the absence of a nameplate from the turret face. *(A Jarski collection)*

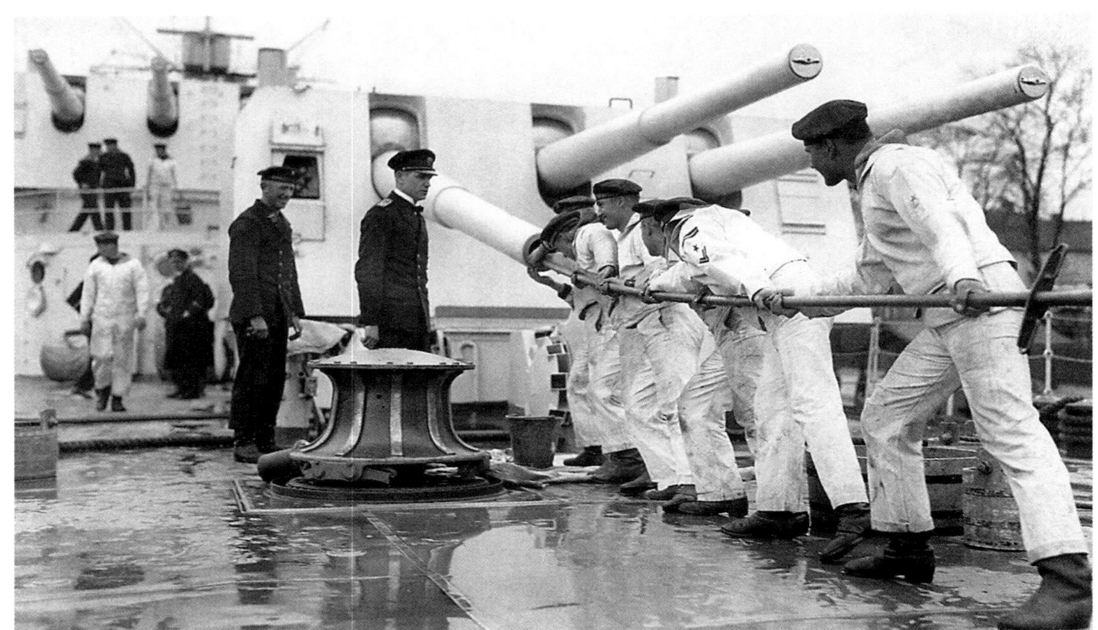

Right: Cleaning the barrels was always one of the most tedious chores for the gunners. *(CAW collection)*

Left: *Königsberg*'s after turrets. Note the turret details. *(T Klimczyk collection)*

Left: *Königsberg*'s gunners removing the empty casings from the baskets outside the turret after gunnery practice. *(CAW collection)*

Below: *Königsberg* moored at the pier in Gdynia harbour. Note the nameplate commemorating SMS *Derfflinger* on the front of 'A' turret. *(A Jarski collection)*

The DrhL C/25 turret

Revolving weight:	136.91 tons
Maximum cradle weight:	2,440kg
Barbette weight:	54,260kg
Sighting equipment weight:	3,500kg
Turret motors weight:	11,120kg
Armour weight:	24,800kg
Ball track diameter:	4,500mm
Barbette internal diameter:	5,700mm
Distance between gun axes:	1,550mm
Recoil distance:	370mm
Maximum elevating speed:	8°/sec
Maximum training speed:	6-8°/sec
Arcs of fire:	
'A' turret	215° – 0°– 145°
'B' and 'C' turret	Theoretically, combined arc of 360°
Turret armour:	Face 30mm; sides 20mm; roof and rear 20mm

them. However, these nets could only hold two cases at a time. During peacetime exercises, crewmen could be stationed behind the turrets to empty the nets as necessary, but this of course would have been impossible in actual combat. Each turret had a crew of fifteen.

Barbettes

Each barbette consisted of a single cylinder 5,700mm in diameter, 1,000mm high and 30mm thick. 'A' and 'C' barbettes were rivetted to the main deck, while the superimposed 'B' barbette was fixed to the after superstructure deck. The barbettes in all ships of the class were identical.

Beneath the barbettes were the internal supports for the turret turntable, a cylinder slightly smaller in diameter than the barbette itself, with beam knees. There were three working levels rotating above that, through which the ammunition was hoisted to the gun platform at the top.

Ammunition

15cm SK C/25 shells

(a) Armour-piercing shell, base-fused, 45.3kg, 550mm long.
(b) High-explosive shell, nose-fused, 45.3kg, 655mm long.
(c) High-explosive shell, base-fused, 45kg, 680mm long.
(d) Star shell, 41kg

The propellant charge was 19.3kg of either RPC/32 or RPC/38 in a 32.8kg brass case. The armour-piercing shell could penetrate 60mm of armour at 3,200m, but only 20mm at 11,200mm

'K' class ammunition stores

Magazines and shell rooms were positioned close to the barbettes, in section III for both after turrets and sections XII and XIV for the forward turret. 'B' and 'C' turrets being offset meant that the magazines could be positioned between them, while they had to be split fore and aft of 'A' turret. *Köln* had a different arrangement, with 'C' turret's magazines in section III and 'B's in section IV. In all ships, the ammunition supply equated to 120 rounds per gun.

Below: Two photos of *Königsberg* moored to the pier at Gdynia. Note the differences in the external equipment of the C/25 turrets: the ladder on the glacis of 'A' turret was offset to the right and set between the right and centre barrels. In 'B' and 'C' turrets it was offset to the left, and fixed between the left and centre guns. *(CAW collection)*

Above: The cruiser *Karlsruhe* steaming under the Levensau bridge, *en route* to Wilhelmshaven. Note the turrets are still lacking their glacis nameplates and emblems over the hatches. *(CAW collection)*

Below: *Karlsruhe* entering the Holtenau lock of the Kiel Canal, just after the nameplates had been fitted to the turrets. In this photo, however, the front turret's plaque, commemorating SMS *Moltke*, is obscured by a black rectangle. *(CAW collection)*

Below: Turrets 'B' and 'C' of the cruiser *Königsberg* ready for firing. Note the baskets to catch empty cases hanging from the rear of the turrets. *(CAW collection)*

Above: *Karlsruhe* in the Holtenau lock. Note absence of the nameplates and emblems on 'B' and 'C' turrets. *(CAW collection)*

Right: External details of *Karlsruhe*'s after C/25 turrets. *(CAW collection)*

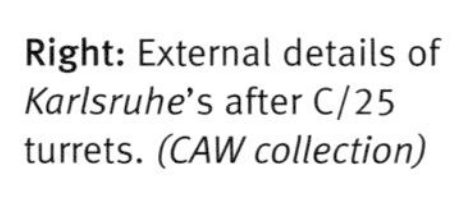

Left: *Karlsruhe* in Wilhelmshaven roads, showing her 'B' and 'C' turrets. Note the Reichsmarine ensign flying at her stern. *(A Jarski collection)*

Above: *Karlsruhe* in the Holtenau lock again – but this time the shiny nameplates are clearly visible on 'B' (SMS *Breslau*) and 'C' (SMS *Goeben*) turrets. *(CAW collection)*

Top left: *Karlsruhe*'s 'C' turret showing the brass plaque commemorating SMS *Goeben*. *(CAW collection)*

Top right: External details of *Karlsruhe*'s after C/25 turrets. *(CAW collection)*

Left: The cruiser *Köln*, still with no turret nameplates mounted. She also had three identical C/25 triple turrets. *(CAW collection)*

Above: One of the most interesting photographs of *Köln*. Note that the 'A' turret does not have her 'Helgoland' nameplate on the glacis, but some longer name or perhaps a two-line warning sign. Note also the white circle painted on top of the 'B' turret as a recognition sign for the Luftwaffe. *(A Jaskuła collection)*

Right: Slight differences between the turrets of the 'K' class cruisers aid in identifying them. In this case, *Köln*'s 'B' and 'C' turrets had two rows of awning attachment points at the sides. *(CAW collection)*

Above: Unofficial graffiti were not uncommon on the cruisers' turrets during wartime. This one was painted at the front of *Köln*'s 'A' turret. *(NHC collection)*

Left: 'B' and 'C' turrets showing their nameplates, 'Doggerbank' and 'Skagerrak' respectively. *(CAW collection)*

Above and left: 'B' turrets with distinctive features enabling their ships' positive identification – above the cruiser *Köln*, to the right, *Karlsruhe*. *(CAW collection)*

Turret names

The 'K' class began the practice of naming main turrets after famous ships and battles of the German Navy. These names were on brass plates fixed to the front of the turret, just below the centre gun port. Careful examination of the available photographs has determined the following names:

Königsberg: 'A' turret = 'SMS Derfflinger'
'B' turret = 'SMS Lützow'
'C' turret = 'SMS Seydlitz'

Karlsruhe: 'A' turret = 'SMS Moltke'
'B' turret = 'SMS Breslau'
'C' turret = 'SMS Goeben'

Köln: 'A' turret = 'Helgoland'
'B' turret = 'Doggerbank'
'C' turret = 'Skagerrak'

They also carried the appropriate coat of arms above the entrance hatch. Of course, all such identifying badges were removed on the outbreak of war.

Below: 150mm shells being loaded aboard a 'K' class cruiser. *(CAW collection)*

Above: *Köln* ended her career scuttled in Kiel harbour. *(MMW collection)*

Left: 'B' turret of the scutttled *Köln*. *(S Breyer collection)*

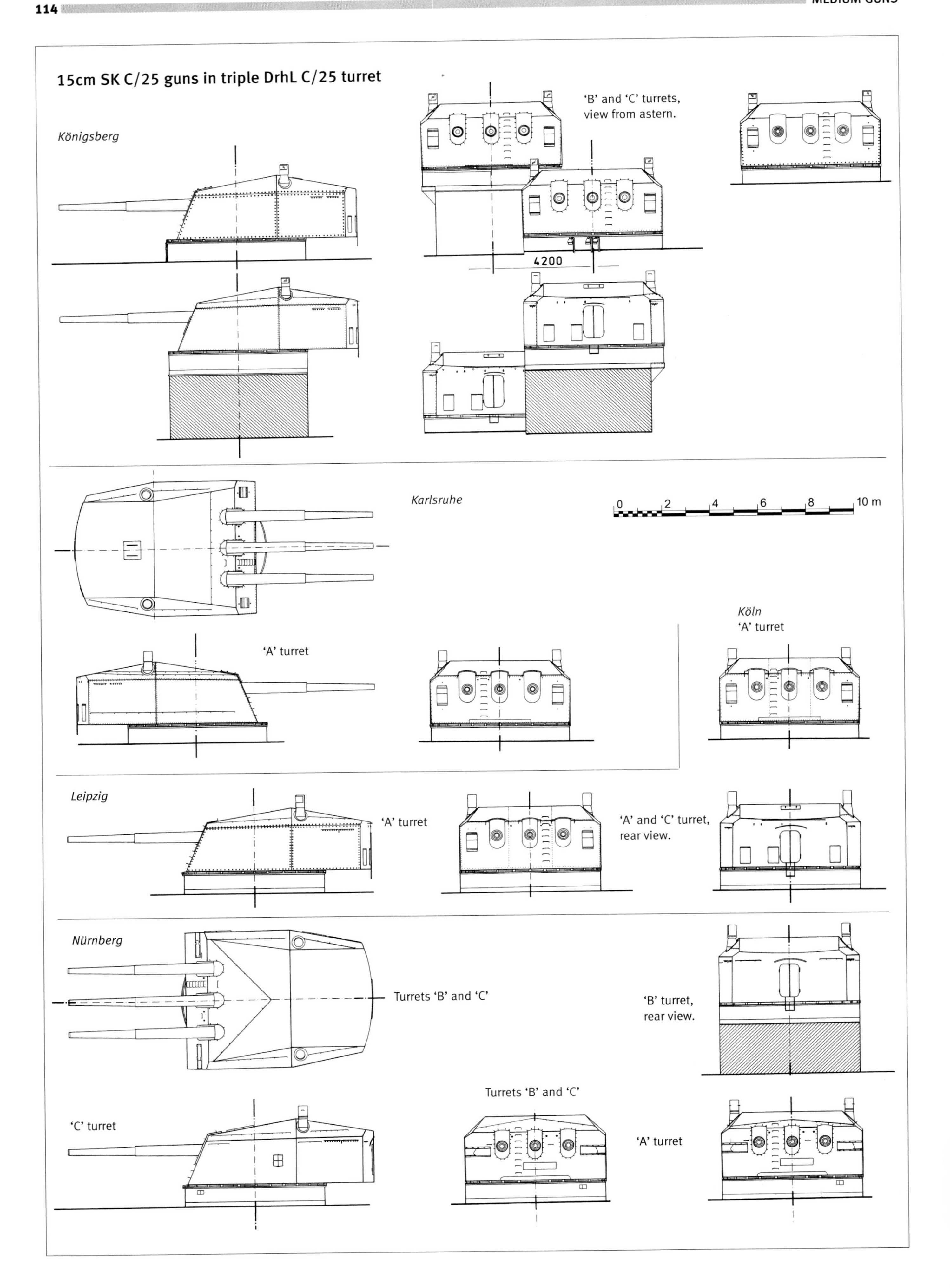
15cm SK C/25 guns in triple DrhL C/25 turret
Königsberg
'B' and 'C' turrets, view from astern.
4200
Karlsruhe
0 2 4 6 8 10 m
'A' turret
Köln
'A' turret
Leipzig
'A' turret
'A' and 'C' turret, rear view.
Nürnberg
Turrets 'B' and 'C'
'B' turret, rear view.
'C' turret
Turrets 'B' and 'C'
'A' turret

THE 15cm SK C/25 GUN

ABOARD THE CRUISER *LEIPZIG*

Cruiser 'E' (*Leipzig*) was designed in 1927 as a revised version of the 'K' class. These minor alterations resulted in her being a little larger than her predecessors, but the use of welding rather than riveting resulted in some weight being saved, allowing larger magazines to be fitted. *Leipzig*'s after turrets were not offset, being on the centreline. She was armed with nine 15cm SK C/25 guns (specifications as above) in three DrhL C/25 triple turrets.

The turrets

Leipzig had the same turrets as the 'K' class (see specifications above), but some sources claim that she was fitted with DrhL C/28 turrets like *Nürnberg* (see below). Close examination of the photographic evidence rules this out, however, as she can be seen to have had DrhL C/25 turrets throughout her career. It is possible that this confusion may have arisen because of the existence in the builder's drawings of an intermediate design of triple 150mm turret, identical to the DrhL C/25 in most respects, apart from being a little longer. The internal layout remained the same as the previous turret.

Turret names

Leipzig's main turrets were named after German cities, with the nameplate on the front of the turret and the respective city's coat of arms on both sides. 'A' turret was 'Dresden', 'B' turret was 'Leipzig' and 'C' turret was 'Nürnberg'.

Below: *Leipzig*'s 'A' turret had a Dresden nameplate on the glacis and the city's coat of arms over the hatch. This photo, however, was taken shortly after she was commissioned, and as yet she has neither nameplates nor coats of arms on her turrets. *(A Jarski collection)*

Below: *Leipzig* shortly after commissioning. Like the previous 'K' class cruisers, she had a main battery of nine quick-firing 15cm SK C/25 guns in triple DrhL C/25 turrets. *(A Jarski collection)*

Right: The cruiser *Leipzig* putting out of Swinemünde. Note that all the turrets have their nameplates and emblems fitted. *(M Skwiot collection)*

Below: *Leipzig* in dock. *(Photo Drüppel, A Jarski collection)*

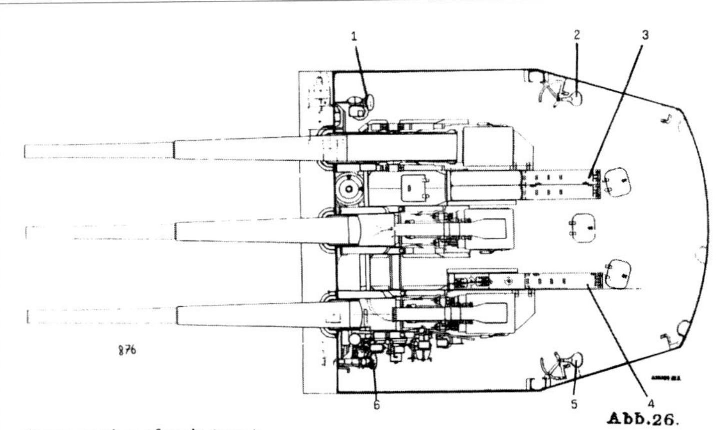

Cross-section of main turret with the 15cm L/60 guns in C/25 mounts

1. Trainer's station.
2. Turret commander's post;
3. Ammunition hoists (right and centre gun).
4. Ammunition hoist (left gun).
5. Alternative turret command post.
6. Elevation station.

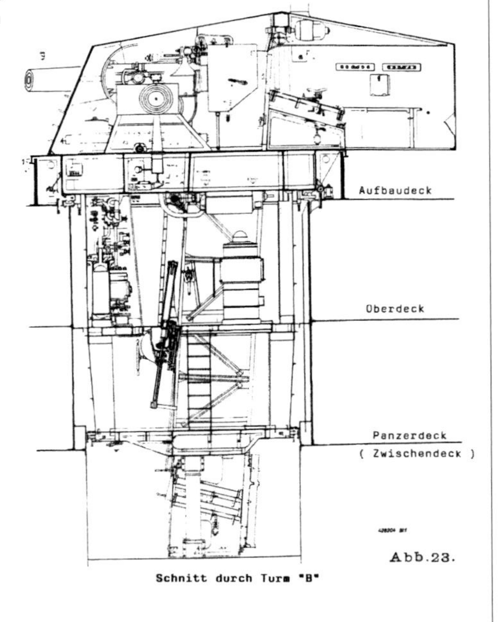

Left: 'A' turret of *Leipzig* with the Dresden coat of arms on the side. *(CAW collection)*

THE 15cm SK C/25 GUN
ABOARD THE CRUISER *NÜRNBERG*

Cruiser 'F' (Ersatz *Nymph*) was designed in 1927 at the same time as Cruiser 'E'. A more extensively altered version of the 'K' class, there were changes to her engine room and to her armament, with her main guns being mounted in new DrhL C/28 triple turrets, longer and better armoured than the DrhL C/25.

Nürnberg was not laid down until 4 November 1933, four years after her near-sister *Leipzig*. This delay was fortunate insofar as it allowed lessons learnt from experience with the earlier ship to be incorporated in her design. The delay was partly due to a lack of available guns, with the *Deutschland* class 'pocket battleships' getting priority. The 150mm gun was once again forming the secondary armament of capital ships, the MPL C/28 single mount of the *Deutschland* class being highly regarded. The succeeding *Scharnhorst* class had the same gun but on the improved MPL C/35 mount. Twin and triple mounts were also being investigated for these weapons.

Nürnberg had nine 15cm SK C/25 guns (see above for specifications) in three DrhL C/28 triple turrets designed and built by Rheinmetall.

The DrhL C/28 turret

Nürnberg's new turrets were, at 7,700mm, longer than their predecessors, and had different gun cradles, modified training and elevating gear and new optical equipment. The turret now had a fume extractor system and an automatic case ejector, replacing the previous manual system. The spent cases were ejected

Below left: 'B' and 'C' turrets of *Nürnberg* in action in the Baltic, October 1944. This photo shows the life rafts attached to the sides of the turrets and the additional anti-aircraft armament, a quadruple 2cm Flakvierling 38 on top of 'B' turret. *(Photo Drüppel, A Jarski collection)*

Below: The cruiser *Nürnberg* moored to a dolphin in Kiel roadstead. Note 'A' turret – the new DrhL C/28 model, longer and better armoured than the C/25 it replaced. *(CAW collection)*

The DrhL C/28 turret

Barbette weight:	54,260kg
Sighting equipment weight:	3,500kg
Turret motors weight:	11,120kg
Armour weight:	24,800kg
Ball track diameter:	4,500mm
Barbette internal diameter:	5,700mm
Distance between gun axes:	1,550mm
Recoil distance:	370mm
Maximum elevating speed:	8o/sec
Maximum training speed:	6-8°/sec
Arcs of fire: turrets A, B and C	290°, 145° each side of the centerline
Turret armour:	Face 80mm: sides 20mm; roof 20-30mm; rear 35mm

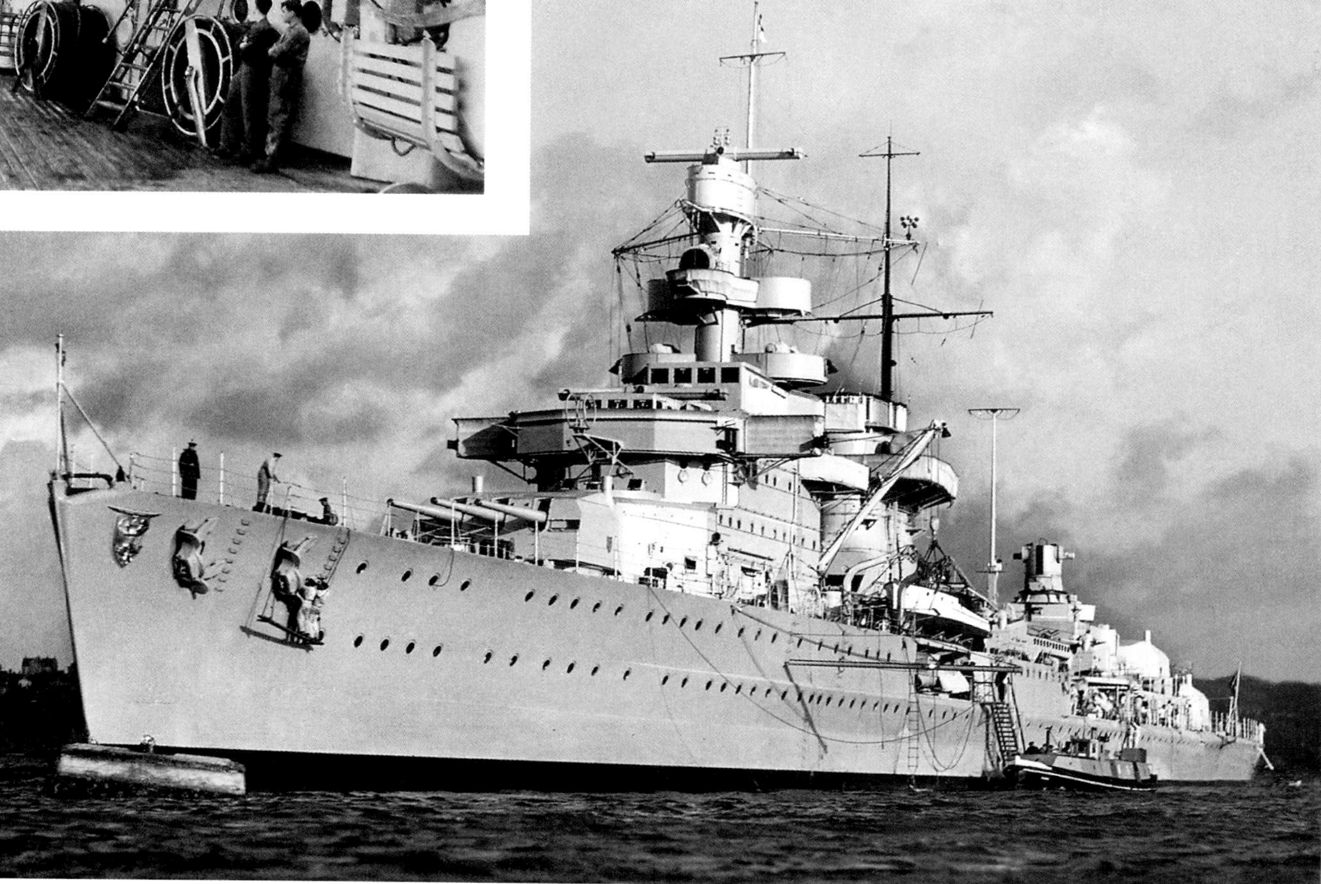

Above: 'B' and 'C' turrets of *Nürnberg*. This photo shows they were named 'Falkland' and 'Coronel', although some sources say that 'B' turret was named 'Ösel' and 'C' turret 'Spee'. *(Photo Urbhans, M Skwiot collection)*

Above: Unlike in the previous type of turret, where spent cases were thrown manually through the ejection ports into the baskets, in the new turrets they were ejected through flaps in the rear floor, onto the deck. *(Photo Drüppel, S Breyer collection)*

through an opening in the rear of the turret floor, falling onto the deck. Rubber mats were placed around the turrets to protect the deck from damage. The new sights resulted in the reshaping and resizing of the ports in the front of the turret. In late 1944, a single 4cm Bofors 28 L/56 anti-aircraft gun was mounted on top of 'A' turret.

Barbettes

These were similar in design to those in previous cruiser classes: single cylinders 5,700mm in diameter, 1,000mm high and 60mm thick. Barbettes 'A' and 'C' were fixed to the main deck, while 'B' was fixed to the after superstructure deck

Turret names

Nürnberg's turrets were named after First World War naval engagements, with the nameplates in the usual place just below the centre gunport. 'A' turret was 'Ösel' with the arms of Rear Admiral Ludwig von Reuter, 'B' turret was 'Falkland' with the arms of Captain Karl von Schönberg, and 'C' turret was 'Coronel' with the arms of Admiral Maximilian Graf von Spee.

Above: *Nürnberg*'s 'A' turret in late 1944. New optics changed the shape and size of the sighting ports in the glacis. *(Photo Drüppel, S Breyer collection)*

Left: Broadside view of *Nürnberg* showing coats of arms fitted on the sides of all three main turrets. *(Photo Urbhans, M Skwiot collection)*

9

THE 15cm SK C/28 GUN

ABOARD *DEUTSCHLAND* CLASS 'POCKET BATTLESHIPS'

The 150m secondary battery for the *Deutschland* class first appeared in proposals I/28 (Entwurf I/28) and II/28 (Entwurf II/28). These had different numbers of guns in different positions, and the failure to choose between the two saw both of them shelved. The Design Bureau produced further proposals, but no decision was made. Indeed, new requirements were issued: these called for a ship with a main battery of six 280mm guns and a secondary battery of six to eight 125mm guns, still capable of a top speed of 26-27 knots. The real challenge was to accommodate all this in a ship restricted by the Treaty of Versailles to a maximum of 10,000 tons.

Finally, on 11 April 1928, Battleship 'A' was authorised with six 280mm guns, eight 150mm guns, five 88mm and four 37mm anti-aircraft guns, and six 533mm torpedo tubes. Although subsequent political developments in Germany were to have a considerable effect on the construction and characteristics of this class, the secondary battery remained unchanged with eight single mounts, four on each side amidships. The mounts and guns were designed and built by Rheinmetall.

The guns

The *Deutschland* class's secondary battery consisted of 15cm SK C/28 guns on MPL C/28 single pivot mounts. The guns had semi-automatic vertical sliding breeches and loose barrel liners. The gun crews were protected by an armoured gun house, open at the rear. Ammunition was supplied from ready-use lockers on deck.

Above: The 'pocket battleship' *Deutschland* at Wilhelmshaven, where she was to be commissioned. Her secondary battery was placed amidships. *(A Jarski collection)*

The 15cm SK C/28 gun

Calibre:	149.1mm
Weight of gun:	9,026/9,080kg*
Overall length:	8,200mm
Length bore:	7,816mm
Length chamber:	1,152mm
Volume chamber:	21.7dm^3
Length rifling:	6,588mm
Grooves:	44 (1.7mm x 6.14mm)
Weight projectile:	45.3kg
Propellant charge:	14.15kg of RPC/38 (7.5/3)
Muzzle velocity:	875m/s
Working pressure:	3,000kg/cm^2
Approximate service life:	1,100 effective rounds
Maximum range:	22,000m at 35°, 23,000m at 40°

*Gun weight varied as shown according to the grade of steel used in its manufacture.

Below: The 'pocket battleship' *Admiral Scheer* arriving at Gdañsk in July 1937. Her secondary battery comprised of single-mounted 15cm SK C/28 guns. *(MMW collection)*

Above: *Deutschland* amidships, with secondary battery guns in the foreground. These were designated as follows (from bow to stern): starboard – Stb I, II, III and IV; port – Bb I, II, III and IV. *(T Klimczyk collection)*

Above: A 15cm SK C/28 gun in a single MPL C/28 pedestal mount. It was fitted on the main deck amidships and designated Stb II. Both the guns and the mounts were designed and manufactured by Rheinmetall. *CAW collection)*

Above: *Lützow* (ex-*Deutschland*) during operations in the Baltic, late 1944. Note additional armour fitted to the fronts of the gun houses. *(CAW collection)*

Left: *Admiral Graf Spee*, her secondary battery clearly visible. Note the additional armour on the sides of the gun houses. *(CAW collection)*

The MPL C/28 gun mount

At the beginning of their service careers, all three ships of the class had identical MPL C/28 mounts for their 150mm guns, but in *Admiral Scheer* and *Admiral Graf Spee*'s last pre-war refits, additional armour was added to the front and sides of the gun houses, as can be seen in wartime photographs of both ships. Furthermore, photographs taken of *Admiral Graf Spee* entering Montevideo harbour in December 1939 show the rears of the gun houses closed in with double doors to protect both guns and crews from the elements. Photographs of *Admiral Scheer* taken during her Atlantic raiding cruise show additional armour plates added to the front of the gun house, just below the gun port.

The MPL C/28 semi-enclosed gun mount

Weight of gun house:	24,830kg
Maximum elevating speed:	8°/s (electric), 1.04°/sec (manual)
Maximum training speed:	9°/sec (electric), 1.09°/sec (manual)
Rate of fire:	8rpm
Depression/elevation:	−10° to +35°

Left: *Admiral Graf Spee* amidships with secondary battery guns. Note brass nameplate on the Stb I gun house, partly obscured by the crew members. *(CAW collection)*

Left: *Admiral Graf Spee* in Montevideo, after the battle of the River Plate. Additional armour has been added to the front and front sides of the 150mm gun houses. They were also fitted with double doors at the back, to protect both guns and crews from severe weather. *(National Archives collection)*

Above: *Admiral Graf Spee*, her secondary battery clearly visible. Note the additional armour on the sides of the gun houses. *(CAW collection)*

Above, right: *Admiral Scheer* leaving Swinemünde. The secondary battery gun houses are fitted with additional side armour. *(S Breyer collection)*

Right: *Admiral Graf Spee* at the arsenal wharf in Kiel, during fitting-out. The secondary battery has already been installed. *(S Breyer collection)*

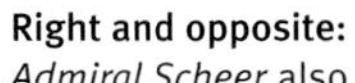

Right and opposite: *Admiral Scheer* also had brass nameplates on her secondary battery gun houses. It is difficult, however, to determine their names: they probably consisted of two words (see photos). Because of the distance they are not readable and one can only speculate if they started with the word 'Batterie' as was the case on her sister-ship, the *Deutschland*. *(Z Bogdanowicz and M Skwiot collections)*

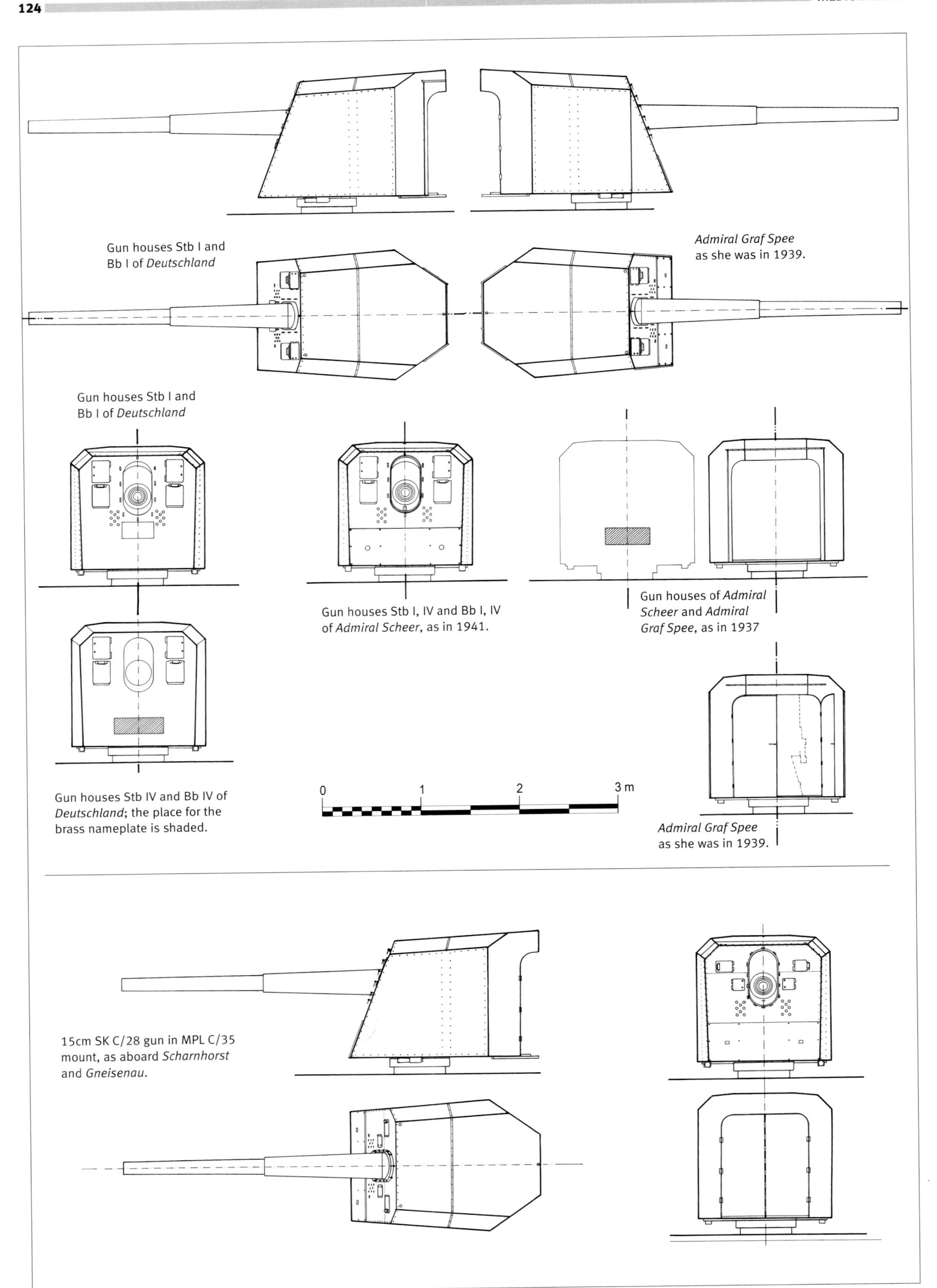
Gun houses Stb I and
Bb I of *Deutschland*
Admiral Graf Spee
as she was in 1939.
Gun houses Stb I and
Bb I of *Deutschland*
Gun houses Stb I, IV and Bb I, IV
of *Admiral Scheer*, as in 1941.
Gun houses of *Admiral*
Scheer and *Admiral*
Graf Spee, as in 1937
Gun houses Stb IV and Bb IV of
Deutschland; the place for the
brass nameplate is shaded.
0
1
2
3 m
Admiral Graf Spee
as she was in 1939.
15cm SK C/28 gun in MPL C/35
mount, as aboard *Scharnhorst*
and *Gneisenau*.

Above: *Admiral Scheer* amidships, 150mm gun houses in the foreground. Note nameplates on Stb I and IV. *(T Klimczyk collection)*

Below: *Admiral Scheer* photographed during her raiding cruise in the Atlantic. Note additional armour on the front of the gun house, below the gun port. *(S Breyer collection)*

Ammunition

Projectiles for the 15cm SK C/28 gun

(a) Armour-piercing shell L/3.8 with Bd Z 38 (1.043kg Fp 1) base fuse, weighing 45.3kg and 550mm long.
(b) High-explosive shell L/4.5 with Bd Z 38 (3.253kg Fp 1.5 – Fp 10) base fuse, weighing 45.3kg and 578.5mm long.
(c) High-explosive shell L/4.3 with Bd Z 38 (2.285kg Fp 5, Fp15, Fp 20) base fuse, weighing 5.3kg and 578.5mm long.
(d) High-explosive shell L/4.6 with KZ 27 (4.086kg Fp 1) nose fuse, weighing 45.3kg and 655mm long.
(e) High-explosive shell L/4.6 Kz Br with KZ 27 (3.0kg Fp 1) nose fuse, weighing 46.8kg and 655mm long;
(f) Star shell (illuminating) L/4.3 with ZZ S/60 or ZZ S/60n.A. time fuse.

The shells were colour-coded as follows: armour-piercing – blue; high-explosive – yellow; practice rounds – red; and star shell – green.

The main propellant charge was 14kg of RPC/32 in an 865mm-long brass case with the C/12n.A. primer. There were also 5.23kg and 7.9kg fore charges, also of RPC/32.

Ammunition stores aboard the *Deutschland* class

These were on the upper platform deck in section VII on the starboard side and section X. The magazines were on the lower platform deck in two places, sections VI and VII to starboard and IX and X to port. The ship carried between 110 and 150 rounds per gun.

Gun designations and names

Secondary-battery guns were designated by an abbreviation of the side of the ship they were on – Stb (Steurbord) for starboard guns and Bb (Backbord) for

Right: *Deutschland*'s four starboard 15cm SK C/28 guns. The background of this photograph has been removed by the censor.

port guns – followed by a roman numeral, counting from bow to stern on both sides. Thus the four starboard guns were Stb I, Stb II, Stb III and Stb IV, and the four port guns Bb I, Bb II, Bb III and Bb IV.

In addition, some of the guns had individual names on brass plates on the front of the gun house, just below the gun port. All that can be seen in the photographs are the names of *Deutschland*'s two forward guns: Stb I was 'Batterie Tirpitz' and Bb I was 'Batterie Köster'. Guns Stb IV and Bb IV also have nameplates but they cannot be read on the photographs. The other four turrets appear to have been unnamed. Photographs of *Deutschland* taken in May-June 1934 show the nameplates already in place, possibly for the ship's cruise to Norway with Hitler on board.

Both *Admiral Scheer* and *Admiral Graf Spee* appear to have had the same arrangement of nameplates, but they cannot be read on the available photographs, although they seem to be the same two-word format, probably beginning with 'Batterie'. There are no records of what these names were, and, as Siegfried Beyer, a leading authority on the Kriegsmarine, has pointed out, the few members of the ships' crews who are still alive joined them after the outbreak of war, when all identifying badges were removed from the ships, so they can be of no help either.

THE 15cm SK C/28 GUN

ABOARD *SCHARNHORST* CLASS BATTLESHIPS

The secondary armament of Battleship 'D' was first considered at a meeting on 23 June 1933. Her design was largely based on that of Battleship 'A' (*Deutschland*), incorporating the fruits of service experience with the previous ships. Armour protection was the main issue, but changes were also planned for the 150mm guns. In order to improve protection for both the guns and their crews, it was intended to mount them in enclosed twin turrets rather than in shielded open mounts. These turrets were ordered from Rheinmetall, but in the event four out of the twelve 150mm guns that made up the secondary battery of

Below: The secondary battery of the battleship *Gneisenau* consisted of twelve 15cm SK C/28 guns in four MPL C/28 single, semi-enclosed gun houses and four twin C/34 turrets. *(M Skwiot collection)*

Above: *Gneisenau* leaves for sea trials, May 1939. Her secondary battery remained the same throughout her service life. *(M Skwiot collection)*

Above: *Gneisenau* while docking at Brest. In the foreground a single 15cm SK C/28 gun is visible. *(S Breyer collection)*

Scharnhorst and *Gneisenau* were mounted in MPL C/35 single semi-enclosed pivot mounts amidships, two on each side of the ship (see above for gun details).

The MPL C/35 single pivot mount

Having proved itself aboard the *Deutschland* class, the 15cm SK C/28 gun was retained as the secondary armament for the *Scharnhorsts*. The four single guns were mounted in new MPL C/35 semi-enclosed pivot mounts. These were very similar to the earlier C/28 mounts, but with improved armour protection which increased their weight to 26,710kg.

Ammunition stores aboard *Scharnhorst* and *Gneisenau*

Magazines and shell rooms for the secondary armament were housed within the armoured citadel, in sections VI and XIII on the upper platform deck, on both sides just forward of the fuel tanks. On the middle platform deck, they were also placed on both sides in sections VII, X and XVI, again just forward of the fuel tanks.

Gun designations

The four single mounts were given the standard secondary-battery gun designations: the two starboard guns were Stb II and III, and the port ones were Bd II and Bd III. There is no evidence to suggest any of these guns were individually named.

Above: Secondary and anti-aircraft batteries of *Gneisenau* during gunnery practice. *(A Jarski collection)*

Left: The 15cm guns in MPL C/35 mounts had only their standard markings – starboard ones were designated Stb II and Stb III, and port – Bb II and Bb III. Gun houses bore neither names nor any other designations. *(S Breyer collection)*

Below: *Gneisenau* had four single-mounted 15cm SK C/28 guns – two of which are clearly visible in the photo. *(S Breyer collection)*

Right: The 15cm SK C/28 gun (in the background) had served well as the secondary battery on the *Deutschland* class 'pocket battleships' and was retained for the next generation of German battleships – this photo shows *Gneisenau* – but in a new MPL C/35 pedestal mount. *(S Breyer collection)*

Below: The DrhL C/34 twin turrets with two 15cm SK C/28 guns were built by Rheinmetall. The first of these were mounted in *Scharnhorst* and *Gneisenau*. The design was a development of the C/25 triple turret, modernised and adapted for two 15cm guns. *(S Breyer collection)*

THE 15cm SK C/28 GUN

ABOARD THE AIRCRAFT CARRIER *GRAF ZEPPELIN*

The initial design for the *Graf Zeppelin* included a main battery of 150mm guns, but in spring 1934, Admiral Raeder, influenced by the armament of the Japanese carriers *Kaga* and *Akagi*, suggested changing it to two twin 203mm turrets. This, however, was ruled out almost immediately: only a single such turret, possibly augmented with casemated guns on either side of the ship, could be fitted if the ship were to remain within its other performance parameters. The 150mm battery was therefore confirmed. Originally there were to be eight guns, in four single mounts port and starboard, but this was later increased to sixteen guns in eight twin turrets ordered from Rheinmetall. But at that time the company had a backlog of work on gun mounts for *Admiral Graf Spee*, *Scharnhorst* and *Gneisenau*, and so the carrier's guns were delayed for some time. In the end, the carrier's armament was to consist of sixteen 15cm C/28 L/55 guns in twin casemated MPL C/36 pivot mounts.

The MPL C/36 gun mount

Designed specifically for the main battery of the *Graf Zeppelin*, this casemate mount had a semicircular shield 2m high and 3m in diameter. The guns were mounted very close together – only 800mm between axes – on a common cradle, and as a result the mount was quite cramped for the crew to work in. The mount had an arc of fire of 122° and maximum depression/elevation was -10°/+35°. The individual fields of fire for each mount were as follows: mounts at frame no. 60 – starboard 53° to 175°, port 192° to 314°; mounts at frame no. 68.1 – starboard 41° to 163°, port 197° to 319°; mounts at frame no. 206.8 – starboard 12° to 134°, port 226° to 348°; and mounts at frame no. 214.5 – starboard 0° to 122°, and port 238° to 360°. Training and elevation were powered by electric motors with an emergency manual system. Each mount, apart from Stb I and Bb I right forward had two electric ammunition hoists. The total weight of the mount including shield was 47,600kg

Ammunition

Projectiles for the *Graf Zeppelin*'s guns

a. High-explosive shell L/4.5 with base fuse, weighing 41.314 (45.3) kg.
b. High-explosive shell L/4.6 with nose fuse, weighing 41.314 (45.3) kg.
c. Star shell L/4.3 weighing 9.768kg.

Ammunition stores

The doubling of *Graf Zeppelin*'s 150mm battery took place without any increase in the size or capacity of the magazines. This therefore ruled out any further guns being fitted to the ship, apart from light anti-aircraft weapons which required no major structural changes to accommodate them.

The 150mm magazines were situated on both sides of the hull at section IV, separated by the aircraft ordnance store, and in section XIV, at upper and lower platform deck levels. The ammunition load was 912 nose-fused high-explosive shells, 912 based-fused high-explosive shells, 240 star shell, 1,824 C/28 propellant charges and 249 charges for star shell, with a total weight of 152.94 tons.

Coastal mounts

When the *Graf Zeppelin* was disarmed in 1940, some of her guns were mounted in single coast artillery mounts, designated Kst MPL C/36.

Left: The aircraft carrier *Graf Zeppelin* was also to have sixteen 15cm SK C/28 L/55 guns, in twin pedestal MPL C/36 mounts. *(S Breyer collection)*

15cm SK C/28 GUNS IN DrhL C/34 TURRETS
ABOARD *SCHARNHORST* AND *GNEISENAU*

Eight of *Scharnhorst* and *Gneisenau*'s twelve 15cm SK C/28 guns were mounted in four DrhL C/34 twin turrets, the remainder being in single mounts (see above)

The DrhL C/34 turret

These were specifically designed for the *Scharnhorst* class by Rheinmetall, and were developed from the DrhL C/25 triple turrets of the 'K' class cruisers, modified for just two guns. The turret had five working levels: the gun platform was inside the turret itself, while the training platform, machinery platform, intermediate platform and ammunition handling space were inside the barbette.

The turrets on both ships were identical. Being the first of their type, and adapted from an existing design, there were a number of problems with them, not the least of which were the entry hatches. For reasons of economy, existing components from the DrhL C/25 turret were used in their construction, including the rear turret plates which had an entrance hatch on the left-hand side. However, the revised layout of the new twin turret meant that a hatch in this position could not be used, so it was bolted shut and a ladder fitted over it to allow the turret crews to get in and out using the emergency escape hatch in the roof. Later, each LC/34 turret aboard *Scharnhorst* and *Gneisenau* was fitted with a pair of stowage bins on the rear slope of the roof.

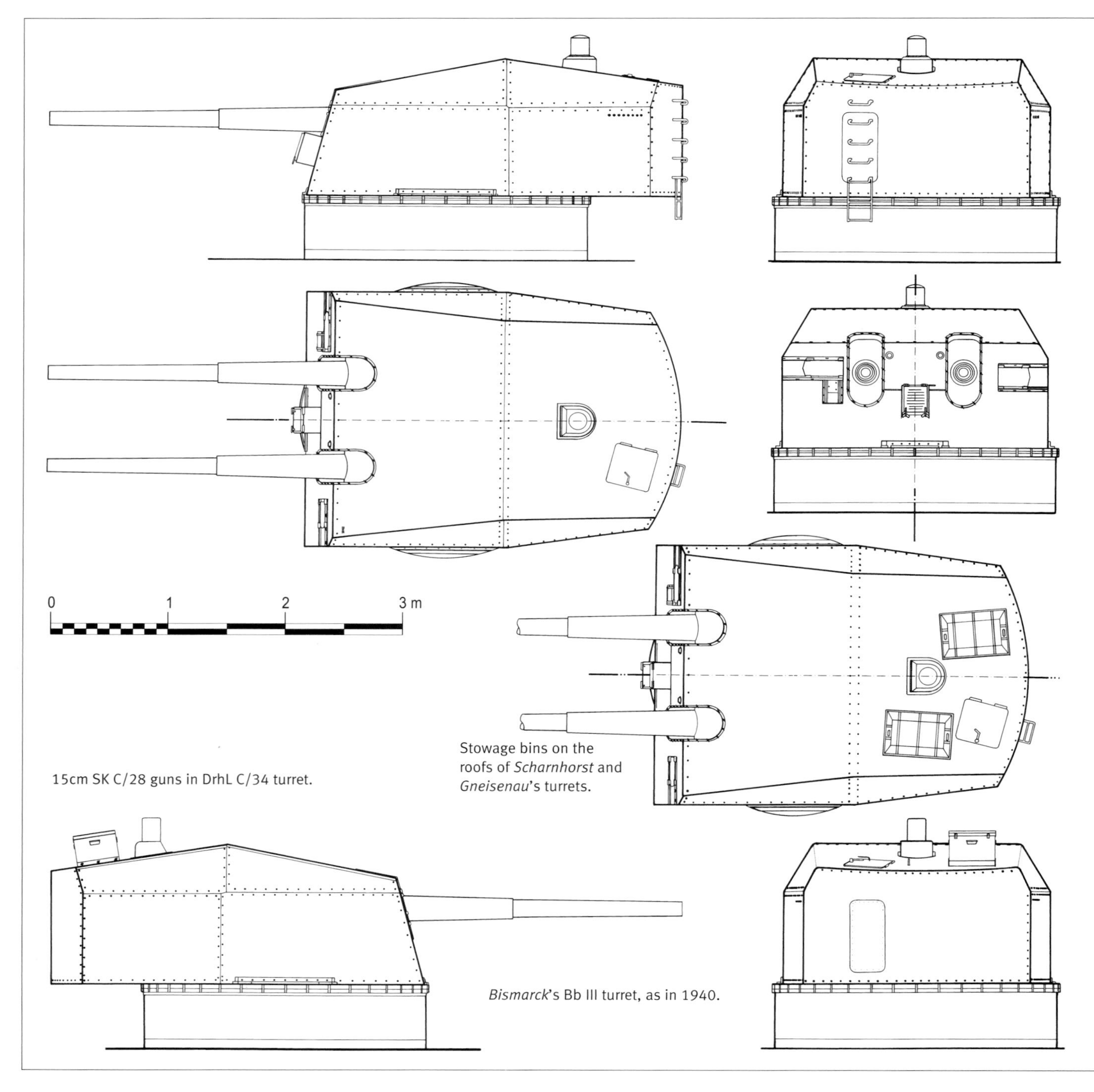

15cm SK C/28 guns in DrhL C/34 turret.

Stowage bins on the roofs of *Scharnhorst* and *Gneisenau*'s turrets.

Bismarck's Bb III turret, as in 1940.

Left: The DrhL C/34 turrets benefited from new techniques of rolling armour plates, enabling more parts of the turrets to be manufactured in this novel way. This photo shows the forward slopes rolled together with the turret roof as one part, the riveted to the turret framework. *(CAW collection)*

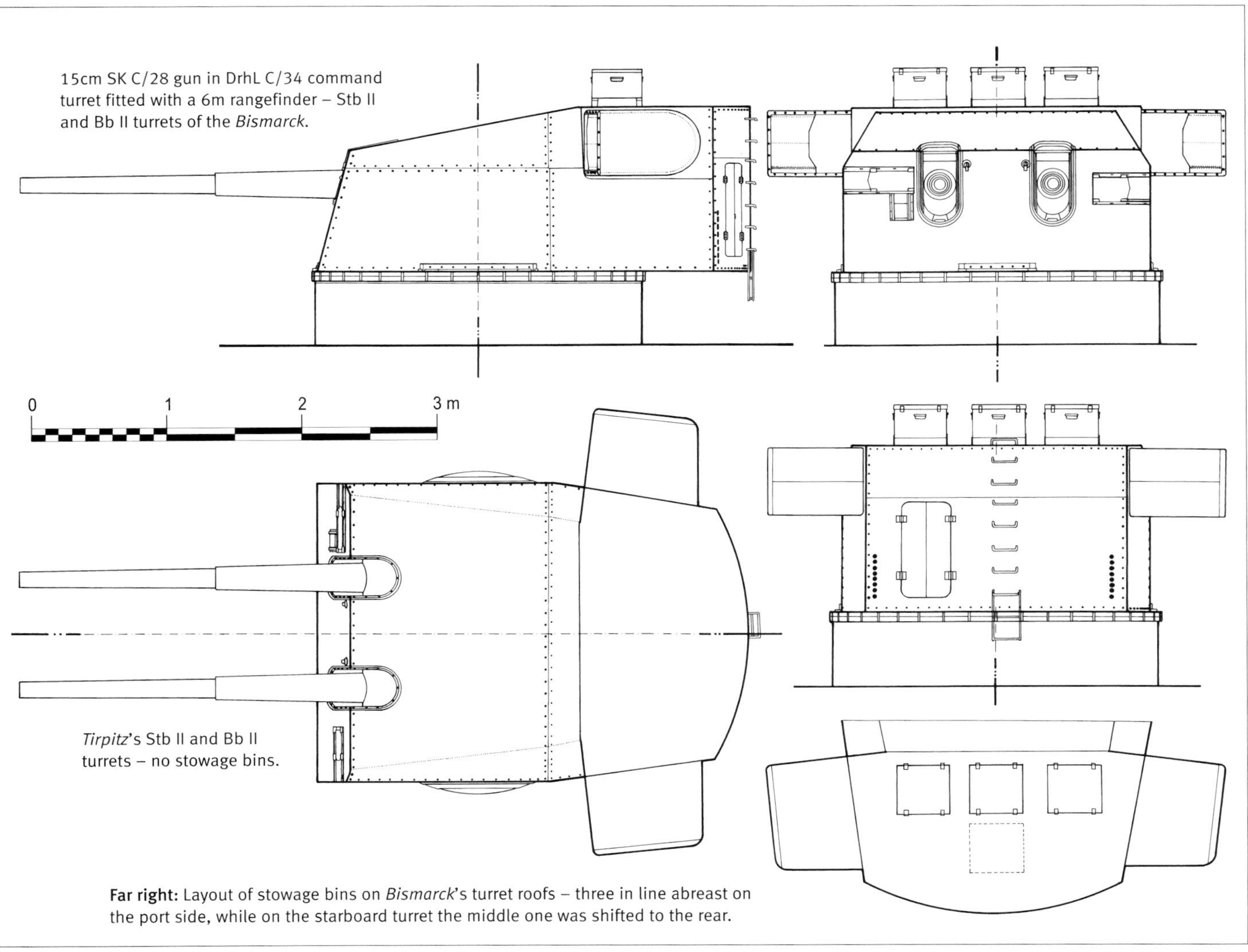

15cm SK C/28 gun in DrhL C/34 command turret fitted with a 6m rangefinder – Stb II and Bb II turrets of the *Bismarck*.

Tirpitz's Stb II and Bb II turrets – no stowage bins.

Far right: Layout of stowage bins on *Bismarck*'s turret roofs – three in line abreast on the port side, while on the starboard turret the middle one was shifted to the rear.

Above: After C/34 turrets of *Scharnhorst*. They were of partially welded construction, contrary to the traditional practice of riveting. *(S Breyer collection)*

Above: After C/34 turrets with stowage bins on their roofs. *(S Breyer collection)*

Above: The DrhL C/34 turrets benefited from new techniques of rolling armour plates, enabling more parts of the turrets to be manufactured in this novel way. This photo shows the forward slopes rolled together with the turret roof as one part, the riveted to the turret framework. *(CAW collection)*

Left: The C/34 design was somewhat experimental and had some faults. One of these was external entrance to the turret. It was meant to be in the rear, but due to the installation of new equipment inside, this became impossible. To spare the additional cost of redesigning the turrets, the already manufactured parts of the turret, with the hatches, were assembled, and the openings were sealed with bolted-up doors (note the bolt-heads clearly visible here). A ladder was welded over it and the crew entered the turret using the roof hatch. *(A Jarski collection)*

The DrhL C/34 turret aboard *Scharnhorst* and *Gneisenau*

Turret weight:	110 tonnes
Gun cradle weight:	2,440kg
Mount weight:	2,835kg
Barbette weight:	41,830kg
Training mechanism weight:	2,350kg
Electric installation weight:	10,300kg
Armour weight:	32,480kg
Turret diameter:	3,630mm
Barbette diameter:	4,800mm
Distance between gun axes:	800mm
Recoil distance:	370mm
Maximum elevating speed:	8°/sec (electric), 1.04°/sec (manual)
Maximum training speed:	9°/sec (electric), 1.09°/sec (manual)
Rate of fire:	8rpm per gun
Depression/elevation:	–10°/+40°

Barbettes
These, like the main battery barbettes, reached right down to the level of the armoured deck.

Turret designations and names
The two starboard turrets were Stb I and Stb IV, and the two port ones Bb I and Bb IV. Pre-war photographs of both ships show no nameplates or other distinguishing features on any of these turrets.

Coastal batteries
Some of the spare guns and turrets held for these ships were later used to arm shore batteries. One of them, made up of two C/34 turrets on the island of Fano off the Jutland peninsula, was christened 'Batterie Gneisenau' in honour of the turrets' 'donor'.

15cm SK C/28 GUNS IN DrhL C/34 TURRETS
ABOARD *BISMARCK* AND *TIRPITZ*

The *Bismarck* class battleships' secondary battery consisted of twelve 15cm SK C/28 guns in six DrhL C/34 twin turrets. Four of these were similar to those aboard *Scharnhorst* and *Gneisenau*, while the centre pair were a variant with integral 6.5m optical rangefinders, known as the 'command turrets'. (See above for details of the guns and ammunition.)

Bismarck and *Tirpitz*'s DrhL C/34 turrets

While the new battleships were being designed, new grades of steel were developed, with greater strength and better suited to welding. Also, the technology for rolling armour plate had improved, enabling thicker slabs to be used for the turret armour. Thanks to these developments, and the use of welding instead of riveting, *Bismarck* and *Tirpitz*'s turrets were much lighter than those of their predecessors.

The foremost pair of turrets, Stb I and Bb I, had five working levels, the gun platform in the turret itself, the training platform, machinery platform and intermediate platform within the barbette, and the ammunition handling space below the armoured deck. The other four turrets (Stb II and Stb III, Bb II and Bb III) had shorter barbettes with no intermediate platform and the ammunition handling space was inside the barbette. Stb I and Bb I weighed 150.5 tons each, and Stb III and Bb III weighed 97.7 tons each (see below for details of the 'command turrets' Stb II and Bb II).

When *Bismarck* was first commissioned, turrets Stb I and Bb III each had a stowage bin on the right-hand side of their roof, while Stb III had one at the rear of

Below and left: On entering service the C/34 turrets had no stowage bins on top of them – these were added later. Both *Bismarck* and *Tirpitz* got two of these mounted on each of the turrets, on their rear slopes. *(S Breyer collection)*

Above: *Bismarck* in the Kiel Canal, December 1940. Note the C/34 turret's stowage bins are still in place. *(M Skwiot collection)*

Above: On entering service the C/34 turrets had no stowage bins on top of them – these were added later. Both *Bismarck* and *Tirpitz* got two of these mounted on each of the turrets, on their rear slopes. *(CAW collection)*

Above, right: The DrhL C/34 turrets of *Bismarck* and *Tirpitz* were almost identical with those of *Scharnhorst* and *Gneisenau*. The only difference was that the rear walls were solid, with no bolted-up doors. In this photo *Bismarck* is moored at the Blohm & Voss wharf, during fitting-out. *(M Skwiot collection)*

Middle, right: The middle C/34 turrets were of the modernised design. They had a 6.5m rangefinder installed, allowing the turret crew to aim and fire independently, as well as transmit fire data to the subordinated fore and after turrets. *(S Breyer collection)*

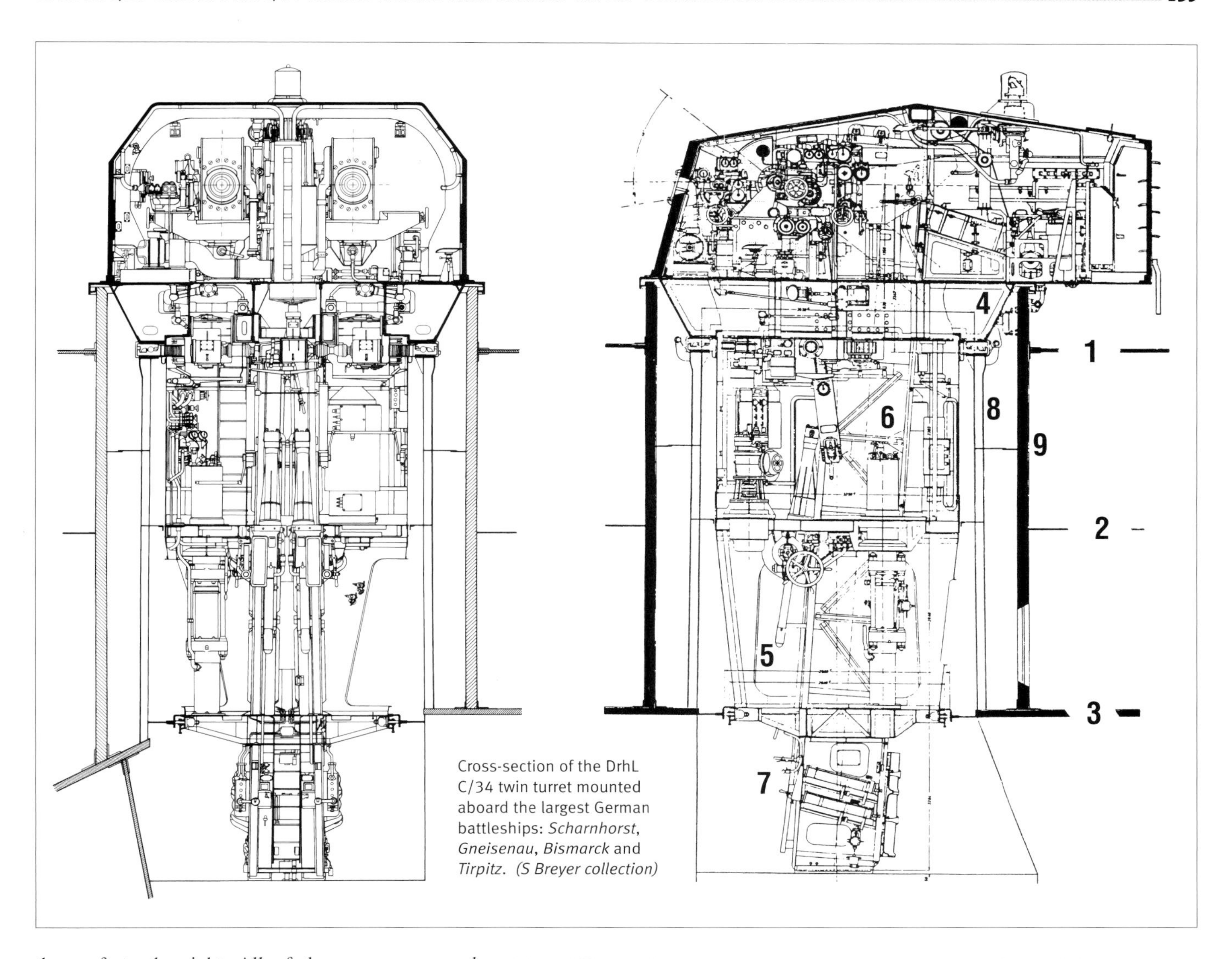

Cross-section of the DrhL C/34 twin turret mounted aboard the largest German battleships: *Scharnhorst*, *Gneisenau*, *Bismarck* and *Tirpitz*. *(S Breyer collection)*

the roof, to the right. All of these were removed between October and November 1940, as a photograph taken of *Bismarck* in the Kiel Canal in December 1940 shows no stowage bins on any of these turrets.

The DrhL C/34 command turret

The 'command turrets', Stb II and Bb II, were each fitted with an integral 6.5m-base optical rangefinder, which allowed them to engage targets independently and pass firing data to the other turrets on their side of the ship, which were only equipped with a C/4 episcope, trainable up to 90° off the bore axis. The command turrets each weighed 131.6 tons.

Bismarck's command turrets originally each had three stowage bins on their roofs. Bb II's bins were in a straight line, while on Stb II the middle one was set slightly further back. These had also been removed by the time the December 1940 photograph referred to above was taken. (*Tirpitz* never had any such stowage bins.)

Stb I and Bb I had arcs of fire of 135°, and the rest 150°. The turret armour, made of Whn/A and KCn/A steels, was 100mm thick on the turret front, 40mm on the sides and rear, and 20-35mm on the roof.

Barbettes

The first pair of barbettes, set closer to the ship's centreline, rested on the armoured deck like the main battery barbettes, while the other four, closer to the ship's sides, reached to the slope of the armoured citadel. Each one consisted to two co-axial cylinders, one on top of the other. The first, resting on the citadel, reached up almost to main deck level. A second, thicker cylinder, made of 80mm Whn/A steel (Siegfried Beyer gives 100mm) was set on top of it.

DrhL C/34 turrets aboard *Bismarck* and *Tirpitz*

Turret weight:	116.25 tonnes (long barbette and rangefinder), 110 tonnes (long barbette), 108 tonnes (short barbette)
Gun cradle weight:	2,440kg
Mount weight:	2,835kg
Barbette weight:	41,830kg
Training mechanism weight:	2,350kg
Electric installation weight:	10,300kg
Armour weight:	32,480kg
Turret diameter:	3,630mm
Barbette diameter:	4,800mm
Distance between gun axes:	800mm
Recoil distance:	370mm
Maximum elevating speed:	8°/sec (electric), 1.04°/sec (manual)
Maximum training speed:	9°/sec (electric), 1.09°/sec (manual)
Rate of fire:	8rpm per gun
Depression/elevation:	–10°/+40°

Ammunition stores

Magazines and shell rooms for the 150mm battery were housed within the armoured citadel, in sections IX, XII and XIV. The magazines were on the upper

Opposite: The *Bismarck* had three stowage bins on top of each command turret. These differed in layout on the port and starboard sides. The port ones were mounted in a line abreast, while on the other side, the middle bin was set back to form a 'Vee' layout. All these were later removed. *(S Breyer collection)*

Above: The after C/34 turrets, like the forward ones, had stowage bins on their roofs. These were laid out as follows: Stb I turret had one on the right, Bb I had none, Bb III – one on the right, while Stb III – one on the right, at the end of the roof. *(S Breyer collection)*

Above: To avoid excessive wear on the 150mm guns during loading practice, special dummy training guns were installed on board the battleships. They consisted of a complete breech section, with a special short tube screwed in, which enabled loading of inert practice rounds. This photo shows the practice gun of the *Scharnhorst*. *(A Jarski collection)*

Above: The command turrets of the *Tirpitz* did not have any bins on their roofs, as this photo proves. *(S Breyer collection)*

platform deck, directly above the shell rooms on the middle platform deck. A total of 1,800 rounds was carried, giving 300 rounds per turret.

Turret designations and names

Apart from the standard Kriegsmarine designations for secondary turrets, they had no other names.

Shore batteries

There was a plan to install two of *Tirpitz*'s spare C/34 turrets in a shore battery on Oxby Island in Denmark.

150mm training gun

To allow 150mm loading drills to take place aboard *Bismarck* and *Tirpitz* without causing wear and tear to the actual guns, a practice gun was installed on deck between 'C' and 'D' turrets. This consisted of an entire breech piece and a shortened barrel mounted on a stand, to allow gun crews to train with inert practice rounds.

Shells and cased propellant charges for the 28cm guns of *Scharnhorst* and *Gneisenau*.

150mm shells and charges.

a. Armour-piercing shell with base fuse, weighing 45.3kg and 550mm long.
b. High-explosive shell with nose fuse, weighing 45.3kg and 655mm long.
c. High-explosive shell with base fuse, weighing 45kg and 680mm long.
d. Star shell, weighing 41kg.

Propellant charge – 19.3kg of RP C/32 or RP C/38 powder charge in a primed case, total weight 32.8kg.

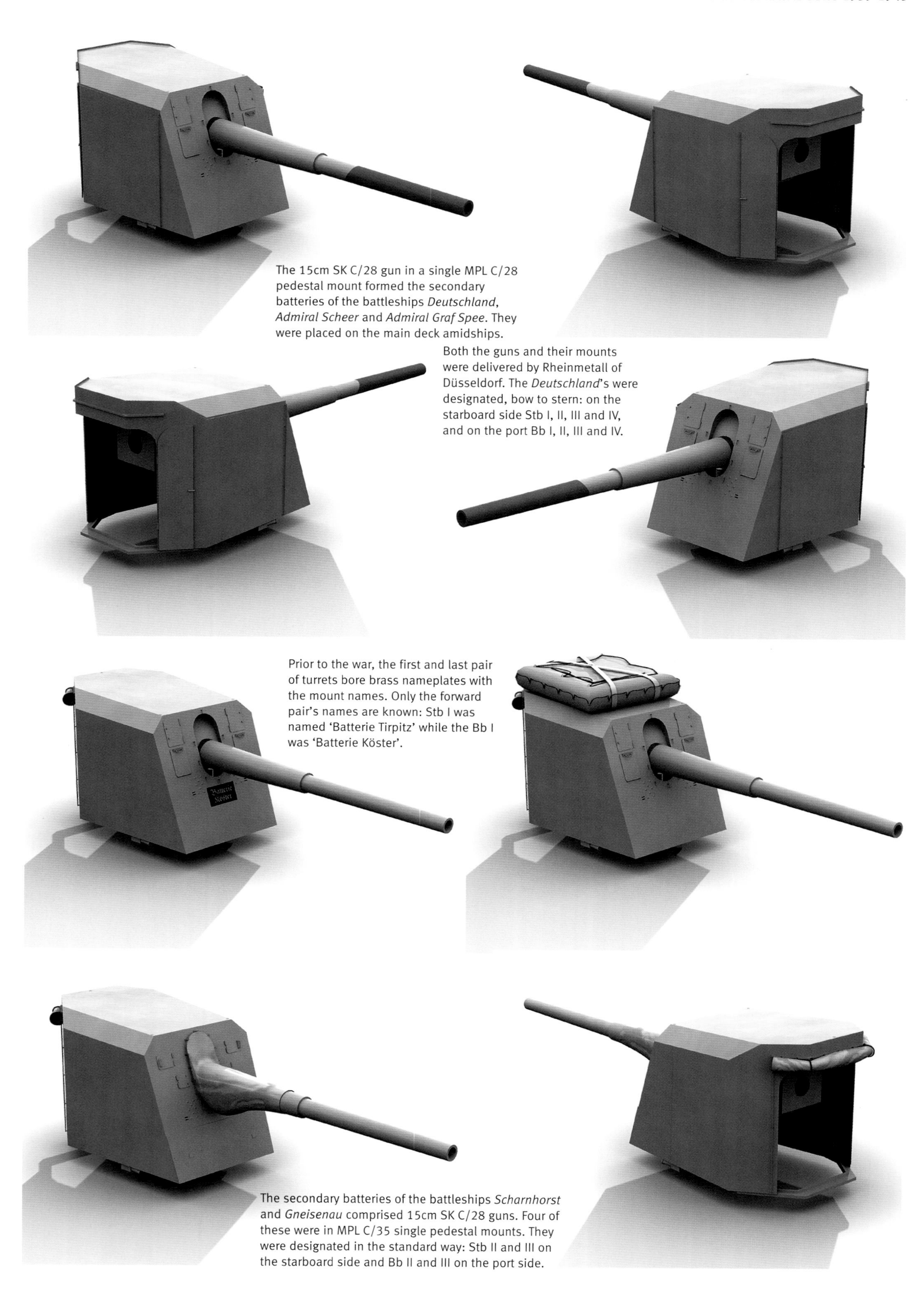

The 15cm SK C/28 gun in a single MPL C/28 pedestal mount formed the secondary batteries of the battleships *Deutschland*, *Admiral Scheer* and *Admiral Graf Spee*. They were placed on the main deck amidships. Both the guns and their mounts were delivered by Rheinmetall of Düsseldorf. The *Deutschland*'s were designated, bow to stern: on the starboard side Stb I, II, III and IV, and on the port Bb I, II, III and IV.

Prior to the war, the first and last pair of turrets bore brass nameplates with the mount names. Only the forward pair's names are known: Stb I was named 'Batterie Tirpitz' while the Bb I was 'Batterie Köster'.

The secondary batteries of the battleships *Scharnhorst* and *Gneisenau* comprised 15cm SK C/28 guns. Four of these were in MPL C/35 single pedestal mounts. They were designated in the standard way: Stb II and III on the starboard side and Bb II and III on the port side.

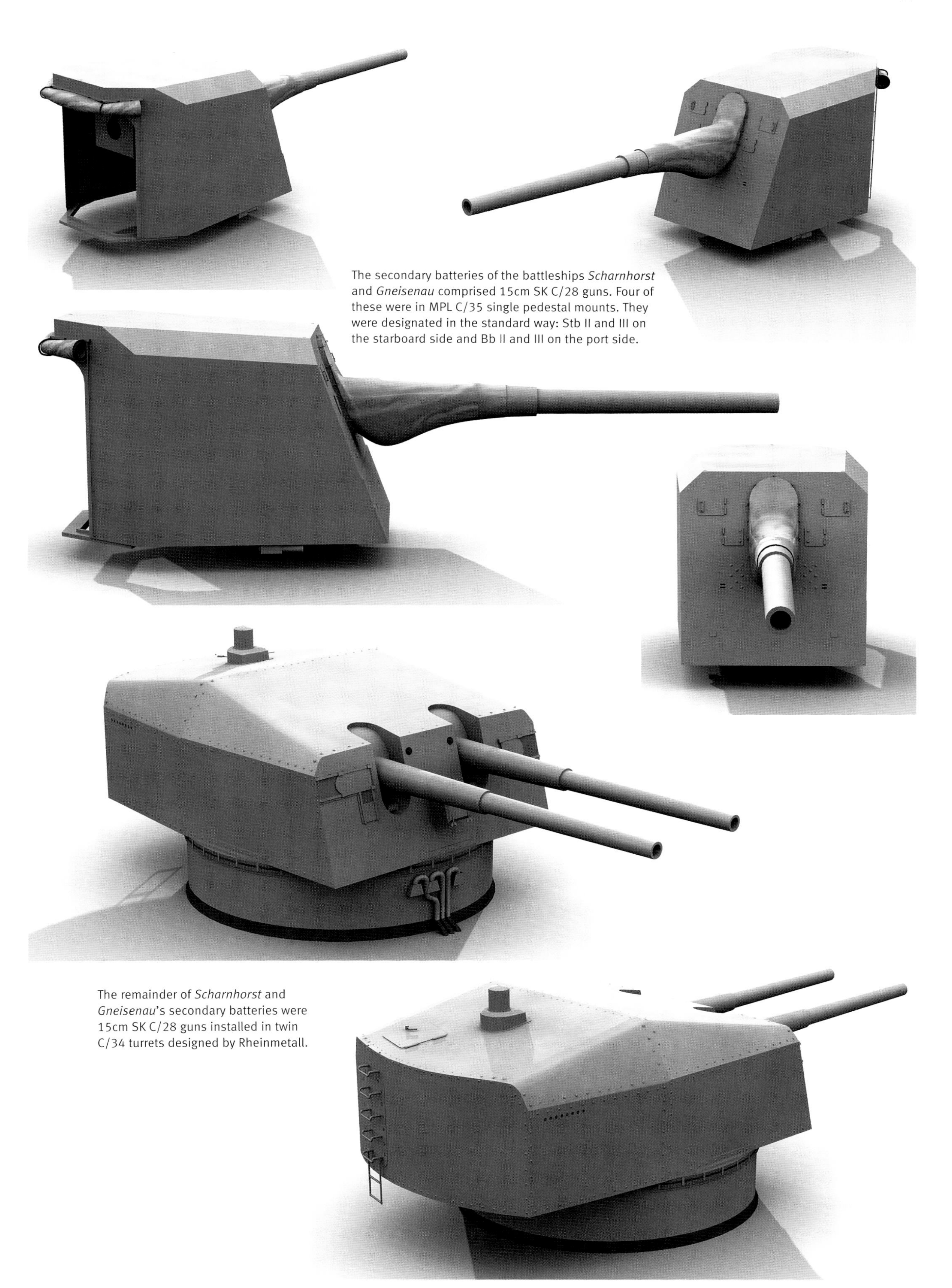

The secondary batteries of the battleships *Scharnhorst* and *Gneisenau* comprised 15cm SK C/28 guns. Four of these were in MPL C/35 single pedestal mounts. They were designated in the standard way: Stb II and III on the starboard side and Bb II and III on the port side.

The remainder of *Scharnhorst* and *Gneisenau*'s secondary batteries were 15cm SK C/28 guns installed in twin C/34 turrets designed by Rheinmetall.

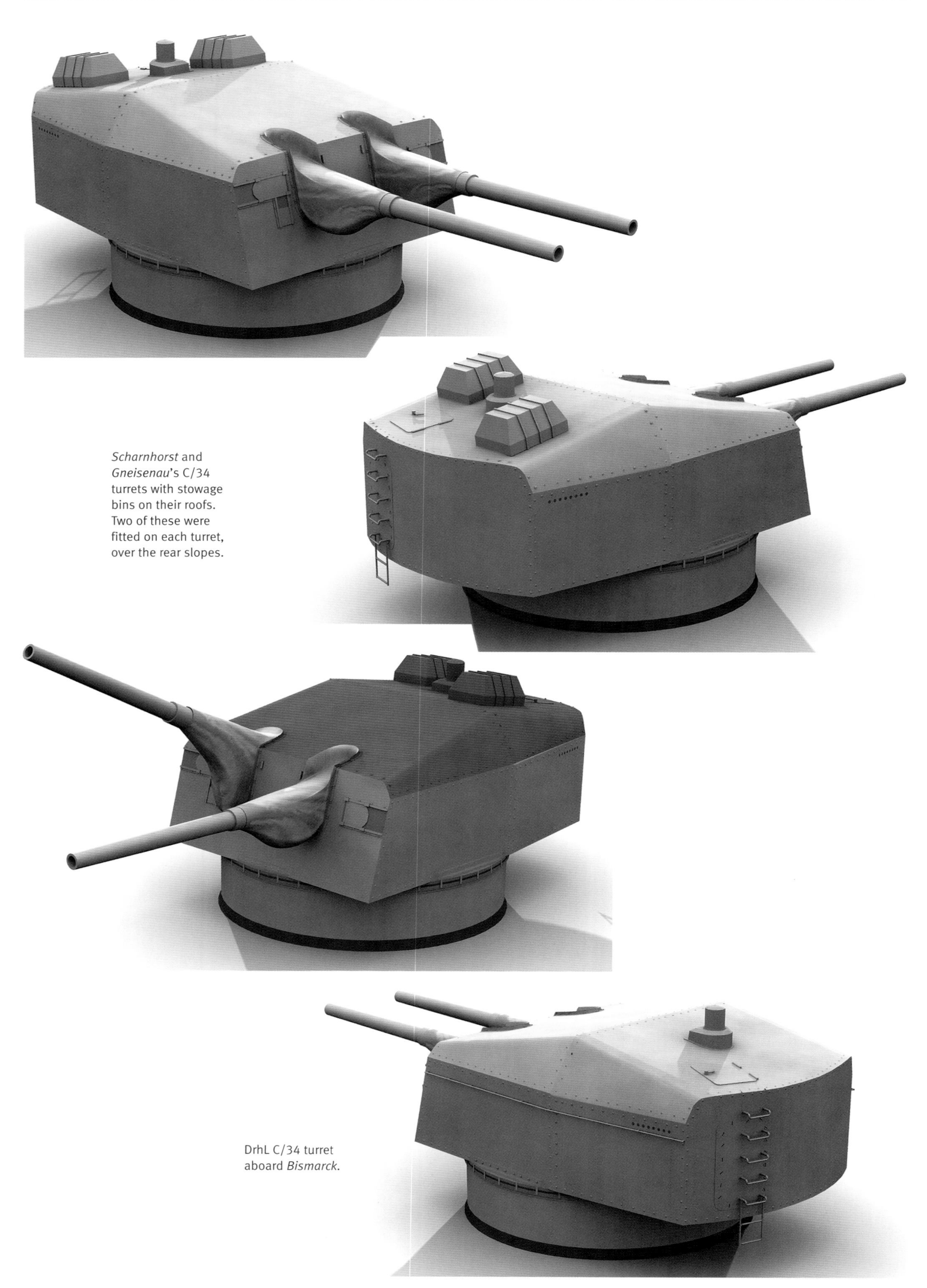

Scharnhorst and *Gneisenau*'s C/34 turrets with stowage bins on their roofs. Two of these were fitted on each turret, over the rear slopes.

DrhL C/34 turret aboard *Bismarck*.

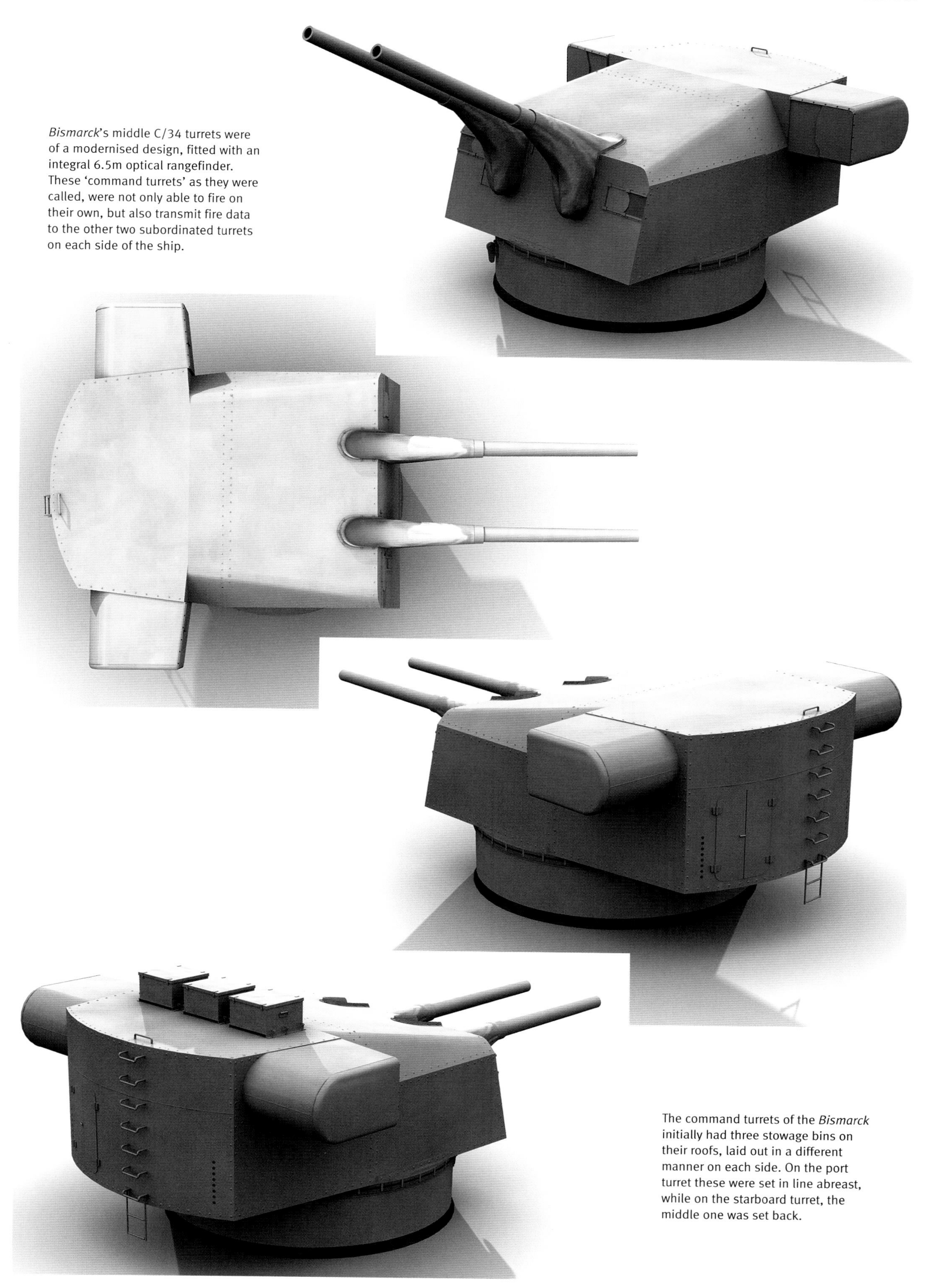

Bismarck's middle C/34 turrets were of a modernised design, fitted with an integral 6.5m optical rangefinder. These 'command turrets' as they were called, were not only able to fire on their own, but also transmit fire data to the other two subordinated turrets on each side of the ship.

The command turrets of the *Bismarck* initially had three stowage bins on their roofs, laid out in a different manner on each side. On the port turret these were set in line abreast, while on the starboard turret, the middle one was set back.

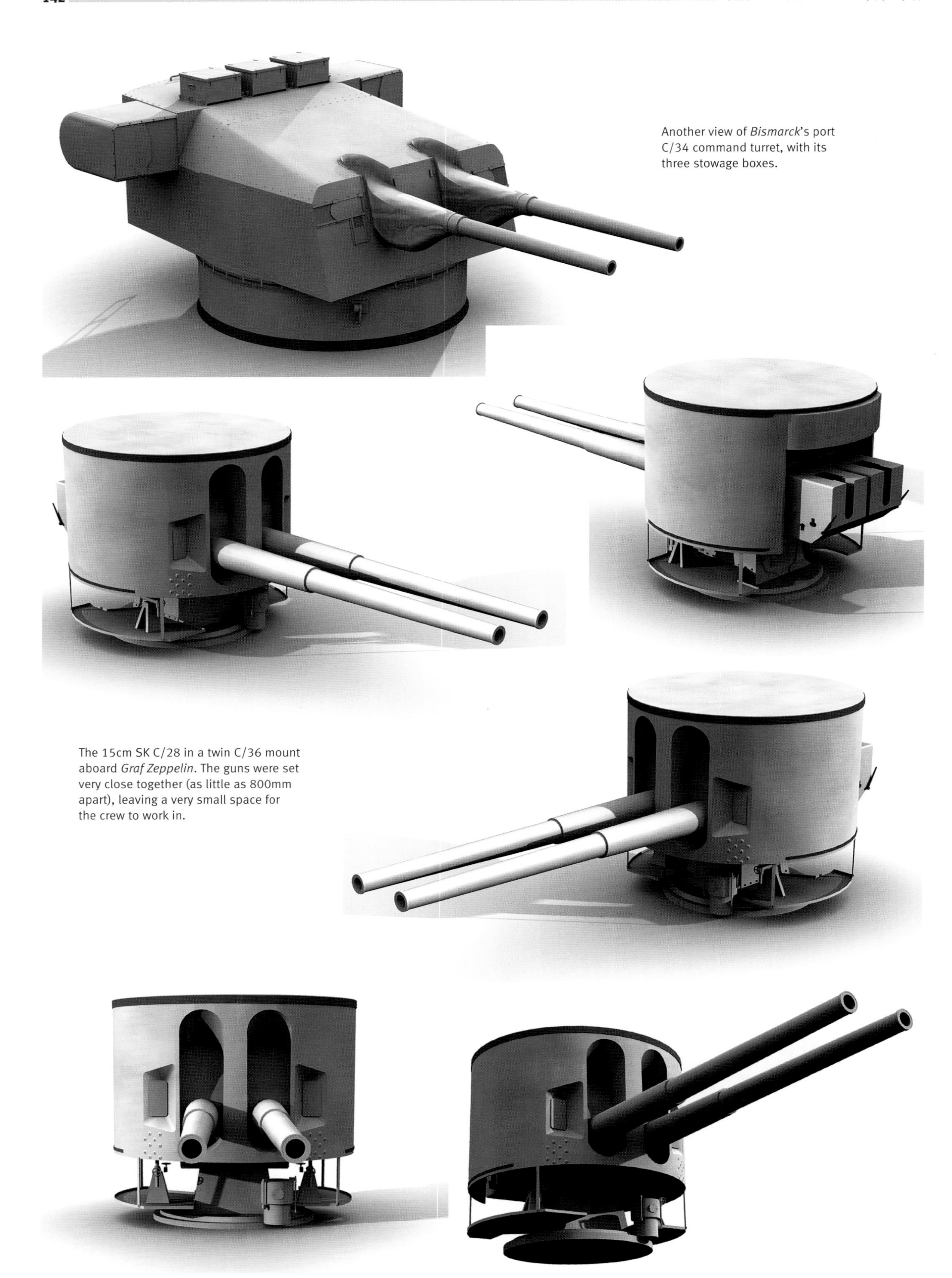

Another view of *Bismarck*'s port C/34 command turret, with its three stowage boxes.

The 15cm SK C/28 in a twin C/36 mount aboard *Graf Zeppelin*. The guns were set very close together (as little as 800mm apart), leaving a very small space for the crew to work in.

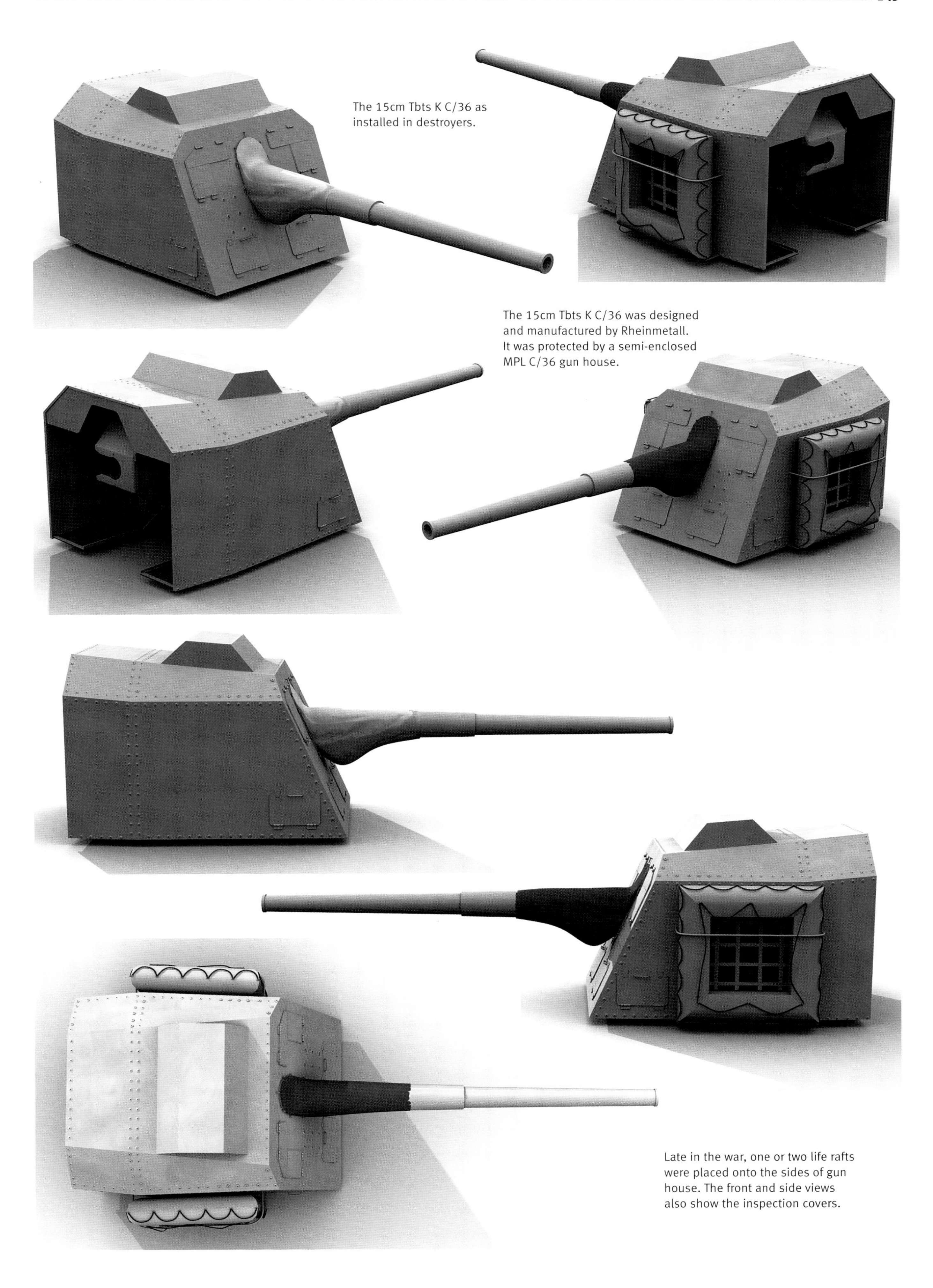

The 15cm Tbts K C/36 as installed in destroyers.

The 15cm Tbts K C/36 was designed and manufactured by Rheinmetall. It was protected by a semi-enclosed MPL C/36 gun house.

Late in the war, one or two life rafts were placed onto the sides of gun house. The front and side views also show the inspection covers.

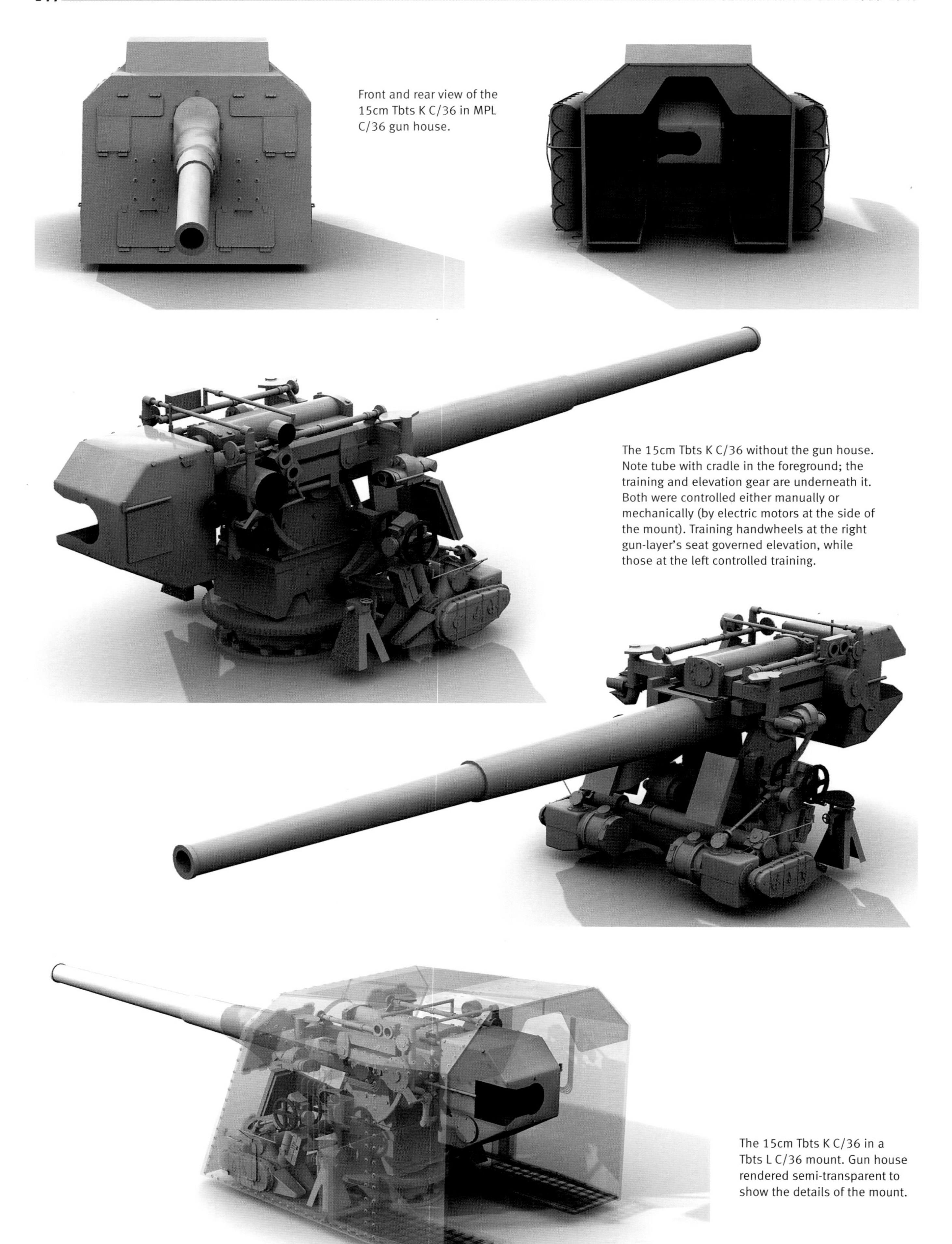

Front and rear view of the 15cm Tbts K C/36 in MPL C/36 gun house.

The 15cm Tbts K C/36 without the gun house. Note tube with cradle in the foreground; the training and elevation gear are underneath it. Both were controlled either manually or mechanically (by electric motors at the side of the mount). Training handwheels at the right gun-layer's seat governed elevation, while those at the left controlled training.

The 15cm Tbts K C/36 in a Tbts L C/36 mount. Gun house rendered semi-transparent to show the details of the mount.

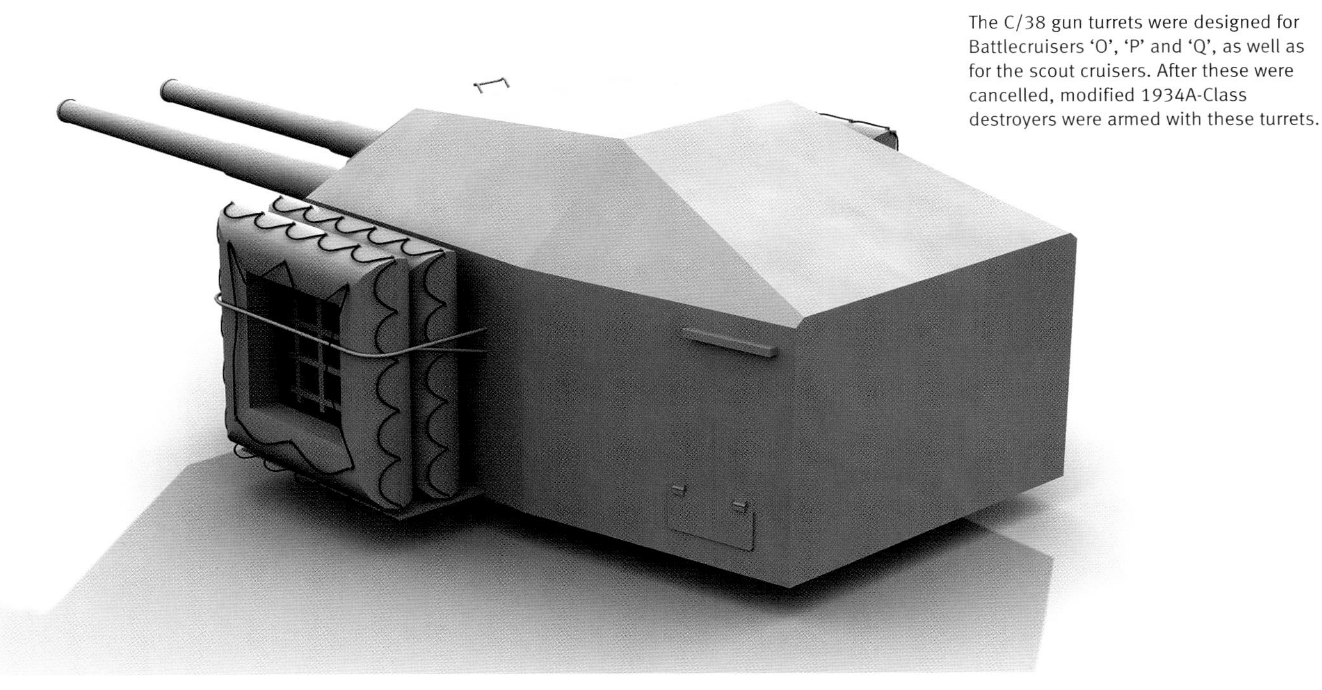

The C/38 gun turrets were designed for Battlecruisers 'O', 'P' and 'Q', as well as for the scout cruisers. After these were cancelled, modified 1934A-Class destroyers were armed with these turrets.

Life rafts were a common sight on the sides of the gun houses at the end of the war.

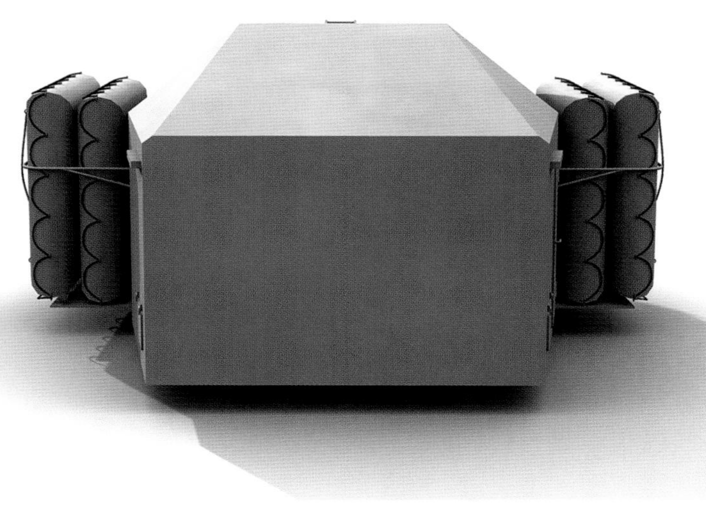

C/38 turret with life rafts.

The 12.7cm SK C/34 gun in MPL C/34 mount, was also installed in large torpedo boats. Design work began in 1930 at Rheinmetall. The drawings show the prototype gun.

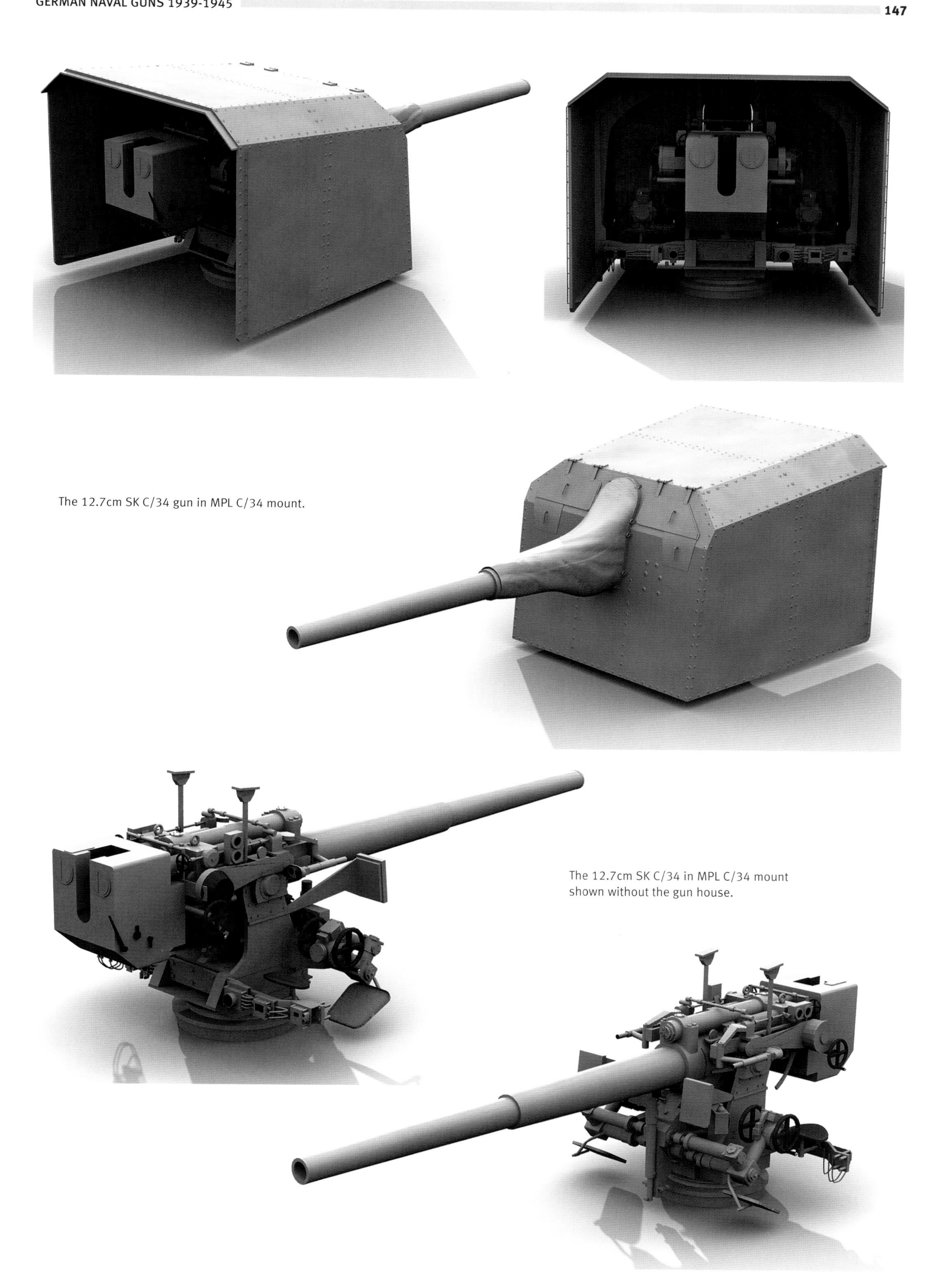

The 12.7cm SK C/34 gun in MPL C/34 mount.

The 12.7cm SK C/34 in MPL C/34 mount shown without the gun house.

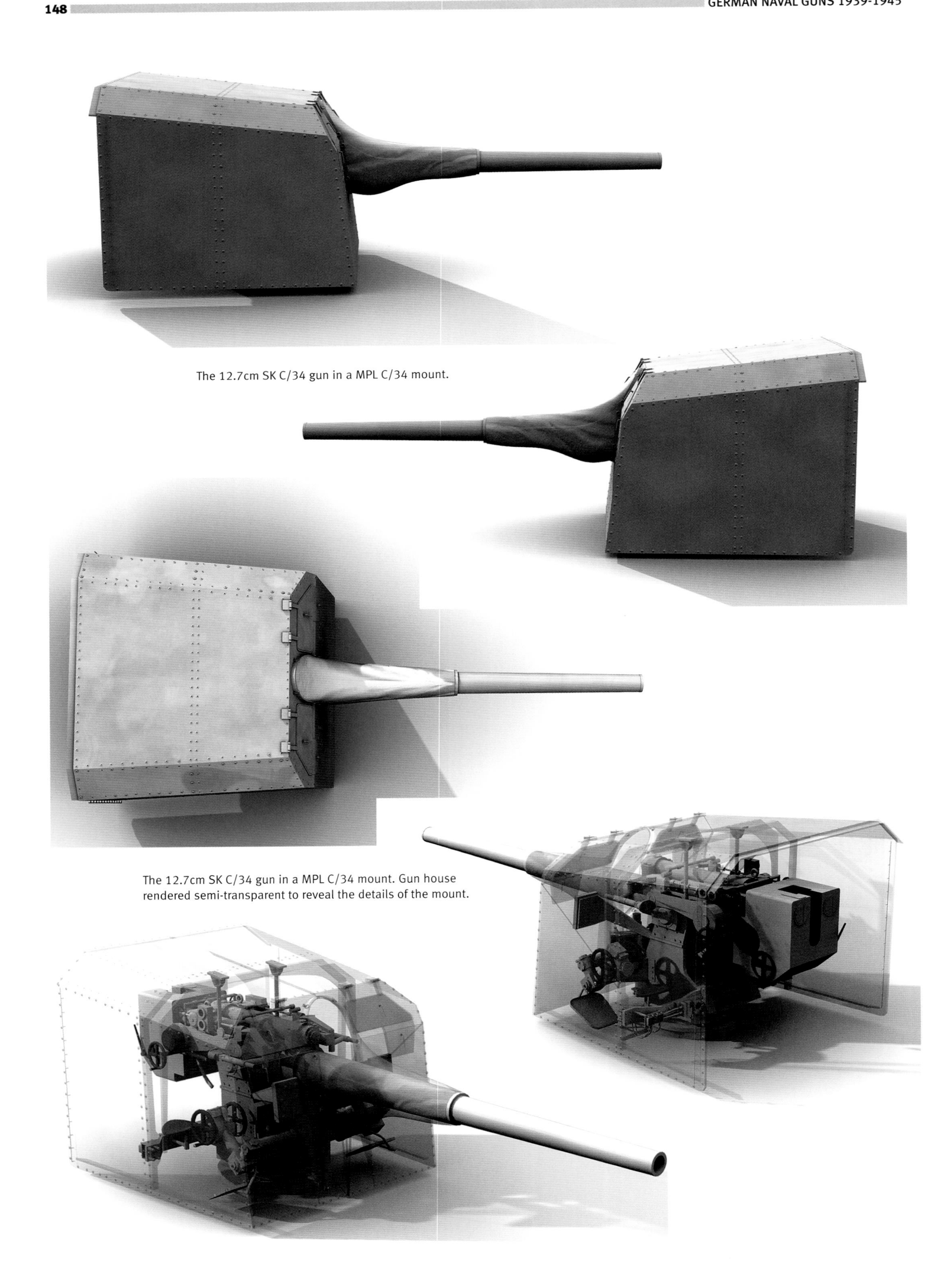

The 12.7cm SK C/34 gun in a MPL C/34 mount.

The 12.7cm SK C/34 gun in a MPL C/34 mount. Gun house rendered semi-transparent to reveal the details of the mount.

The 10.5cm SK C/32 in an MPL C/30 single pedestal mount with shield. Note the sighting-port covers on both sides of the tube, which were removed for firing.

The 10.5cm SK C/32 in an MPL C/30 single pedestal mount with shield. The gun shield in this drawing is made transparent to show the details of the gun.

The 10.5cm SK C/32 in an MPL C/30 single pedestal mount with shield. Note the elevated tube with recuperators on top, on either side.

The 10.5cm SK C/32 in an MPL C/30 single pedestal mount with shield. Some of the gun shields had rounded lower edges at the back, like the one shown here.

The 10.5cm SK C/32 in an MPL C/30 single pedestal mount with shield.

The 10.5cm SK C/32 in an MPL C/30 single pedestal mount with gE shield, enlarged to protect the cradle and breech-ring from the elements. The opening in the roof of the gun house could be covered with canvas. The sighting ports were also enlarged.

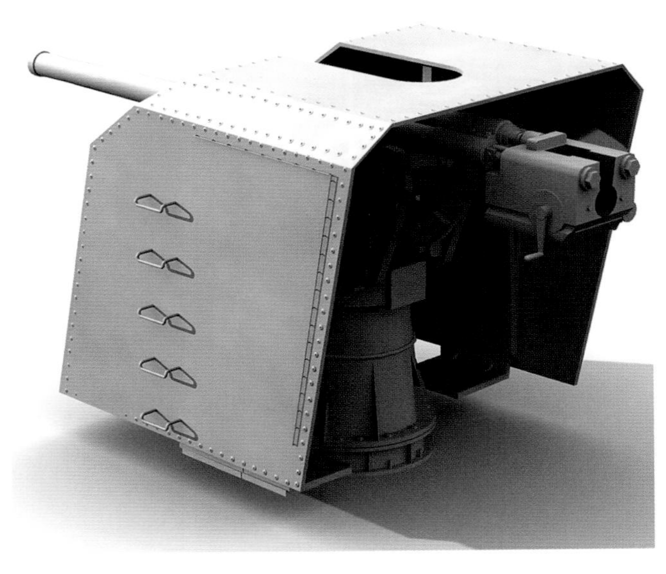

The 10.5cm SK C/32 in an MPL C/30 single pedestal mount with gE shield. The gun shield has been made transparent to show the details of the gun.

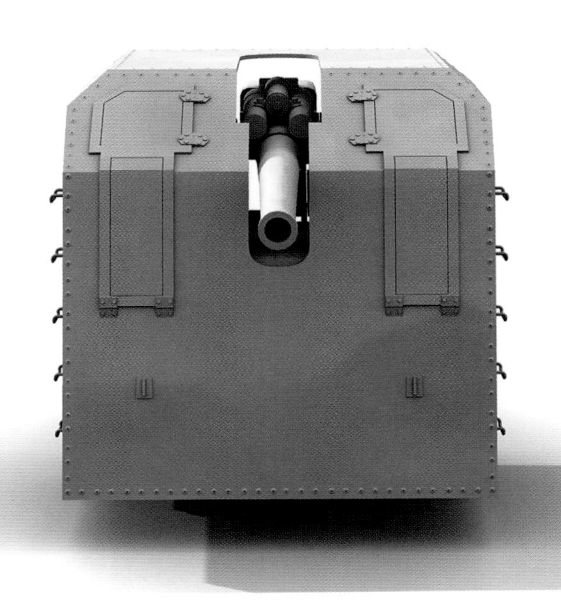

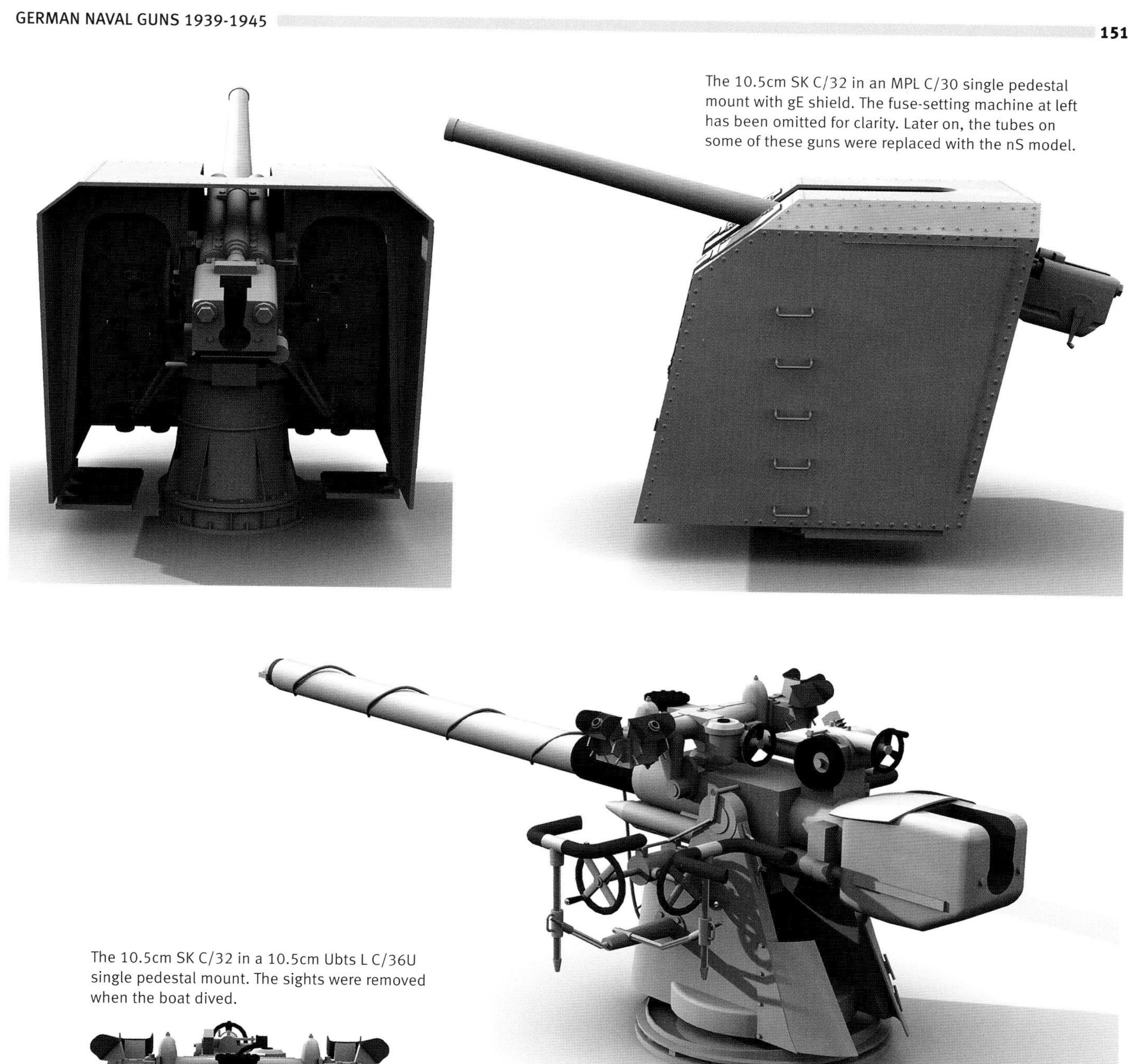

The 10.5cm SK C/32 in an MPL C/30 single pedestal mount with gE shield. The fuse-setting machine at left has been omitted for clarity. Later on, the tubes on some of these guns were replaced with the nS model.

The 10.5cm SK C/32 in a 10.5cm Ubts L C/36U single pedestal mount. The sights were removed when the boat dived.

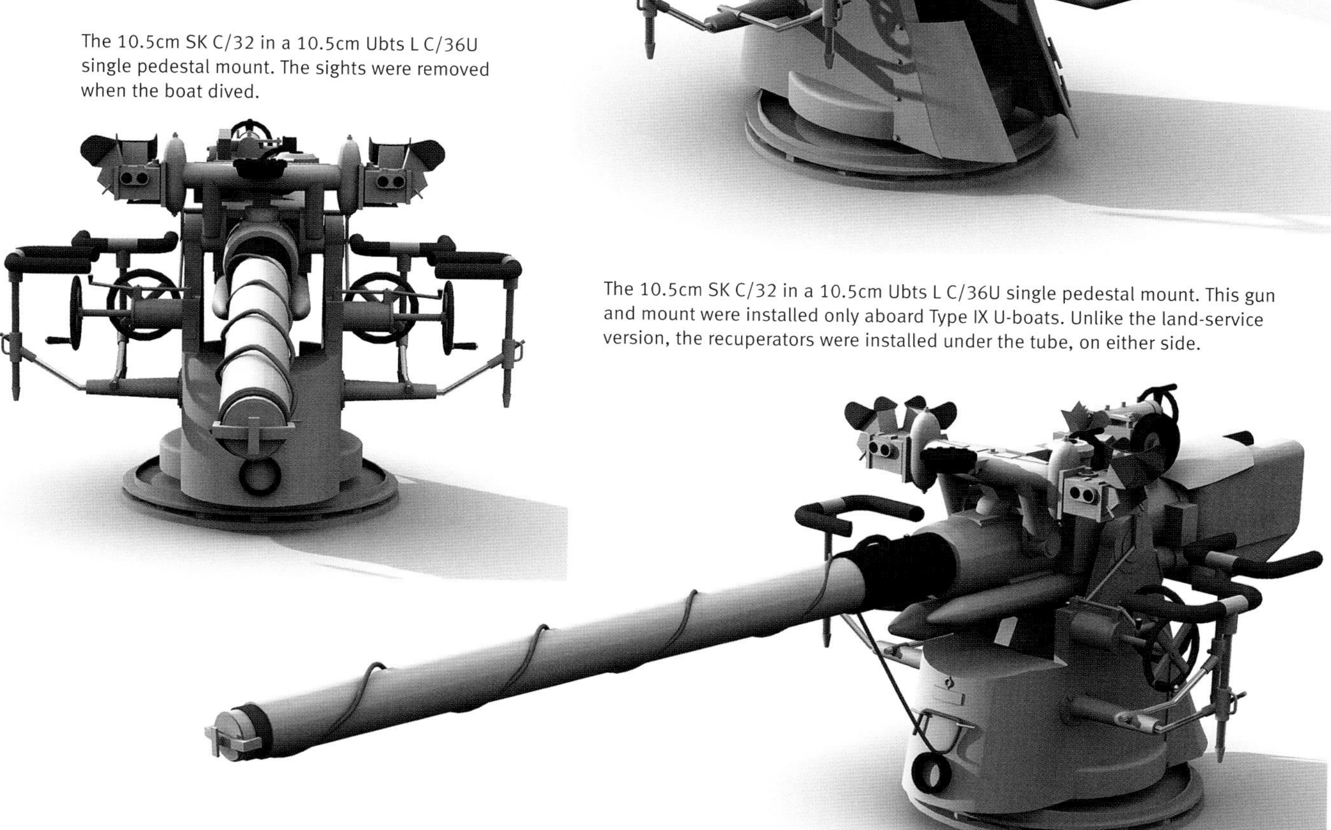

The 10.5cm SK C/32 in a 10.5cm Ubts L C/36U single pedestal mount. This gun and mount were installed only aboard Type IX U-boats. Unlike the land-service version, the recuperators were installed under the tube, on either side.

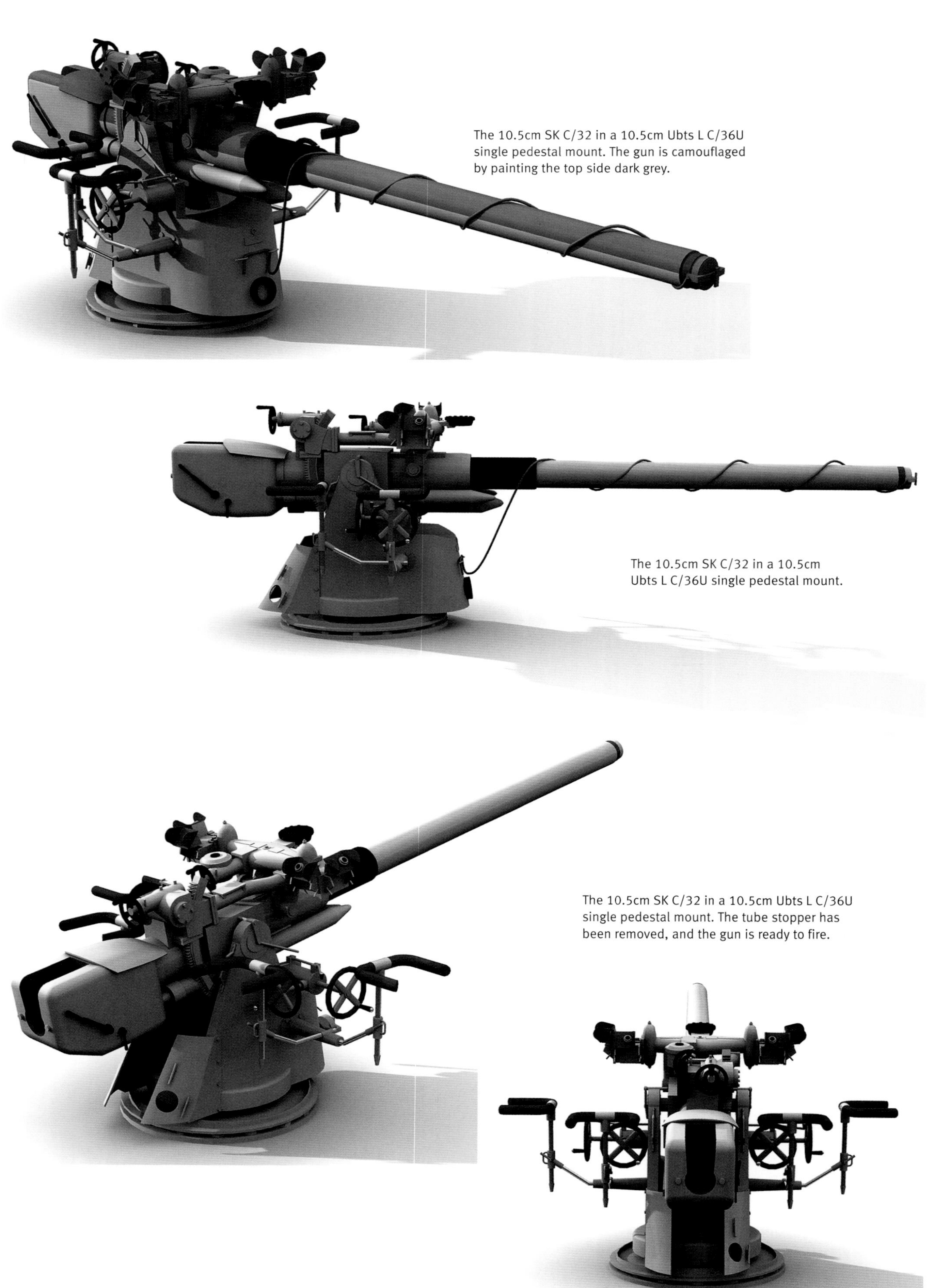

The 10.5cm SK C/32 in a 10.5cm Ubts L C/36U single pedestal mount. The gun is camouflaged by painting the top side dark grey.

The 10.5cm SK C/32 in a 10.5cm Ubts L C/36U single pedestal mount.

The 10.5cm SK C/32 in a 10.5cm Ubts L C/36U single pedestal mount. The tube stopper has been removed, and the gun is ready to fire.

8.8cm Dopp. L C/31 twin mount with 10.5cm SK C/33 guns. In this variant, with the gE shield, the fuse-setting machines were placed outside the shield, on either side of the mount.

8.8cm Dopp. L C/31 twin mount with 10.5cm SK C/33 guns. *Scharnhorst* and *Gneisenau* were the first ships to get these mounts.

8.8cm Dopp. L C/31 twin mount with 10.5cm SK C/33 guns and the gE shield. Note the interior details.

8.8cm Dopp. L C/31 twin mount with 10.5cm SK C/33 guns and the gE shield. The upper surfaces of these mounts were painted dark grey during *Scharnhorst* and *Gneisenau*'s raids into the North Atlantic.

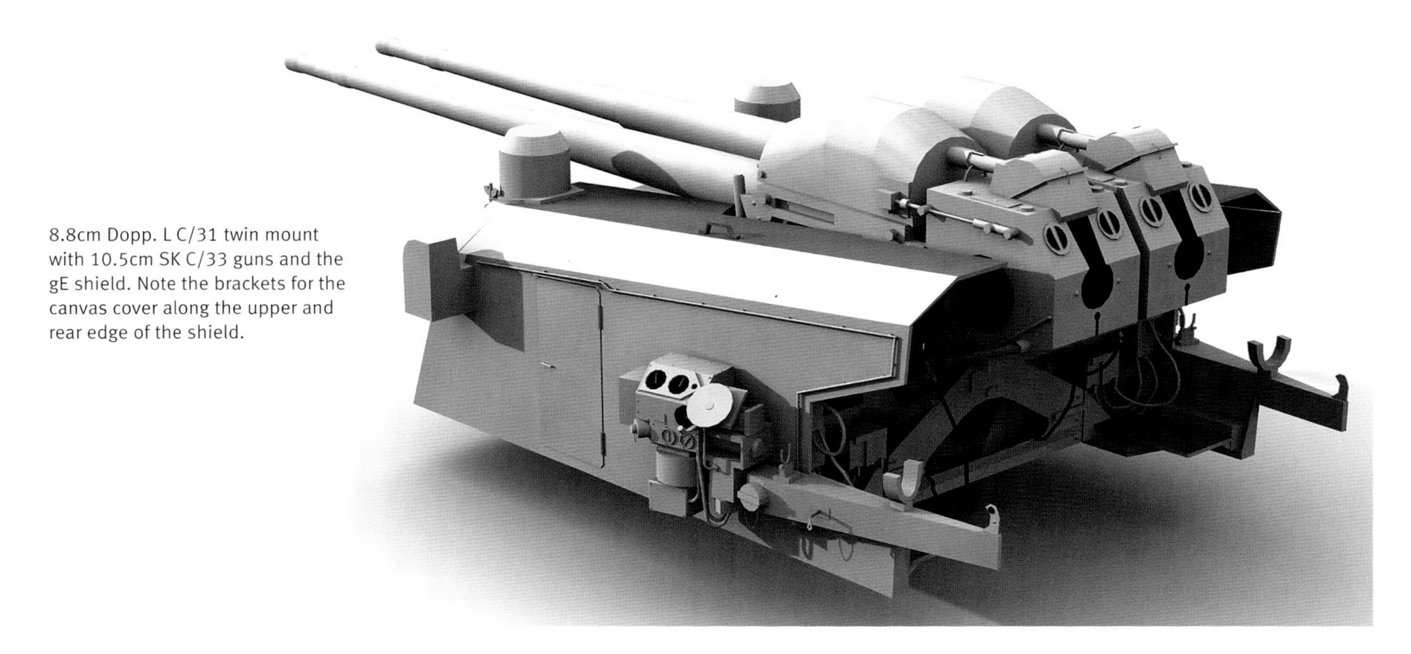

8.8cm Dopp. L C/31 twin mount with 10.5cm SK C/33 guns and the gE shield. Note the brackets for the canvas cover along the upper and rear edge of the shield.

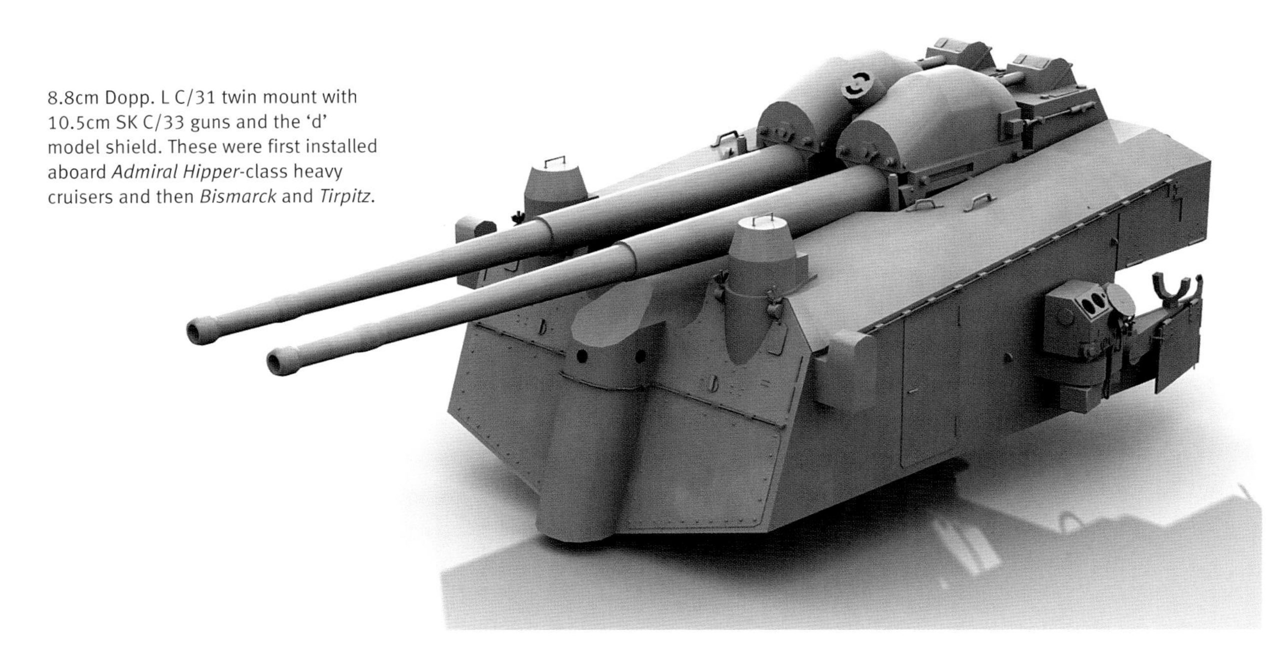

8.8cm Dopp. L C/31 twin mount with 10.5cm SK C/33 guns and the 'd' model shield. These were first installed aboard *Admiral Hipper*-class heavy cruisers and then *Bismarck* and *Tirpitz*.

8.8cm Dopp. L C/31 twin mount with 10.5cm SK C/33 guns and the 'd' model shield. These were first installed aboard *Admiral Hipper*-class heavy cruisers and then *Bismarck* and *Tirpitz*.

8.8cm Dopp. L C/31 twin mount with 10.5cm SK C/33 guns and the 'd' model shield. This was slightly enlarged, compared to the previous model, with flaps added at the rear, covering the fuse-setting machines. Note the brackets for the canvas cover close to the upper rim of the shield.

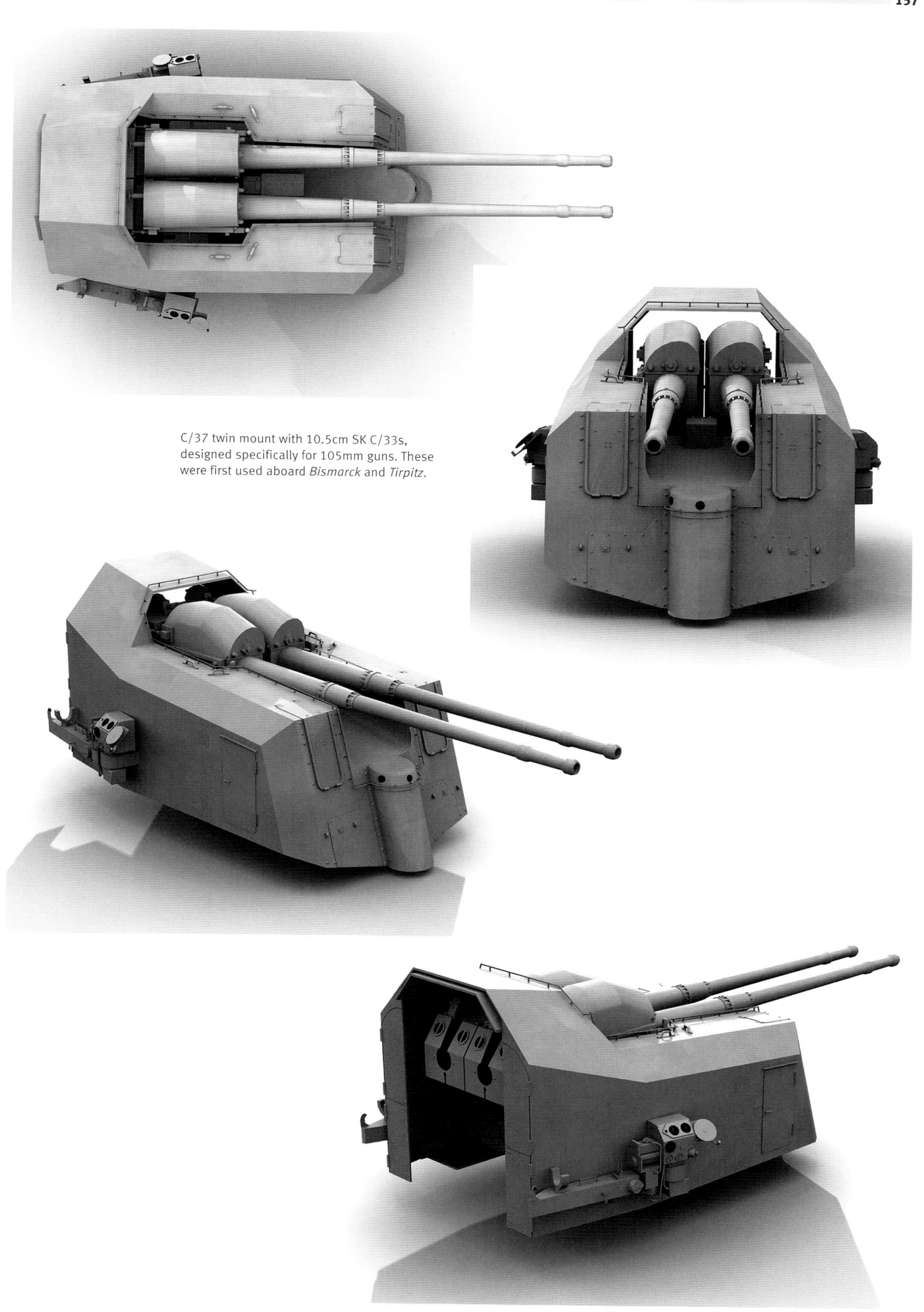

C/37 twin mount with 10.5cm SK C/33s, designed specifically for 105mm guns. These were first used aboard *Bismarck* and *Tirpitz*.

The 8.8cm SK C/30 gun in an MPL C/30 single pedestal mount. There are slight differences between individual guns and their shields.

The 8.8cm SK C/30 gun in an MPL C/30 single pedestal mount. Note brackets for the canvas cover on the upper and rear edges of the sides of the shield.

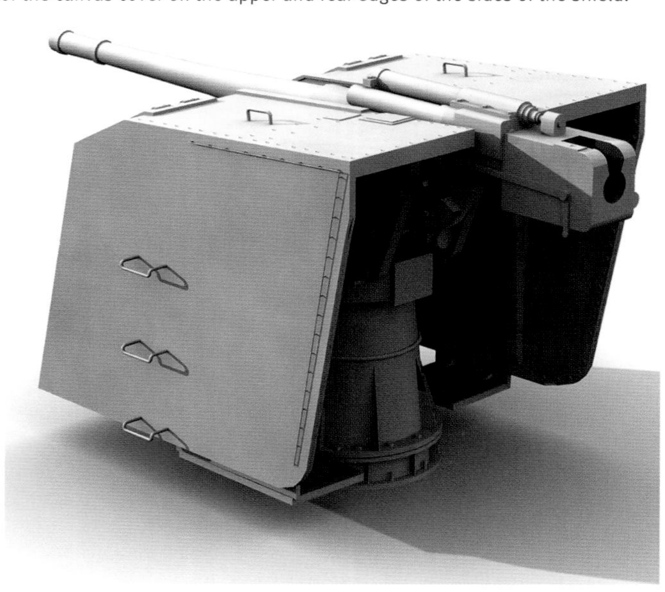

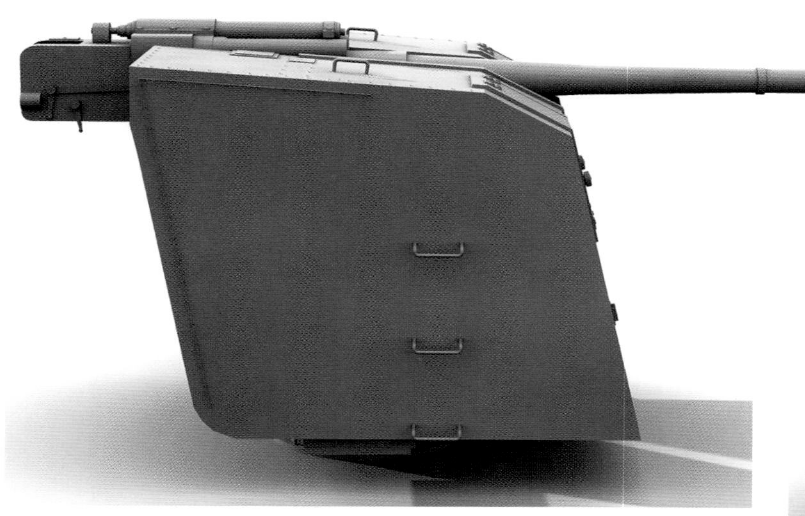

The 8.8cm SK C/30 gun in an MPL C/30 single pedestal mount.

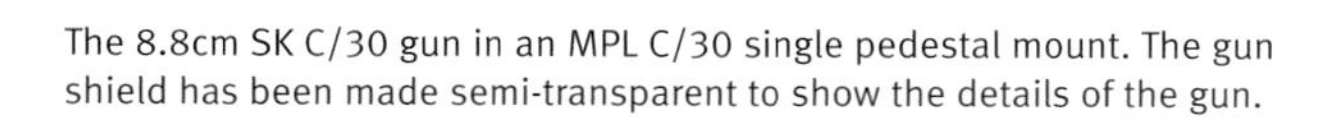

The 8.8cm SK C/30 gun in an MPL C/30 single pedestal mount. The gun shield has been made semi-transparent to show the details of the gun.

The 8.8cm SK C/30 gun in an MPL C/30 single pedestal mount, front and rear view.

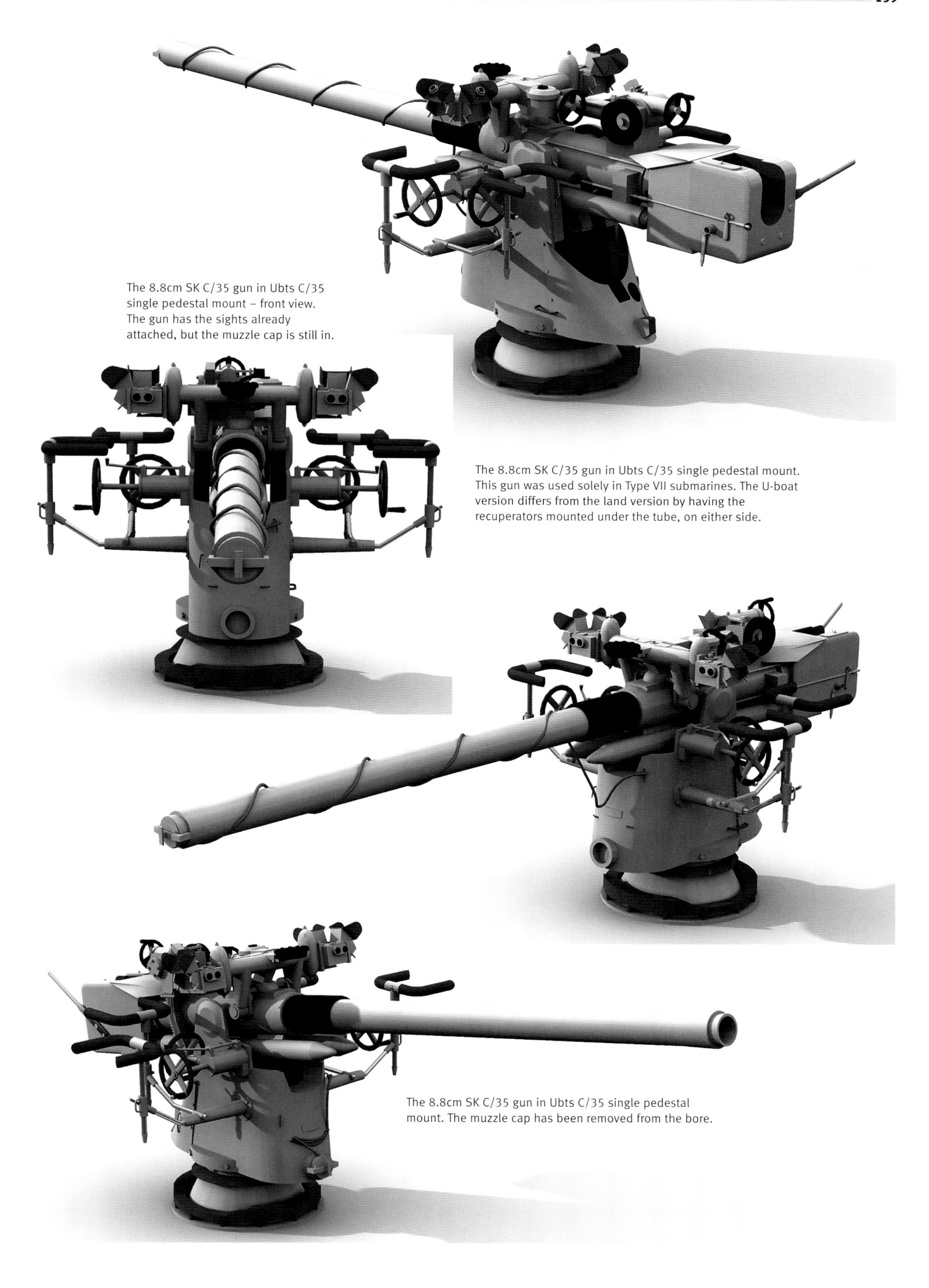

The 8.8cm SK C/35 gun in Ubts C/35 single pedestal mount – front view. The gun has the sights already attached, but the muzzle cap is still in.

The 8.8cm SK C/35 gun in Ubts C/35 single pedestal mount. This gun was used solely in Type VII submarines. The U-boat version differs from the land version by having the recuperators mounted under the tube, on either side.

The 8.8cm SK C/35 gun in Ubts C/35 single pedestal mount. The muzzle cap has been removed from the bore.

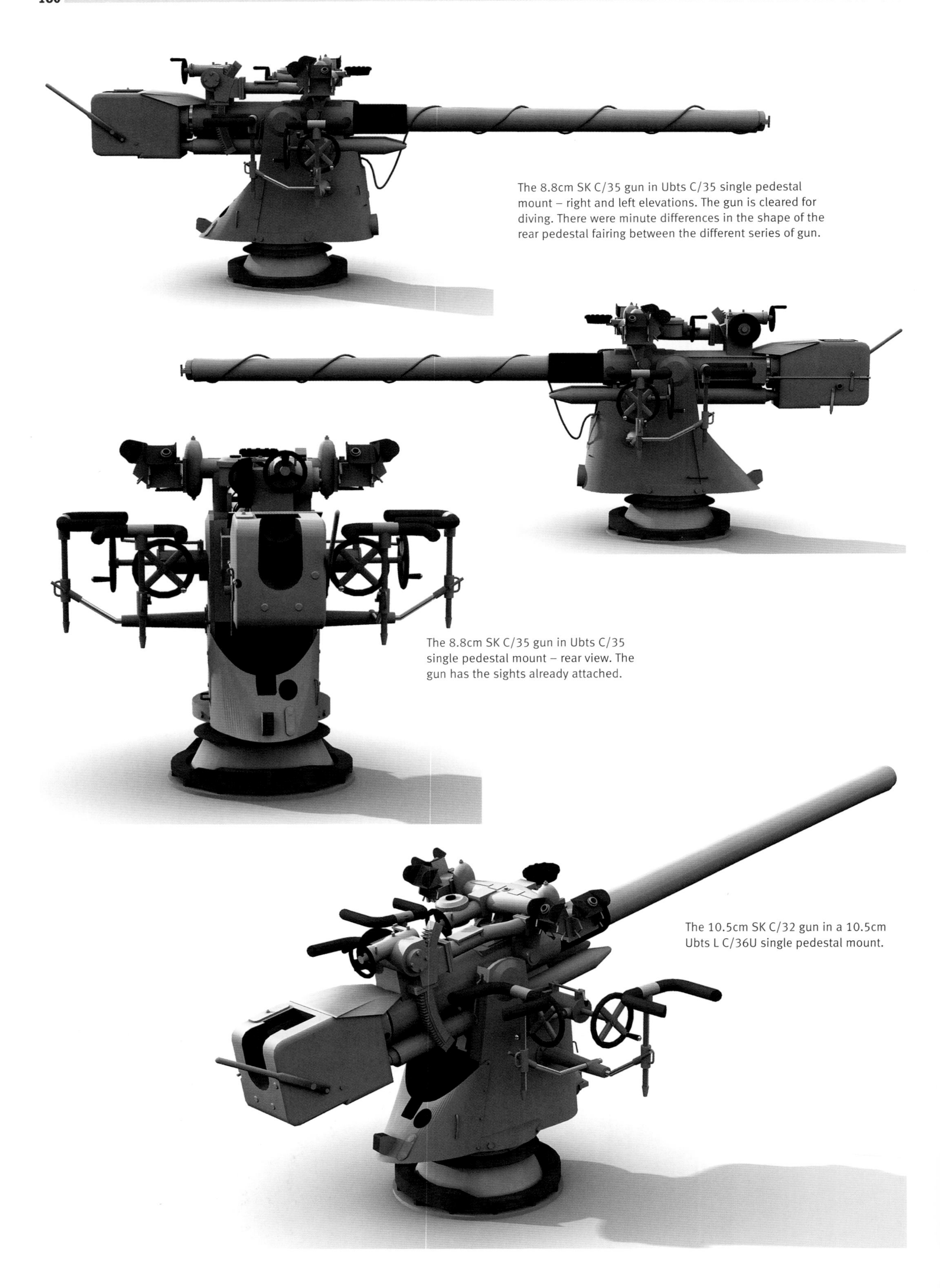

The 8.8cm SK C/35 gun in Ubts C/35 single pedestal mount – right and left elevations. The gun is cleared for diving. There were minute differences in the shape of the rear pedestal fairing between the different series of gun.

The 8.8cm SK C/35 gun in Ubts C/35 single pedestal mount – rear view. The gun has the sights already attached.

The 10.5cm SK C/32 gun in a 10.5cm Ubts L C/36U single pedestal mount.

10

THE 15cm TBTS K C/36 GUN

ABOARD DESTROYERS

The political changes in Germany in 1932-3 had a profound effect on naval construction. After the repudiation of the restrictions imposed by the Treaty of Versailles in 1932, the Kriegsmarine high command immediately approved a new destroyer programme for 1,500-ton ships, and design work on two projects began at the Vulcan Shipyard in Stettin and the F Schichau yard in Elbing. Both designs were to be armed with 127mm guns to match the 120-130mm guns that were the norm in other countries' destroyers at that time.

The Rheinmetall 15cm Tbts K C/36 was originally designed for torpedo boats, but was rapidly adapted for destroyers, the first studies into rearming the 1934 and 1934A class destroyers with these weapons having began as soon as the ships had been commissioned. The high command considered their original 127mm armament inferior compared to that of potential enemy ships, and the new 1936 class was designed for 150mm guns from the start. The destroyer *Bruno Heinemann* had her 127mm guns replaced by five single 150mm guns for trials in 1938, in which it was rapidly discovered that not only were there problems with the guns themselves but that mounting such heavy weapons on a ship not designed for them was positively dangerous. The additional weight high

Left: The Rheinmetall-built prototype of the 15cm Tbts K C/36 gun. This gun was installed in the semi-enclosed Tbts L C/36 gun house. *(AJ-Press collection)*

Above: The 15cm Tbts K C/36 prototype without the gun house. *(AJ-Press collection)*

Left: When commissioned the first modernised 1936A class destroyers (*Z 23 – Z 30*) had four 150mm guns. From late 1942/early 1943 this was increased to five guns of the same calibre. *(CAW collection)*

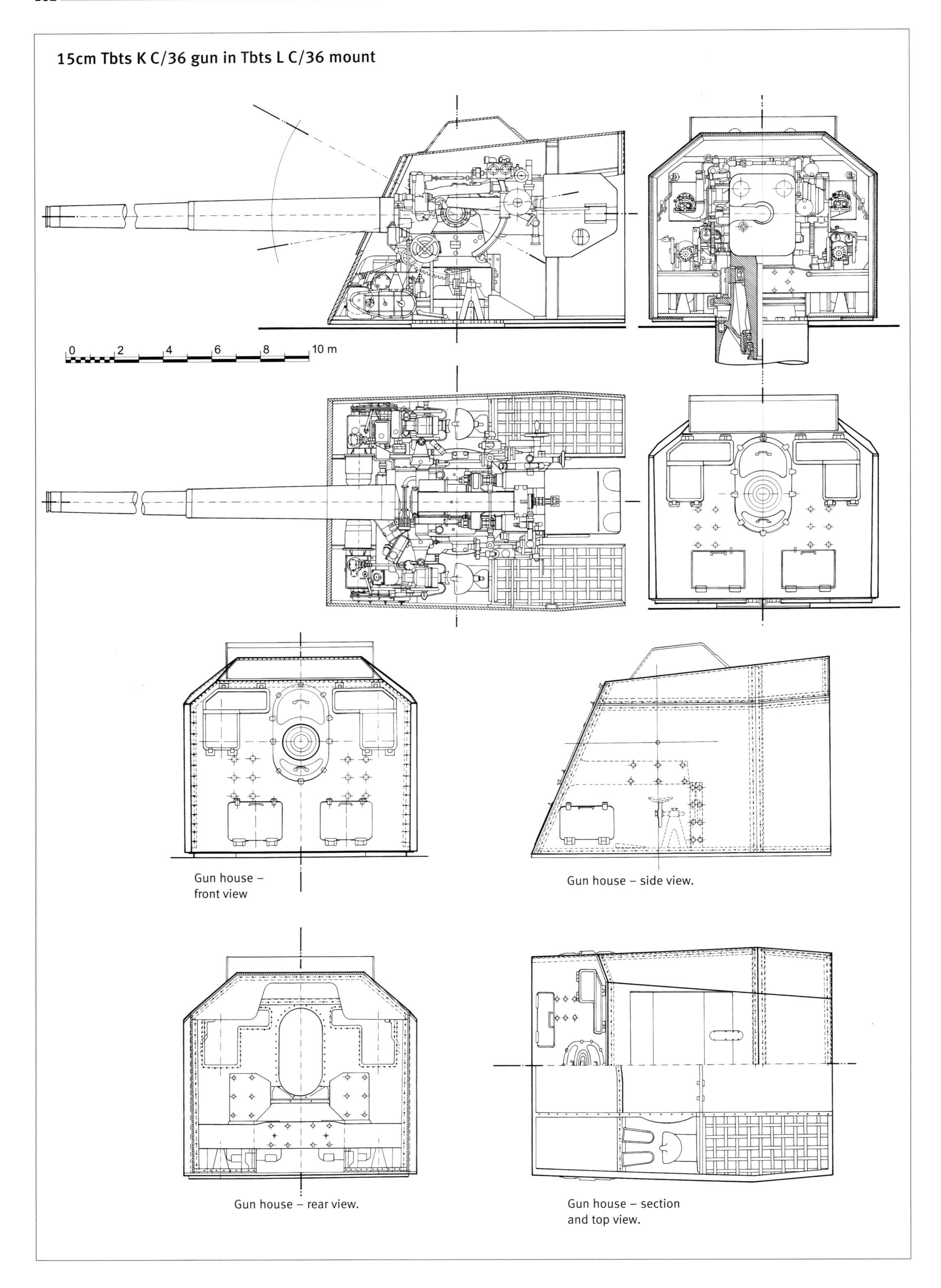

Gun house – front view

Gun house – side view.

Gun house – rear view.

Gun house – section and top view.

Above: Front view of the 15cm Tbts K C/36 gun. Training and elevation gear in the foreground. Both training and elevation could be done manually or by electric motors fitted at the side of the mount. Handwheels at the right gun-layer's seat governed elevation, at the left one training. *(AJ-Press collection)*

Above: Rear view of the gun. Breech ring with horizontal sliding block in the foreground.

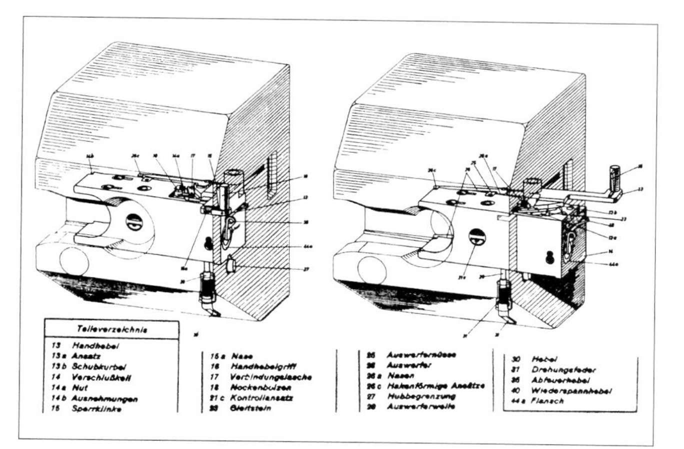

Above: Gun breech – closed (left) and open (right).

Above: Rear view of the Rheinmetall prototype. *(AJ-Press collection)*

above the waterline seriously affected stability, and in heavy seas only two of the five guns could be worked. One mount was removed in an attempt to remedy these problems, but when this was found to be insufficient, the original 127mm armament was quickly reinstalled. Later on, the 12.7cm SK C/34 guns were replaced by the new 12.7cm SK C/41 in DrhL C/41 twin turrets.

The gun

The 15cm Tbts K C/36 was a semi-automatic weapon with a horizontal sliding breech, which had to be opened manually to load the first shot, using the breech lever on the right-hand side of the breech ring. The loose barrel was anchored at the breech end with a breech nut. The electromagnetic trigger circuit was backed up by a mechanical system for emergency use. In 1943, a muzzle heater to prevent the barrel icing-up in freezing conditions was tested, but the idea was abandoned when it was found that the heater consumed too much electric power and also its additional weight strained the mount's elevating gear.

The mount

The mount sat on a cylindrical pillar, fixed to the base with fourteen bolts. The vertical shaft bearing was in the centre of the pillar, and it was topped by the toothed training ring. The mount itself consisted of the splinter-proof shield, the training and elevation mechanisms and buffer stops, the gun-layers' seats, sights, triggers, remote-control mechanisms and the electric motors. The gun cradle consisted of a hollow tube, two hydraulic buffers to absorb the recoil force of 58,000kg

The 15cm Tbts K C/36 L/48 gun

Calibre:	149.1mm
Weight of gun:	7,200kg
Overall length:	7,165mm
Length bore:	6,815mm
Length chamber:	1,088mm
Volume chamber:	21.2dm^3
Length rifling:	5,587mm
Grooves:	44 (1.75mm x 6.14mm)
Weight projectile:	45.3kg
Propellant charge:	13.5kg of RPC/38 (7.5/3)
Muzzle velocity:	875m/s
Working pressure:	3,000kg/cm^2
Approximate service life:	1,600 effective rounds
Maximum range:	23,550m at 47°

at 0°

Above: Right and left gun-layers' stations. *(AJ-Press collection)*

elevation, and a single pneumatic recuperator.

Training and elevation were either manual or powered by the electric motors controlled by hydraulic clutches. The left-hand gun layer controlled training and the right elevation. With power training on, the hand wheels simply controlled the movement of the gun, moving through an arc of 150° only. The clutches had to be disengaged to revert to manual training. In an emergency, control of either training or elevation could be taken over by the layer on the opposite side.

There were two trigger mechanisms, electromagnetic and mechanical. Each layer had a foot-pedal for the mechanical system, which could also be fired directly by a lanyard attached to the trigger level in case of damage to the main system. Each layer also had a trigger switch built into his right hand-wheel for the electromagnetic circuit, which could also be fired remotely from the conning tower. Both layers had linked stereoscopic sights with 5-10x power zoom. The right-hand layer was also responsible for elevation corrections supplied by two sets of compensating gear. The first of these, the so-called 'Regler', provided corrections according to the type of ammunition being used, while the second compensated for barrel wear.

Optical sights used with the 15cm Tbts K C/36 gun in the Tbts L C/36M mount

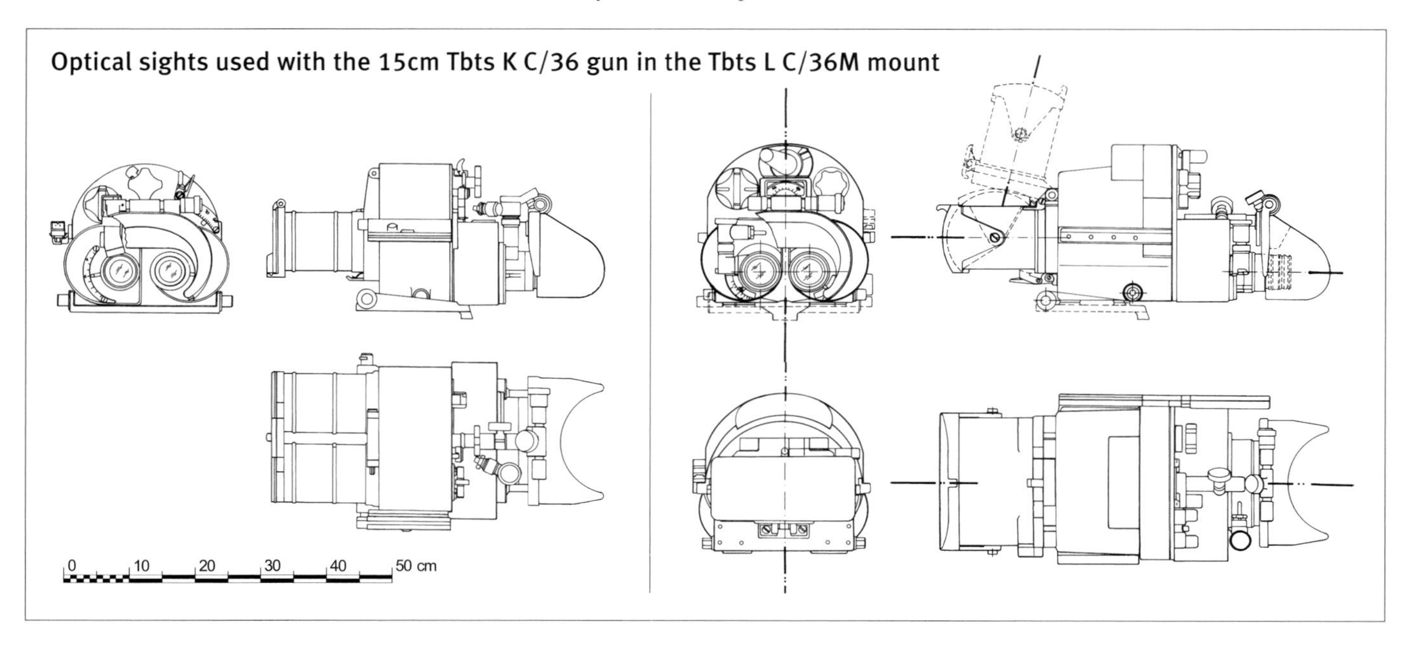

Firing information was transmitted to the guns by wire from the fire-direction centre. Each layer had his own receiver and trained and elevated the gun accordingly, these settings being transmitted back the fire-direction centre, which was also linked to the guns by intercom.

The semi-enclosed C/36 gun house

The splinter-proof shield covered the front, sides and top of the mount, the rear being open. In the front, there were two flap-covered sighting ports, one either side of the central gun port. There were also four inspection flaps at the foot of the shield, two in the front and one each at the front on either side, to allow servicing of the power-training equipment.

The mount's electrics ran from the ship's main supply at 220V DC. This powered the trigger circuit

C/36 gun house weights

Item	Weight
Barrel and breech:	7,200kg
Cradle and recuperating gear:	1,730kg
From 1942:	1,500kg
Mount:	3,885kg
Shield with frame:	4,153kg
Sights:	650kg
Electric wiring and equipment:	580kg
Total weight:	18,800kg
Auxiliary equipment (including securing gear):	330kg

C/36 mount training arcs aboard 1934A class destroyers

Turret 'A'	30° – 0° – 330°	Turret 'D'	27° – 0° – 333°
Turret 'B'	40° – 0° – 320°	Turret 'E'	42° – 0° – 318°
Turret 'C'	20° – 0° – 340°	Depression/elevation:	–10°/+30°

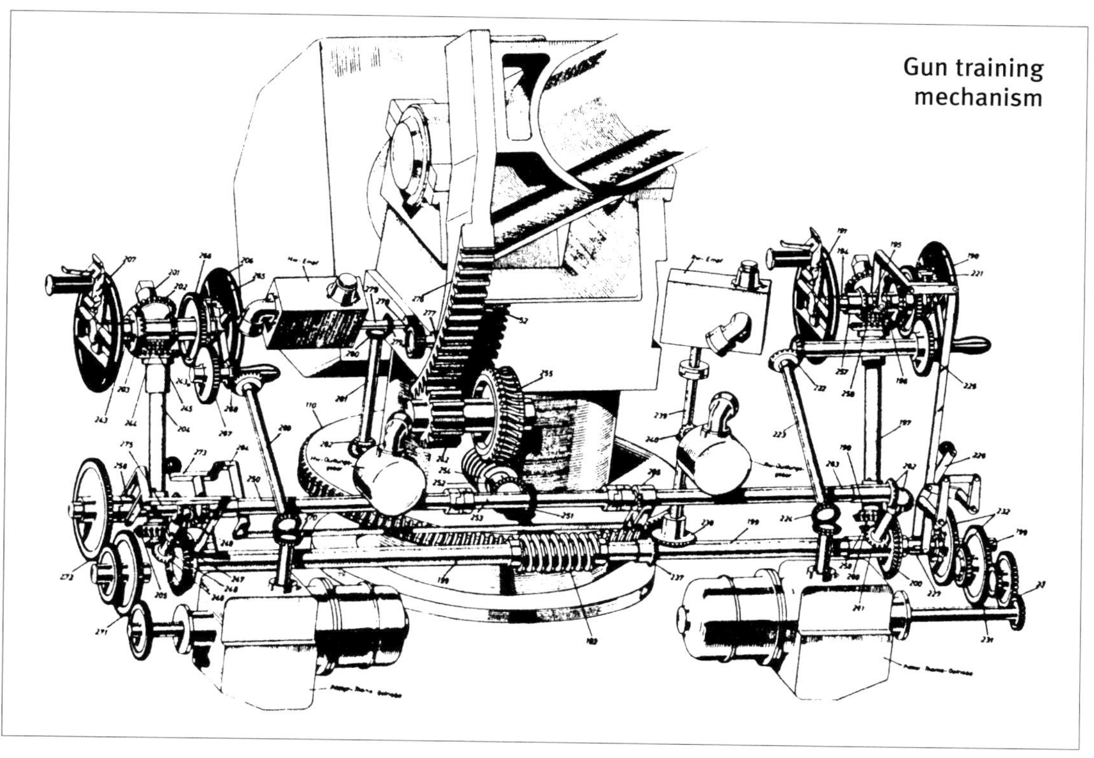

Gun training mechanism

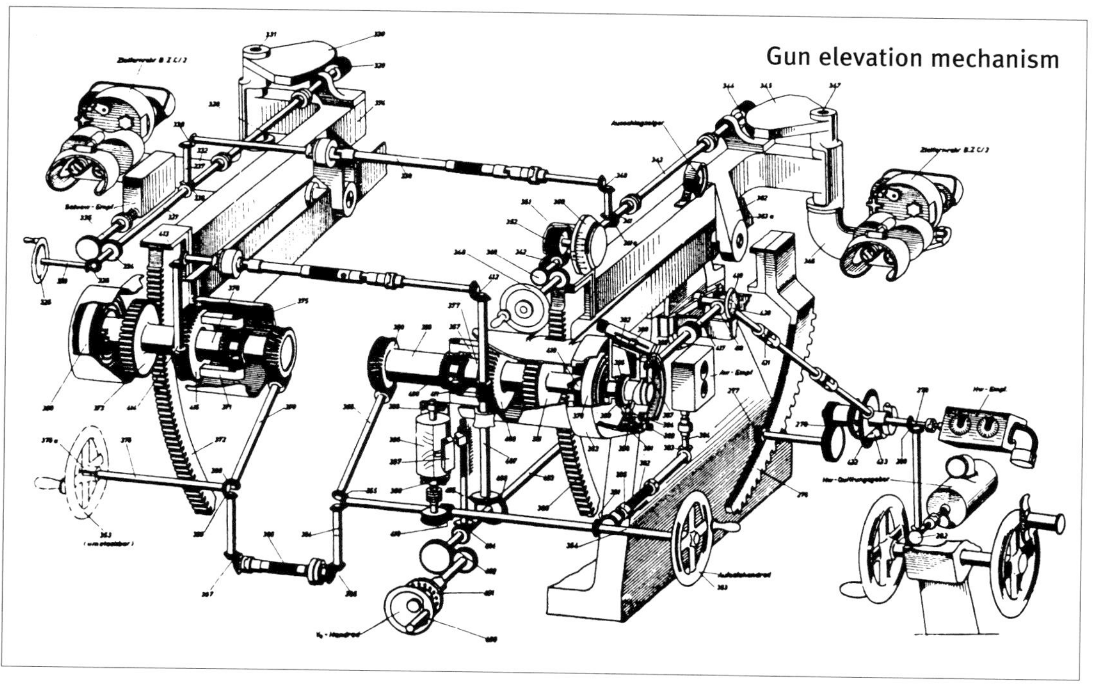

Gun elevation mechanism

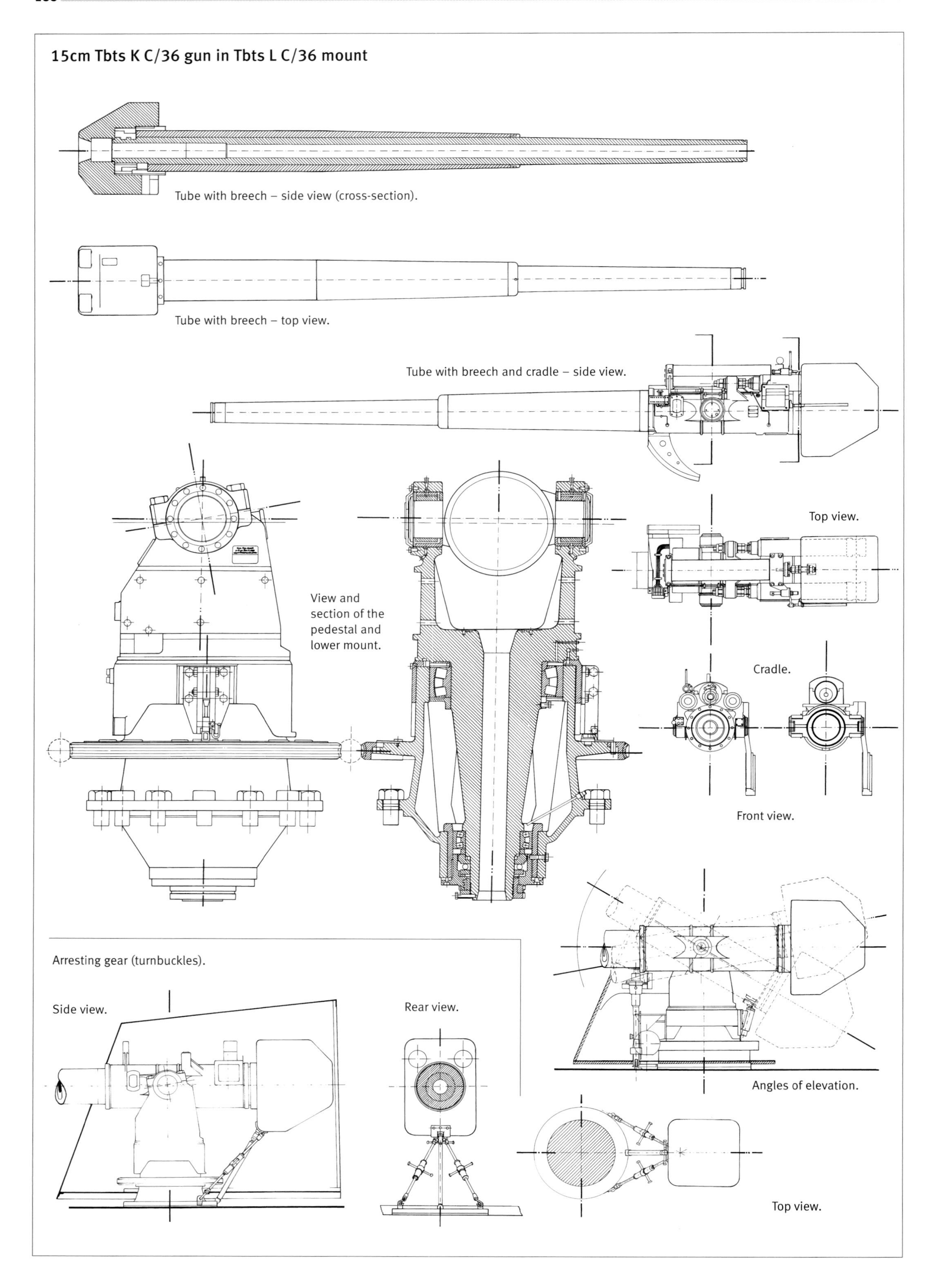
15cm Tbts K C/36 gun in Tbts L C/36 mount
Tube with breech – side view (cross-section).
Tube with breech – top view.
Tube with breech and cradle – side view.
Top view.
View and section of the pedestal and lower mount.
Cradle.
Front view.
Arresting gear (turnbuckles).
Side view.
Rear view.
Angles of elevation.
Top view.

solenoid, the 1kW permanent and 3kW peak output training and elevating motors and the portable auxiliary lighting for the mount. A 4V transformer also powered lights for the sights, the control positions and the breech, as well as the firing warning system (blue and red lights and a buzzer).

The DrhL C/38 twin turret

The DrhL C/38 was originally designed for Battlecruisers 'O', 'P' and 'Q' and the scout cruisers, but when these were cancelled it was decided to arm the modernised 1934A class destroyers with them. Stability problems had handicapped these ships by forcing the reduction of their 150mm battery from five single mounts to four, and it was hoped that mounting the twin turret in place of the forward single mount would restore the fifth gun without causing the same stability problems.

Two 15cm Tbts K C/36 guns were therefore fitted in a new 'lightweight gun turret', in which extensive use of welding and other modifications were expected to result in considerable weight savings. However, despite all this, the turret still weighed almost twice as much as the single mount it was to replace. There were also problems integrating the new twin turret into the ships' existing fire-control systems. Future destroyer classes were planned to mount two of these turrets, but nothing came of this before the end of the war.

Above: One of only a few photos which show brass nameplates on individual gun houses. *(CAW collection)*

Above, left: A destroyer's stern – in the foreground no. 3 gun barrel. *(CAW collection)*

Left: Destroyer armed with 127mm guns steams by one of her sister-ships. Later on this armament was replaced by 150mm guns. *(CAW collection)*

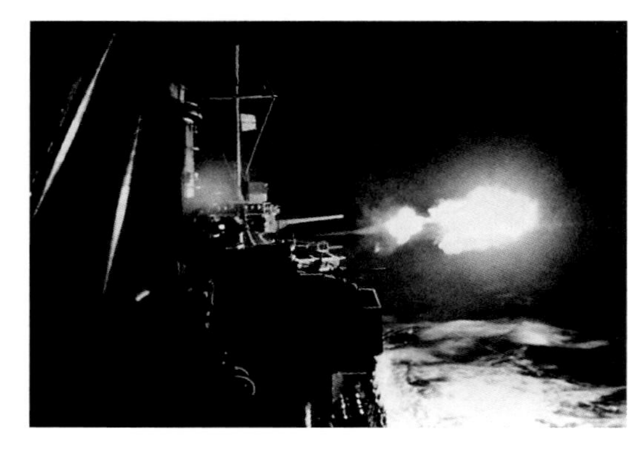

Above: Night gunnery practice onboard a destroyer. *(CAW collection)*

Above: Stern guns of destroyer fire a salvo during gunnery practice. *(CAW collection)*

Above: Destroyer amidships. Two 15cm guns were fitted astern. *(CAW collection)*

Left: A destroyer fires her guns. *(CAW collection)*

Above: The destroyer *Z 34* was armed with five single 15cm Tbts K C/36 guns. *(A Jarski collection)*

Below and right: Two photos of a destroyer in a Norwegian fiord. This ship was fitted with five single 15cm Tbts K C/36 guns. *(A Jarski collection)*

Above, left and right: After 150mm gun. *(CAW collection)*

Left: After guns of a destroyer and their crew. Note the details of the gun. *(CAW collection)*

Above: The DrhL C/38 twin turret aboard *Z 25*. *(M Skwiot collection)*

Left: Gun crew at battle stations. Note the details of the 150mm gun house. *(CAW collection)*

Below: The 15cm Tbts K C/36 gun, designed for large torpedo boats, was soon adopted for destroyers. It was decided to re-arm the 1934 and 1934A-class destroyers immediately upon their commission. This photo shows after guns nos. 3, 4 and 5. *(CAW collection)*

Right and below: The first ships to be fitted with twin C/38 turrets were the destroyers *Z 23*, *Z 24* and *Z 25*. Each of them got one such turret installed in place of the forward single gun. *(CAW collection)*

Right: *Z 38* in Norwegian waters, 1942. *(A Jarski collection)*

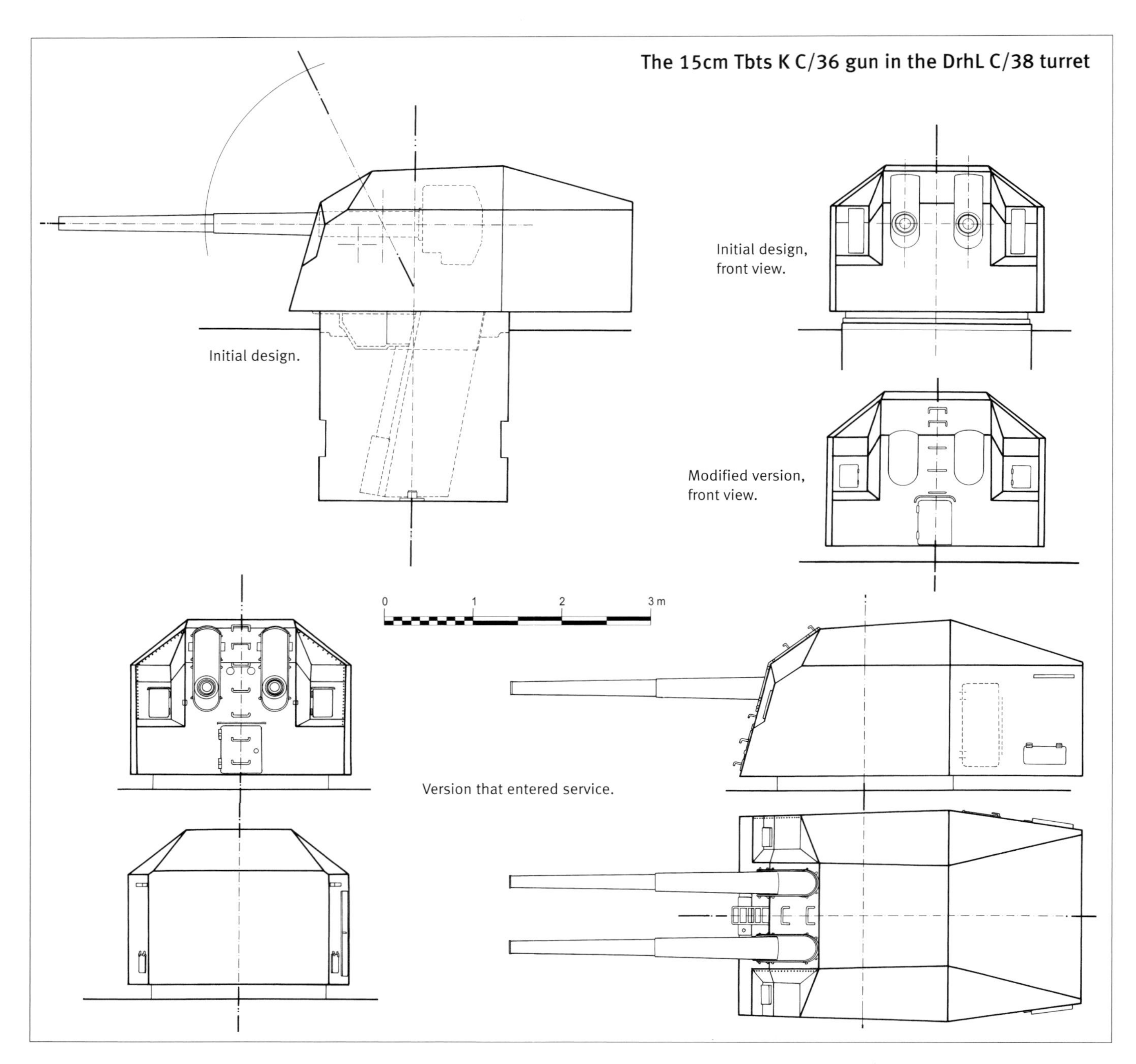

Left: The destroyer *Z 25* was fitted with one DrhL C/38 twin turret. *(M Skwiot collection)*

Left: C/38 twin turrets were installed aboard the 1936A class (*Z 23–Z 25, Z 29*) and the modernised 1936A class destroyers (*Z 31–Z 34, Z 37–Z 42*) during 1942. The photo shows *Z 34*. *(A Jarski collection)*

The new turret made for 60 tons of weight high up above the waterline, which compromised handling in heavy seas and also reduced speed. These problems were not ironed out in the sea trials, and therefore all subsequent modernised 1934B class destroyers, otherwise sister-ships of the 1934A class, reverted to a 127mm main battery.

The DrhL C/38 twin turret

Turret weight:	62.5 tonnes
Turret diameter:	2,800mm
Barbette diameter:	3,200mm
Distance between gun axes:	1,070mm
Recoil distance:	440mm
Maximum elevating speed:	8°/sec
Maximum training speed:	8°/sec
Depression/elevation:	–10°/+65°
Arcs of fire, destroyers *Z 37-Z 39*:	
'A' turret, DrhL C/38:	30°–0°–330°
'B' gun, C/36:	42°–0°–318°
'C' gun, C/36:	27°–0°–333°
'D' gun, C/36:	20°–0°–340°

Arcs of fire varied in other ships of the class.

C/38 turret weights

Barrel and breech (single):	7,200kg
Cradle and recuperator gear:	4,300kg
Mount:	22,250kg
Turret shield:	13,750kg
Sights:	650kg
Electric wiring and equipment:	2,400kg
Weight, total:	60.4 tons
Armour:	Front 30mm; sides 20mm; roof 20mm; rear 15mm

Elevation in the C/38 turret was by Pittler-Thoma hydraulic gear powered by electric motors, and training was by electric motors. Manual training was available in emergencies. The internal layout of the mount differed little from the C/36 mount and the guns and their equipment were identical. There was an Ardelt electric ammunition hoist for each gun, as well as a ten-round ready-use ammunition supply at the rear of the turret, allowing the gun crews to load and open fire at short notice without waiting for shells and charges to come up on the hoists. The ready-use cased charges were kept dry by putting them in airtight

Below: *Z 25* in dry dock during an overhaul and modernisation of the armament, including exchanging the single 150mm gun for the C/38 twin turret. It was mounted on the forecastle. *(Photo Drüppel, M Skwiot collection)*

Above: *Z 32* in camouflage scheme. Note the twin DrhL C/38 turret on the forecastle. *M Skwiot collection)*

aluminium containers which were them locked in galvanised steel boxes.

The DrhL C/38 turret was mounted in destroyers *Z 23*, *Z 24*, *Z 25* and *Z 29* of the 1936A class and *Z 31*, *Z 32*, *Z 33*, *Z 34*, *Z 37*, *Z 38*, *Z 39*, *Z 40*, *Z 41* and *Z 42* of the modified 1936A class.

Ammunition

The 15cm Tbts K C/36 fired the same ammunition as the 15cm SK C/28 (see above).

Destroyer ammunition stores

These were housed below the main deck, close to the gun positions. Aboard *Z 37*, *Z 38* and *Z 39* those for the after guns were in sections II and III, with ammunition hoists nearby. The hoists for the superfiring guns on the after superstructure were longer. Once the shells and charges had reached the upper deck level, they were placed on a wheeled tray and pushed to the guns, where they were loaded by hand.

Gun designations and names

In destroyers, guns were simply designated by numbers, counting from the bows, so the forward gun was No 1 etc. The guns were not officially named, but crews often gave them unofficial names, usually commemorating the ship's successful engagements and the like.

Coastal batteries

Many of these guns armed coastal batteries, on a version of the naval mount that lacked power training. This was designated the C36/H for 'Handbetrieb' – 'Manual'. The shipboard power mounting was the C36/M for 'Maschinenbetrieb' – 'powered'.

11

THE 12.7cm SK C/34 GUN

ABOARD DESTROYERS

Rheinmetall began designing the new 127mm gun in 1930, to arm the large torpedo boats ('Torpedoboot', 'T-Boot') which were what the German navy had to have instead of destroyers, thanks to the prohibition on building torpedo vessels over 800 tons in the Treaty of Versailles. However, in 1934, just before the final repudiation of the Treaty, these ships were reclassified as destroyers ('Zerstörer').

Progress on the new 127mm design had been rapid, and the first six prototype guns had been ready by 1932. These had been mounted abroad the 1924 class torpedo boats *Leopard* and *Luchs* for sea trials, replacing their original 105mm guns. Having successfully completed these trials, the new 12.7cm SK C/34 gun on the MPL C/34 pivot mount was formally adopted as the main gun for Germany's future destroyers.

In fact, the calibre of the gun was actually 128mm, with a 47-calibre barrel and a semi-automatic vertically-sliding breech, firing a 28kg shell. With a muzzle velocity of 830mps, maximum range was 17,400m. The MPL C/34 mount was fitted with a splinter-proof shield of 8mm-thick Wsh steel. The rate of fire, with manual loading of separate ammunition, was estimated at 18-20rpm, but even the best gun crews never got above 15-18rpm.

Ships armed with the 12.7cm SK C/34 gun

The Type 1934 class destroyers (*Z 1* to *Z 16*) all had five 12.7cm SK C/34 guns in MPL C/34 single mounts, two forward and three aft, apart from *Z 5*, *Z 10* and *Z 15* which had an anti-aircraft gun in place of No.

Above: One of the 1934B class destroyers at sea. In the early part of her career, her main armament consisted of 127mm guns. *(M Skwiot collection)*

Below: Only two torpedo boats were armed with these guns – *Leopard* and *Luchs*. Their 12.7cm SK C/34 guns were fitted in modified MPL C/28 mounts. *(A Jarski collection)*

Left: Design of the 127mm gun commenced at Rheinmetall in Düsseldorf in 1930. This is the prototype of the 12.7cm SK C/34 gun. *(AJ-Press collection)*

Above: 12.7cm SK C/34 gun without the gun house. *(AJ-Press collection)*

Above: Gun crew at action stations. The troughs in the foreground delivered ammunition to the gun. *(CAW collection)*

3 gun aft. The second series of ships (*Z 17* to *Z 22*) and the final 1936B class (*Z 35*, *Z 36*, *Z 43*, *Z 44* and *Z 45*) also had the five guns in single mounts. The gunboat *Grille* and the gunnery training ship *Bremse* also had the same guns and mounts.

Leopard and *Luchs*, the test ships for the new gun, were the only torpedo boats to be re-armed with them, on older MPL C/28 mountings. The remaining torpedo boats all retained their original armament of five 10.5cm SK C/32 guns on MPL C/32 pivot mounts with g.E. splinter shields.

The gun

The barrel consisted of an outer tube and an inner liner which was inserted through the breech ring and secured with a bronze nut. The liner was rifled with 40 grooves of increasing pitch. The semi-automatic breech had to be opened manually with the breech lever on the right-hand side of the breech ring to load the first shot. Opening the breech cocked the trigger

Right: The 1934, 1934A and 1936 class destroyers had their guns mounted in single MPL C/34 mounts. There were five of these on each ship, designated no. 1 through 5 (of which nos. 2 and 4 were superfiring). *(CAW collection)*

Above: Crew during routine gunnery drill. *(A Jarski collection)*

mechanism, which was fired either from the gun layer's position or remotely from the conning tower. There was an emergency mechanical trigger operated by foot pedals in the layers' positions. Safety fittings prevented accidental discharge or premature opening of the breech.

Opening the breech after firing automatically ejected the spent case. If there was a misfire, the trigger mechanism could be re-cocked without opening the breech, and if there was a major malfunction in it (i.e. a broken striker) the whole trigger mechanism could be removed and replaced while the breech stayed safely closed.

The barrel lay in the cradle, attached to the cradle yoke by the recoil-control gear, which consisted of a hydraulic buffer and a pair of spring-loaded recuperators. Two parallel toothed arcs meshed with the elevating gear.

The 12.7cm SK C/34 gun

Calibre:	128mm
Overall length:	5,760mm
Length bore incl. chamber:	5,430mm
Length chamber:	894mm
Length initial combustion chamber:	819mm
Volume initial combustion chamber:	12.1dm^3
Length rifling:	4,536mm
Grooves:	40 (1.5mm x 4mm)
Initial rifling pitch:	35 calibres (4,480mm)
Final rifling pitch:	30 calibres (3,840mm)
Height of centre of gravity above deck:	1,556mm

The mount

This consisted of a fixed post, with a rotating body and cradle. The post contained a vertical upper mount shaft with bearings supporting the cylindrical upper body shaft, with the cabling for the electric motors and the communication link between the gun and the fire-direction centre running up the middle of it. On top of the post was a toothed training ring which meshed with the gun's traversing cogs, installed in the rotating upper mount. The supports for the gun shield, the layers' seats, handwheels, sights and firing data indicators well all fitted to the rotating upper body, comprising the cradle trunnion pivots and needle bearings.

Above: Sequence of photos that illustrate the complete procedure of transporting (shoving in this case) shells from the ammunition hoist via the ammunition troughs to the guns where they were then hand-loaded into the breech. *(CAW collection)*

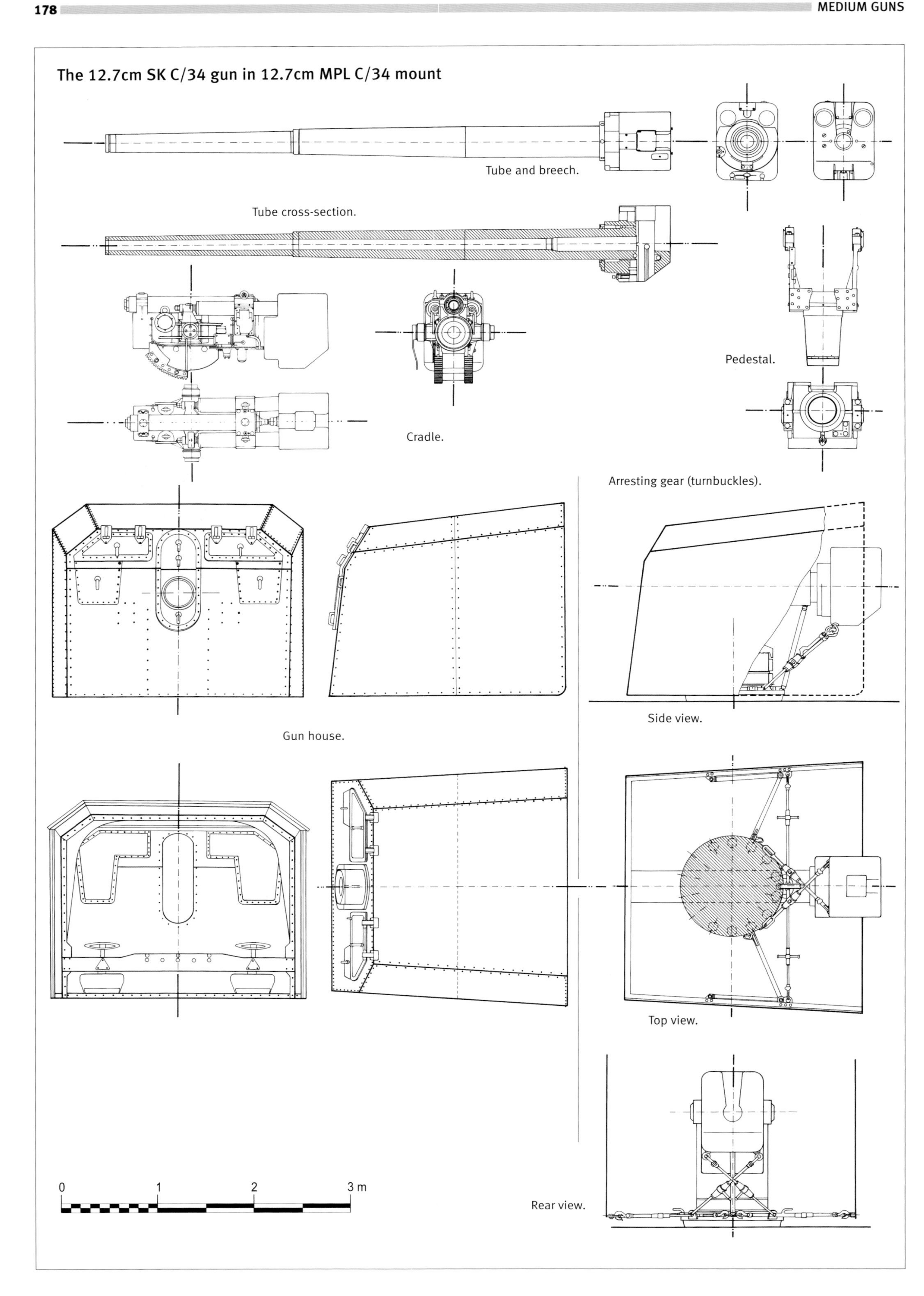
The 12.7cm SK C/34 gun in 12.7cm MPL C/34 mount
Tube and breech.
Tube cross-section.
Pedestal.
Cradle.
Arresting gear (turnbuckles).
Side view.
Gun house.
Top view.
Rear view.
0
1
2
3 m

Above: *Z 21* (*Paul Jacobi*) before the war. The ship was armed with five 127mm guns. *(A Jarski collection)*

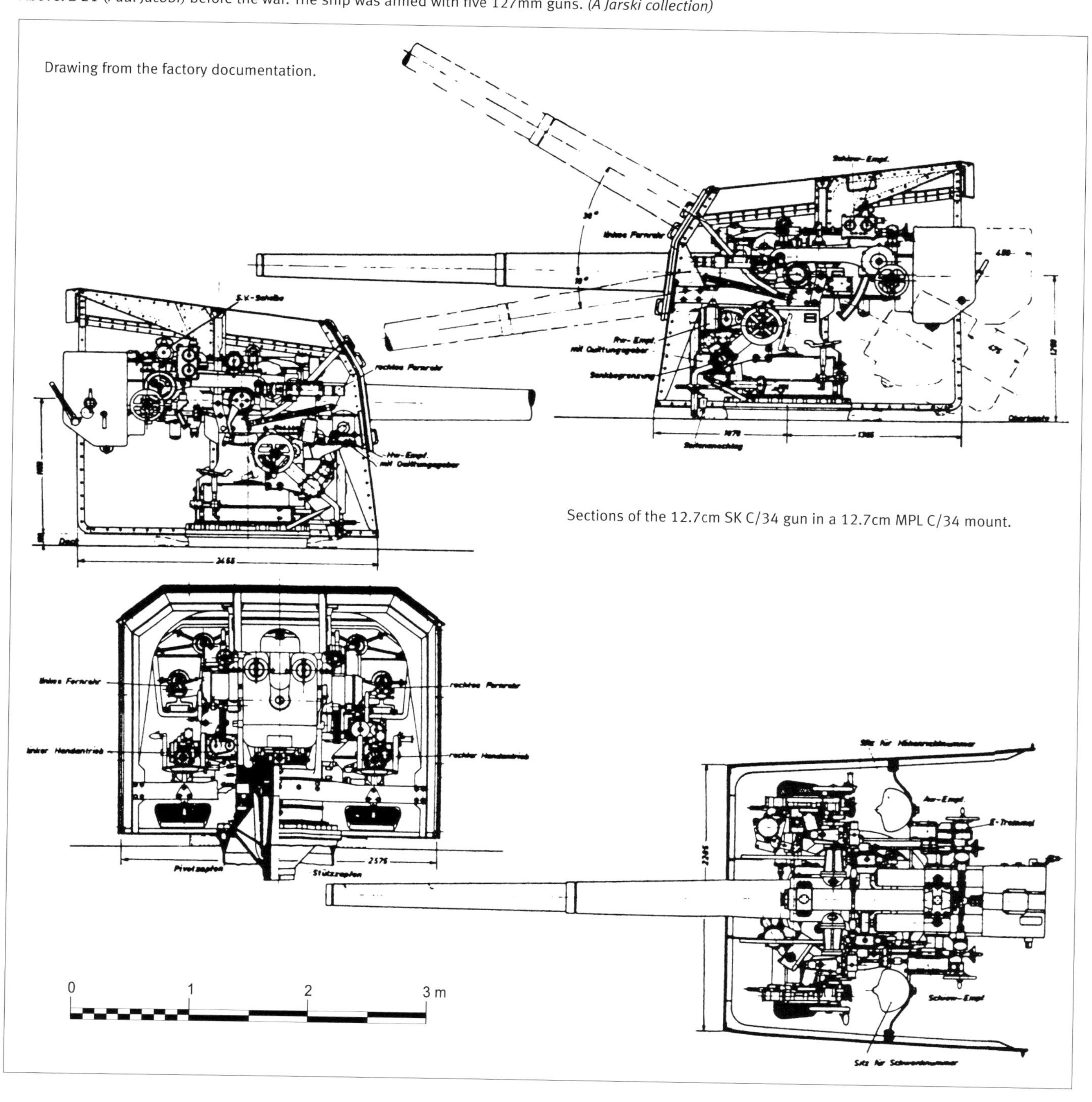

Drawing from the factory documentation.

Sections of the 12.7cm SK C/34 gun in a 12.7cm MPL C/34 mount.

Above: A destroyer division in line ahead. Each of them had five single 12.7cm SK C/34 guns. *(CAW collection)*

Left: Towards the end of the war, life rafts were mounted to the sides of the turrets on most ships. *(CAW collection)*

Below: The *Leberecht Maass* class destroyers were the first to be armed with these guns. *(A Jarski collection)*

Above: *Z 16* (*Friedrich Eckholdt*) in Norwegian waters early in the war. Note the five gun houses with 127mm guns. Some time later the ship was sunk by the British cruiser HMS *Sheffield*. *(A Jarski collection)*

Left: Gun crew aboard *Z 7* (*Herman Schoemann*) during gunnery practice. *(A Jarski collection)*

Below: The first series of destroyers, *Z 1*–*Z 4*, *Z 6*–*Z 9*, *Z 11*–*Z 14* and *Z 16*, had five single 12.7cm SK C/34 guns in MPL C/34 mounts; two of them were mounted forward, while the rest were fitted aft. The photo shows one of these destroyers in heavy weather. *(CAW collection)*

Above: One of *Tirpitz*'s escorting destroyers, photographed from the battleship. She is armed with 127mm guns. *(CAW collection)*

The cradle

Tube shaft diameter:	330mm
Cradle shaft diameter:	130mm
Recoil brake cylinder diameter:	155mm
Recoil brake cylinder volume:	16.8dm^3
Recoil brake cylinder fluid volume:	15.8l
Recoil distance at 0° elevation:	445mm
Recoil distance at 30° elevation:	450mm
Recoil distance to the bumper:	475mm
Elevation toothed arc radius:	532mm
Force of recoil at 0° elevation:	38,000kg

The MPL C/34 single pivot mount

These mounts equipped all 1934, 1934A and 1936 class destroyers. In standard destroyer gun designation practice, the mounts were numbered 1 to 5, with mounts 2 and 4 superfiring.

There were three ports in the front of the splinter shield, the central gun port and sighting ports with flaps either side of it. The gap around the barrel in the gun port could be filled by a canvas blast bag, but this was replaced by a steel cover on the two forward mounts. Training and elevation were controlled by hand wheels, the left layer controlling the former and the right the latter, though in emergencies either position could take over both functions. The layers' handwheels each had an electric trigger switch built in.

The fire-control equipment was fitted above the handwheels, with indicators for the fire-control data transmitted from the conning tower – training on the left, elevation on the right – and two identical optical sights. Two types of sight were used with this mount. Guns with serial numbers up to 209 (210 was a spare) had C/47 monocular variable magnification (4x-20x) sights, while from gun 211 they had C/1 stereoscopic sights with magnification of 6x to 12x. Both sights could be fitted with a series of progressive darker protective filters – the darkest, almost like the glass in a welder's mask – to prevent gun layers' being blinded by searchlight beams in night actions. The sights were also illuminated for night fighting. The C/47 sight had been lit with white light, but the C/1 changed to red light. At the right-hand layer's position there was an additional gravity sight (a pendulum in a canister of glycerine) for firing star shell. Gear was also provided for securing the gun and mount in heavy weather.

Below: The stern of a torpedo boat. Note part of the gun house in the foreground. *(CAW collection)*

Above: Operating in Arctic waters or in winter caused the guns to get covered with ice, which could put them out of action. Experiments with a muzzle heater to prevent this began in 1943, but due to very high electricity consumption and excessive weight, the project was eventually abandoned. *(CAW collection)*

The mount

Distance between cradle axis and center of post:	303mm
Distance of bore axis at 0° elevation from front edge of post collar:	1,140mm
Traverse ring diameter:	672mm
Post collar diameter:	1,030mm
Diameter between post bolt centres:	910mm
Post bolt diameter:	45mm
Number of post bolts:	14
Maximum width of splinter shield:	2,575mm
Distance between front edge of splinter shield and center of post:	1,070mm

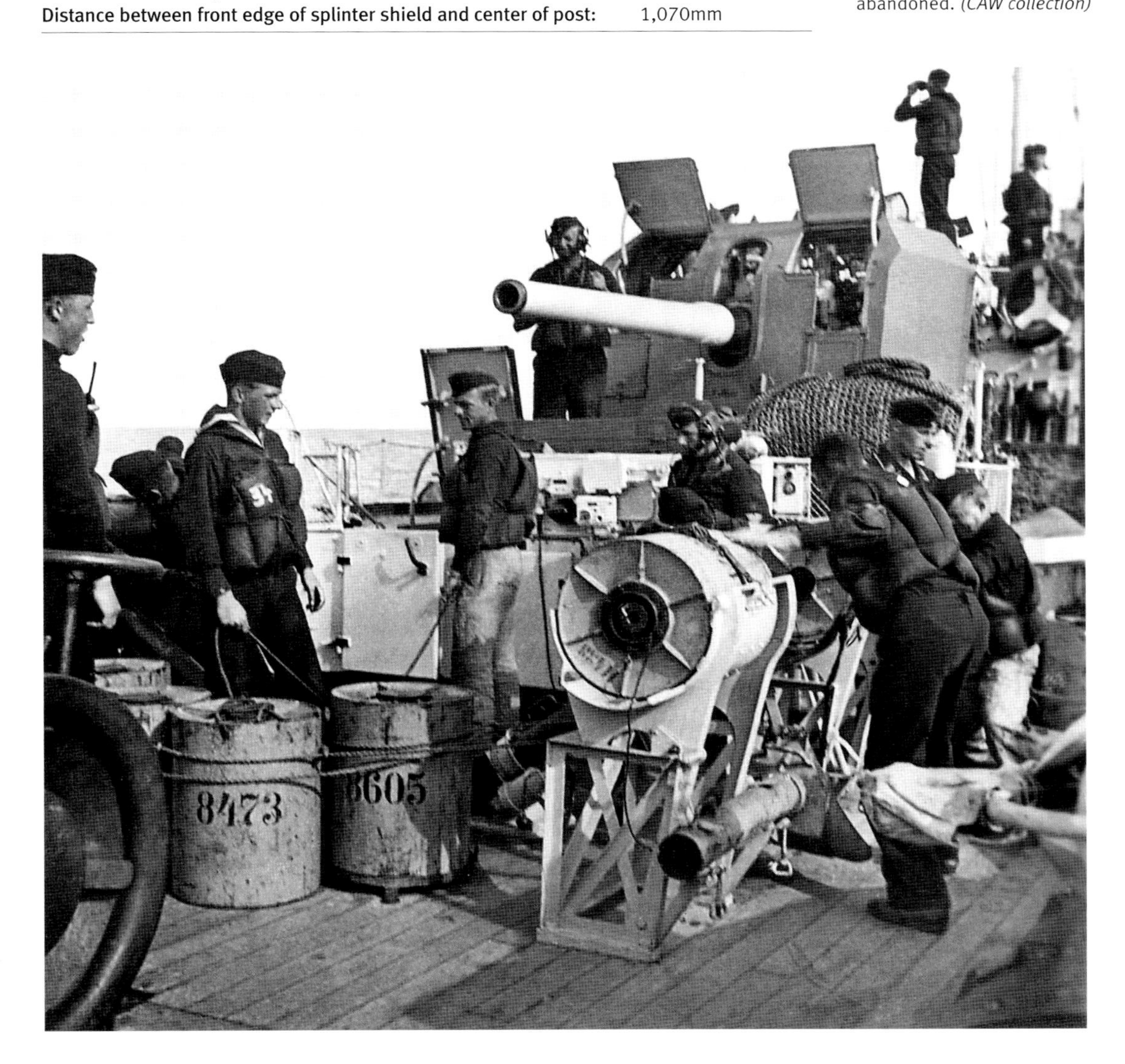

Left: Destroyer crew at battle stations. In the background is a 12.7cm SK C/34 gun. *(CAW collection)*

Mount operating angle

Traverse:	~360°
Maximum tube elevation:	+30°
Maximum tube depression:	−10°
Change of training per turn of hand wheel:	3.08°
Change of elevation per turn of hand wheel:	2.95°

C/34 gun house weights

Barrel and breech:	3,635kg
Cradle and recuperating gear:	1,320kg
Upper mount:	2,605kg
Splinter shield and frame:	1,870kg
Sighting equipment:	530kg
Electric wiring and equipment:	260kg
Complete mount:	10,220kg
Auxiliary equipment (incl. securing gear):	532kg

Ammunition

Destroyers carried two types of 127mm ammunition:

a. Armour-piercing shell, base-fused (Fp 02), weighing 28kg and 564.7mm long.
b. Star shell.

Propellant charges

Weight of propellant load:	8.6kg
Weight of case with charge:	16kg
Length of case:	732mm

Ammunition stores

Aboard the torpedo boats *Leopard* and *Luchs*, the magazines and shell rooms were in sections III and X, while the destroyers all had four ammunition stores, two forward and two aft. Each had its own electric hoist up to the guns. The magazines had no ventilation and each gun's shells and charges were stored in their respective ammunition lockers.

Above: Late in the war, destroyers had their armament increased. Every available space was used for additional guns. In this photo an additional 12.7cm SK C/34 gun has been squeezed between the funnels of a destroyer. *(CAW collection)*

Right: Torpedo boats – like the one in this photo – also had 127mm guns. *(CAW collection)*

12

105mm AND 88mm GUNS

INTRODUCTION

After the First World War, military aviation developed rapidly. Improved engines enabled the new breed of aircraft to fly far higher and faster than their predecessors, rendering the anti-aircraft guns of the previous war useless, and forcing the world's weapons designers to meet the challenge of creating guns with the rate of fire, range and effective ceiling to engage them.

This was a particular problem for Germany, since the Treaty of Versailles had imposed a specific ban on the development and possession of anti-aircraft guns, over and above the general prohibition on artillery. There were two exceptions to this ban, however. Firstly, the Germans were allowed to keep a small number of 88mm, 105mm and self-propelled 75mm anti-aircraft guns to defend the city of Königsberg from potential Soviet air attack, although they were forbidden to manufacture anti-aircraft fire-control equipment and gun mounts capable of elevation above 42°, and secondly the navy, such as it was, was permitted to equip its ships with anti-aircraft guns. It was even allowed to develop new weapons, at the rate of one new 77mm and 105mm design every five years and an 88mm design every other year. This exception gave rise to the establishment in 1930 of the Ausbildungsstab-3 (ASTA-3) committee, to review existing anti-aircraft guns and decide on the course of future development. In fact, its real purpose was to find ways to circumvent the Treaty restrictions.

Having reviewed the experience of the First World War, ASTA-3 concluded that the 88mm was the most effective anti-aircraft gun – the performance of the 77mm gun was insufficient while the 105mm was too heavy. However, an interim 75mm gun, the Flak (short for 'Fliegerabwehrkanone' – anti-aircraft gun) L/60 for the army, was the first new design to enter service for a short period in 1932. Even when this weapon was in the prototype stage, the Army had asked for a more powerful weapon, and it was therefore redesigned as an 88mm gun.

However, this did not mean that the designers had to go right back to the drawing board. In fact, a prototype 88mm gun had been built as early as 1928, by the Swedish armaments company Bofors, with which Krupp's had set up a joint venture in order to circumvent Treaty restrictions on weapons development. Designed as an army weapon, it had been designated the 8.8cm Flak 18. The year number 18, for 1918, was to give the impression that it had been designed before the ban imposed in 1920. The first 88s therefore entered service in 1933 and became the

Below: The 8.8cm SK C/30 in an MPL C/30 triaxially-stabilised single pedestal mount. Guns like these were used on smaller surface craft, like this minesweeper *M 6*. *(CAW collection)*

Right: 10.5cm (105mm) U-boat guns, such as this one on display in London's Imperial War Museum, were the predecessors of the modern shipborne anti-aircraft gun. *(A Jarski)*

Below: The 8.8cm SK C/31 gun in a Dopp. L C/31 twin pedestal mount, installed amidships board *Nürnberg*. *(A Jarski)*

Above: This 10.5cm SK C/32 nS in an MPL C/32 gE single pedestal mount was one of the first sea-going triaxially-stabilised 105mm mounts. Such guns were fitted aboard smaller surface craft, like this torpedo boat. *(CAW collection)*

Below: The first 8.8cm SK C/32 L/76 guns in twin mounts were tested on board the 'K' class light cruisers. These guns, seen here aboard *Köln*, in front of 'B' turret, have not yet been fitted with shields. *(CAW collection)*

Below: The 10.5cm SK C/32 in the Ubootlafette MUbtes L C/32U single pedestal mount. This photo shows a gun on board the Type IA U-boat *U 25*. *(CAW collection)*

backbone of the German anti-aircraft artillery.

The ubiquitous 88's naval career began in earnest when it was selected as the anti-aircraft armament for the most famous warship of the Weimar period, the light cruiser *Königsberg*. This was Rheinmetall-Borsig's first big contract since 1918, and designing and building an entire weapons system for a large warship was a major undertaking for the company's chief engineer Herman Westphälinger. The company did a splendid job, as shown by the letter of congratulation sent to it by the cruiser's chief designer Professor Carl Waninger.

In early 1932 Rheinmetall reached an agreement with Krupp's and Bofors about the production of both land- and sea-service guns, which allowed for the development of anti-aircraft guns and also, more importantly, provided the means to pay both for that development and later manufacturing, giving the German companies an outlet for their products. The agreement continued into the Second World War, allowing deliveries via neutral Sweden of armaments both to neutrals and to countries with co-operation agreements with Germany, the Imperial Japanese Navy being a major beneficiary of this. The two German companies also divided up the artillery market between them. Krupp's were to have all guns over 200mm, while Rheinmetall had everything smaller, as well as all guns for submarines.

The 8.8cm Flak 18, 36 and 37 guns were the mainstays of German tactical anti-aircraft artillery, both at sea and on land. During the early part of the war, they were usually deployed in four- or six-gun batteries. They served in both fixed and mobile mounts, and also on railway cars, either the specially-designed four-axle 'Flak-wagen' or improvised mounts on flat cars, to defend freight trains or as part of armoured trains. They also served as mobile anti-invasion batteries as part of the coastal defences.

The heavier 10.5cm Flak guns had a slightly different role. These were part of the strategic air defences of the Reich, protecting key targets. Again, they could be deployed on mobile mounts or in fixed emplacements, including the massive Flak towers that sprang up in major cities such as Berlin, Hamburg and Vienna. In late 1939 and 1940, special anti-aircraft trains ('Eisenbahnflak') were created to give heavy Flak batteries some mobility in defence of vital locations.

13

105mm GUNS

SINGLE MOUNTS

The 10.5cm C/32 gun in the C/30 mount

Designed by Rheinmetall, this gun was the model for other weapons installed either on pedestal mounts, twin mounts or in turrets. Guns, cradles and mounts varied in minor details according to model, year or manufacture and intended purpose. They served both afloat and in shore batteries. The earliest variant armed torpedo-boats on a single pedestal mount, designated the 10.5cm MPL AA, and were later fitted aboard minesweepers on the improved C/32 mount which had a new shield designated with the suffix 'gE'. The first version for submarines was designated the Ubts L C/32 U, while the later Type IX and Type X U-boats had the improved Ubts L C/36 U mount.

The gun consisted of a tube set in a cradle, with a semi-automatic falling-block breech. The hydraulic recoil buffer was mounted above the barrel, between two spring-loaded recuperators. The cradle trunnions were set at the height of the upper mount's bearing, 1,900mm above the base. The vertical axis of the mount passed through the exact centre of the ball bearing on top of the pedestal. The manual training and elevation gear was on the upper mount, with the frame for the sights attached to the front. The gun could be fired either by a foot-pedal on the left-hand layer's position or by a lanyard attached to the end of the trigger lever on the breech block, although some more sophisticated naval mounts introduced electro-

Below: An early 10.5cm SK C/32 nS in a 10.5cm MPL C/32 single pedestal mount, unshielded. *(Author's collection)*

Bottom: The 10.5cm SK C/32 nS in a 10.5cm MPL C/32 single pedestal mount with gE shield, aboard a German torpedo boat. The crew is at action stations. *(CAW collection)*

mechanical trigger circuits. The crew was protected by a semi-enclosed splinter shield, open at the rear, which was fixed to the upper mount.

The gun tube was not uniform. The rear section was cylindrical, the middle 2,360mm section tapered towards the bore, and the final 360mm was cylindrical again, capped by the muzzle ring. Lines indicating the bore axis were marked on both the chamber and muzzle flats, and the rear flat was engraved with such information as the tube serial

Above: One of the earliest 10.5cm SK C/32 nS guns in a 10.5cm MPL C/32 single pedestal mount with gE shield. *(Author's collection)*

Below: The 10.5cm SK C/32 nS in a 10.5cm MPL C/32 single pedestal mount with gE shield, aboard a German auxiliary ship, during gunnery practice. Note the sailor with portable 1.5m optical rangefinder, at top right of the photo. *(CAW collection)*

Above: The 10.5cm SK C/32 nS in a 10.5cm MPL C/32 single pedestal mount with gE shield, aboard a German auxiliary ship, seen during gunnery practice. Note the crew's steel helmets strapped to the shield. *(CAW collection)*

Left: Small Kriegsmarine craft were fitted with 10.5cm SK C/32 nS guns in 10.5cm MPL C/32 single pedestal mounts with gE shield. This ship has it fitted on the forecastle. *(CAW collection)*

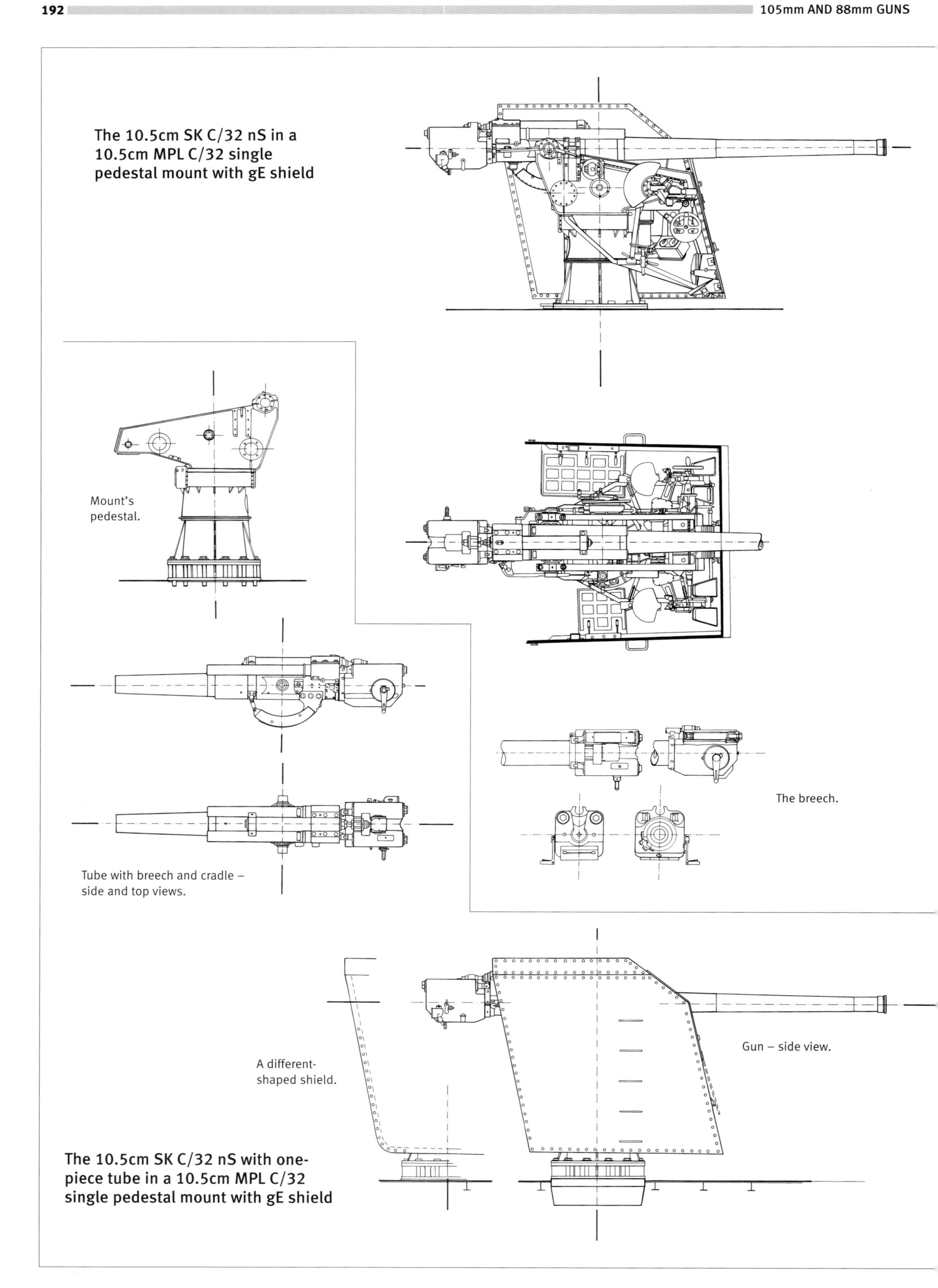
The 10.5cm SK C/32 nS in a 10.5cm MPL C/32 single pedestal mount with gE shield
Mount's pedestal.
Tube with breech and cradle – side and top views.
The breech.
A different-shaped shield.
Gun – side view.
The 10.5cm SK C/32 nS with one-piece tube in a 10.5cm MPL C/32 single pedestal mount with gE shield

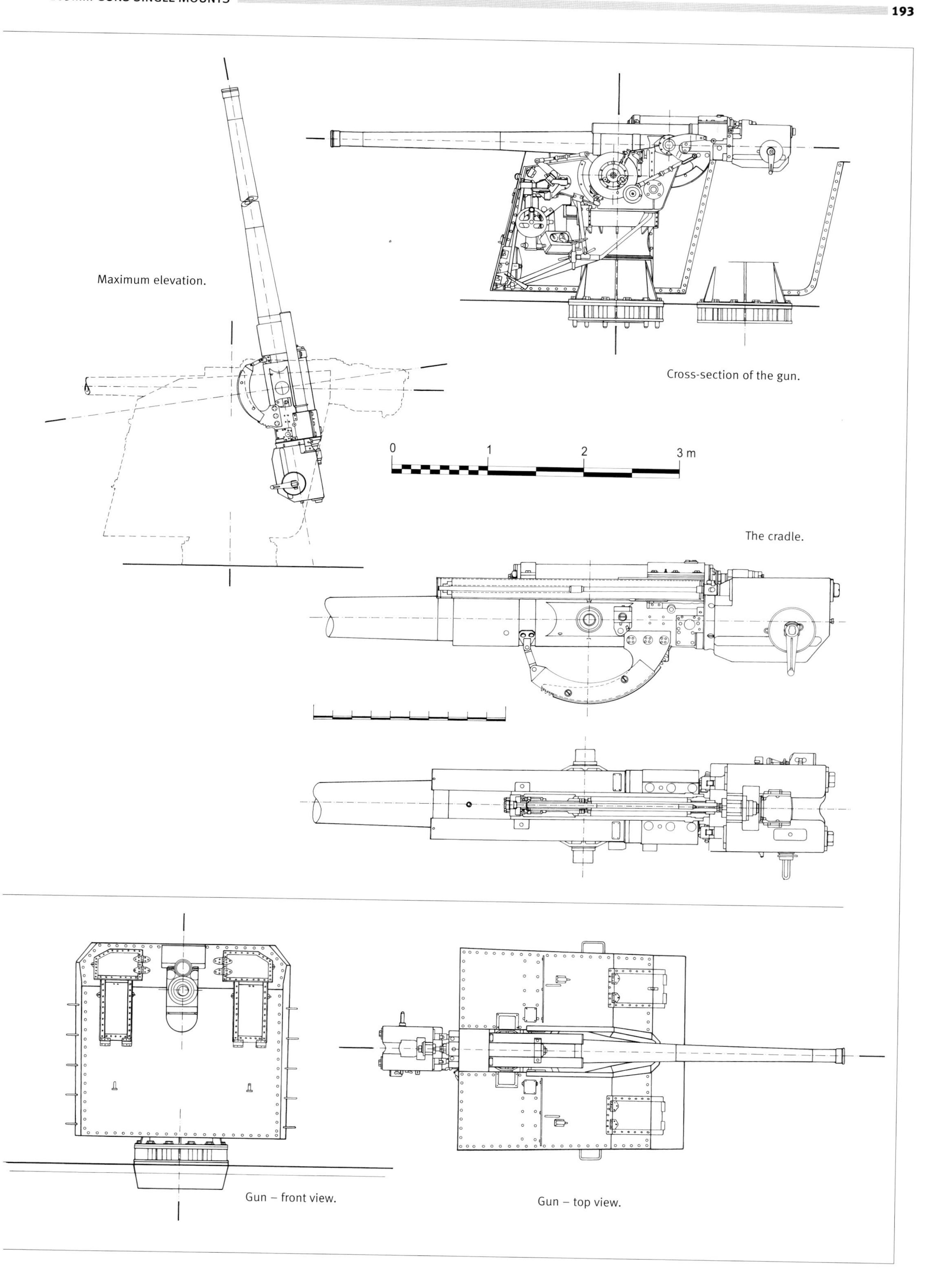

Maximum elevation.

Cross-section of the gun.

The cradle.

Gun – front view.

Gun – top view.

Above: Winter and Arctic navigation often resulted in ice caking the guns, sometimes putting them out of action. This photo illustrates the problem well enough... *(CAW collection)*

number, its weight, the manufacturer's name, etc.

The rear end of the tube fitted into the rectangular breech, secured by a brass ring. The block slid in a rectangular opening in the breech ring, the fore end of which was aligned with the bore axis, while the rear end inclined downwards slightly to facilitate opening the breech. The breech opening was perpendicular to the loading opening, concentric with the bore axis and leading to the slightly tapering chamber which was connected to the bore by the forcing cone (or lead). The bore was rifled with thirty-two right-hand grooves of constant width and depth. If this gun was mounted in the 8.8cm MPL C/30 mount, the weight of the breech was balanced by a counterweight bolted to the breech ring.

The semi-automatic falling-block breech had a manual opening lever on the left-hand side, fitted with a safety latch to prevent accidental operation. With the breech block fully raised, the handle of the lever pointed downwards, indicating the breech was closed. To open it, the crewman had to squeeze the handle, releasing the safety latch, and only then could he pull the lever back, lowering the breech block and opening the bore. Opening the breech automatically ejected the spent case and cocked the firing pin. An alleviating spring was fitted to the breech-block crank case to help raise the block back up when the gun had been loaded. A safety catch on the trigger prevented the gun being fired until the breech was fully closed. The trigger lever was on the right-hand side of the breech, fitted with a lanyard ring at the end and a rotating safety bolt. With this bolt turned vertically, the word 'Sicher' ('Safe') was exposed, and until this was turned horizontally, revealing the word 'Feuer' ('Fire'), the gun could not be fired. The breech was designed so that the trigger mechanism, safety bolt and breech block could all be removed without tools.

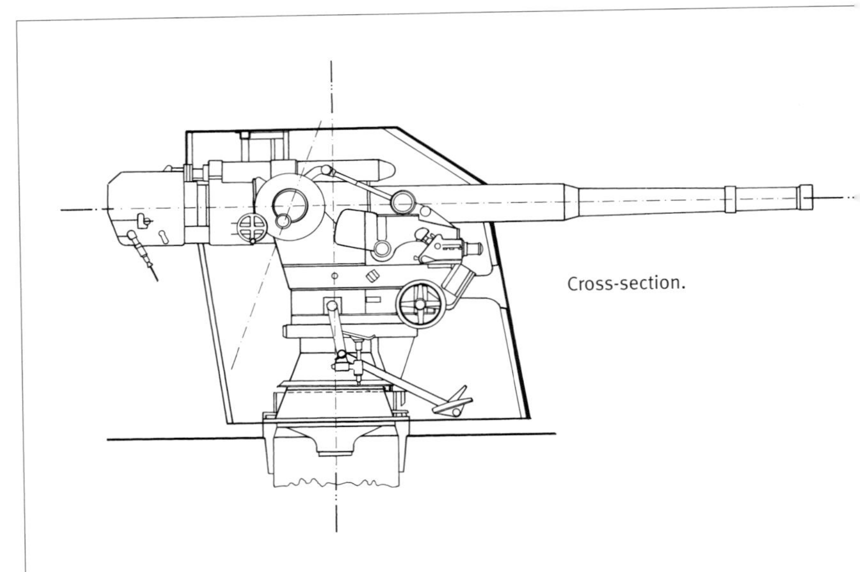

Cross-section.

The 10.5cm SK C/32 nS with two-piece tube in a 10.5cm MPL C/32 single pedestal mount with gE shield

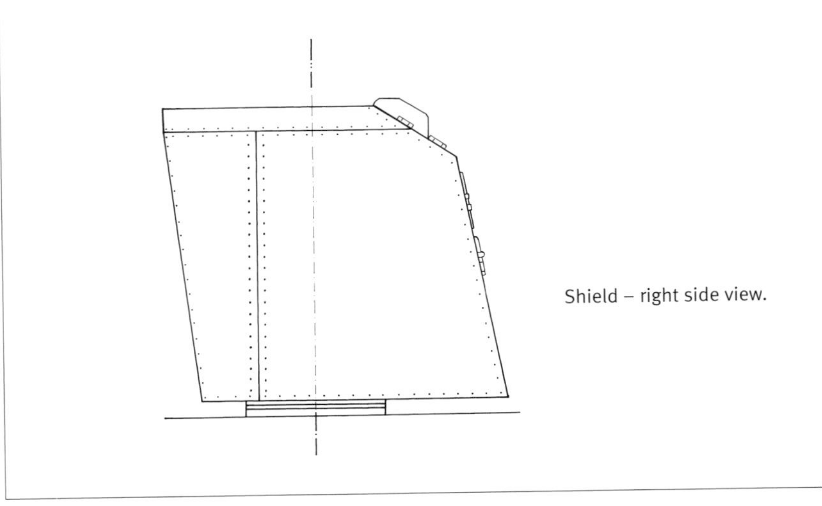

Shield – right side view.

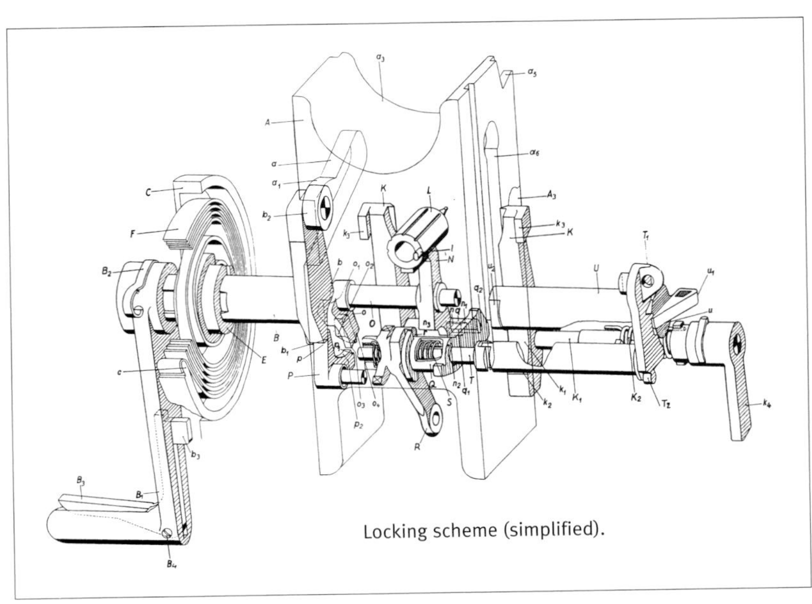

Locking scheme (simplified).

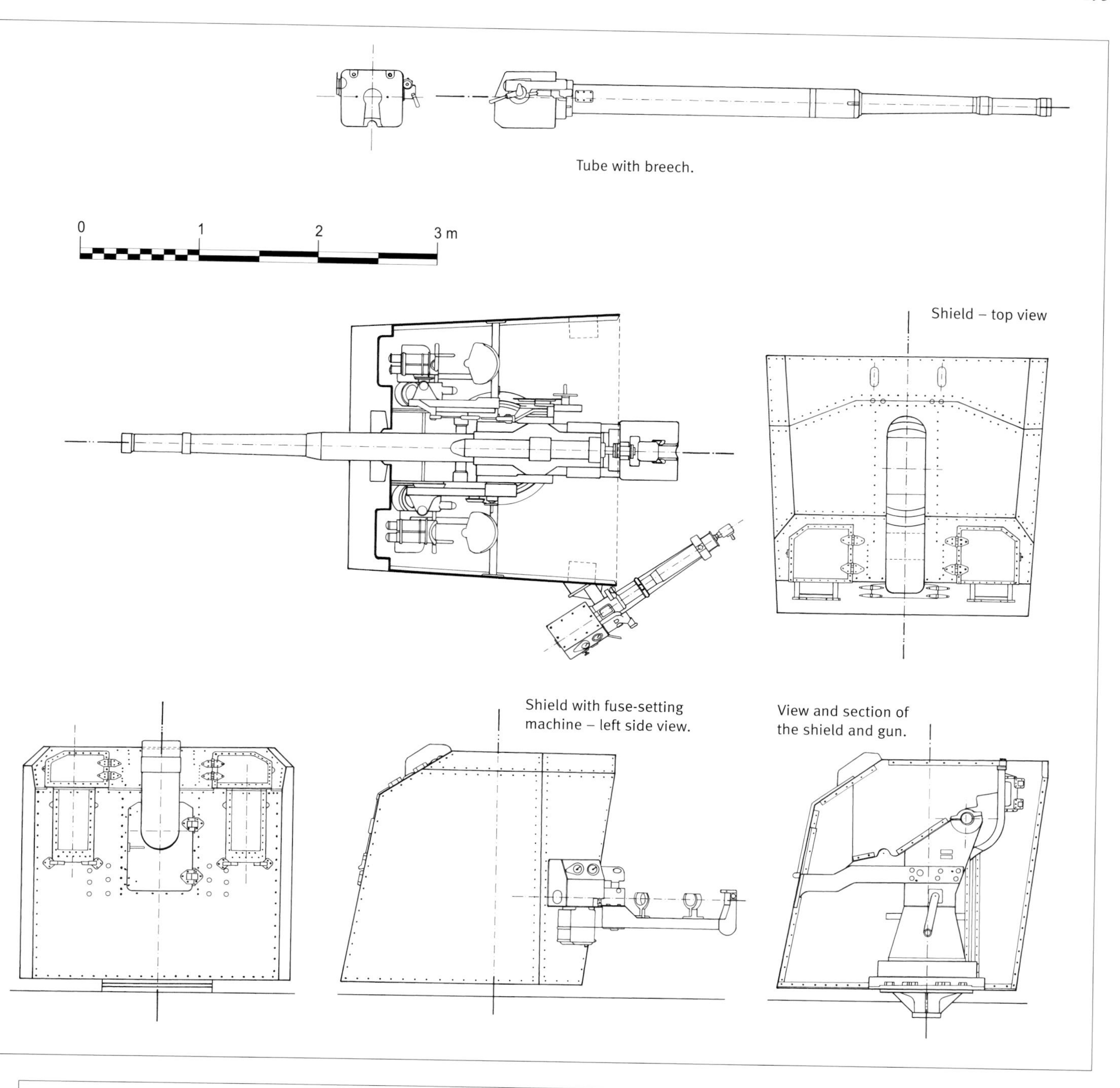

Tube with breech.

Shield – top view

Shield with fuse-setting machine – left side view.

View and section of the shield and gun.

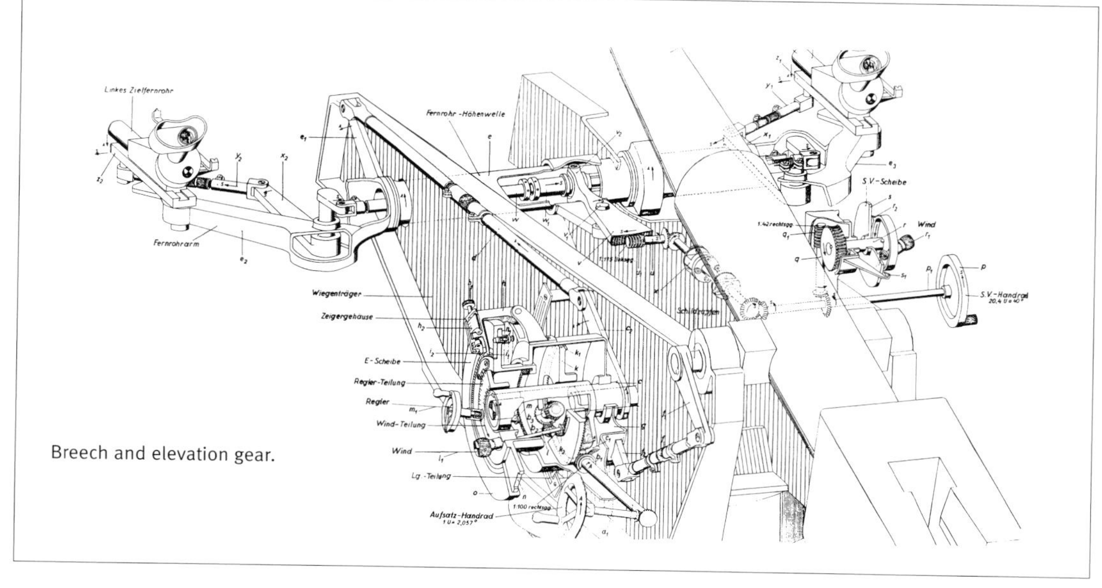

Breech and elevation gear.

Above: The 10.5cm SK C/32 nS with two-piece tube in a 10.5cm MPL C/32 single pedestal mount with gE shield. Note the crew at action stations. *(CAW collection)*

Right: The 10.5cm SK C/32 nS with two-piece tube in a 10.5cm MPL C/32 single pedestal mount with gE shield, probably aboard a torpedo boat. *(CAW collection)*

Ammunition and ballistic data for the 10.5cm SK C/32 (in C/30 mount)

Weight of projectile:	15.1kg
Weight of entire round:	24.0kg
Length of round:	1,052mm
Maximum muzzle velocity:	785mps
Maximum range:	15,175m at 44°
Maximum ceiling:	10,200m at 79°

The cradle was a one-piece seamless tube that enclosed the cylindrical rear section of the barrel. Welded to it were the brackets for the recoil buffer and recuperators at the top, the trunnions on either side, and the toothed arc for the elevation gear and the elevation stops underneath. It also had two brass lubricating cylinders at either end to reduce friction between the fixed cradle and the recoiling barrel.

The upper mount, resting on the turntable, had the cradle trunnion bearings at the top on each side, with

Left: Two-piece tube of the 10.5cm SK C/32 nS gun. *(CAW collection)*

Cradle measurements for the 10.5cm SK C/32 gun (in C/30 mount)

Inner diameter of tube sleeve:	250mm
Inner diameter of recoil buffer:	100mm
Volume of oil in recoil buffer:	5.6l
Diameter of cradle trunnions:	100mm
Recoil distance (mean):	480mm
Recoil distance (maximum):	500mm
Radius of toothed elevating arc:	448mm
Maximum recoil force:	18,500kg

the sight base set below the axis of elevation. The upper ring of the training bearing was bolted to the base of the turntable. At the centre of the ring was a tubular shaft, the training axis (pivot) of the mount, set into the welded steel pedestal which had the training bearing at the top.

The layers' linked telescopic sights – left and right – were fixed to the upper mount co-axial with the cradle trunnions. They had 5x magnification with a 14° field of view and angled eyepieces. Various grades of coloured filter could be fitted to prevent the layers being blinded by searchlight beams in night actions. There was also a special elevation-indicator scale on the left side of the mount, used when firing star shell. There were compartments on each side of the mount housing 4V batteries to light both the reticules and the fire-control indicators.

The right-hand layer controlled training, while the left-hand one controlled elevation. In an emergency, the left-hand layer could also take over training. Both layers had fire-control indicators, linked to the fire-direction centre.

The 10.5cm SK C/32 gun in single mounts

The prototype of this weapon was designed in 1932 and was in series production and Kriegsmarine service two years later. Designed for smaller vessels, the first to receive it were the torpedo boats *T 1* to *T 21* (the 35 and 37 classes). The 'F' class sloops and the *M261* (40 class) minesweepers were also armed

Weights of the 10.5cm SK C/32 (in C/30 mount)

Tube with breech and counterweight:	1,720kg
Complete cradle with buffer and recuperators:	620kg
Mount with power unit:	1,120kg
Pedestal with lower training bearing:	830kg
Sighting equipment, complete:	320kg
Splinter shield with fittings and counterweight:	1,955kg
Fire-control indicators:	50kg
Electrical equipment:	25kg
Total weight:	c. 6,640kg
Spares and tackle:	c. 130kg

Tube measurements for the 10.5cm SK C/32 gun

Calibre:	105mm
Overall length:	4,740mm
Length bore and chamber:	4,400mm
Length chamber and forcing cone:	706mm
Length chamber:	586.5mm
Volume chamber	5.38l
Distance chamber to centre of gravity:	1,270mm
Length rifling:	3,694mm
Grooves:	32 (1.25mm x 6.8mm)
Width of fields:	3.5mm
Initial pitch (45 calibres):	4,725mm
Final pitch (30 calibres):	3,150mm

Pedestal measurements for the 10.5cm SK C/32 (in C/30 mount)

Distance bore axis to pedestal base:	1,900mm
Pedestal training ring diameter:	800mm
Cradle trunnions spacing:	476mm
Pedestal base diameter:	980mm
Number of pedestal mounting bolts:	12
Maximum distance between pedestal mounting bolts:	880mm
Diameter of pedestal mounting bolt:	38mm
Maximum width of splinter shield:	2,150mm
Distance from front edge of shield to mount pivot:	1,300mm
Radius of crew area:	3,370mm
Training:	360°
Depression/elevation:	–9°/+79°

Above: 10.5cm rounds waiting to be transferred to the ship moored at the pier. *(CAW collection)*

Below, left: One of *Scharnhorst*'s crewmen cleaning the grease off a 10.5cm round. *(A Jarski collection)*

Below, right: The 10.5cm rounds with the storage grease removed, ready to be loaded into the magazine.

with it, and it is claimed that the later torpedo boats, *T 22* to *T 51*, also had it. The mount was ideally suited to small craft, requiring only reinforcement of the section of deck to which it was to be bolted, with none of the heavy barbettes or ammunition hoists of turret guns. Ammunition was stored as close to the guns as possible, in lockers in the superstructure on surface ships and in special watertight lockers underneath the deck aboard U-boats, the individual rounds being kept in special containers to protect them from damage.

The main difference between this modified gun and the original SK C/32 was the design of the barrel. The original gun had a one-piece liner in a one-piece jacket, with the breech block screwed on, as did the submarine model, the SK C/32 U in C/32 and C/36 pedestal mounts. The later version, designated the SK C/32 nS, had a two-piece tube, which was lighter and gave improved ballistic performance.

The 8.8cm MPL C/30 AA pedestal mount

This was also designed for smaller surface craft, and was originally intended to take 88mm guns. But it was later decided to upgrade the armament to 105mm guns, and Rheinmetall undertook a highly successful adaptation of the C/30 AA mount,

Above: The 10.5cm SK C/32 in a 10.5cm Ubts L C/32U single pedestal mount, aboard *U 26*, a Type IA submarine. *(T Klimczyk collection)*

Left: The 10.5cm SK C/32 in a 10.5cm Ubootslafette MUbtes L C/32U single pedestal mount. This photo was taken on board *U 25*, the second of the two Type IA submarines. *(CAW collection)*

Below: The 10.5cm SK C/32 in a 10.5cm Ubts L C/36U single pedestal mount on board a Type IX U-boat, front view, taken during gunnery practice. *(CAW collection)*

Right: Supplies being loaded aboard a Type IX submarine. Note the details of the 10.5cm SK C/32 in a 10.5cm Ubts L C/36U pedestal mount. *(CAW collection)*

Below: The 10.5cm SK C/32 in a 10.5cm Ubts L C/36U single pedestal mount of a Type IX U-boat being serviced while the boat is dry-docked in a French port. *(CAW collection)*

Below: Type IX U-boat preparing for a patrol. The 10.5cm SK C/32 in a 10.5cm Ubts L C/36U pedestal mount seen here on the right, in front of the submarine's conning tower, was the standard surface armament of Type IX U-boats. *(CAW collection)*

Opposite: A Type IX U-boat moored at the base. *(A Jarski collection)*

Above: The 10.5cm SK C/32 in a 10.5cm Ubts L C/36U single pedestal mount on board the Type IX U-boat, front view. The boat is covered with camouflage netting. *(CAW collection)*

Right: The 10.5cm SK C/32 in a 10.5cm Ubootslafette MUbtes L C/32U single pedestal mount on board a U-boat. *(CAW collection)*

The 10.5cm SK C/32 in a 10.5cm Ubts L C/36U pedestal mount.

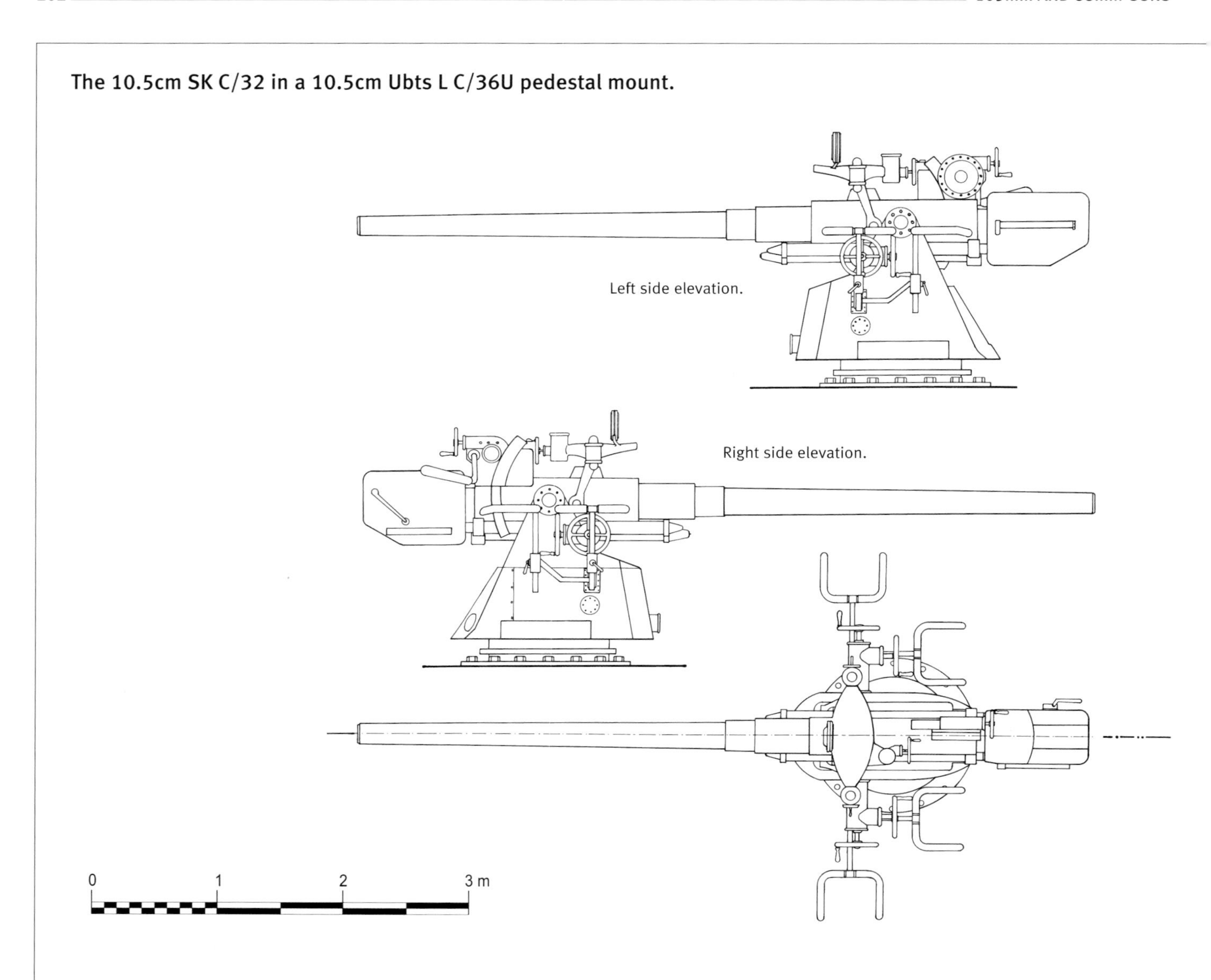

Right: Crew during gunnery practice on the 10.5cm SK C/32 in a 10.5cm Ubts L C/36U pedestal mount on board a Type IX U-boat. *(CAW collection)*

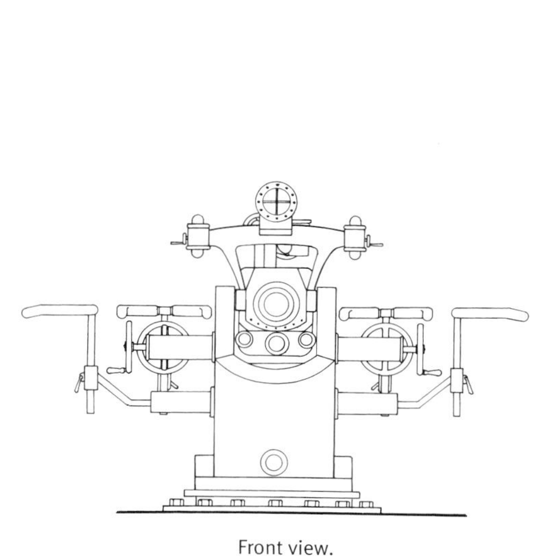

Front view.

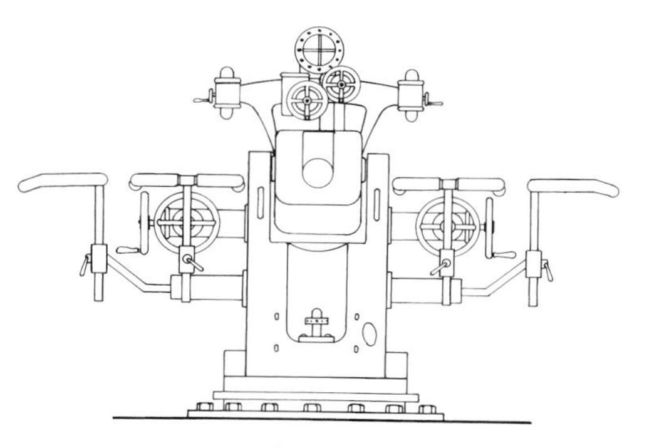

Rear view.

Top: The 10.5cm SK C/32 in a 10.5cm Ubts L C/36U pedestal mount aboard *U 124*, a Type IXB U-boat, leaving Lorient on the French coast. *(CAW collection)*

Above: The 10.5cm SK C/32 in a 10.5cm Ubts L C/36U pedestal mount is about to take a plunge. Note that the barrel is closed with a special stopper. *(A Jarski collection)*

Left: Two Type IX U-boats meeting at sea. Note the 10.5cm SK C/32 in a 10.5cm Ubts L C/36U pedestal mount in the foreground. *(CAW collection)*

The 10.5cm SK C/32 in the 8.8cm MPL C/30 AA pedestal mount

Total weight, mount with gun:	6,910kg
Maximum training speed (manual):	3°/sec
Maximum elevating speed (manual):	3°/sec
Training arc:	360°
Depression/elevation:	–9°/+80°
Maximum length of shield:	2,337mm
Width of shield (fore):	2,050mm
(aft):	2,150mm
Height of shield:	2,100mm

The 10.5cm SK C/32 with nS tube

Calibre:	105mm
Overall length of tube:	4,760mm
Length of first tapering section:	3,113.5mm
Length of second tapering section:	1,646.5mm
Length bore:	3,694mm
Length chamber:	586.5mm
Volume chamber:	5.38l
Grooves:	32 (1.25mm x 6.8mm)
Field width:	3.5mm
Initial rifling pitch (45 calibres):	4,725mm
Final rifling pitch (30 calibres):	3,150mm

The 10.5cm MPL C/32 gE pedestal mount

Total weight:	6,750kg
Mean Recoil distance:	400mm
Maximum training speed (manual):	3°/sec
Maximum elevating speed (manual):	3°/sec
Training arc:	360°
Depression/elevation:	–10°/+70°
Maximum length of shield:	2,145mm
Width of shield (front):	2,108mm

The 10.5cm Ubts L C/32 U pedestal mount

Total weight of mount:	4,970kg
Maximum training speed (manual):	3°/sec
Maximum elevating speed (manual):	3°/sec
Training arc:	360°
Depression/elevation:	–10°/+35°

The 10.5cm Ubts L C/36 U pedestal mount

Total weight of mount:	4,600kg
Maximum training speed (manual):	3°/sec
Maximum elevating speed (manual):	3°/sec
Training arc:	360°
Depression/elevation:	–10°/+30°

creating a partially-enclosed mount for a 105mm gun ideally suited for service aboard smaller vessels. These weapons armed minesweepers, torpedo boats and auxiliary vessels. As the gun went into series production, an improved mount was also introduced for the newer U-boats and small surface warships. The table below lists only the differences between this mount and the basic version, the gun itself remaining the same.

The 10.5cm MPL C/32 gE pedestal mount

This was a modified version of the original MPL C/32 mount, the main change being an increased angle of elevation. They were fitted as the anti-aircraft armament aboard the pre-dreadnoughts *Schliesen* and *Schleswig-Holstein*, the cruiser *Emden* and various smaller craft, including the 35 and 39 class torpedo boats and the 35 and 43 class minesweepers. Most of the guns in these mounts were fitted with the SK C/32 nS barrel (see above), with Rheinmetall's trademark rifling profile. Aboard torpedo boats and minesweepers, the standard ammunition supply was 120 rounds per gun.

The 10.5cm Ubts L C/32 U submarine mount

As the new Type I U-boats came into service, they were experimentally armed with 10.5cm guns, larger than boats of their size would usually have had. The older SK C/30 U mount for the 8.8cm gun was adapted to take the heavier weapon. The sea trials were successful and the U-boat crews were pleased to have a more powerful gun, so the gun and mount went into series production to arm the large new ocean-going U-boats, the Type IXs and the Type X minelaying submarines, although they were soon removed from the latter (see below). Aboard the Type I boats, the normal ammunition supply was 120 round per gun, while aboard the Type IXs it was 110 rounds per gun.

The 10.5cm SK C28 gun

Calibre:	105mm
Weight of gun:	3,660kg
Overall length:	5,760mm
Length bore:	5,431mm
Length chamber:	814mm
Volume chamber	8.4l
Weight projectile:	14.7kg
Propellant charge:	5.37kg of RP C/32
Muzzle velocity:	925mps
Maximum range:	17,250m at 30°
Rate of fire:	15rpm

The 10.5cm Ubts L C/36 U pedestal mount

This was an improved version of the earlier C/32 U, introduced when the Type IX U-boats went into series production. Originally, the Type X minelaying U-boats were also armed with them, but they were soon removed, since these boats' role was stealthy minelaying, not fighting gunnery duels on the surface. Their guns were used to arm the 40-class minesweepers.

The 10.5cm SK C/28 MPL C/30 gun

This gun was designed in 1928 and entered service two years later. They were mounted in single semi-enclosed mounts aboard the three *Bremse* class ships and the four *Wolf* class torpedo boats. In the 1930s, most of these ships were re-armed with the new 10.5cm SK C/32, although *Jaguar* retained her original armament until late 1944. When *Leopard* and *Luchs* were modernised in 1932, their 10.5cm guns were replaced with 12.7cm SK C/34s.

The MPL C/30 pedestal mount

Total weight of mount:	Not available
Maximum training speed (manual):	3°/sec
Maximum elevating speed (manual):	3°/sec
Training arc:	360°
Depression/elevation:	–10°/+30°

The 10.5cm SK C/28 Ubts K L/45 gun

The 10.5cm Ubts K L/45, which fired the same round as the SK C/28, only equipped one submarine, *U A* (ex-Turkish *Batiray*). Other First World War 10.5cm C/28 Flak L/45 guns armed *Möwe* class torpedo boats, 'F' class sloops and 40-class minesweepers in the Ubts and Tbts L C/16 mount. As the anti-aircraft defences of occupied Norway were reinforced, these guns armed 'Flak-Schiff' such as the *Nymphe* (ex-Norwegian *Tordenskjøld*). Also, some Type VII U-boats received these guns if newer types were unavailable. Some of them were mounted in 8.8cm MPL C/30 mounts.

The 10.5cm SK C/28 gun

	Ubts SK C/28	Ubts K L/45
Calibre:	105mm	105mm
Weight of gun:	3,660kg	2,135kg
Overall length:	5,760mm	5,092mm
Length bore:	5,430.5mm	4,725mm
Length chamber:	814mm	814mm
Volume chamber:	8.4l	8.4l
Weight projectile:	14.7kg	14.7kg
Propellant charge	5.37kg of RP C/32	5.37kg of RP C/32
Muzzle velocity:	925mps	890mps
Maximum range	17,250m at 30°	?

105mm GUNS
TWIN MOUNTS

The first twin anti-aircraft mounts were introduced with the 'K' class cruisers, which had 8.8cm SK C/25 guns on triaxially-stabilised mounts. Several years of tests aboard *Leipzig* and *Nürnberg*, first with open and then with semi-enclosed mounts, helped in the development of effective seaborne anti-aircraft systems. Of course, Germany was still bound by the terms of the Treaty of Versailles, but the arrangement with Bofors in Sweden allowed the development of the new twin C/31 mount with SK C/31 guns to proceed steadily, albeit slowly.

The twin 105mm mount was a conversion of the existing 88mm mount, fitted with a semi-enclosed gun house. After thorough testing of the prototype, the first twin mount, the C/31, entered series production. Later versions had different cradles, sights and shields.

The most obvious differences between the various mounts were the shape of the shield and the position of the Zünderstellmaschine, the fuse-setting machines. In the earliest versions, these were on the deck outside the mount itself, while in later mounts they were fitted either to the inside or the outside of the shield. There were other minor variations in the design of the pedestal mount and in the equipment included in it. Different types of gun were also mounted. The 10.5cm SK C/33, as aboard the *Deutschland*, had a one-piece barrel liner inside a one-piece jacket, while the later 10.5cm SK C/33 nT had a two- or even three-part liner in a two- or three-layer outer tube. These shorter liner sections were easier to manufacture, and also made it simpler to replace a damaged section in the gun.

Bismarck and *Tirpitz* had the latest C/37 mounts, in which the shield covered the top of the mount at the rear, protecting both the gun breeches and the gun crews from shell splinters and the elements. The armour protection, made of Whn/A steel, also gradually increased as new mounts were introduced.

The standard gun equipping these mounts was the 10.5cm SK C/33.

Left: *Deutschland* amidships. The 150mm secondary battery guns can be seen in the foreground, with a 10.5cm SK C/31 in an 8.8cm Dopp. L C/31 mount behind them. *(S Breyer collection)*

Right: Propaganda photo illustrating the successful Operation 'Berlin' in the North Atlantic, early 1941. Note the 10.5cm SK C/31 in twin 8.8cm Dopp. L C/31 gE mount. *(CAW collection)*

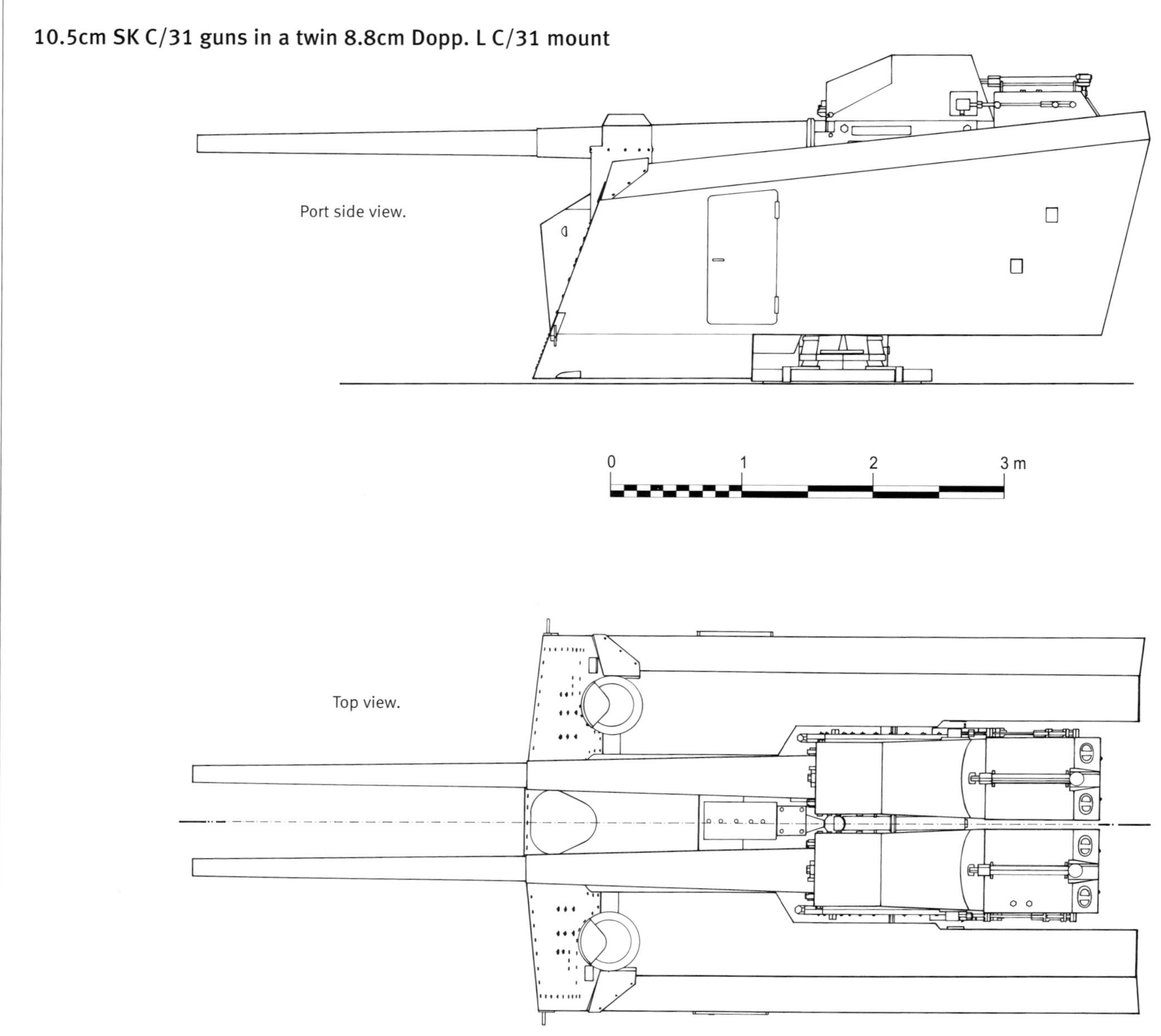

Left: The 'pocket battleship' *Lützow* (ex-*Deutschland*) limps for home after being torpedoed by the British submarine *Spearfish*. Note the twin 10.5cm SK C/31 guns in a 8.8cm Dopp. L C/31 mount just above 'B' turret. *(S Breyer collection)*

The 8.8cm Dopp. LC/31 twin mount

The Spanish Civil War was an opportunity to test the German Navy's new anti-aircraft guns in service conditions, and all the ships that were to be deployed to Spanish waters had their anti-aircraft batteries upgraded. The first ships to receive the C/31 twin 88mm mounts were the 'pocket battleships' *Deutschland*, *Admiral Scheer* and *Admiral Graf Spee*, with smaller vessels, e.g. the cruiser *Nürnberg*, next in line. Although the gun proved very successful, it still did not meet the Anti-Aircraft Armaments Bureau's requirements, and it was therefore decided to replace the 88mm guns with the new 10.5cm SK C/33 whilst retaining the same mount, with minor modifications, thus creating the semi-enclosed 10.5cm SK C/33 auf 8.8cm Dopp. LC/31 mount.

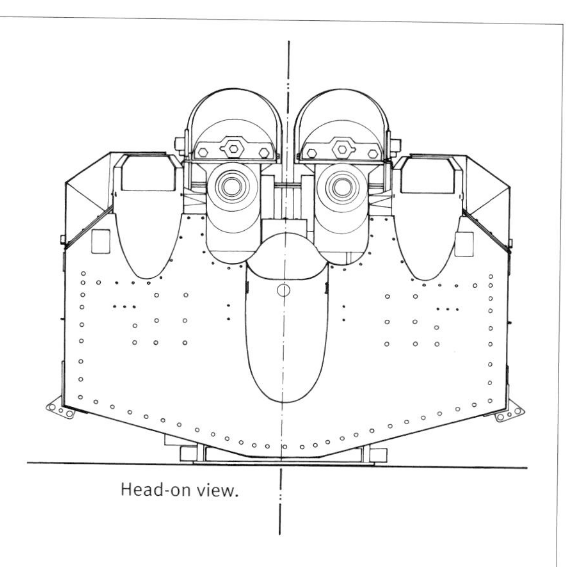

Head-on view.

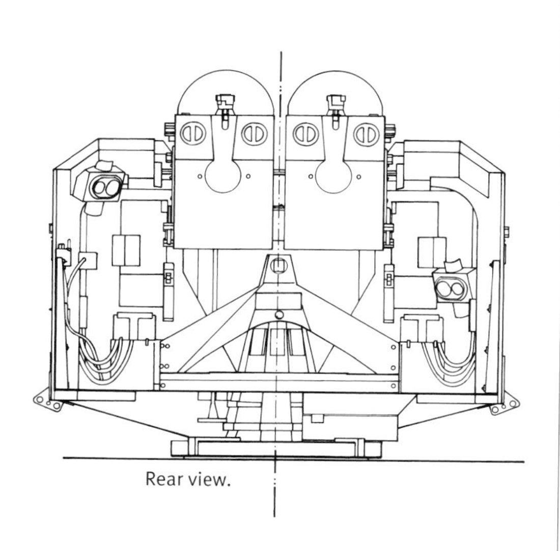

Rear view.

The 10.5cm SK C/33 gun

Calibre:	105mm
Breech:	Semi-automatic falling block
Weight of gun:	4,560kg (solid tube) 4,695kg (nS tube) 4,300kg (nT tube)
Overall length:	6,840mm*
Tube design	Outer tube with loose-fit inner tube
Length of tube:	6,348mm
Length chamber:	698mm
Volume chamber:	7.31l
Length:	5,531mm
Grooves:	36 (1.3mm x 5.5mm)
Weight projectile:	15.1 kg*
Propellant charge:	6.05kg of RP C/40 N (5.5/2.1)
Muzzle velocity:	900mps
Working pressure:	2,850 kg/cm^2
Approximate service life:	2,950 effective rounds
Maximum range:	17,700m
Maximum ceiling:	12,500m at 80°
Rate of fire:	15rpm

* Different sources give different figures.

The 8.8cm C/31 twin pedestal mount

Total weight, mount and guns:	27,805kg
Distance between gun axes:	680mm
Recoil distance:	410mm
Maximum elevating speed:	12°/sec
Maximum training speed:	8°/sec
Training arc:	360°
Depression/elevation:	–9°/+80°
Shield armour:	10-15mm

Above and right: The 10.5cm SK C/31 in a twin 8.8cm Dopp. L C/31 gE mount. One of *Gneisenau*'s mounts is in the upper photo, while the lower one shows one of *Scharnhorst*'s. *(A Jarski collection)*

The 8.8cm Dopp. L C/31gE twin mount

Experience in the Spanish Civil War rapidly lead to the development of an improved version of the C/31 mount. The pedestal mount was redesigned, with each gun elevating independently in its own cradle, driven by a hydraulic RPC system powered by electric motors. A roller track was fitted to bring shells from the ammunition hoist directly to the breeches of the guns. New fuse-setting machines were also installed on the insides of the shield. The first of these mounts were fitted aboard the *Scharnhorst* class battleships.

The 8.8cm Dopp. L C/31 d twin mount

The next modifications were to the mounts to equip the *Admiral Hipper* class heavy cruisers, involving minor changes to the equipment of the mount and its shield. Each cruiser had twelve 10.5cm SK C/33 guns in six 8.8cm Dopp. LC/31 d twin mounts. A total of 6,200 rounds of 10.5cm ammunition was carried aboard, mostly air-burst anti-aircraft rounds but with a proportion of nose-fused shells for surface targets, the exact balance depending on the requirements of the ship's mission, and 240 star shell.

The next ships to get these guns were *Bismarck* and *Tirpitz*. Both ships had eight twin mounts, four on each side, mounted on the superstructure. *Bismarck*'s heavy Flak battery in fact consisted of two types of mount. The four forward mounts were C/31s, installed before the ship was commissioned, the after four being the newer C/37 mount (see below) which were fitted later, although sources differ as to when this actually happened. Some German publications say it was in the latter half of October 1940, when the ship was at Kiel, but photographs of *Bismarck* taken during her machinery trials in the Baltic on 23 October 1940, show her still without her after 105mm guns. It seems likely that they had been fitted by 27 November, because a

The 8.8cm C/31 gE twin pedestal mount

Total weight, mount and guns:	27,805kg
Distance between gun axes:	680mm
Recoil distance:	410mm
Maximum elevating speed:	12°/sec
Maximum training speed:	8°/sec
Training arc:	360°
Depression/elevation:	–9°/+80°
Shield armour:	10-15mm

The C/31 d twin pedestal mount

Total weight of mount:	27,350kg
Cast cradle weight:	1,455kg
Mount weight:	2,300kg
Foundation weight:	7,150kg
Electric equipment weight:	1,295kg
Optical equipment weight:	745kg
Armour weight:	6,130kg
Distance between gun axes:	680mm
Recoil distance:	410mm
Maximum elevating speed:	1.33°/sec (manual), 10°/sec (powered)
Maximum training speed:	1.5°/sec (manual), 8°/sec (powered)
Depression/elevation:	–8°/+80°
Armour:	Front 15mm; sides 10mm; mount 10mm

Left: Maintaining 10.5cm SK C/31 gun tubes. *(A Jarski collection)*

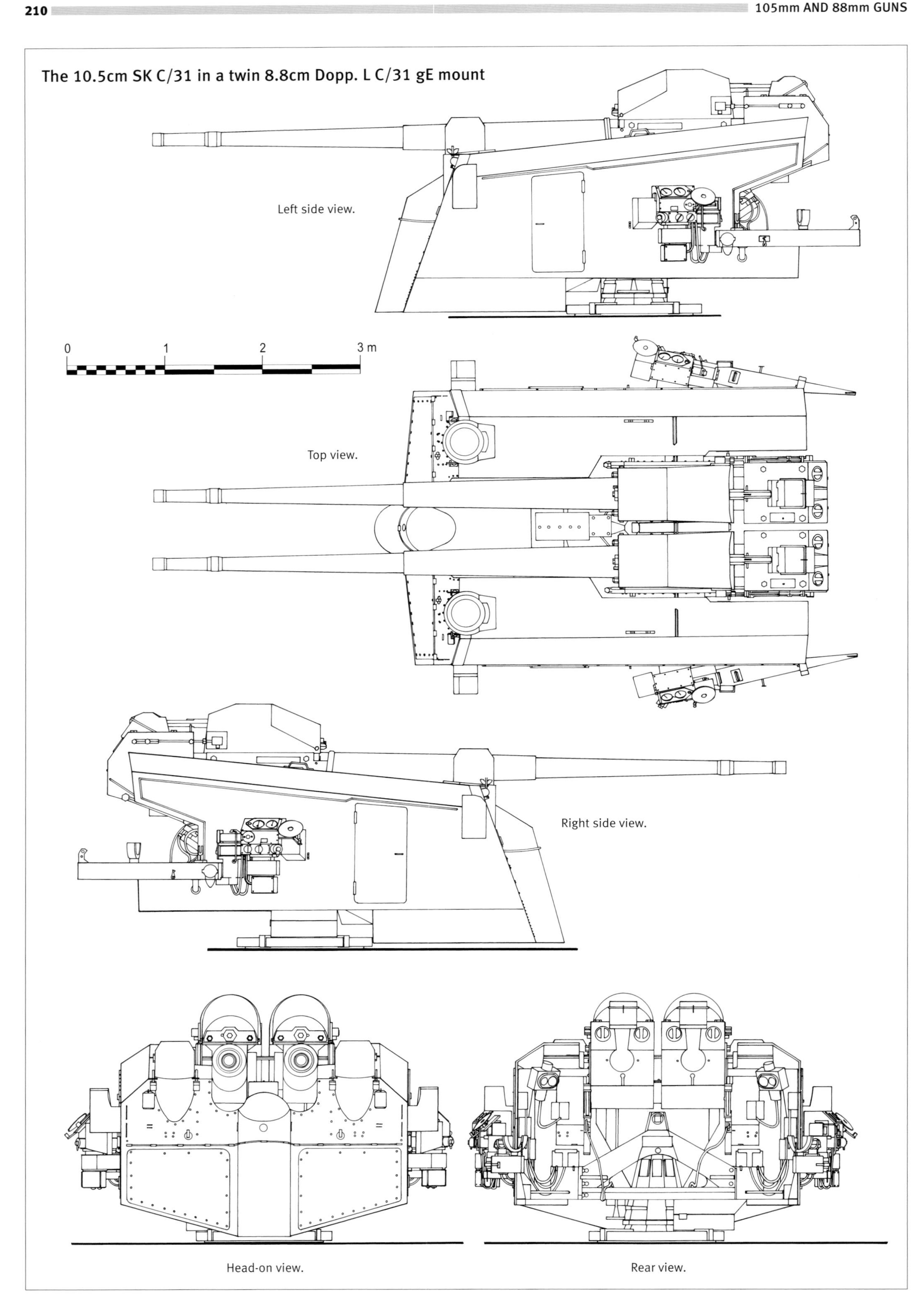
The 10.5cm SK C/31 in a twin 8.8cm Dopp. L C/31 gE mount
Left side view.
0
1
2
3 m
Top view.
Right side view.
Head-on view.
Rear view.

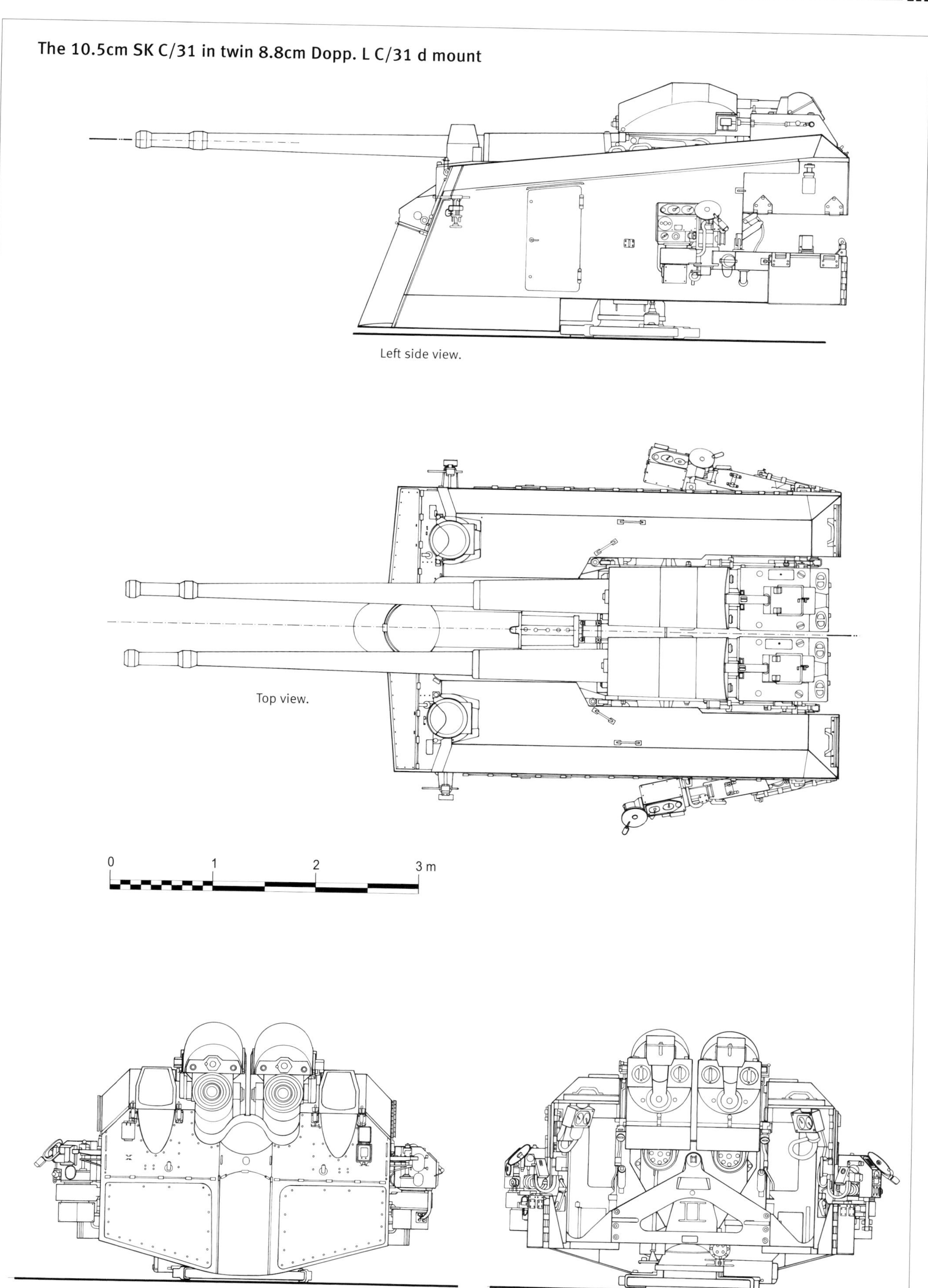
The 10.5cm SK C/31 in twin 8.8cm Dopp. L C/31 d mount
Left side view.
Top view.
0
1
2
3 m
Head-on view.
Rear view.

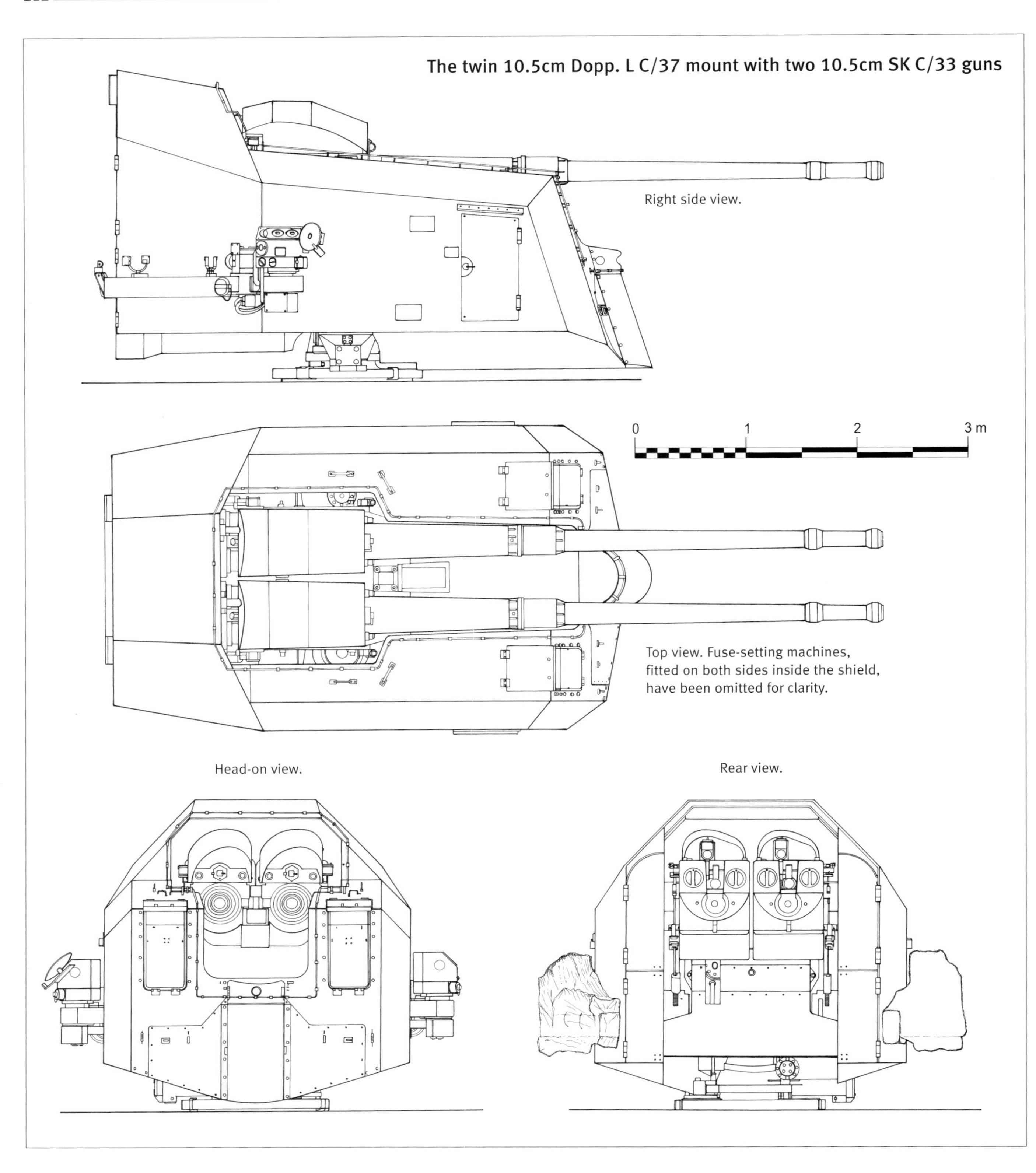

Right and opposite, left: Four detailed views of the 10.5cm SK C/31 in twin 8.8cm Dopp. L C/31 d mount aboard the heavy cruiser *Prinz Eugen*. These photos were taken prior to the Operation 'Crossroads' atomic test in 1946. *(National Archives)*

report of that date states that blast from the after Bb turret (150mm) and Stb III and IV mounts (i.e. the after 105s) had slightly damaged the aircraft hangar doors during gunnery trials. This suggest they may have been fitted in early November, when the ship was at Gotenhafen (Gdynia).

The 10.5cm Dopp. L C/37 twin mount

These were a thoroughly updated version of the previous mounts, to arm the *Bismarck* class battleships. They had a single cradle, eliminating the space between the guns, new training and elevation gear was fitted, and there was a new arrangement for the fuse-setting machines. The gun was the new 10.5cm SK C/33 nT with a multi-part barrel liner in a multi-layer tube jacket. The shield now covered the top of the mount at the rear, protecting both guns and their crews from shell splinters and the elements.

Only *Bismarck* (see above for details) and *Tirpitz* received these mounts. Initially, *Tirpitz* had six of the C/37 mounts, with the after pair being C/31s, which were replaced with C/37s in late 1941, making her heavy Flak battery sixteen 10.5cm SK C/33 guns in eight 10.5cm Dopp. L C/37 twin mounts. These triaxially-stabilised mounts were controlled by their own director, stabilised in the same way. The mounts were designated in the standard Kriegsmarine system, beginning with Stb I (Starboard I) and Bb I (Port I) forward and working back to Stb IV and Bb IV aft.

The 10.5cm Dopp. L C/37 twin mount

Total weight of mount:	26,425kg
Weight of cast cradle:	1,455kg
Weight of pedestal:	2,300kg
Weight of base:	7,150kg
Weight of electrical equipment:	1,295kg
Weight of optical equipment:	560kg
Weight of armour:	5,270kg
Distance between gun axes:	660mm
Recoil distance:	380mm
Maximum elevating speed:	1.75°/sec (manual), 12°/sec (powered)
Maximum training speed:	1.5°/sec (manual), 8.5°/sec (powered)
Depression/elevation:	–8°/+80°
Armour protection:	Front 20mm; sides 10mm; base and rear 8mm; front and rear oblique flats 8mm

It was intended to fit these mounts to the heavy cruisers *Seydlitz* and *Lützow*, but the ships were cancelled.

The 10.5cm Dopp. L C/38 twin mount

This was intended to be a new type of fully-automatic mount, to arm the 'H' class battleships, with the gun crew only there to step in if the power failed. The RPC system would control everything – training, elevation, etc – and each gun had its own automatic loading system, the first of its kind. Two prototypes were built, a long and short trunk version, but they were

Below: *Tirpitz* steaming out of Westfjord to take part in Operation 'Sportpalast'. Note the twin 10.5cm Dopp. L C/37 mount with elevated barrels in the foreground. *(S Breyer collection)*

Bottom: *Bismarck* amidships. Note the twin 10.5cm Dopp. L C/37 mount in the foreground. *(S Breyer collection)*

Right: The 10.5cm SK C/31s in a twin 8.8cm Dopp. L C/31 d mount shown firing aboard the heavy cruiser *Admiral Hipper*. *(CAW collection)*

cancelled along with the battleships they were to equip before any more could be completed.

10.5cm training gun

To allow 105mm loading drills to take place aboard *Bismarck* and *Tirpitz* without causing wear and tear to the actual guns, a practice gun was installed on deck between 'C' and 'D' turrets. This consisted of an entire breech piece and a shortened barrel mounted on a stand, to allow gun crews to train with inert practice rounds.

Below: The newly-commissioned *Prinz Eugen* at Kiel. Note the 10.5cm SK C/31 in a twin 8.8cm Dopp. L C/31 d mount in the left foreground. *(S Breyer collection)*

Above, left: A 10.5cm SK C/31 in a twin 8.8cm Dopp. L C/31 d mount aboard *Admiral Hipper*, photographed during the Norwegian campaign. *(CAW collection)*

Above, right: Senior officers visiting *Tirpitz*. A twin 10.5cm Dopp. L C/37 mount with 10.5cm SK C/33 guns is in the background. *(CAW collection)*

Above: The 105mm ammunition hoists aboard *Prinz Eugen*. *(NHC)*

The 10.5cm Dopp. L C/38 twin mount

Total weight of mount:	44,000kg
Distance between gun axes:	970mm
Recoil distance:	400mm
Maximum training speed:	10°/sec
Maximum elevating speed:	12°/sec
Training arc:	360°
Depression/elevation:	−10°/+80°

Right: A twin 10.5cm Dopp. L C/37 mount aboard *Bismarck*. Note the fuse-setting machine at the side of the shield with a canvas cover. *(Author's collection)*

14

88mm GUNS

THE 8.8cm SK C/31 GUN

This was the first naval version of the highly-successful 88mm anti-aircraft gun, which was introduced a year after the original land-service version (see above). The first ship to be armed with them was the 'pocket battleship' *Deutschland*, in semi-enclosed twin mounts.

The tube

This consisted of a one-piece liner inside a one-piece outer jacket and a breech ring. The liner was attached to the breech ring with a brass nut and to the jacket by a ring with an asbestos seal to keep out water and other debris. The breech ring was held fast by a special lug. Sockets for the recuperating gear were at the front of the breech ring, and the breech block was housed in a rectangular opening. The front of this opening was perpendicular to the bore, while the rear was inclined slightly downwards. The chamber ended

Right: 8.8cm SK C/30 guns in an MPL C/30 single pedestal mount, fitted fore and aft aboard the minesweeper *M1*.

Right: An 8.8cm SK C/30 gun in an MPL C/30 single pedestal mount, aboard the minesweeper *M 8*. These ships were fitted with two such guns each, one forward and one aft. *(CAW collection)*

The 8.8cm SK C/30 gun in an MPL C/30 single pedestal mount

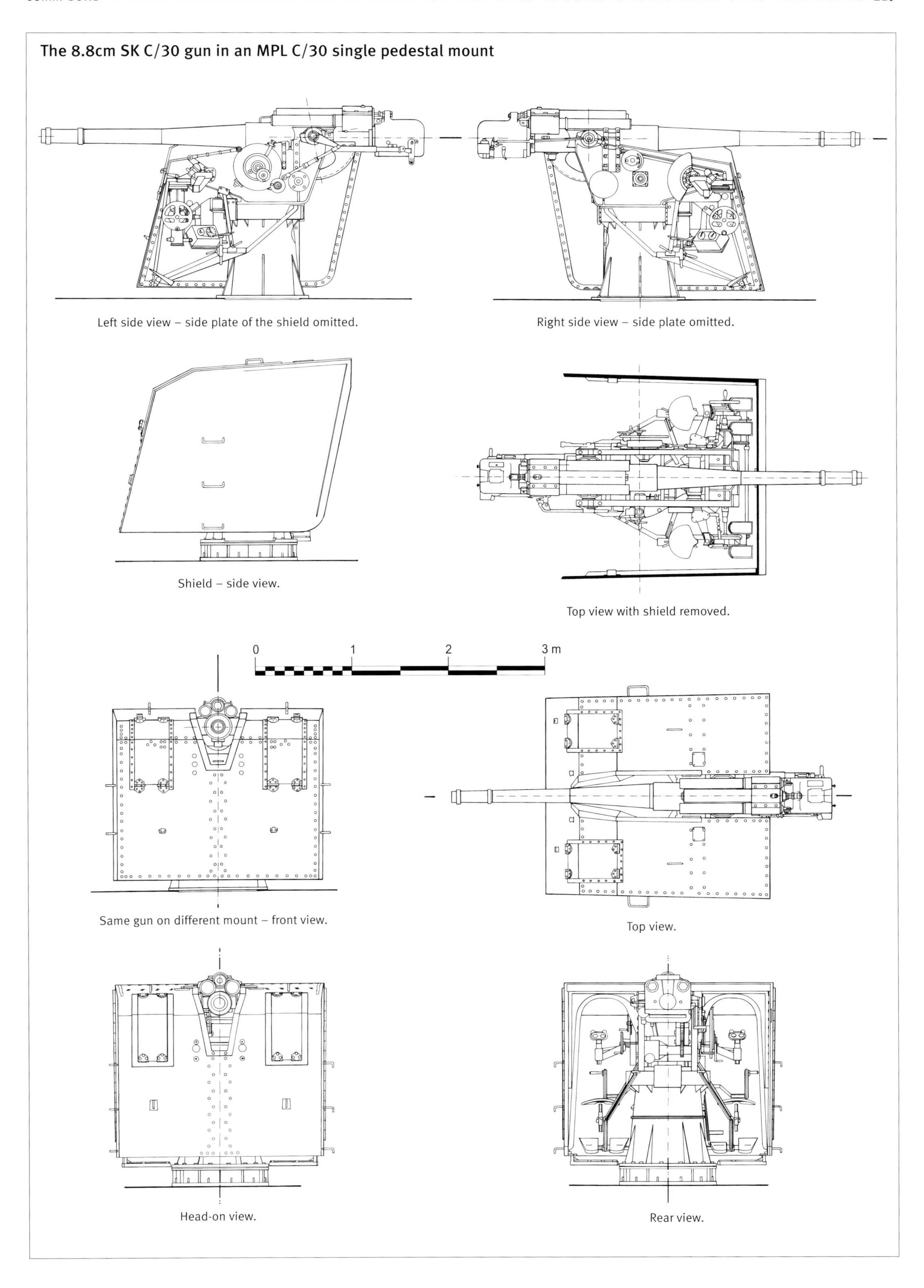

Left side view – side plate of the shield omitted.

Right side view – side plate omitted.

Shield – side view.

Top view with shield removed.

Same gun on different mount – front view.

Top view.

Head-on view.

Rear view.

Left: 8.8cm SK C/30 guns in single MPL C/30 pedestal mounts aboard minesweepers. The stern gun of one ship is visible in the foreground, with the bow gun of another in the background. *(CAW collection)*

Right: Two 8.8cm SK C/30 guns in single Flak L C/30 anti-aircraft pedestal mount, installed aboard a gun lighter. The guns are firing at a towed target. *(CAW collection)*

in a forcing cone, where the rifling began. The rifling was progressive, with twenty-eight right-hand grooves of increasing pitch.

The 8.8cm SK C/31 tube

Calibre:	88mm
Overall length (tube + breech):	6,870mm
Length chamber:	918.5mm
Length rifling:	5,421.5mm
Grooves:	28 (1.2mm x 5.97mm)
Width fields:	3.9mm
Rifling pitch – initial:	50 calibres (440mm)
Rifling pitch – terminal:	35 calibres (3,080mm)

The 8.8cm SK C/31 cradle

Tube ring inner diameter:	288mm
Cradle trunnion diameter:	110mm
Distance between trunnion bearings:	390mm
Recuperator inner diameter:	130mm
Recuperator cylinder volume:	7.6l
Recuperator oil volume:	7.22l
Recoil distance:	175-300mm
Maximum allowed recoil:	350mm
Recoil force:	c. 17,000kg

The breech

The gun had a semi-automatic vertical sliding block breech. The breech opened (i.e. the block was lowered) either automatically when the tube reached its maximum recoil position after firing or manually by a lever on the right-hand side of the breech ring. It was closed (i.e. the block was raised) likewise either manually or automatically once a round was chambered. The main trigger was a solenoid-operated electric circuit, but the gun could also be fired by a lanyard attached to the trigger lever. The recoil automatically activated a circuit breaker in the trigger, and the firing pin was cocked automatically when the breech was opened, but this again could also be done manually. The spent case was ejected from the chamber when the breech opened. A safety catch blocked the firing mechanism and prevented the breech being opened accidentally. Both the firing pin and its spring could be removed and replaced from both sides of the gun with the breech closed. Electrically-driven rollers were fitted at the entrance to the chamber to facilitate chambering a round at high angles of elevation.

The mount

The triaxially-stabilised SK C/31 mount was protected by a semi-enclosed splinter shield. The lower mount was a conical pedestal, bolted to the base of the mount. On top of the pedestal was a toothed ring which meshed with the training cogwheel. The revolving upper mount was set above the training

Twin C/31 mount for the 8.8cm SK C/31

Distance between gun axes:	680mm
Distance between cradle trunnions and vertical axis of mount:	545mm
Vertical distance between cradle trunnions and stabilisation axes:	455mm
Tube height above deck:	1,900mm
Pedestal diameter:	1,220mm
Number of pedestal bolts:	16
Pedestal bolt diameter:	60mm
Maximum width of shield:	2,700mm
Distance of shield from pedestal axis:	2,350mm
Depression/elevation:	−10°/+80°
Maximum stabilisation angle:	17°

Below: An 8.8cm SK C/30 gun in Ubts C/30 single pedestal mount aboard *U 47*. The light cruiser *Emden* is in the background, with her crew manning the rails to salute Prien's return from the successful Scapa Flow raid. *(A Jarski collection)*

gear, with three parallel axes of stabilisation. The shield and floor of the mount were suspended on the centre axis, with the individual guns on the side axes. The guns and mounts were simultaneously and uniformly stabilised for both pitch and yaw up to 17° in each direction. Both powered and manual training were available.

The hydraulic recoil buffer and two spring-loaded recuperators were mounted above the tube, between the breech ring and the cradle flange. The shield protected three crew positions. The left-hand layer controlled training and the right-hand one elevation. Both layers' stations had fire-control indicators linked to the director. Wide-angle telescopes for target acqui-

Right: An 8.8cm SK C/30 gun in Ubts C/30 single pedestal mount aboard Type VII U-boat moored alongside a submarine tender. *(CAW collection)*

Below: An 8.8cm SK C/30 gun in Flak L C/30 single pedestal mount, on the after superstructure of a small surface vessel, probably a minesweeper. *(CAW collection)*

Above and below: Gunnery drill on the 8.8cm SK C/30 gun in Flak L C/30 single pedestal mount at the bows of a 'KFK' class auxiliary ship. *(CAW collection)*

Left and below: Gunnery drill on the 8.8cm SK C/30 gun in Flak L C/30 single pedestal mount at the bows of a 'KFK' class auxiliary ship. Note ready ammunition containers lining the rail in the right photo. *(CAW collection)*

Below: Gunnery drill on the 8.8cm SK C/30 gun in Flak L C/30 single pedestal mount on board a Kriegsmarine auxiliary ship. *(CAW collection)*

Above: Gunnery drill on the 8.8cm SK C/30 gun in Flak L C/30 single pedestal mount on board a Kriegsmarine auxiliary ship. *(CAW collection)*

Above: The commander of a minesweeper flotilla addressing his men from the fantail. The 8.8cm SK C/30 gun in single Flak L C/30 pedestal mount is clearly visible in the middle of the photo. *(CAW collection)*

Below: The 8.8cm SK C/30 gun in Flak L C/30 single pedestal mount on board an auxiliary ship – front view. *(CAW collection)*

Gun group weights

A: Tube	
Tube with breech ring:	c.4,190kg
Breech block:	c.45kg
Breech block transport mechanism:	c.27kg
Loading gear (minus engine):	c.33kg
Total:	**4,250kg**
B: Cradle	
Cradle with recuperator unit:	1,300kg
Tube recoil brake:	100kg
Tube recuperator (incl. 2 springs):	150kg
Cradle mount with helical gears:	c.600kg
Total:	**2,150kg**
C: Mount	
Stabilisation gear with counterweight:	c.2,100kg
Shield with crew seats:	4,650kg
Upper mount with training mechanism:	2,100kg
Pedestal:	1,500kg
Total:	**10,350kg**
D: Sights	
Sight mount:	c.200kg
Sighting unit with scopes:	c.435kg
Sighting scope:	26.5kg
Stabilisation scope:	15kg
Fire controls:	50kg
Total:	**727kg**

E: Electrical equipment	
Electric trigger units:	c.145kg
Loading unit motors with starter:	c.85kg
Fire control unit:	110kg
Elevation motor with remote control gear:	210kg (incl. 65kg motor)
Check relay:	c.21kg
Cables, mounts, etc.:	680kg
Sights lighting:	20kg
Total:	**1,250kg**

Total weights	
Remote control unit:	200kg
Two guns:	8,500kg
Two cradles:	2,600kg
Two mounts:	1,200kg
Lower mount:	10,350kg
Sights:	700kg
Electric equipment:	1,250kg
Grand total:	**24,800kg**

sition were mounted in the outer viewports of the mount, while closer to the centre the variable-zoom telescopic gunsights were mounted in cylindrical sleeves.

Between the two gunlayers was a third crewman, who controlled the stabilisation of the mount. He had his own telescopic sight and hand-wheels to control the stabilisation gear. At cruising stations, the stabilisation system was disconnected, the mount being secured using the brackets along the lower edge of the shield. The guns were also fixed in place with special ring braces.

Above: An 8.8cm round is being chambered in an SK C/30 gun in Flak L C/30 single pedestal mount. Note the details of the breech. *(CAW collection)*

Left: A senior Kriegsmarine officer is addressing a torpedo-boat's crew on the fantail. The 8.8cm SK C/30 in single Flak L C/30 mount is visible in the middle of the photo, with a shielded quadruple 2cm Flakvierling 38 anti-aircraft gun in the background. *(CAW collection)*

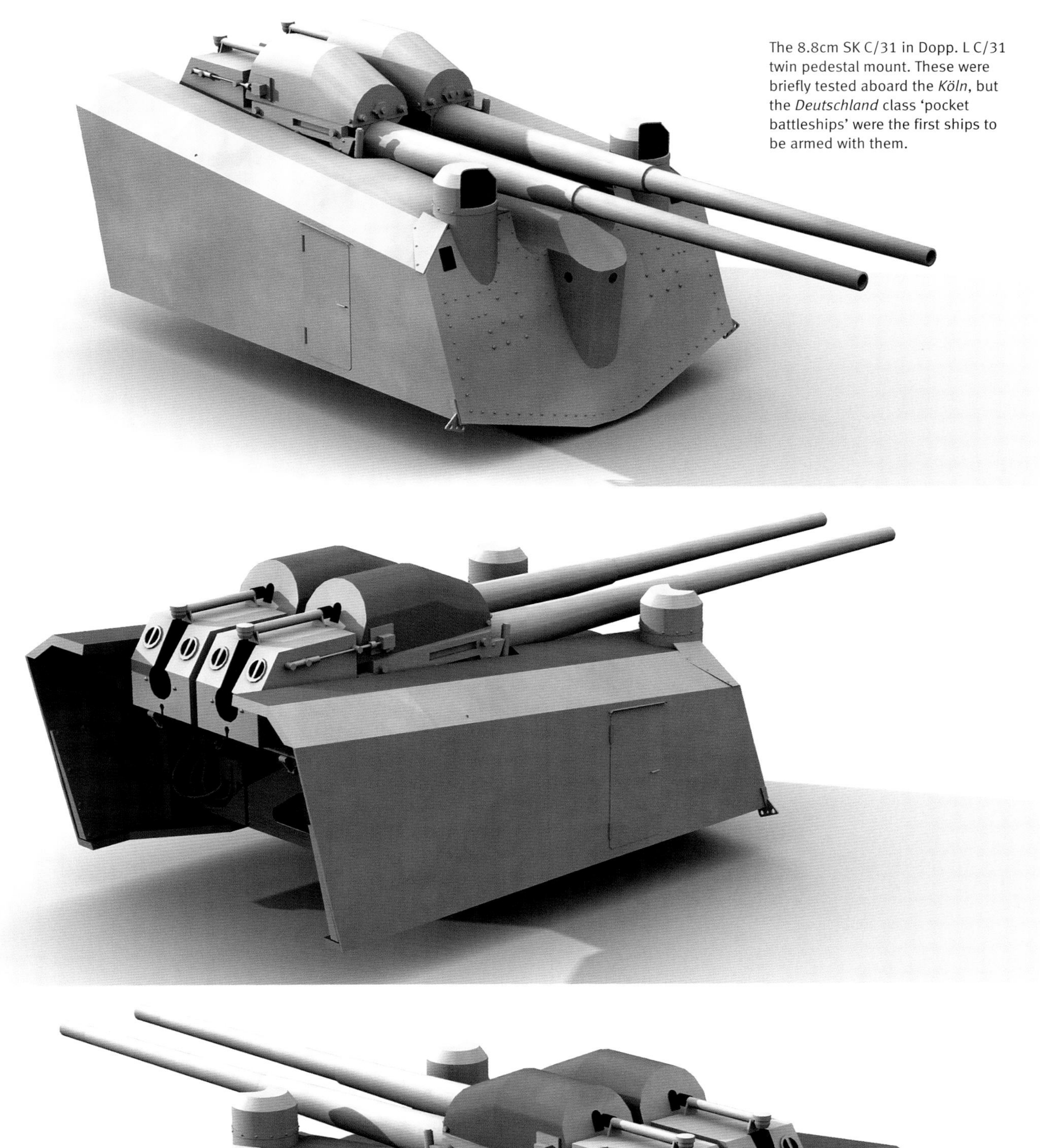

The 8.8cm SK C/31 in Dopp. L C/31 twin pedestal mount. These were briefly tested aboard the *Köln*, but the *Deutschland* class 'pocket battleships' were the first ships to be armed with them.

The 8.8cm SK C/31 in a Dopp. L C/31 twin pedestal mount from the *Deutschland*, front, rear and side views.

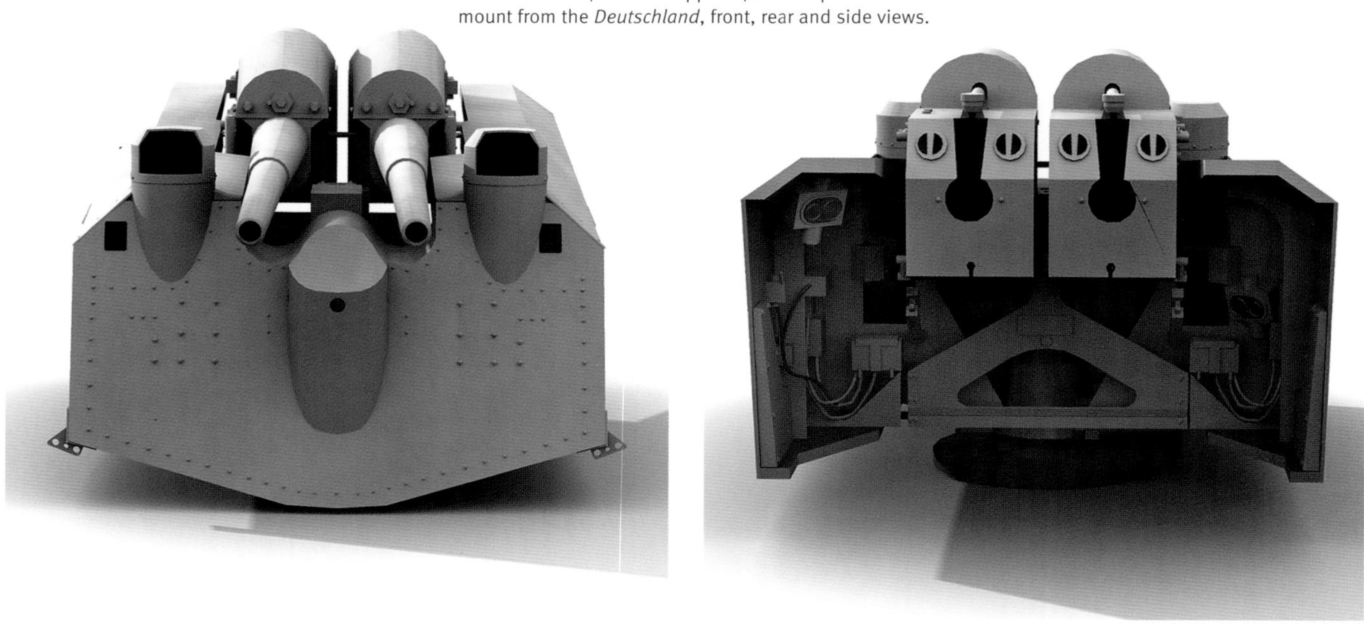

The 8.8cm SK C/31 on pedestal twin mount Dopp. L C/31 on board the 'pocket battleship' *Deutschland*. Their blast-shields were not perfected yet – their chief disadvantage was the lack of built-in fuse-setting machines. Prior to chambering, each round had to be carried by hand to the fuse-setter installed some distance from the mount, resulting in a reduced rate of fire.

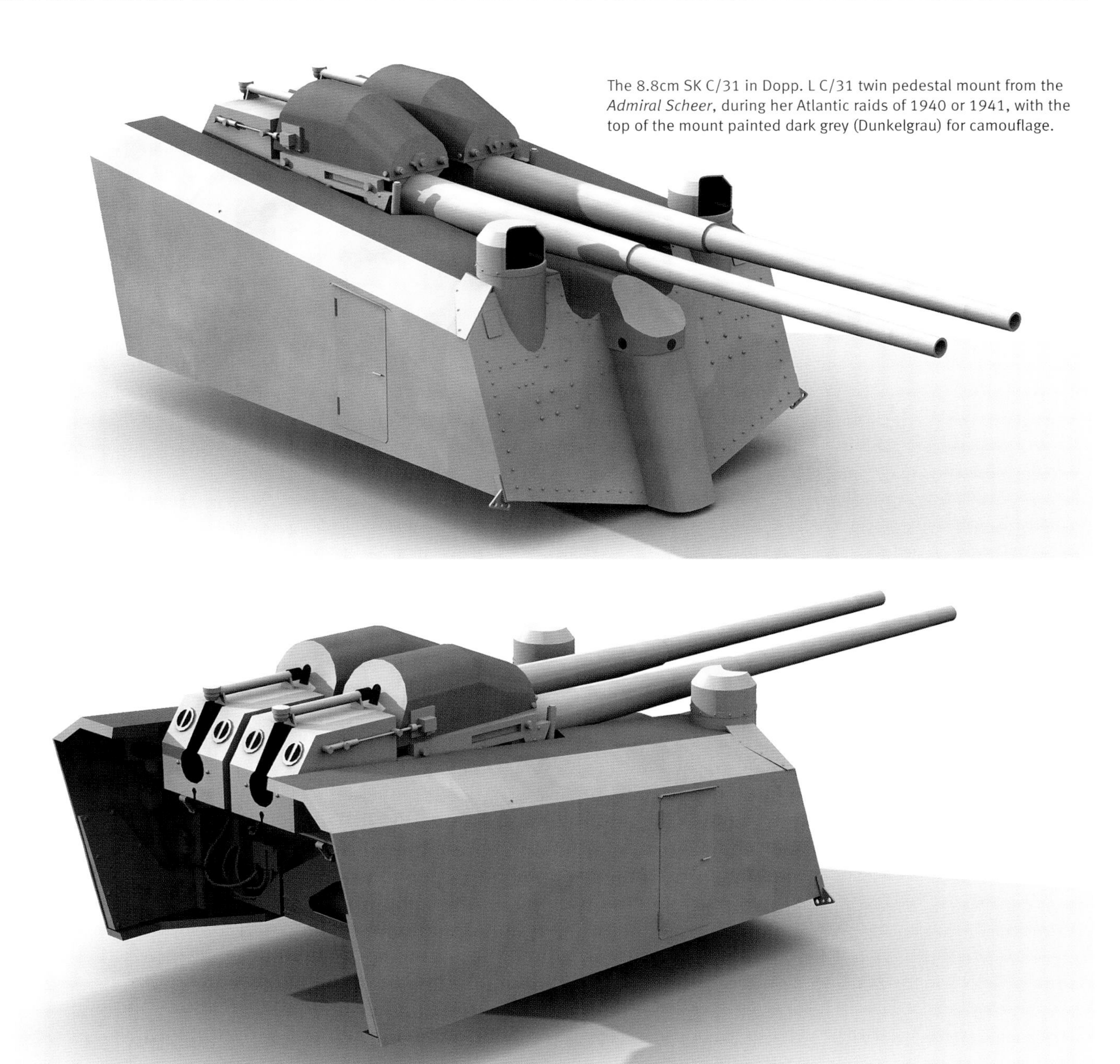

The 8.8cm SK C/31 in Dopp. L C/31 twin pedestal mount from the *Admiral Scheer*, during her Atlantic raids of 1940 or 1941, with the top of the mount painted dark grey (Dunkelgrau) for camouflage.

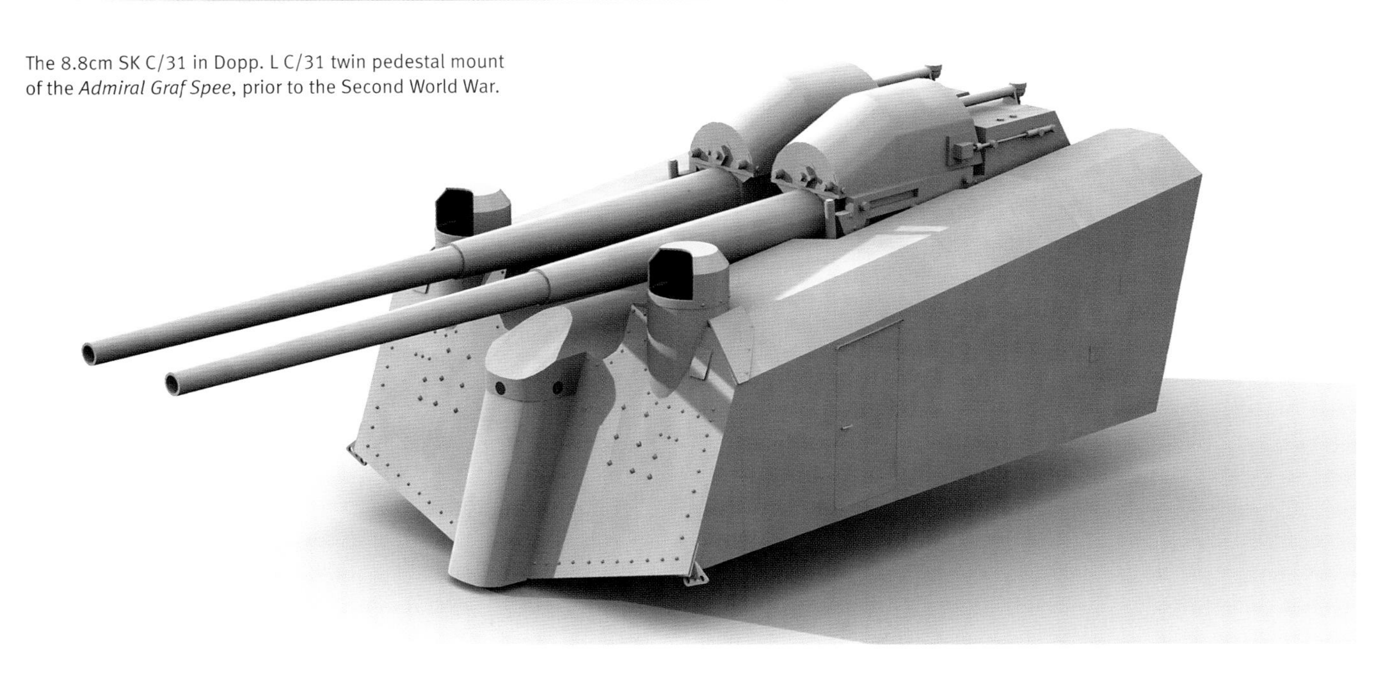

The 8.8cm SK C/31 in Dopp. L C/31 twin pedestal mount of the *Admiral Graf Spee*, prior to the Second World War.

The 8.8cm SK C/31 in Dopp. L C/31 twin pedestal mount of the *Admiral Graf Spee*, prior to the Second World War.

The 8.8cm L/45 gun in an MPL C/13 single pedestal mount.

The 8.8cm L/45 gun on MPL C/13 single pedestal mount, front and rear views.

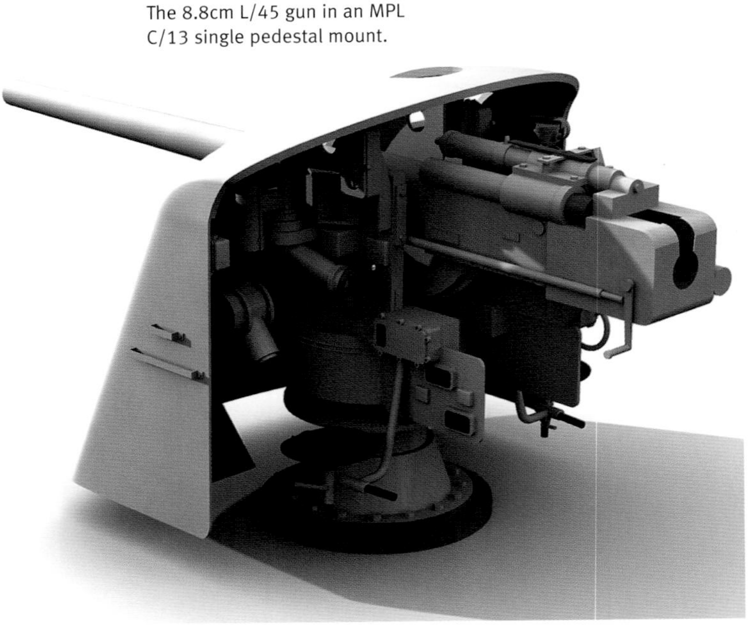

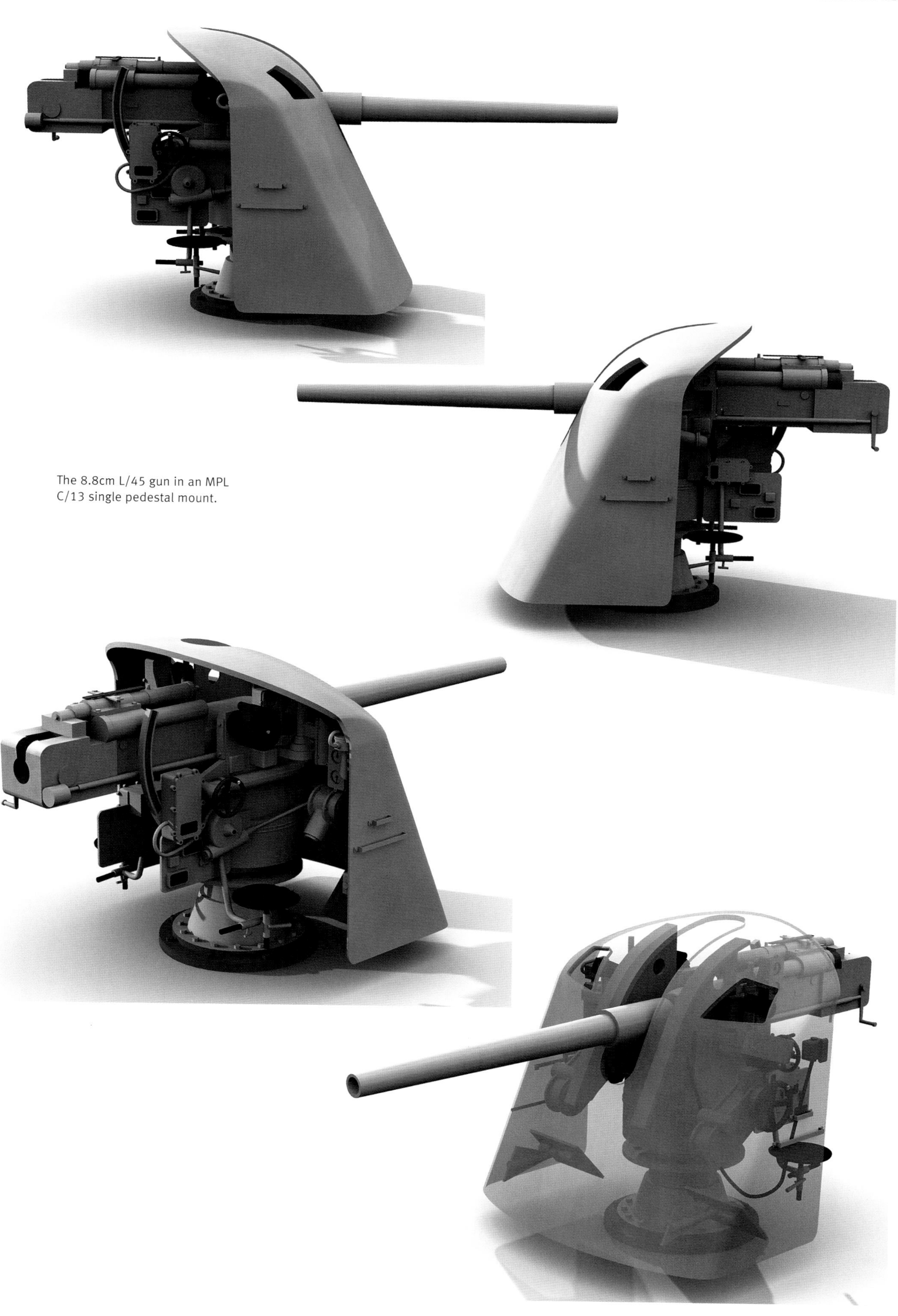

The 8.8cm L/45 gun in an MPL C/13 single pedestal mount.

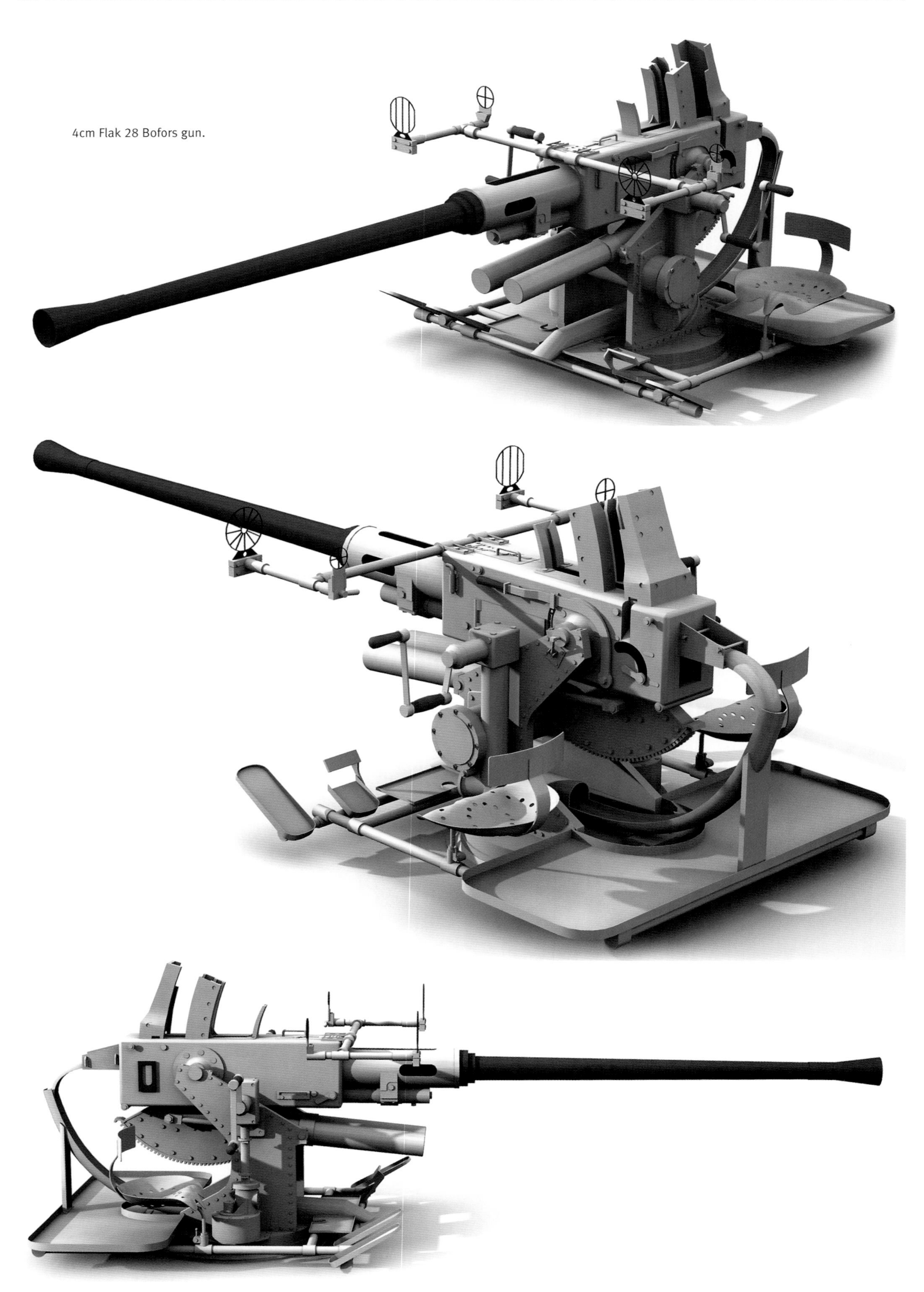

4cm Flak 28 Bofors gun.

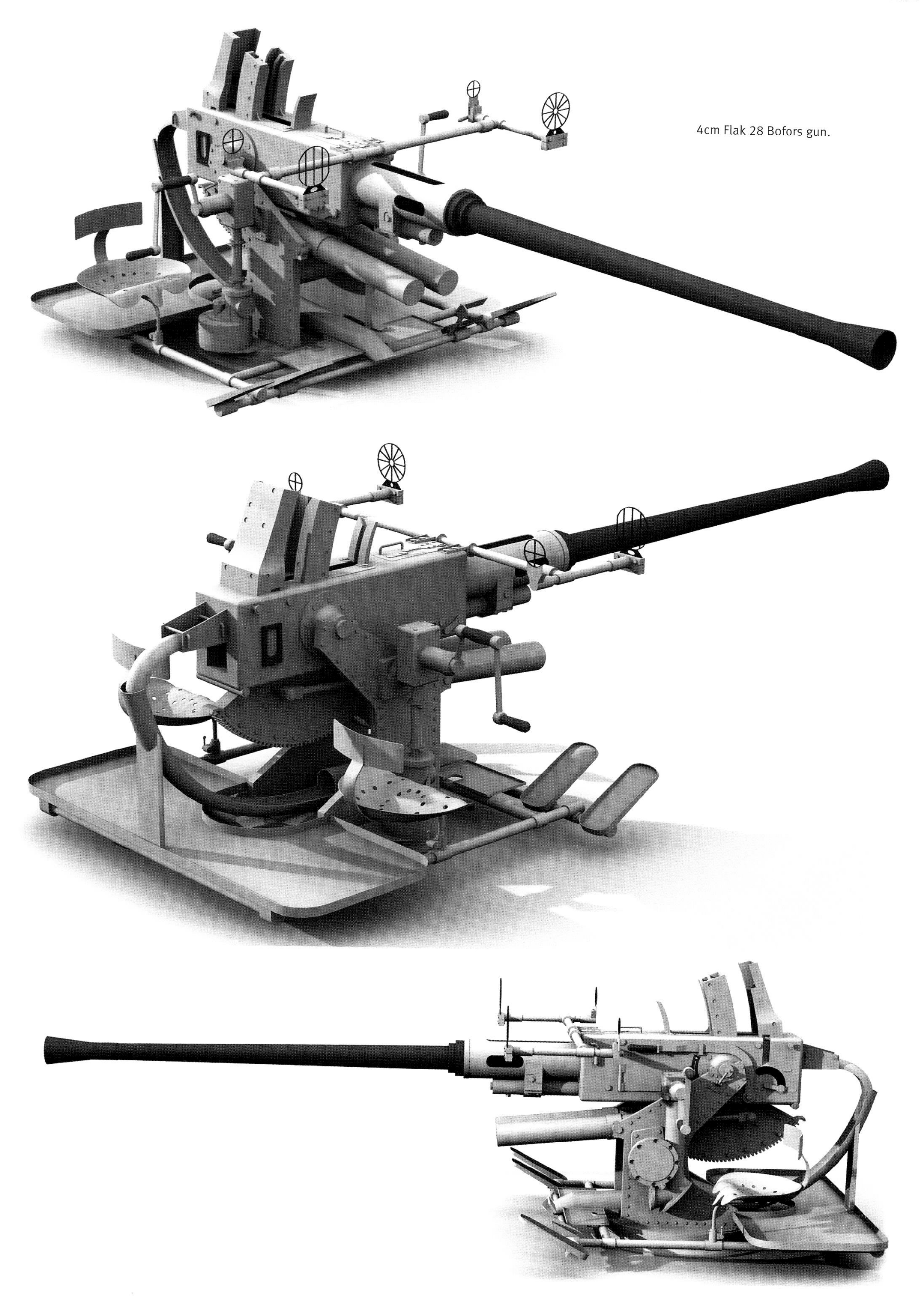

4cm Flak 28 Bofors gun.

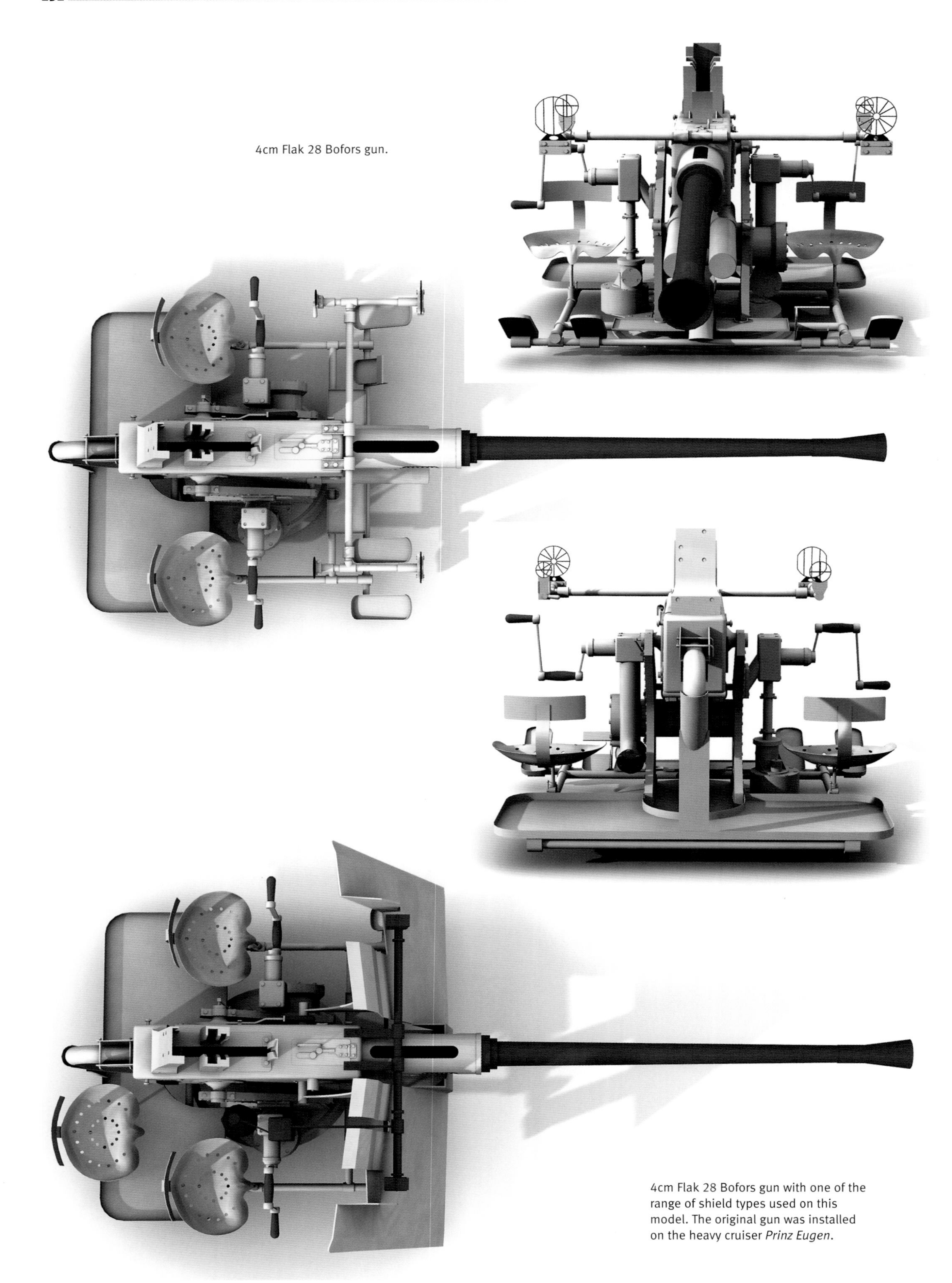

4cm Flak 28 Bofors gun.

4cm Flak 28 Bofors gun with one of the range of shield types used on this model. The original gun was installed on the heavy cruiser *Prinz Eugen*.

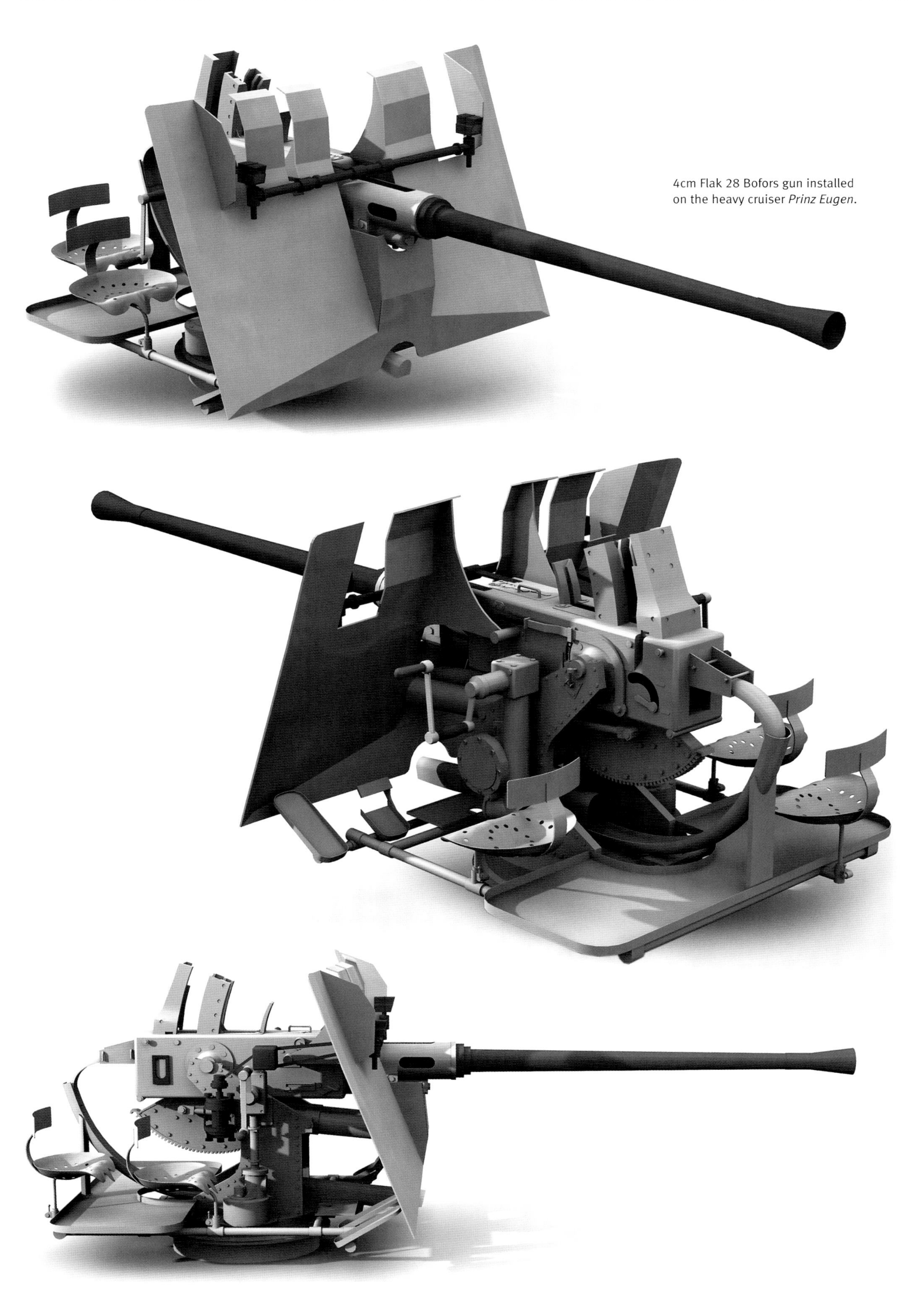

4cm Flak 28 Bofors gun installed on the heavy cruiser *Prinz Eugen*.

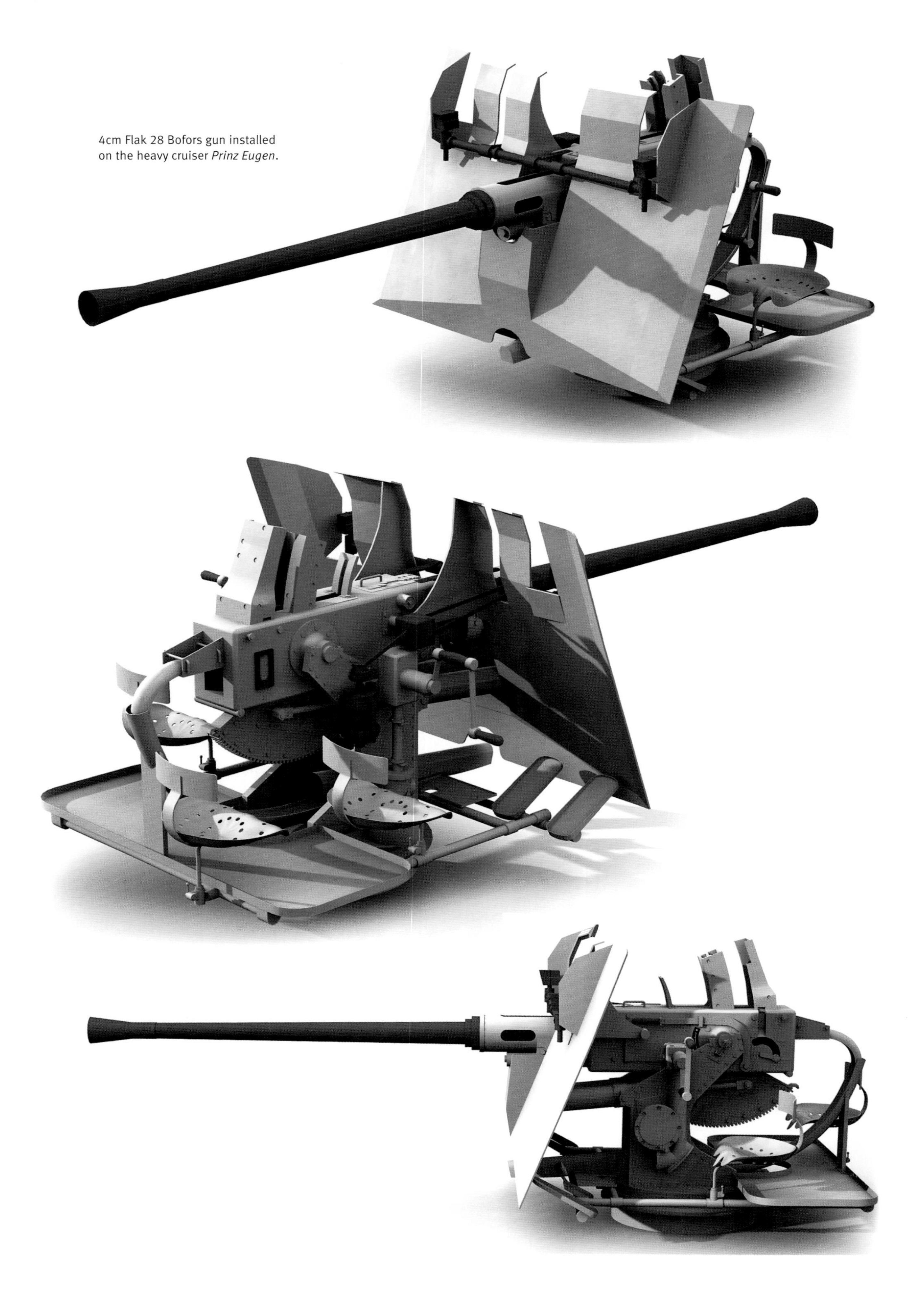

4cm Flak 28 Bofors gun installed on the heavy cruiser *Prinz Eugen*.

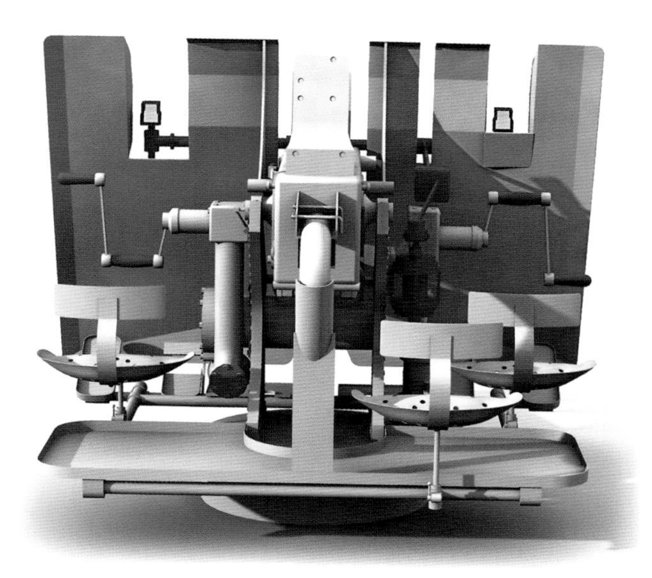

Modification of previous naval versions of the Bofors gun included installation of shields and replacing the sights with newer models.

3.7cm SK C/30 guns in Dopp. L C/30 mount, production variant.

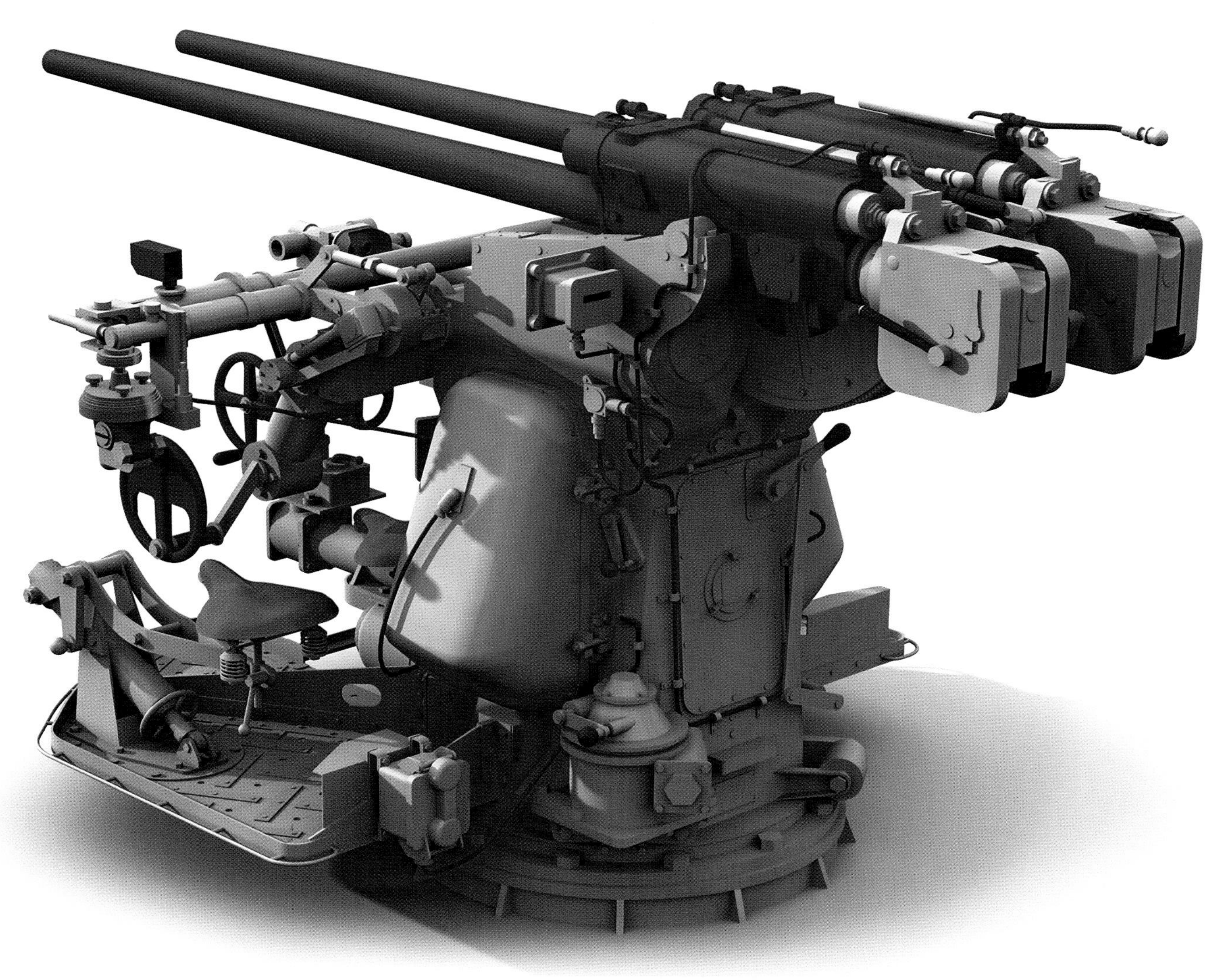

3.7cm SK C/30 guns in Dopp. L C/30 mount, production variant.

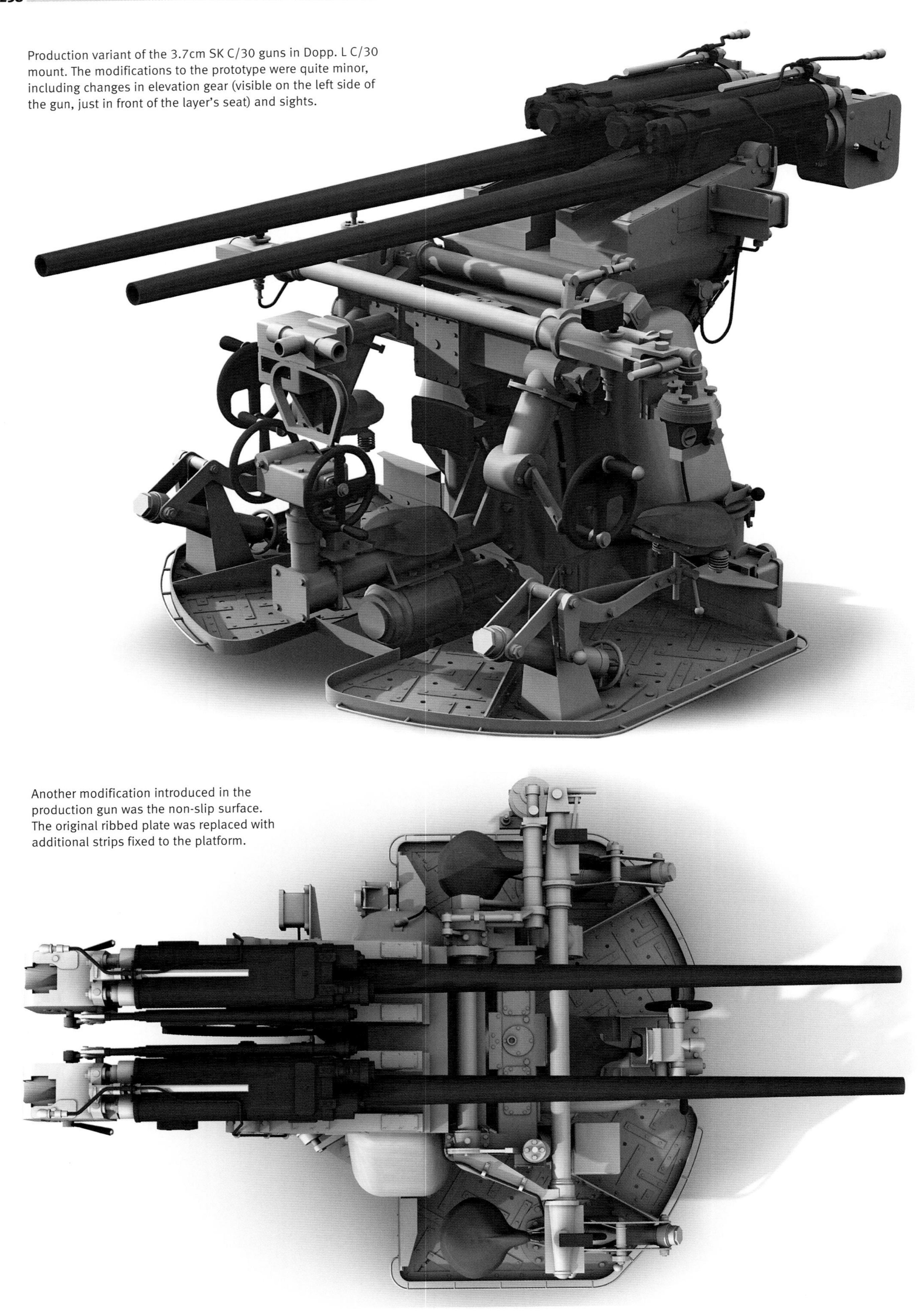

Production variant of the 3.7cm SK C/30 guns in Dopp. L C/30 mount. The modifications to the prototype were quite minor, including changes in elevation gear (visible on the left side of the gun, just in front of the layer's seat) and sights.

Another modification introduced in the production gun was the non-slip surface. The original ribbed plate was replaced with additional strips fixed to the platform.

The 3.7cm SK C/30 guns in Dopp. L C/30 mount were fitted with a triaxial stabilisation system, to compensate for the ship's rolling movement in rough seas.

In 1944 shields to protect the crew from splinters and aircraft fire were introduced for this gun type.

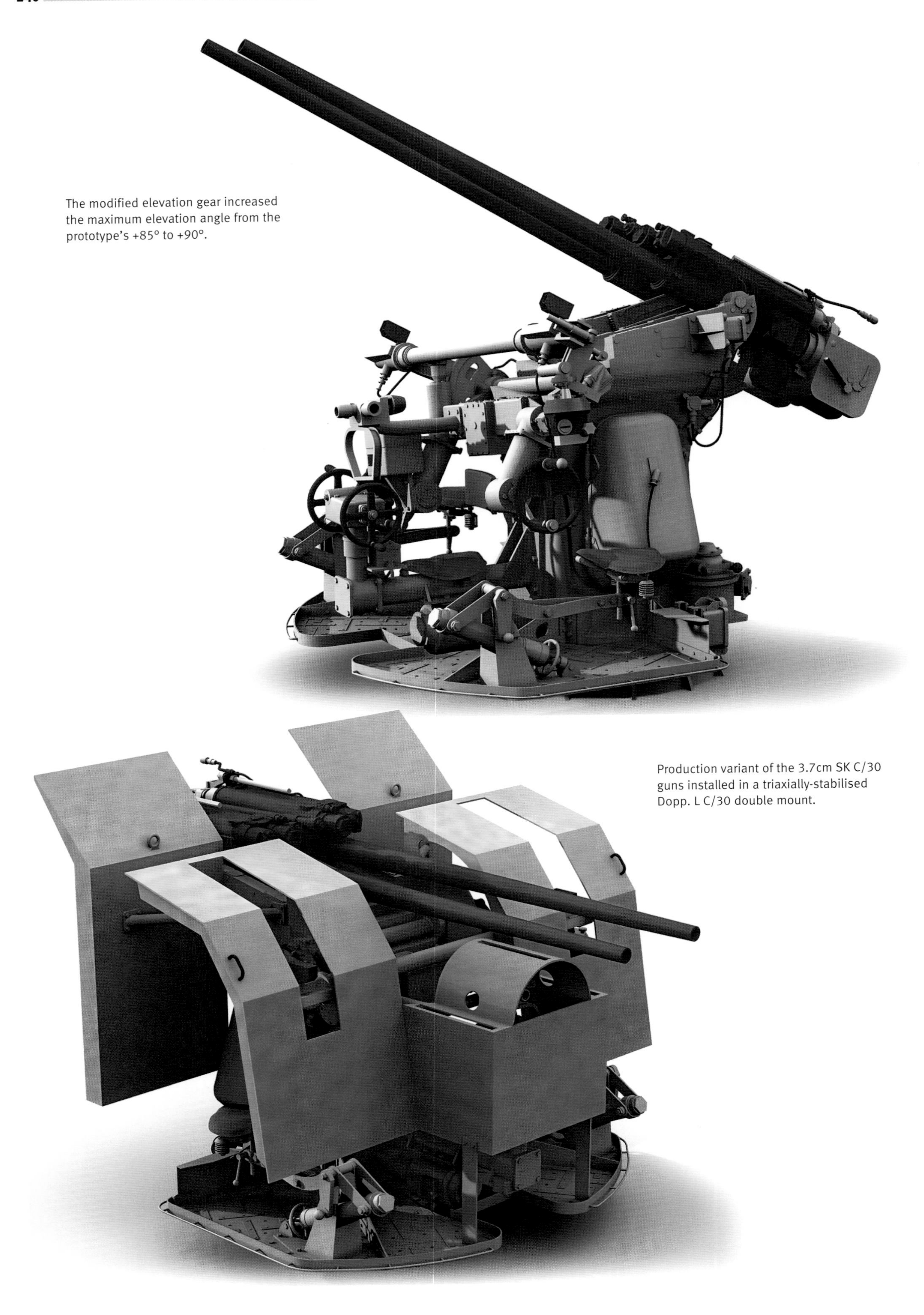

The modified elevation gear increased the maximum elevation angle from the prototype's +85° to +90°.

Production variant of the 3.7cm SK C/30 guns installed in a triaxially-stabilised Dopp. L C/30 double mount.

Introduction of 8mm-thick shields reduced the maximum elevation angle from +90° to +80° degrees.

After some time it was decided to install shields protecting the gun and its crew from splinters and aircraft fire. The first guns of this type were installed aboard the light cruiser *Nürnberg*. They were also used on smaller Kriegsmarine warships like destroyers and torpedo boats.

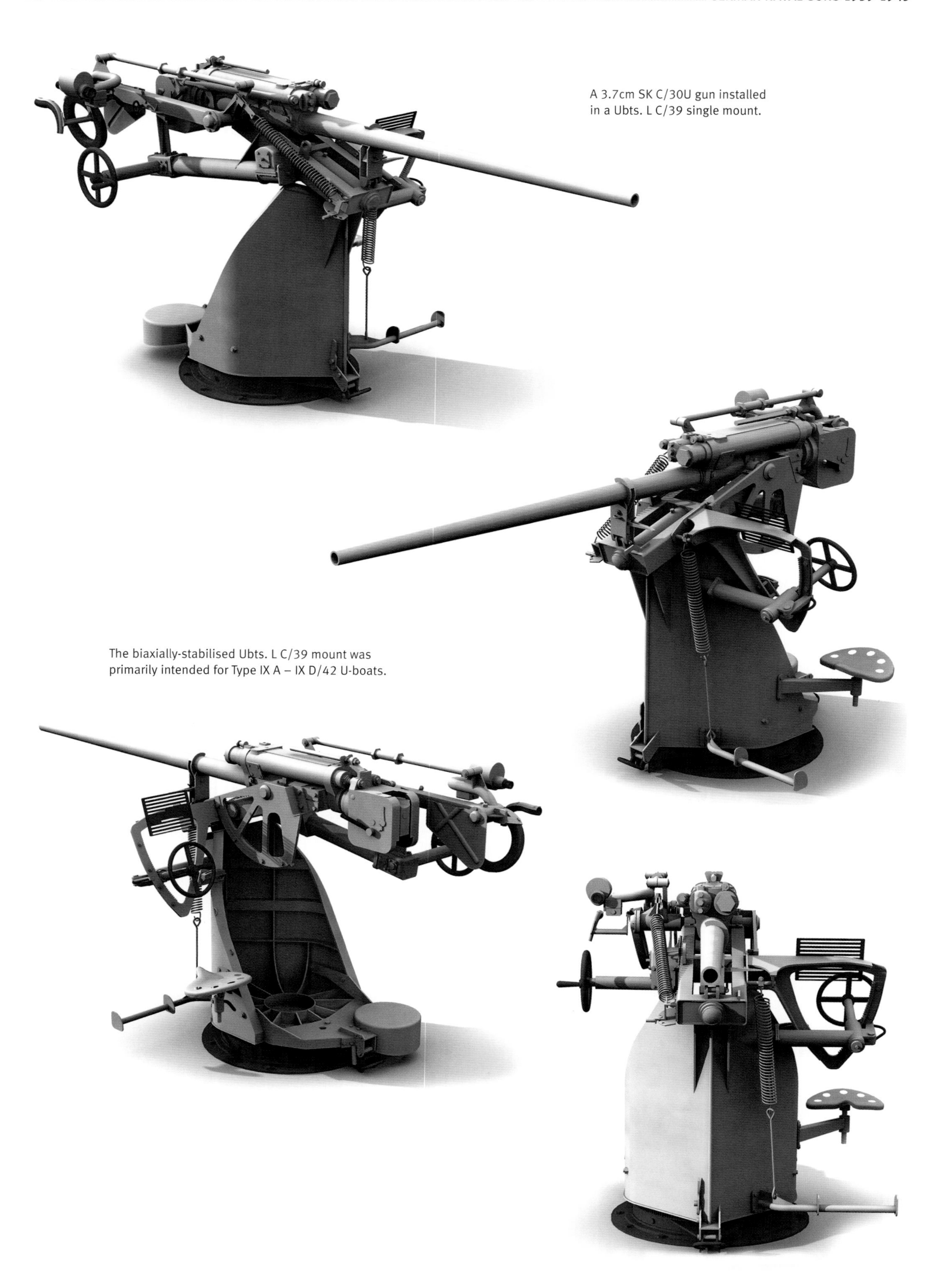

A 3.7cm SK C/30U gun installed in a Ubts. L C/39 single mount.

The biaxially-stabilised Ubts. L C/39 mount was primarily intended for Type IX A – IX D/42 U-boats.

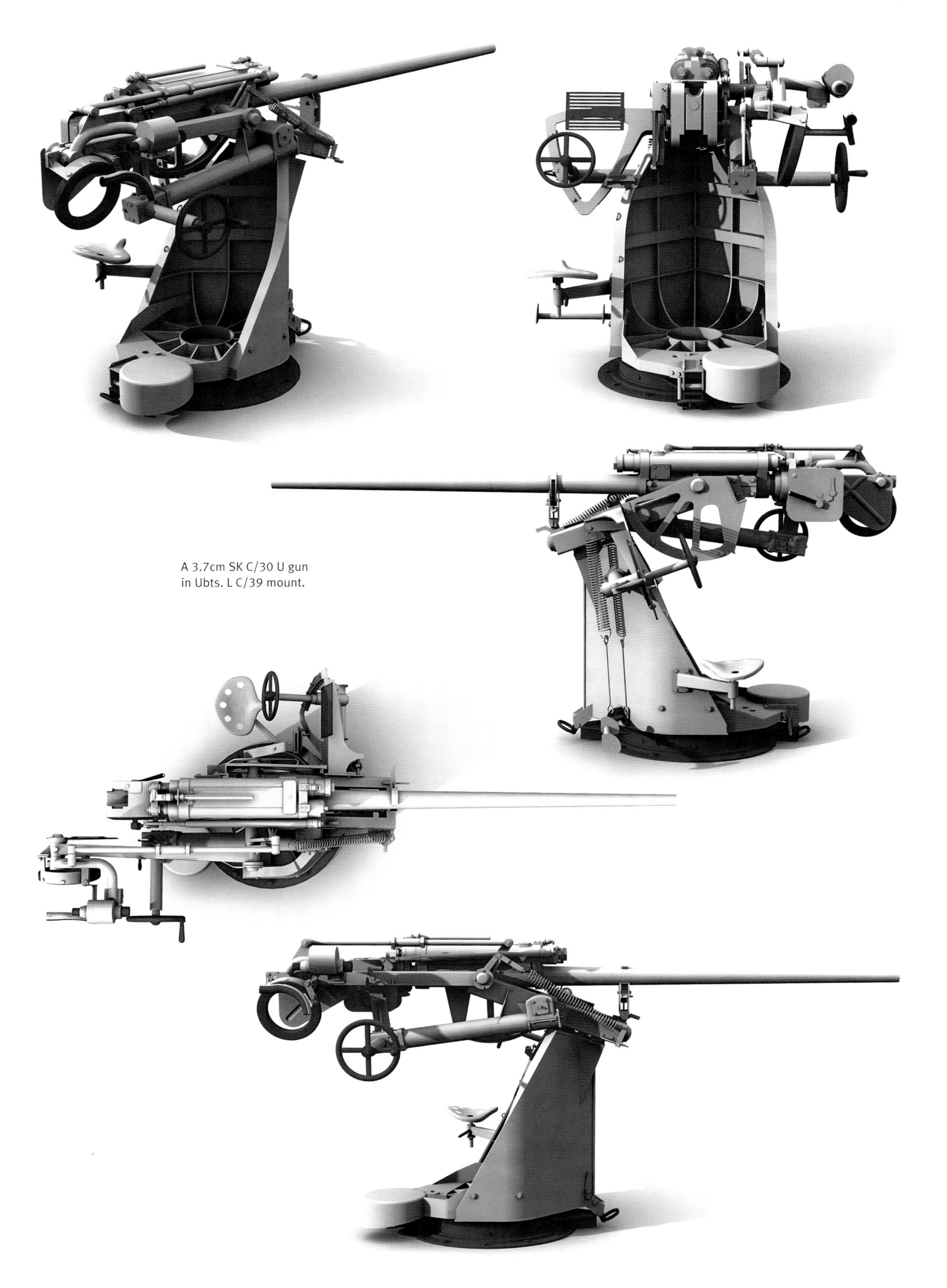

A 3.7cm SK C/30 U gun in Ubts. L C/39 mount.

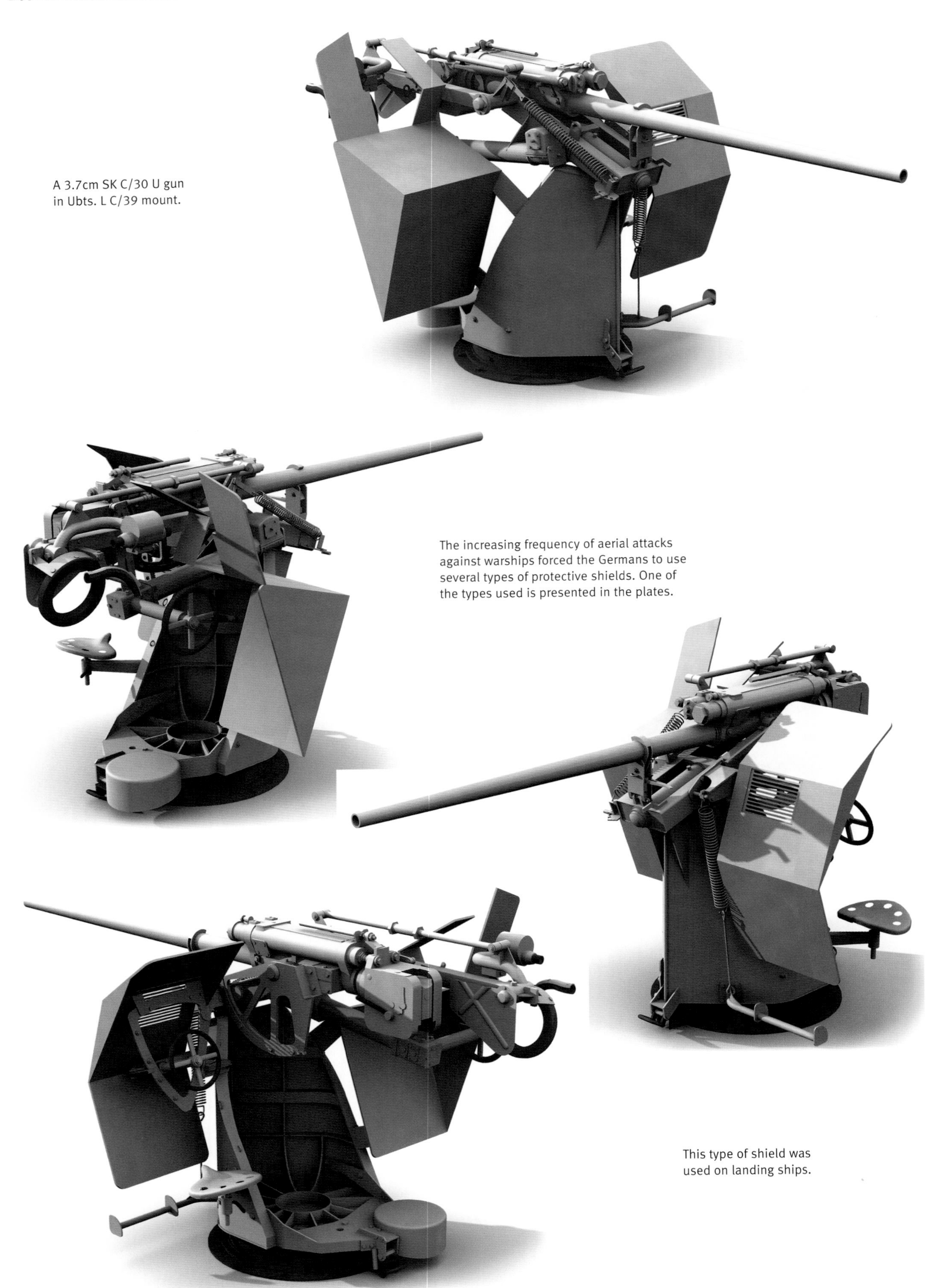

A 3.7cm SK C/30 U gun in Ubts. L C/39 mount.

The increasing frequency of aerial attacks against warships forced the Germans to use several types of protective shields. One of the types used is presented in the plates.

This type of shield was used on landing ships.

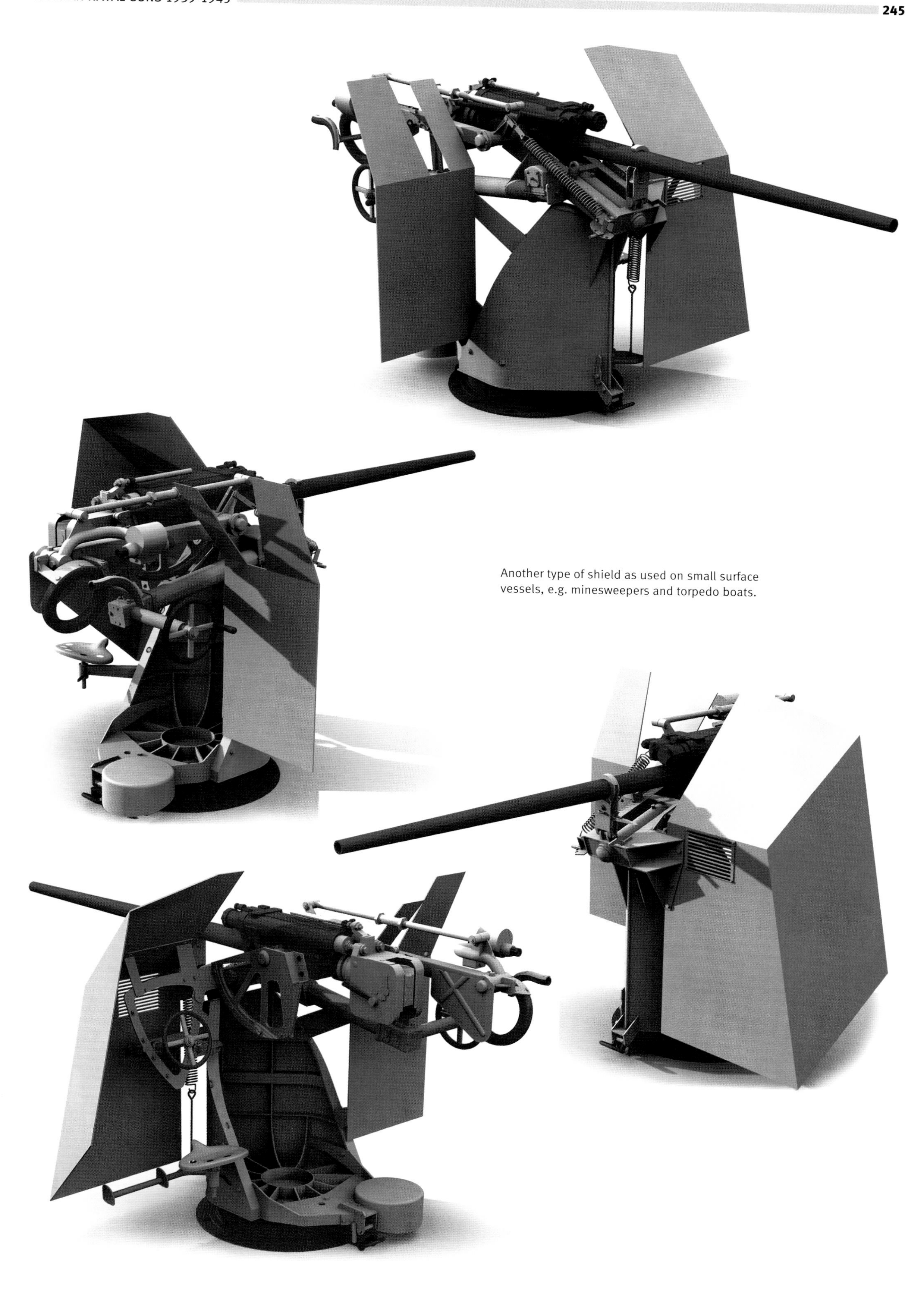

Another type of shield as used on small surface vessels, e.g. minesweepers and torpedo boats.

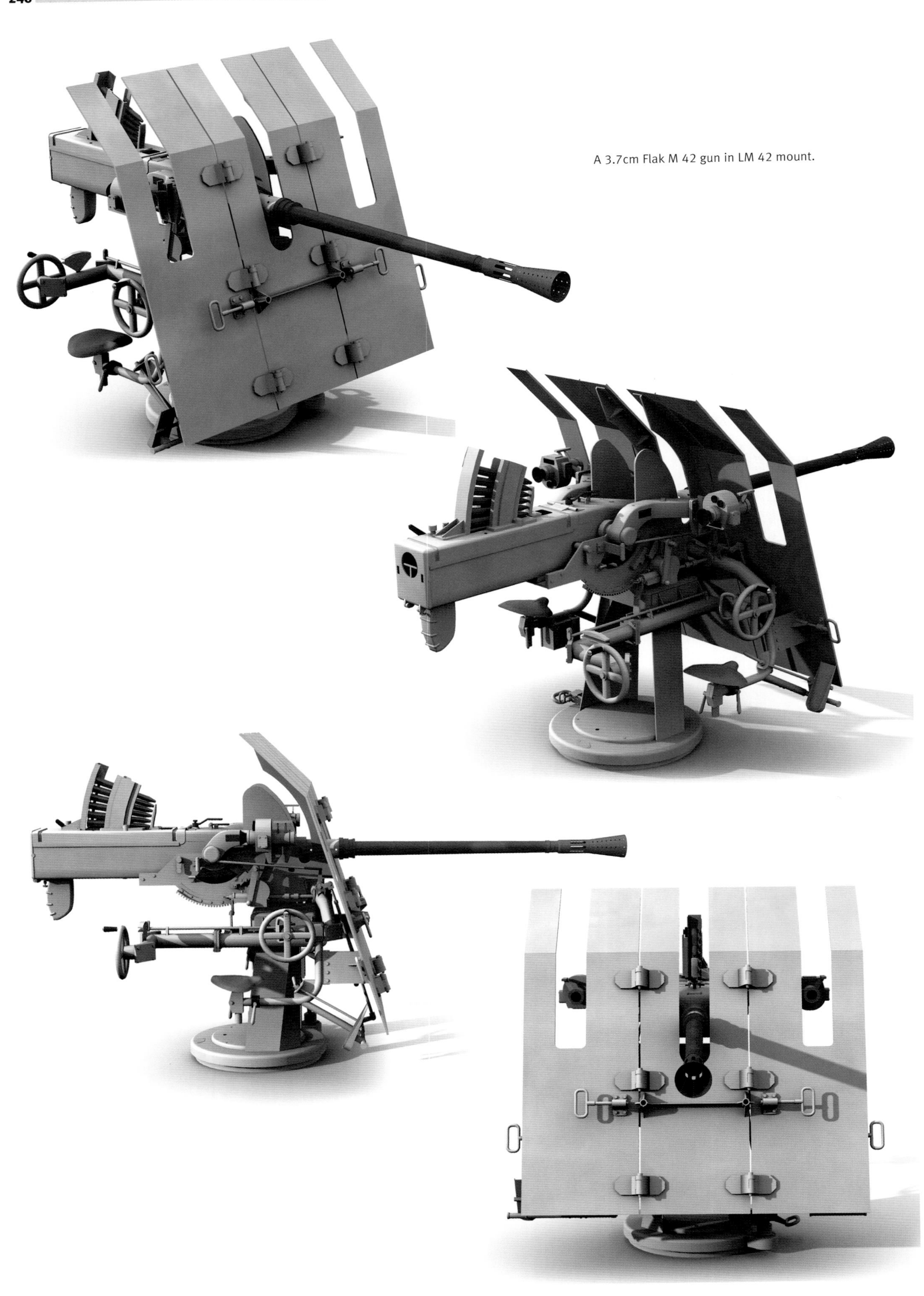

A 3.7cm Flak M 42 gun in LM 42 mount.

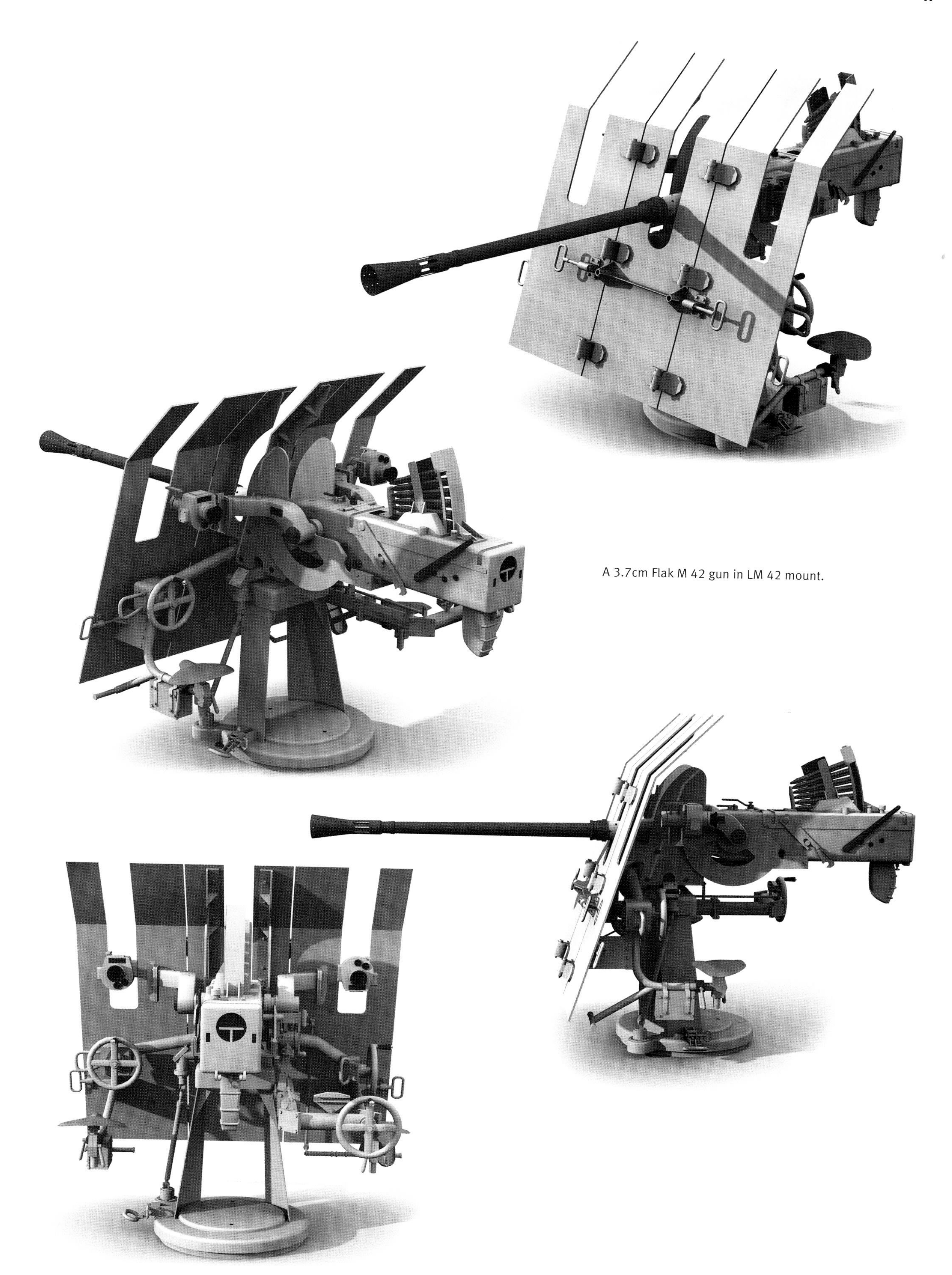

A 3.7cm Flak M 42 gun in LM 42 mount.

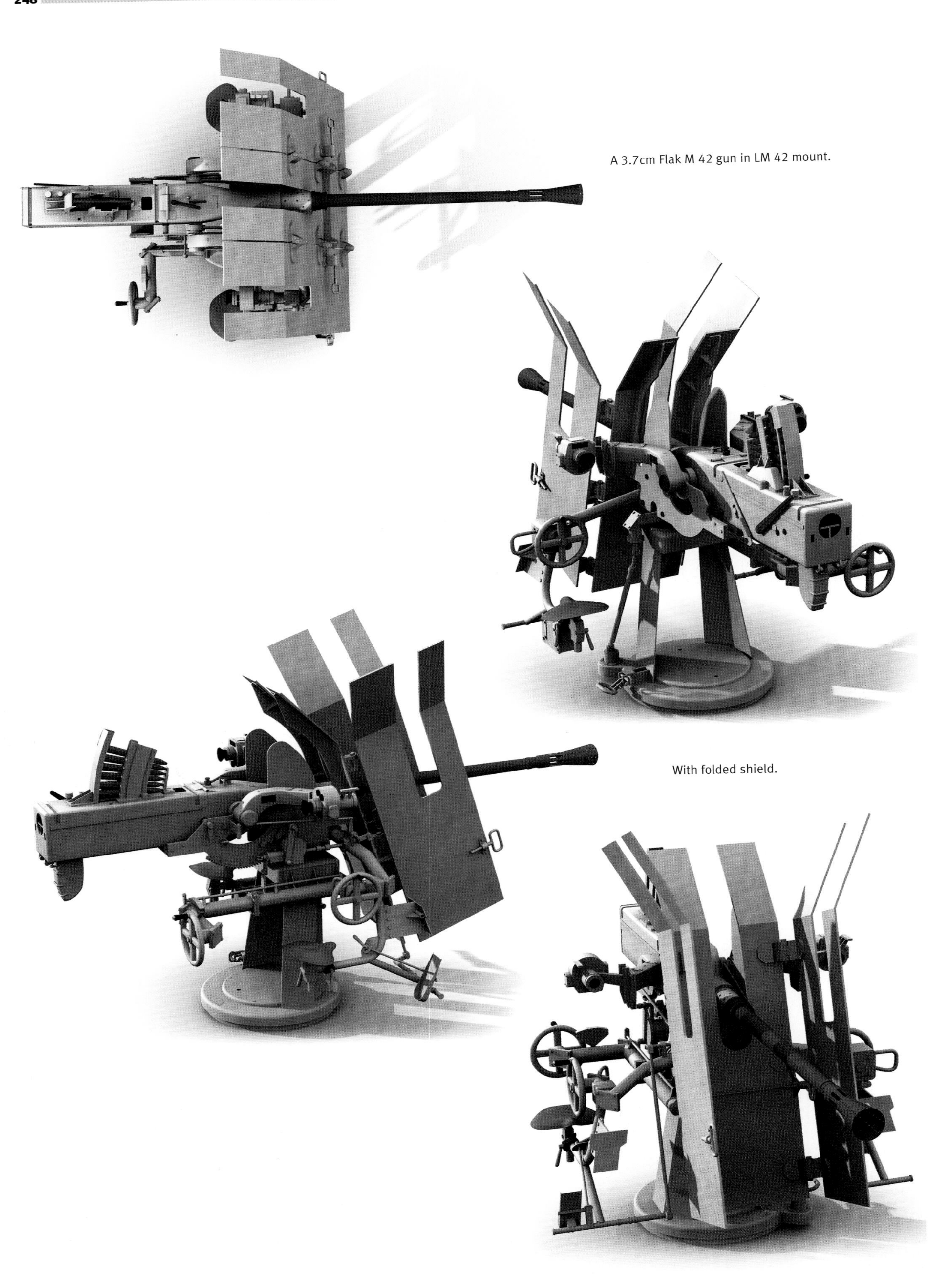

A 3.7cm Flak M 42 gun in LM 42 mount.

With folded shield.

THE 8.8cm SK C/30 GUN IN SINGLE PEDESTAL MOUNTS

Two such 88mm guns will be described here. The first is the SK C/30 in the MPL C/30 mount, with its submarine variant the SK C/30 U, and the second is the SK C/35 in the Ubts L C/35 mount. The former, on a biaxially-stabilised mount, was for surface vessels while the latter was for U-boats.

Development of the SK C/30 began in 1930 and three years later the gun began to enter service aboard smaller Kriegsmarine ships such as minesweepers, Flak ships, sloops and tenders. Although the SK C/30 U had been designed for submarines in 1933, by the later years of the Second World War U-boats had largely abandoned gun actions on the surface, and these weapons were removed and used to arm small transport vessels.

The London Naval Conference, which closed on 22 April 1930, exerted a profound influence on the development of German submarine guns. According to the treaty signed there, 4in (102mm) guns could be mounted on boats up to 1,000 tons, 5in (127mm) on boats up to 2,000 tons and 6in (152mm) only on boats up to 2,800 tons.

The SK C/35 gun was designed for the first Type VII U-boats in 1935, after the Anglo-German naval agreement gave the green light to the expansion of the

Above: The 8.8cm SK C/35 in Ubts C/35 single mount from a German U-boat on show in a museum. *(A Jarski collection)*

Left: The 8.8cm SK C/35 in Ubts C/35 single mount aboard Type VII U-boat. Note the muzzle stopper. *(A Jarski collection)*

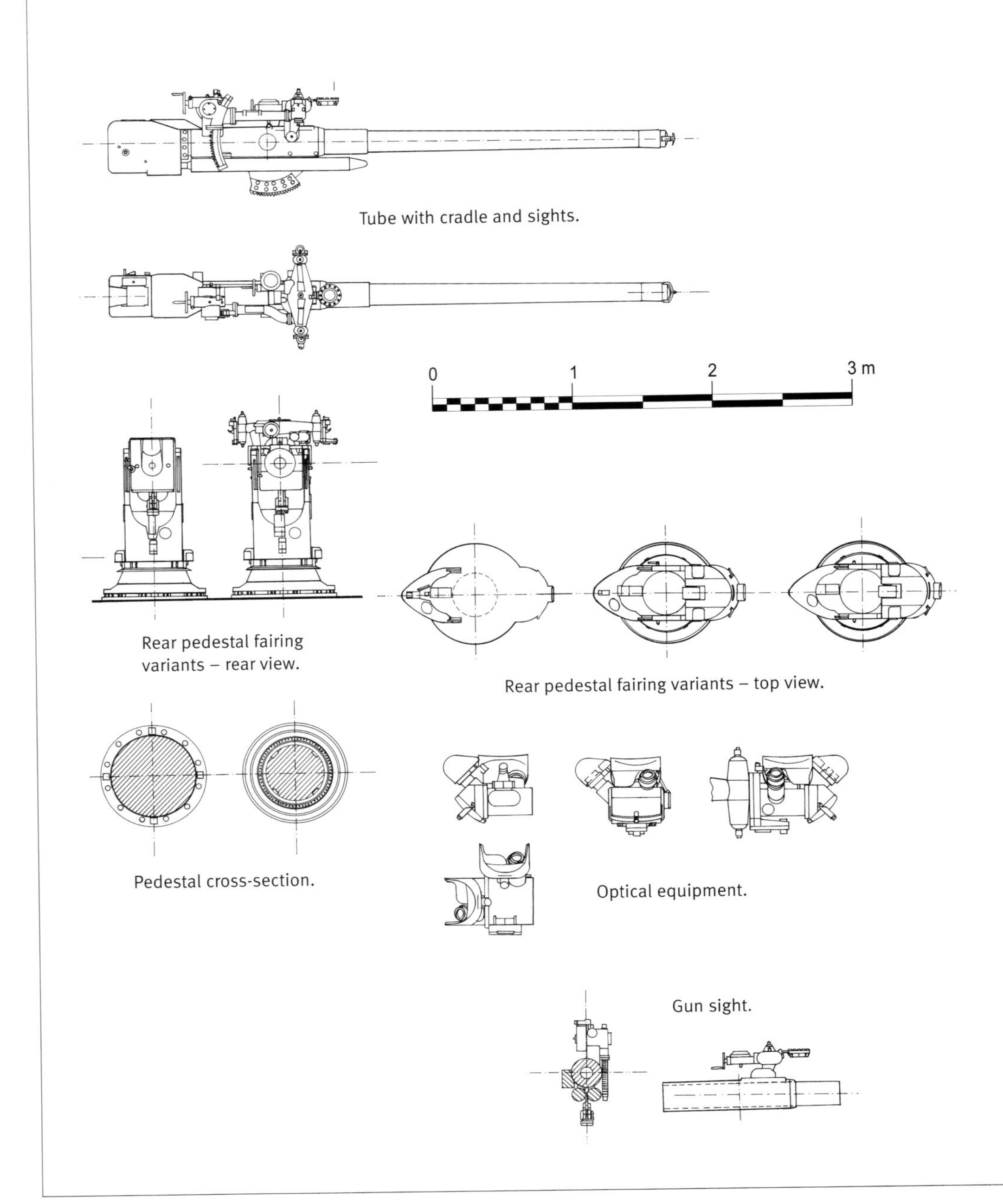

Below: Preparing ready ammunition aboard a Type VII U-boat. The sailor at left is holding a container for a round, while the round itself, thickly greased to ensure watertightness, can be seen on the right. *(ADM)*

Kriegsmarine in general and the building of U-boats in particular. Operational experience during the Spanish Civil War allowed all the gun's teething problems to be dealt with before it went into series production. Guns for submarines required higher-quality steel in their manufacture than surface-ship weapons, to withstand both the force of the water when running submerged and salt-water corrosion. Improvements in steel production, gun-founding techniques and machine tools were very important for naval armaments in this period, allowing such advances as multi-part gun tubes, improved mounts with wider arcs of fire, and lighter components, which reduced the overall weight of the gun.

The 8.8cm SK C/30 and KM41 guns

The barrel of this gun was 45 calibres long, and it was mounted on the MPL C/30 single pedestal mount.

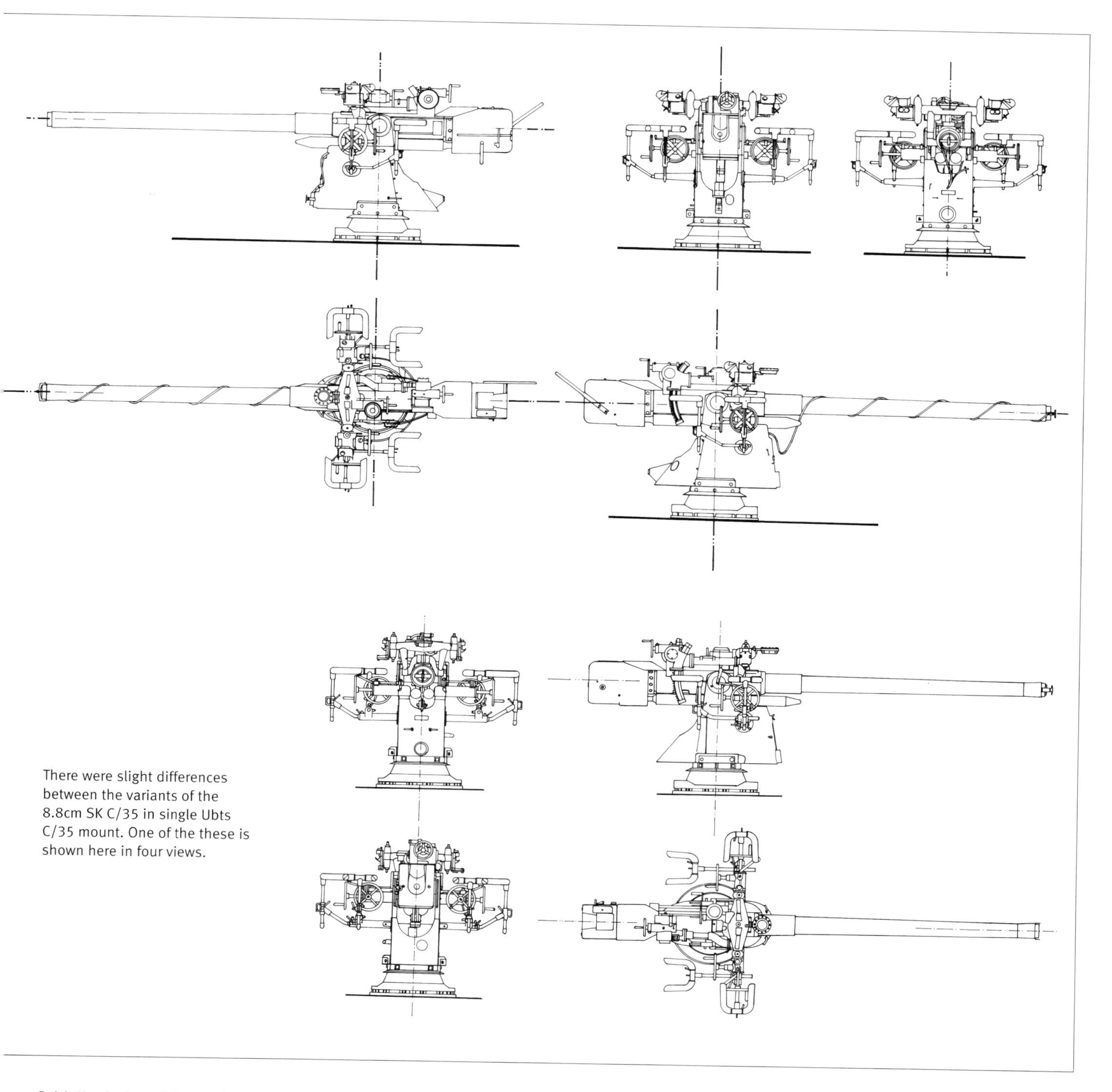

There were slight differences between the variants of the 8.8cm SK C/35 in single Ubts C/35 mount. One of the these is shown here in four views.

Initially designed for surface ships, with its biaxially-stabilised mount, in late 1930 its suitability for submarine service was investigated, with several adapted guns being tested by the Ubootwaffe. Experience with these fed into the design of the new SK C/35 U and KM41 (Ubts Flak L C/31) guns. The main difference between these two was the design of the tube and breech. The SK C/30 had a loose-fitting barrel liner and a falling-block breech, whereas the KM41 had a monobloc tube and a horizontally-sliding breech.

The 8.8cm MPL C/30 pedestal mount

Originally designed for 88mm guns aboard smaller vessels, this mount was later used for 105mm guns. The tables below give the data for the MPL C/30 biaxially-stabilised pedestal mount and the triaxially-stabilised Flak LM 41 mount.

The 8.8cm SK C/30 gun (figures for the KM41 in square brackets)

Calibre:	88mm
Weight of gun:	1,230kg [960kg]
Overall length:	3,960mm
Length bore:	3,706mm
Length chamber:	530mm
Volume chamber:	3.67l
Length rifling:	3,109mm
Grooves:	32 (1.05mm x 5.4mm)
Weight projectile:	9kg
Propellant charge:	2.82kg of RP C/38
Muzzle velocity:	790mps
Working pressure:	2,750kg/cm^2
Approximate service live:	7,000 effective rounds
Maximum range:	14,175m at 43.5°
Maximum ceiling:	9,700m at 70°
Rate of fire:	15rpm

Below: Several photos of the 8.8cm SK C/35 gun in Ubts C/35 single mount on board *U 570*, captured by the British. She was subsequently commissioned into the Royal Navy as HMS *Graph*. *(RAFM)*

The 8.8cm Flak LM 41 pedestal mount

(the successor to the MPL C/30)

Overall (mount and gun):	4,750kg
Training arc:	360°
Depression/elevation:	−10°/+75°

The 8.8cm SK C/35 in single mounts

Originally intended to arm just the first series of Type VIIA U-boats in the Ubts L C/35 U (Ubts L C/36) mount, problems with the new SK C/32 gun and its Ubts L C/32 U (Ubts L C/36) mount meant that it was used aboard later Type VIIs and other classes of U-boat. It also armed Type 40 minesweepers. The gun had a 45-calibre monobloc tube and a horizontally-sliding breech.

The 8.8cm SK C/35 gun

Calibre:	88mm
Weight of gun:	776kg
Overall length:	3,985mm
Length bore:	3,731mm
Length chamber:	348.7mm
Volume chamber:	2.49l
Length rifling:	3,313mm
Grooves:	28 (1.2mm x 6.4mm)
Weight projectile:	9kg
Propellant charge:	2.1kg of RP C/40N (3.6/1.07)
Muzzle velocity:	700mps
Working pressure:	2,400kg/cm^2
Approximate service life:	12,000 effective rounds
Maximum range;	11,950m at 30°
Rate of fire:	15-20rpm

Left and above: Two photos of the 8.8cm SK C/35 in single Ubts C/35 mount aboard a U-boat at high speed on the surface. The design of this version had to take into consideration the exposed position of the gun and permanent flooding by sea water. *(CAW collection)*

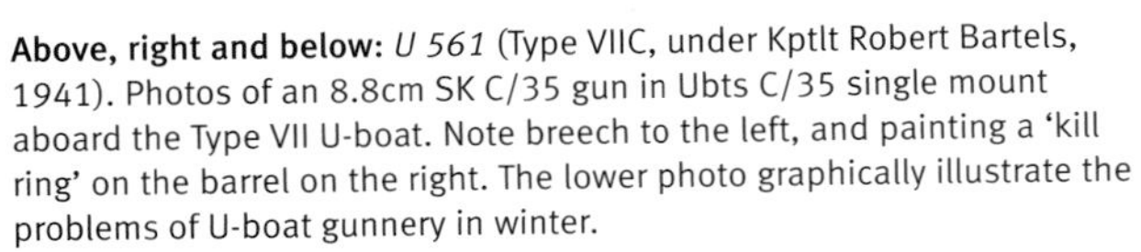

Above, right and below: *U 561* (Type VIIC, under Kptlt Robert Bartels, 1941). Photos of an 8.8cm SK C/35 gun in Ubts C/35 single mount aboard the Type VII U-boat. Note breech to the left, and painting a 'kill ring' on the barrel on the right. The lower photo graphically illustrate the problems of U-boat gunnery in winter.

Left: An 8.8cm SK C/35 gun in Ubts C/35 single mount on board a Type VII U-boat, moored alongside a depot ship in one of the French ports. Note the details of the gun. *(CAW collection)*

Above and below: More photos of an 8.8cm SK C/35 gun in Ubts C/35 single mount taken on board a Type VII U-boat.

Left: The 8.8cm SK C/35 in single Ubts C/35 mount on board a Type VII U-boat on the surface. Heavy weather frequently encountered in the North Atlantic practically ruled out any gun actions, and so the later Type VIIs (Type VIIC/41) had no guns to eliminate drag when submerged. *(CAW collection)*

Above: The 8.8cm SK C/35 gun in Ubts C/35 single mount aboard *U 69* (Type VIIC). *(CAW collection)*

Left: The 8.8cm SK C/35 gun in Ubts C/35 single mount aboard *U 30* (Type VIIA). *(CAW collection)*

Below: Type VII U-boat firing her 8.8cm SK C/35 gun in Ubts C/35 single mount. *(CAW collection)*

Right: Type VII U-boats in their base. The 8.8cm SK C/35 in single Ubts C/35 mount, visible on the right, was the Type VII's main surface gun. *(CAW collection)*

Left: The 8.8cm SK C/35 gun in Ubts C/35 single mount aboard various Type VII U-boats. *(CAW)*

Right: The 8.8cm SK C/35 gun in Ubts C/35 single mount aboard a Type VIIB U-boat. *(A Jarski collection)*

Left: An 8.8cm SK C/35 gun in Ubts C/35 single mount aboard a Type VII U-boat. *(CAW)*

The 8.8cm MPL C/30 pedestal mount

Overall weight (mount and gun):	5,760kg
Maximum training speed (manual):	1.3°/sec
Maximum elevating speed (manual):	1.3°/sec
Training arc:	360°
Depression/elevation:	–10°/+80°
Shield armour:	10-15mm*

* No shield on submarines

The 8.8cm Ubts L C/35 U mount

Developed at the same time as the SK/35 gun, this mount needed to be strong and streamlined enough to be mounted on a submarine's deck, and reliable enough for long ocean patrols. The designers produced a simple, hard-wearing manually-operated pedestal mount, with fittings such as the sights and the gunners' safety harnesses, that could be removed before the boat dived.

The 8.8cm Ubts L C/35 U pedestal mount

Overall weight (mount and gun):	2,425kg
Maximum training speed (manual):	1.5°/sec
Maximum elevating speed (manual):	1.5°/sec
Training arc:	360°
Depression/elevation:	–10°/+30°

THE 8.8cm SK C/30 GUN IN TWIN PEDESTAL MOUNTS

The light cruiser *Köln* was the first ship to be armed with 88mm guns in twin mountings, receiving a pair of triaxially-stabilised open LC/32 mounts with 8.8cm SK C/32 L/76 guns. The mounts were positioned on the superstructure aft, between the funnel and 'B' turret. The absence of a shield made the crew's life easier in peacetime, but would have been fatal in wartime. *Köln*'s sister-ships were temporarily fitted with older 88mm guns in single MPL C/13 mounts.

At the same time, development began of the second naval 88mm gun, the SK/31, with a longer (78-calibre) tube. These were tested aboard the 'pocket battleship' *Deutschland*, the mounts having a shield for the first time. A new mount, the C/37, was later designed for the 'M' class cruisers, but it was eventually abandoned.

The 8.8cm SK C/31 gun

Developed by Rheinmetall-Borsig, this gun had a monobloc outer tube with a loose-fitted barrel liner and a falling-block breech, the tube weighing 915kg in total. The *Deutschland* was armed with these guns on three Dopp. L C/31 twin pedestal mounts, while her sister-ships *Admiral Scheer* and *Admiral Graf Spee* had different guns, the 8.8cm C/32 in twin triaxially-stabilised L C/31 mounts. In all three ships, the three mounts were positioned on the superstructure, one each side of the funnel, each training 190°, and the third aft, above 'B' turret, training 360°. These guns were all later replaced with new 105mm

The 8.8cm SK C/31 gun

Calibre:	88mm
Weight of gun:	4,255kg
Overall length:	6,870mm
Length bore:	6,341mm
Length chamber:	530mm
Volume chamber:	6.4l
Length rifling:	5,422mm
Grooves:	28 (1.2mm x 5.97mm)
Weight projectile:	18.5kg
Propellant charge:	4.53kg of RP C/32
Muzzle velocity:	790mps
Working pressure:	3,100kg/cm^2
Approximate service life:	1,500 effective rounds
Maximum range:	17,800m at 45°
Maximum ceiling:	13,300m at 80°
Rate of fire:	15-20rpm

Above: 8.8cm SK C/32 L76 guns in triaxially-stabilised C/32 twin mounts (without shields as yet) were tested aboard the light cruiser *Köln*. They were mounted between the after superstructure and 'B' turret. The experience gained in these trials was the foundation for the technical requirements for the next-generation of naval anti-aircraft guns. *(W Danielewicz collection)*

Right: 8.8cm SK C/31 guns in a Dopp. L C/31 triaxially-stabilised twin pedestal mount fitted amidships aboard the light cruiser *Leipzig*. She had two amidships, on either side, and one behind 'B' turret. *(A Jarski collection)*

Below: The first ship to get the production 8.8cm SK C/31 in Dopp. L C/31 triaxially-stabilised twin pedestal mounts was the light cruiser *Leipzig*. The gun mounts were fitted amidships and forward of 'B' turret. *(M. Cieślak collection)*

Right: The breeches of the 8.8cm SK C/31 guns in a Dopp. L C/31 twin pedestal mount. *(Author's collection)*

Above: Right side elevation of the prototype 8.8cm SK C/31 in a Dopp. L C/31 twin pedestal mount manufactured by Rheinmetall-Borsig. *(Author's collection)*

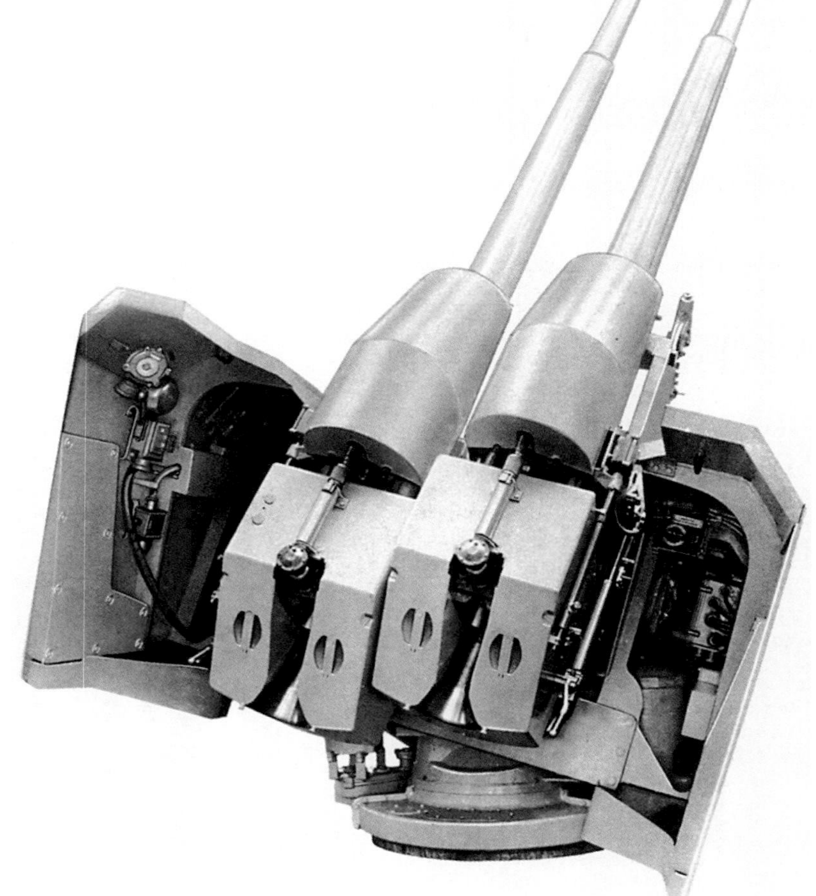

Right: Prototype of the 8.8cm SK C/31 in a Dopp. L C/31 pedestal twin mount with barrels elevated and with simulated list. *(Author's collection)*

Above: Prototype of the 8.8cm SK C/31 in a Dopp. L C/31 twin pedestal mount, rear view. *(Author's collection)*

Above: Prototype of the 8.8cm SK C/31 in a Dopp. L C/31 twin pedestal mount with barrels elevated. *(Author's collection)*

Above: Prototype of the 8.8cm SK C/31 in a Dopp. L C/31 twin pedestal mount with barrels elevated. *(Author's collection)*

Right: Rear view of the prototype of the 8.8cm SK C/31 in a Dopp. L C/31 pedestal twin mount, used in testing triaxial stabilisation. *(Author's collection)*

Right: One of the 8.8cm SK C/31 in Dopp. L C/31 triaxially-stabilised twin pedestal mounts aboard the light cruiser *Nürnberg*. The port gun mount is partially visible below the floatplane. *(A Jarski collection)*

Below: The 8.8cm SK C/31 guns in Dopp. L C/31 twin pedestal mounts were mainly installed in light cruisers. This photo shows such a gun at the moment of firing aboard *Nürnberg*. *(A Jarski collection)*

weapons, *Admiral Graf Spee* receiving hers in 1938, *Admiral Scheer* in September 1939. *Deutschland* got her new guns a little earlier. Some German-language sources say that only the guns themselves were replaced, the original mounts and shields remaining as they were. *Scharnhorst* and *Gneisenau* were scheduled to receive SK C/31s, but the new 105mm gun was developed in the meantime and they were armed with that instead.

The 8.8cm Dopp. L C/31 twin mount

Overall weight (mount and gun):	27,300kg (in some sources 27,805kg)
Distance between gun axes:	680mm
Recoil distance:	410mm
Maximum elevating speed:	10°/sec (powered), 3.6°/sec (manual)
Maximum training speed:	2.5°/sec
Training arc:	360°
Depression/elevation:	–10°/+80°
Shield armour:	10-15mm

The 8.8cm SK C/32 gun

This gun entered service in 1930, aboard the *Köln*. She was originally to have been armed with older 8.8cm SK C/25 guns in Dopp. L C/25 twin mounts, but in trials their training and elevation was too slow against modern aircraft, so they were replaced with newer 8.8cm SK C/32 guns on Dopp. L C/32 twin mounts.

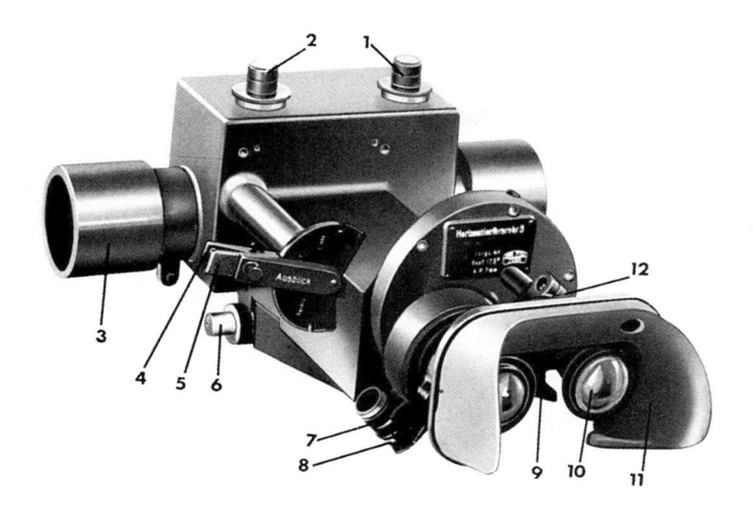

Above: Traverse optical telescope 3 (Horizontierfernrohr 3). *(Author's collection)*

The 8.8cm Dopp. L C/32 twin mount

Overall weight (mount and guns):	23,650kg
Mount weight	6,275kg
Sighting equipment weight:	745kg
Electric power drive weight:	1,280kg
Shield weight:	5,830kg
Maximum training speed:	10°/sec (powered), 3.6°/sec (manual)
Maximum elevating speed:	10°/sec
Training arc:	360°
Depression/elevation:	–10°/+80°
Shield thickness:	Front 12mm; sides 10mm

Below: Layout of gun-laying handwheels. *(Author's collection)*

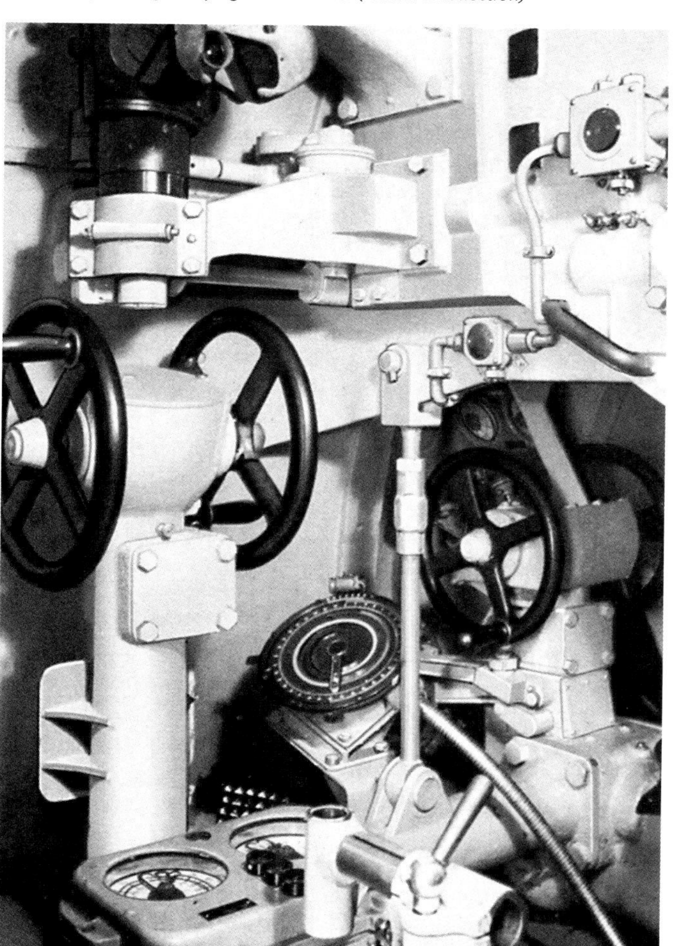

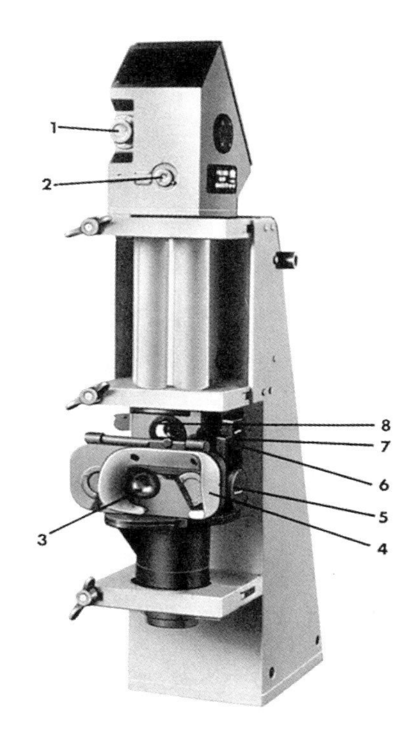

Above: The variable-power sighting periscope C/21 (Pankratisches Winkel-Zielfernrohr C/21), used with the 8.8cm SK C/31. *(Author's collection)*

Below: The 8.8cm SK C/31 in a Dopp. L C/31 twin pedestal mount aboard *Nürnberg*. *(A Jarski collection)*

Above: *Leipzig* had the 8.8cm SK C/31 guns mounted in Dopp. L C/31 twin pedestal mounts, seen here amidships. *(A Jarski collection)*

Compared to the SK C/31, these guns were made of inferior materials. They armed the cruisers *Köln*, *Leipzig* and *Nürnberg* on triaxially-stabilised Dopp. L C/32 twin mounts, although as these ships' careers progressed, they were gradually replaced by 105mm guns. The SK C/32 had a 925kg monobloc tube with loose-fitting barrel liner, 76 calibres long (two calibres shorter than the SK C/31), and a falling-block breech. The C/32 mount resembled the C/31, but was lighter (at 23,650kg) and the shield was thinner (at 10-12mm).

The 8.8cm SK C/32 gun

Calibre:	88mm
Weight of gun:	3,640kg
Overall length:	6,690mm
Length bore:	6,340.5mm
Length chamber:	530.7mm
Volume chamber:	3.67l
Length rifling	5,745.5mm
Grooves:	28 (1.2mm x 6.4mm)
Weight projectile:	15.2kg
Length projectile:	932mm
Propellant charge:	2.93kg of RP C/38 (4.5/1.5)
Muzzle velocity:	950mps
Working pressure:	3,150kg/cm^2
Approximate service life:	3,200 effective rounds
Maximum range:	17,200m at 45°
Maximum ceiling:	12,400m at 80°
Rate of fire:	15-20rpm

The 8.8cm L/45 gun in MPL C/13 single pedestal mounts

The 8.8cm L/45 quick-firing gun was a development of the L/35 gun used aboard torpedo-boats and smaller craft of the Kaiser's navy. The new gun was mounted in the MPL C/13 single pedestal mount, and was introduced around 1915. The first time they were employed after the war was in the 1920s, when they were installed on board the light cruiser *Emden*, then on the *Königsberg*, and finally – until they were replaced by more modern models – aboard the *Deutschland* class 'pocket battleships'. During the later 1930s they were gradually phased out as newer weapons entered service, and in 1939, when the war began, they were finally declared obsolete.

Above: The 8.8cm L/45 gun in an MPL C/13 single pedestal mount, aboard the light cruiser *Königsberg* aft of the stern superstructure, in front of 'B' turret.

Above: An 8.8cm L/45 gun in a MPL C/13 single pedestal mount aboard *Königsberg*. Note the crewman operating the rangefinder in the foreground.

The 8.8cm L/45 SK quick-firing gun

Calibre:	88mm
Weight of gun:	2,500kg
Overall length:	?
Length barrel:	3,960mm (45 calibres)
Weight projectile:	9kg
Length projectile:	385.5mm
Propellant charge:	2.35kg of RP C/38
Muzzle velocity:	790–890mps
Working pressure:	2,750kg/cm2
Approximate service life:	400 effective rounds
Maximum range:	101,694m at 25°
Maximum ceiling:	11,790m at 80°
Elevation/depression:	-10°/70°

Right: Cleaning an 8.8cm L/45 gun on board *Königsberg*. Three crewmen are inserting the pull-through from the chamber end under the watchful eye of a petty officer. Note the bathtub filled with sand and the canvas sheet under the breech, protecting the deck from the bore-cleaning solution dripping from the gun. *(CAW collection)*

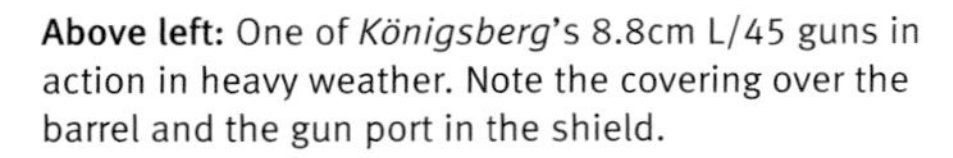

Above left: One of *Königsberg*'s 8.8cm L/45 guns in action in heavy weather. Note the covering over the barrel and the gun port in the shield.

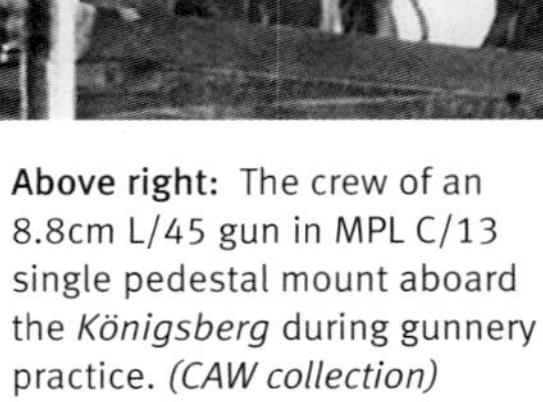

Above right: The crew of an 8.8cm L/45 gun in MPL C/13 single pedestal mount aboard the *Königsberg* during gunnery practice. *(CAW collection)*

Above: 8.8cm L/45 gun in MPL C/13 single pedestal mount.

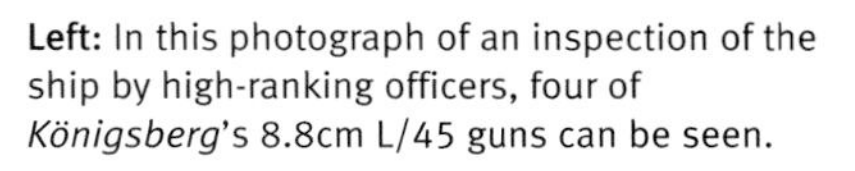

Left: In this photograph of an inspection of the ship by high-ranking officers, four of *Königsberg*'s 8.8cm L/45 guns can be seen.

15

LIGHT ANTI-AIRCRAFT GUNS

INTRODUCTION

The history of the development of German light anti-aircraft guns was directly influenced by the restrictions imposed by the Treaty of Versailles. Forbidden to design and build such weapons in their own country, some of the designers from Krupp of Essen – Germany's largest armaments concern – went abroad to work for other companies in the same field. The best example was the Swedish firm of Bofors, which hired numerous German designers. An agreement signed in 1930 between AB Bofors and Krupp extended their previously-established co-operation to the development and manufacture of 75mm anti-aircraft guns for the German Army. The programme included 75mm and 80mm weapons for the Swedish armed forces as well. During this development work, a 40mm gun was also designed, which was to become one of the best anti-aircraft weapons in history and remains in service with some armies even today. The development of lighter cannon was carried out in a similar way, demand for such weapons being driven by the rapid development of combat aircraft. As the speed and altitude of aircraft increased, existing anti-aircraft weapons were unable to destroy them. New weapons were therefore needed, with two principal features: a higher rate of fire and an increased effective ceiling. At the same time, fire-control systems for such guns were developed – these had to be able to track a fast-flying target and supply appropriate data to the gunners, who would then shoot it down. Bearing in mind how rapidly aircraft performance was improving at this time, this was far from being an easy task.

Using experience gained with anti-aircraft weapons in the First World War, in 1930 Rheinmetall began production of a 37mm automatic cannon, designated the Flak 18.[1] Beginning in 1936, improved versions – the Flak 36 and then also the Flak 37 – entered production. At the same time as these three Army weapons, Krupp and Rheinmetall were also developing a similar weapon for the Navy, the 3.7cm SK ('Schnellfeuerkanone' – quick-firing gun) C/30, for shipboard use. To allow accurate fire from a rolling ship, the gun had to be fitted with a transversal stabilisation system. It also required new target-tracking equipment, new sights and even seats for the gunners! As aircraft performance was improving so rapidly at this time, the sights, mounts, magazines etc, were all designed to allow them to be easily updated after the weapons had entered service. In the early 1930s, target-tracking was still by optical rangefinder. It was not until radar had come into general use that mounting it on small-calibre anti-aircraft mounts suggested itself.

Eventually, the 3.7cm SK C/30 became the first series-built model with a triaxially-stabilised mount. In 1939 the Kriegsmarine high command ordered Rheinmetall to develop a new 37mm anti-aircraft cannon based on that design to arm new classes of warship. This entered series production in 1942 as the 3.7cm Flak M 42.

In 1944, a programme for increasing the anti-aircraft defences of German warships was initiated. This called for new 37mm guns, including 3.7cm M 42s, to be fitted aboard smaller vessels, including submarines. The battleships and cruisers were supposed to be armed with the new Flak 43/M, but this weapon never went into production and the 4cm Flak 28 developed by Bofors took its place.

Above: The land version of 4cm Flak 28 Bofors gun used by the Wehrmacht. The naval variant used on most Kriegsmarine warships and auxiliary vessels was derived from this model. *(A Jarski collection)*

The history of the development of the first 20mm anti-aircraft cannon is very interesting and will be briefly described here. It began with the Becker gun of 1917 which was installed on a 'rotating pedestal mount'. This was in fact a large cartwheel lying on the ground with the gun mounted on the 'axle'. The gunner rested his back against a special cradle, lying flat when higher angles of elevation were required, and traversing the mount with his feet. This simple system was the first in a rapidly-evolving series of anti-aircraft guns, the development of which was driven by the equally rapid development of aircraft. In 1928 Rheinmetall designed the 2cm Flak 28 recoil-operated autocannon, fed from fifteen-round magazines. This was soon adapted for naval use as the 2cm

1 The designation was supposed to suggest that the gun had been designed before the signing of the Treaty of Versailles, which prohibited Germans from developing anti-aircraft artillery.

MG C/30 L, on the SL 30 L pedestal mount and firing from a 100-round magazine. The mount turned out to be a problem, as it did not have a pivoted cradle fork, forcing the gunner to crouch uncomfortably when firing at higher angles of elevation, adversely affecting accuracy particularly in prolonged engagements. They were introduced into Reichswehr and Reichsmarine service respectively in 1928.

Initially, in order to evade Treaty restrictions, Rheinmetall's design and production work had been transferred to the Swiss company Solothurn. They came up with various models of 20mm anti-aircraft gun, originally known as 'Maschinenkanone' (autocannon), and then renamed 'Maschinengewehr' (machine gun). These were designed ST 4, ST 52 and MG C/30.[1] They used the same ammunition as later German designs of the same calibre (i.e. Flak 30 and Flak 38), so they remained in service until the end of the Second World War. The claim that the Flak 30 was just the MG C/30 under a different designation is incorrect. In fact it was an improved version of the gun, developed entirely separately and initially intended as an aircraft weapon designated the MG C/30 L. The MG C/30 was developed specifically for naval use. After it had been introduced aboard warships, it was decided to also produce a land-based variant for coastal defence units.

Intervention in the Spanish Civil War provided a perfect opportunity for the German forces to test their new weapons under combat conditions. The Flak 30 was one such weapon, and its performance was considered quite good, although its (theoretical) rate of fire of 280 rounds per minute was found to be too low. Therefore Mauser-Werke was instructed to redesign the Flak 30 to increase the rate of fire. Several other improvements were also required, including the ability to use the same ammunition as other guns of the same calibre. The prototype of this modified gun was designated the 2cm Flak 38, and after successful trials it was adopted by the Army. A special variant for mountain and airborne units was also developed, designated the 2cm Gebirgsflak 38. However, the most effective variant of this weapon was to be the 2cm Flakvierling 38, a common mount for four guns giving a nominal rate of fire of 4 x 150 rounds per minute. Combat experience proved this to be a deadly weapon and it was used in all theatres of war until the fall of the Third Reich. Its effectiveness is shown by the fact that more than 18,000 such guns were built.

Above: A captured 40mm Bofors gun. The Germans installed some of those guns aboard auxiliary Kriegsmarine vessels. But due to the lack of a triaxial stabilisation system they were soon mostly withdrawn from service. *(CAW collection)*

Top left: One of the most popular anti-aircraft guns in German naval service – the 3.7cm SK C/30 installed in a triaxially-stabilised Dopp. L C/30 mount. *(CAW collection)*

Below: The second most popular German anti-aircraft cannon – the 2cm MG C/30. There were several variants in different mounts in use. The photograph shows the MG C/30 in the SL 30 mount with crew. *(CAW collection)*

1 Designations stand for ST = Solothurn, MK = Maschinenkanone (autocannon), MG = Maschinengewehr (machine gun).

16

THE 4cm FLAK 28 BOFORS GUN

One of the most widely-used and effective anti-aircraft guns of the Second World War was a joint design by the Swedish firm of Bofors and the German Krupp. Development began in 1922 when the Swedish Navy purchased some British 2pdr pompom guns from Vickers. These were soon found not to meet requirements, and Bofors was asked to develop a new gun. The contract signed in 1928 required the company to design and build a prototype, which the Navy would pay for whether the gun was acceptable or not. The issue of possible series production would be agreed on separately. It should be noted that at the same time Bofors had developed a semi-automatic 57mm gun (Luftvärnskanon 57mm/L55 M/89 B and M/24) intended primarily as the main armament for destroyers (the gun had a barrel constructed according to a Nordenfelt patent). The lighter gun was developed using some of the engineering solutions from this design.

The first tests on the new light gun began in 1930, full-automatic burst fire first being tested on 17 October that year. The tests were unsuccessful and further development was in doubt, but at that point Krupp purchased a third of the shares in Bofors and German engineers began a large-scale modernisation of the Swedish factory. While this was being done, development work on the 40mm gun continued in secret, allowing them to gain more time and ensure better security from foreign intelligence services. A new prototype was tested on 10 November 1931 and 21 March 1932. This time the tests were successful and after some minor improvements the gun went into series production in 1936.

In all the countries that adopted it, the gun confirmed its high quality. In fact, it provoked considerable interest among the naval powers of the world,

The prototype Aktiebolaget Bofors 40mm gun as tested

Weight gun:	1,725kg
Weight propellant charge:	0.95kg
Muzzle velocity:	902.2mps
Maximum range:	8,500m
Training arc:	360°
Depression/elevation:	−5°/+90°

Below: A Flak 28 Bofors gun. Details of the gun and its mount can clearly be seen. This is an early variant without the protective shield. *(CAW collection)*

Left: Crew of a German Flak 28 Bofors gun at action stations. *(CAW collection)*

and the British and Americans began to gather information about the operational use of the new weapon. In 1937 the Americans sent their Military Attaché in London, Colonel R R Studler, to Sweden to obtain as much information about the Bofors gun as possible. At test-firing displays on 18 and 20 August, Studler saw for himself how the weapon performed. Limited combat service in the Spanish Civil War only confirmed the gun's quality, and it quickly became the most sought-after anti-aircraft gun in the world. Nevertheless, the gun only saw full-scale combat service in 1939-40 with the German military. This successful design encouraged German engineers to start work on a new version with a slightly larger calibre of 45mm, but it never progressed beyond the stage of a wooden model.

Austria had been one of the countries to purchase a licence to produce the 40mm Bofors gun, and after the 1938 Anschluss the German Army took over the first batch of twenty-four finished guns, as well as a couple

Above: A Flak 28 Bofors gun. Details of the gun and its mount can clearly be seen. This is an early variant without the protective shield. *(CAW collection)*

Right: Training in the operation of a Flak 28 Bofors guns aboard Kriegsmarine auxiliary vessels at bases. The photograph above is notable for two reasons. Firstly there are no sights installed on the gun. Secondly the crews are training in gas-attack conditions wearing gas masks. A support for the gun's barrel when at cruising stations is installed forward of the gun. *(CAW collection)*

Right: One of the measures called for in the programme of increasing anti-aircraft armament of Kriegsmarine vessels was installation of 4cm Flak 28 Bofors guns on smaller vessels, like the KFK visible here. *(CAW collection)*

of dozen more at various stages of completion.[1] On 15 May 1939 the Germans introduced the designation 4cm Flak 28 (Bofors) for the incomplete Austrian guns. These guns, as well as those captured later from conquered countries, were mostly assigned to the Army and the Luftwaffe.

The Bofors design came to the attention of German engineers for a second time after the defeat of Poland. It was discovered that the Swedish guns licence-built in the Polish Starachowice plant outperformed the standard German 37mm Flak 36 and Flak 37 guns built by Rheinmetall. It was therefore decided to carry out a thorough comparison of both types and introduce appropriate modifications in a German gun.

The Germans captured considerable numbers of serviceable Bofors guns in Poland, so they had to find a use for them. Lacking triaxial stabilisation they were unsuitable for service afloat, so the majority were handed over to the Army as part of the 'Polnische Beute' ('Polish Haul'), although the Kriegsmarine did receive a few of them, which were installed aboard small barges in 1940-1.[2]

During the preparations for Operation 'Barbarossa', the entire production output of Bofors guns – manufactured by six factories in occupied countries – was diverted to units intended to take part in the invasion of the Soviet Union, so the Kriegsmarine had to wait. The stabilisation system was also not yet ready. Eventually, in December 1942 800 guns of the new model were ordered from the Norwegian Waffenfabrik Kongsberg plant (formerly Kongsberg Vípenfabrikk). This order was completed and delivered, with a small surplus, by July 1944. In all, the Kriegsmarine received 578 guns, and a further 247 were supplied for coast-defence units.

The first naval 4cm Flak 28 Bofors guns were installed in 1944 aboard the heavy cruisers *Admiral Hipper* and *Prinz Eugen*.[3] The programme reinforcing the anti-aircraft armament of Kriegsmarine warships, 'Program Barbara', called for these guns to be mounted on other vessels as well. Four were intended for the cruiser *Emden*, four more for the cruiser *Leipzig* (planned for 1944 but never done), and the cruiser *Nürnberg* was supposed to get two.[4] The greatest number of 40mm guns were intended for the *Admiral Hipper* class heavy cruisers, which actually received them and kept them until the end of the war. They were installed aboard these ships as follows.

(a) In 1944 *Admiral Hipper* was equipped with six 4cm Flak 28 Bofors guns. In November the same year

Above: Preparation for night-firing drills with a Flak 28 Bofors gun aboard an S-38 class Schnellboot. *(CAW collection)*

1 German documents specify that twenty-four completed guns were taken over and a further twenty-six were 'almost finished'. The Austrian Böhler plant had procured a licence for production of a total of 132 Bofors guns.

2 The development of a naval variant of this gun was begun by the Norwegian Kongsberg Vípenfabrikk. The first naval model, water-cooled and triaxially stabilised, was examined by the British on 14 May 1940 in Portsmouth, aboard the Dutch minelayer *Willem van der Zaan*.

3 Some sources claim that it was also installed aboard Schnellboote which carried 500 rounds of ammunition for them. Nevertheless such information must be treated carefully. As already mentioned those guns were not equipped with triaxial stabilisation, which made them totally unsuitable. Perhaps the authors were referring to the later variant which was used on German torpedo boats.

4 Some German sources claim that four such guns were intended for this ship.

Left: Großadmiral Raeder during an inspection at a naval base. A Flak 28 Bofors gun with an early-type (provisional) protective shield can be seen in the background, installed aboard an auxiliary vessel.

Above: Bofors guns were often installed on smaller vessels as both their main and anti-aircraft armament. *(CAW collection)*

her anti-aircraft armament was augmented again with an additional six such guns, for a total of twelve.

(b) *Prinz Eugen* also received her guns in two stages. In the autumn of 1944, six guns were installed, and further guns were added after her collision with the cruiser *Leipzig* in October that year. At the end of the war, her 40mm armament was as follows: two guns on either side of the forecastle, forward of the capstans, two either side of 'B' turret, one on top of that turret, two on the forward superstructure and one on the forward searchlight platform – a total of eight guns in the forward part of the ship. Two more were installed on the after superstructure either side of the SL 8 fire-control positions, and four more abaft of the after 105mm guns (two on the superstructure deck and two one deck higher). A single gun was mounted on top of 'C' turret, two on the main deck abaft 'D' turret and one right aft. Therefore there were ten guns in the

Right: A Flak 28 Bofors with a shield installed on 'B' turret of *Prinz Eugen*. *(A Jarski collection)*

Right: One of the few Schnellboot photographs showing a Flak 28 Bofors gun installed at the stern. Note the non-standard shields which protected the crew not only from the front, but also from the sides. *(CAW collection)*

after part of the ship, for an overall total of eighteen. The magazines of an *Admiral Hipper* class cruiser could carry approximately 2,000 rounds of 4cm Flak 28 ammunition per gun.

The *Deutschland* class 'pocket battleships' were also included in this programme. In the summer of 1944 it was decided to install six 4cm Flak 28 Bofors aboard the Lützow (ex-*Deutschland*). This was done in two stages – the first four guns were fitted to the fore part of the ship in August 1944 and the last two replaced 37mm guns aft on 27 September 1944. The other surviving ship of the class, the *Admiral Scheer*, was scheduled for a similar upgrade in November 1944. She was to receive six 40mm guns in place of her existing 37mm weapons. Photographs taken in March 1945 show the following layout: one atop each of the two main turrets and four in place of 37mm guns. S Breyer also states in his book that it was planned to increase the number of Bofors guns to nine in 1945. Four would be installed forward – one atop 'A' turret, one abaft the turret on the forward superstructure, and two more either side of the superstructure, aft of the 7m rangefinder. The other five were to be mounted aft: one atop 'B' turret, two on the main deck behind the turret and two on the after superstructure, either side of the 10m rangefinder located there.

In early 1945, as increasing numbers of 4cm Flak 28 Bofors guns were delivered from the Norwegian factory, they were also installed aboard smaller Kriegsmarine vessels – mostly torpedo boats, minesweepers and auxiliary vessels. Most photographs taken of German warships in the final months of the war show them with Bofors anti-aircraft guns. Thanks to the ease of installation, which required no major changes to hull or superstructure, and their high effectiveness and ease of operation, Bofors guns – together with Flakvierlings – were substituted for older anti-aircraft guns aboard almost all German naval vessels, even transport barges.

Above: Bofors gun installed at a Schnellboot's stern. This gun has no shield. *(CAW collection)*

Left: Another type of shield used with Flak 28 Bofors guns seen on a Kriegsmarine auxiliary vessel.

Above: The first Flak 28 Bofors guns installed aboard the heavy cruiser *Prinz Eugen* had no shields as shown in the photograph above. *(M Skwiot collection)*

Below: *Prinz Eugen* in dry dock after a collision with the light cruiser *Leipzig*. A Bofors gun with a freshly installed shield can be seen atop 'B' turret. *(A Jarski collection)*

Left and above: A Flak 28 Bofors gun photographed by the US Navy Technical Mission after the *Prinz Eugen* had been taken over by the Americans – seen from the front and rear. The shape of the shield can be clearly seen. *(NARA)*

Working principle of the 4cm Flak 28 Bofors gun

The 4cm Flak 28 Bofors was a fully-automatic recoil-operated gun. The breech remained locked until the shell had cleared the muzzle. Then the recoil energy divided the main components of the gun into two assemblies. The first of them – moving – consisted of the barrel with recoil spring, the breech ring, the breech block and the loading tray with rammer. The second one – fixed – consisted of the receiver (which was also the cradle) with the barrel guide, ammunition guide and loading mechanism. When the first assembly recoiled, the subsequent operation fell into

Left, above and below: A round of ammunition for the 4cm Flak 28 Bofors gun.

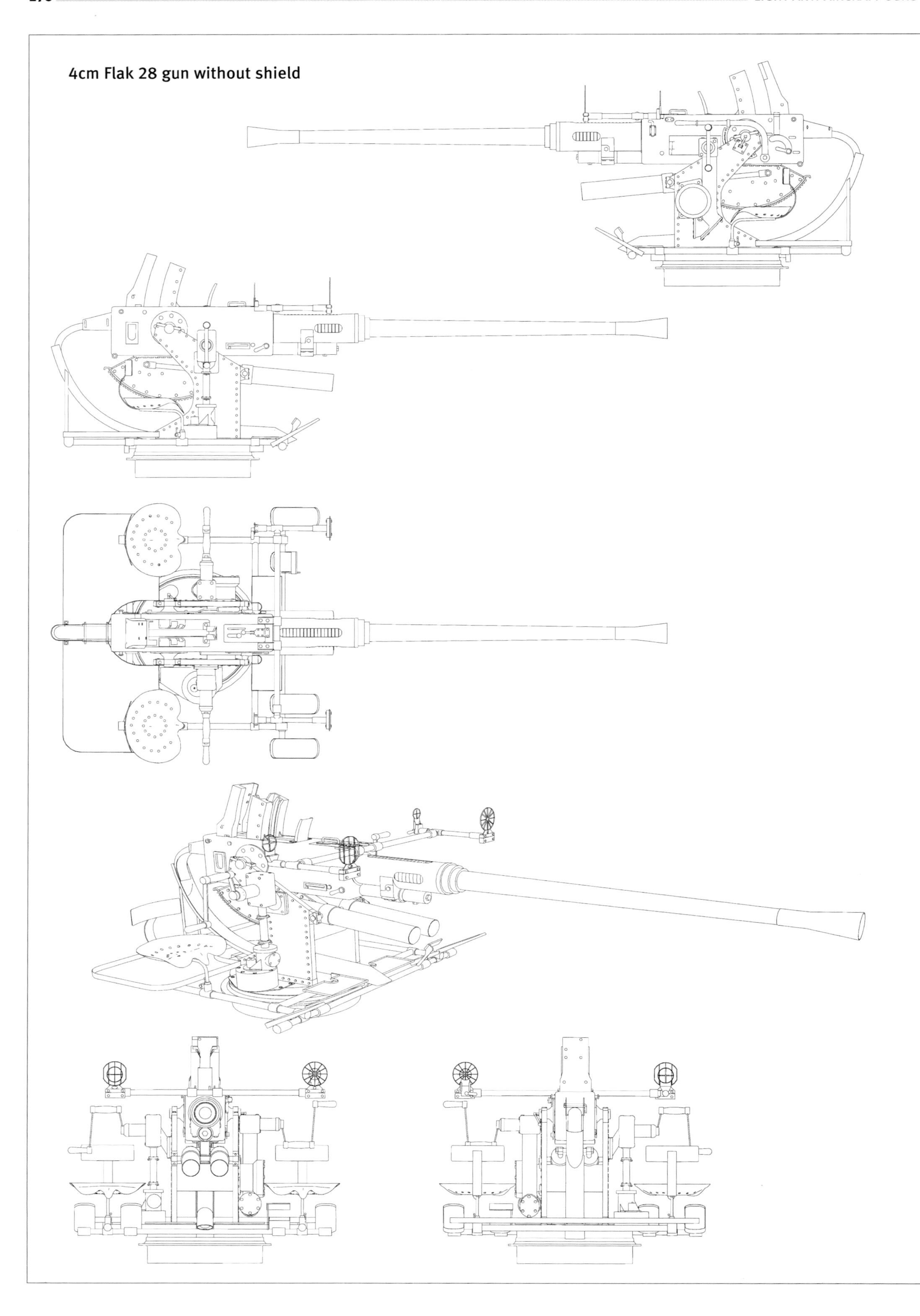
4cm Flak 28 gun without shield

4cm Flak 28 gun with shield aboard *Prinz Eugen*

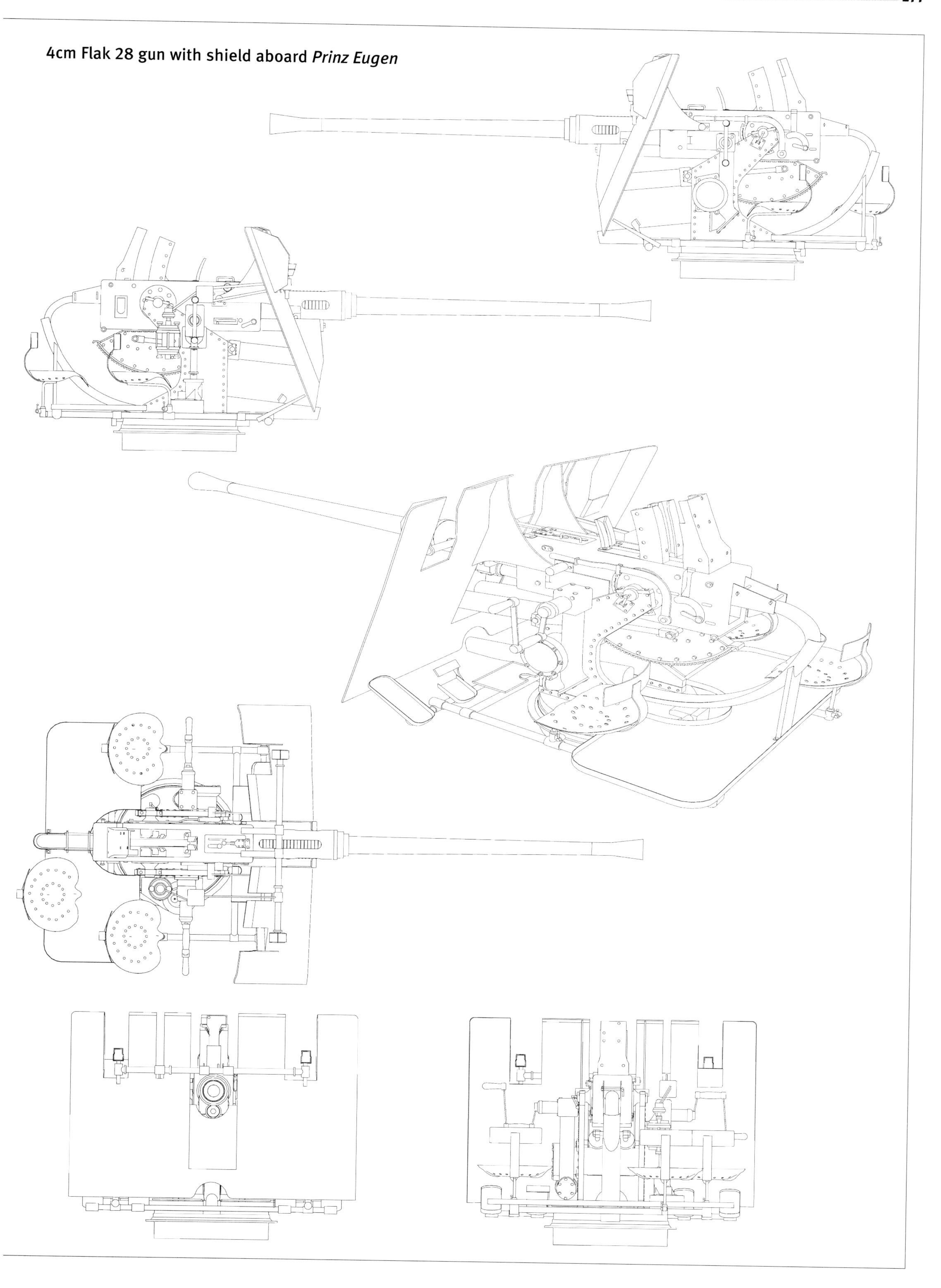

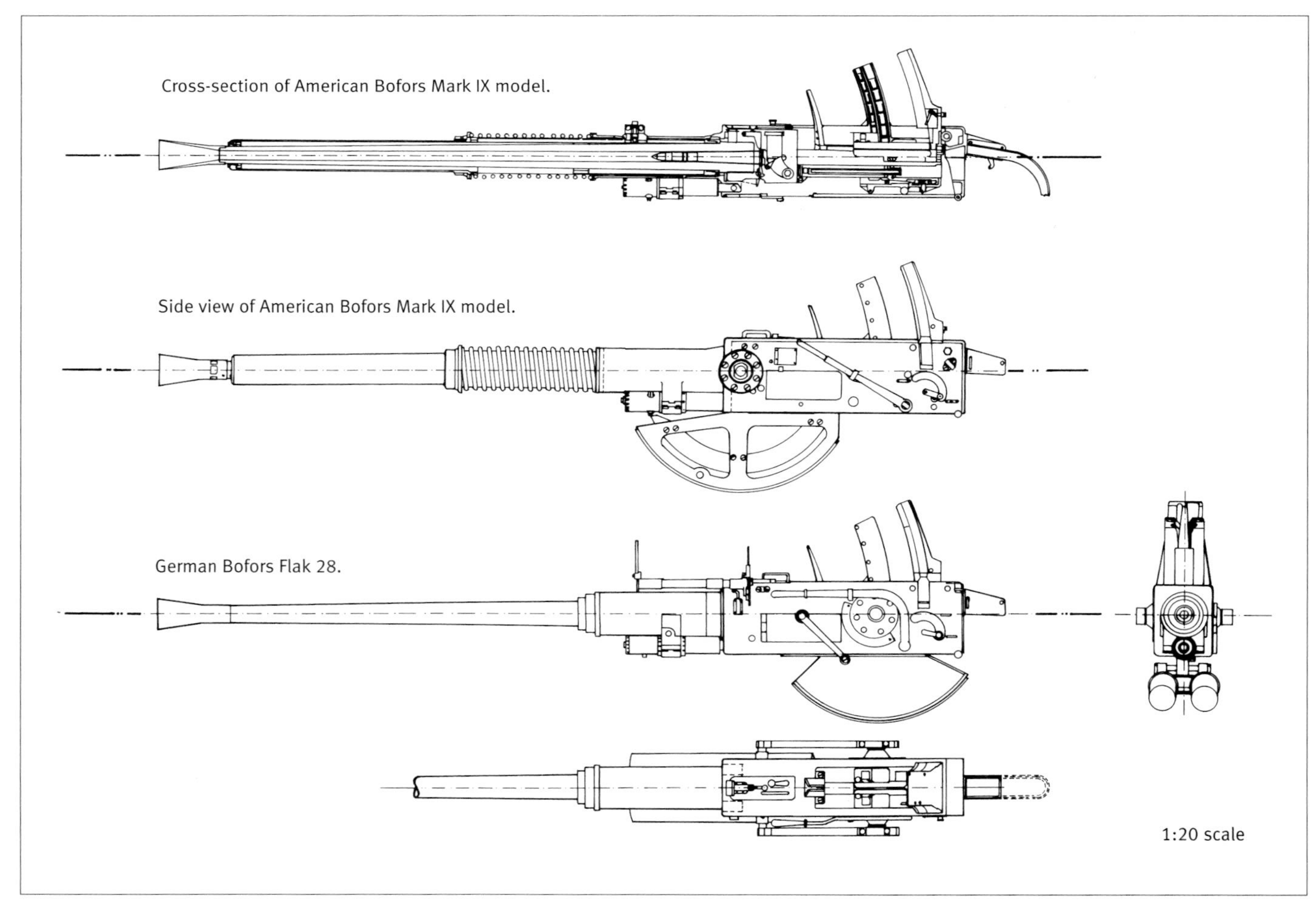

Cross-section of American Bofors Mark IX model.

Side view of American Bofors Mark IX model.

German Bofors Flak 28.

Opposite: *Prinz Eugen* seen from astern. Note the Bofors guns – one atop 'C' turret and another on the after superstructure deck, port side. There was an identical mount on the starboard side. *(NARA)*

Left: Another view of a Bofors gun with a shield installed on the superstructure deck of *Prinz Eugen*. *(NARA)*

three phases. First, the breech block's recoil spring was unlocked and compressed. Second, the empty case was ejected and the rammer spring compressed. Third, and finally, the feeder mechanism fed the next round into the loading tray. The barrel and breech then returned to the forward position, the rammer spring was released chambering the next round, the breech block returned to the upper position (locking the chamber) and the main spring was released. If after the shot the gunner was still holding the trigger down, the entire cycle was repeated. The rounds were inserted between the guide rails manually, from the top, usually in four-round clips although single loading was possible. The theoretical rate of fire was 170 rounds per minute, but in practice it was only 120 rounds per minute. The first round had to be loaded manually, using the charging handle on the left side of the receiver.

The monobloc barrel was made of chromium-nickel steel and was 2,250mm long (excluding flash guard), with progressive right-hand rifling of increasing pitch. There were sixteen grooves, each 41.2mm wide. The barrel was attached to the breech ring with a bayonet joint cut out of the external surface of its base. A recoil spring with retaining collar and adjusting nut was fitted over the rear end of the barrel and a flash guard was fitted to the muzzle. The hydraulic recoil buffer was installed below the cylindrical barrel slide. The brake rod, which controlled the speed of the recoiling breech and barrel assembly inside the chamber, was connected to the breech ring. The gun had a vertical sliding breech block. The firing mode was selected by a switch on the left-hand side of the chamber. It had three settings: fully automatic, semi-automatic and locked. The empty case ejected from the breech was extracted through an opening in the rear of the chamber and fell down a curved chute to below the gun platform. The gun was usually fired by the left-hand gunner, although the right-hand layer's position also included a trigger.

The entire receiver (which was also the cradle) was suspended on trunnions in the bearings on the body of the mount. A toothed arc bolted to the underside of the receiver was connected to the elevation gear, which was attached to the left-hand side of the mount and operated by a two-handed crank lever. An identical

Below: After superstructure of *Prinz Eugen* seen from the side of the funnel. Flak 28 Bofors guns can be seen on the superstructure deck, either side of the rangefinder. *(NARA)*

Above: Another view of the after superstructure of *Prinz Eugen* and her Flak 28 Bofors guns. *(NARA)*

lever on the right-hand side controlled the training of the mount. The gun's centre of gravity was located forward of the trunnions. Two spring-loaded counter-weights installed between the mount's side plates at the front were connected to the rear part of the toothed arc to compensate for the weight of the barrel. The twin sights were installed on a bar fixed across the top of the receiver. Its right side was connected to the predictor. In most cases the Germans used either reflector sights or, less commonly, ring sights, which were only fitted on the simplified version of the gun.

The elevation layer's seat, with pedals, was on the left-hand side of the mount, towards the lower edge. The training layer's seat was on the right. The gun commander had a seat at the rear of the mount, on the right. According to the information received from the range-taker, he could operate the predictor. The loader stood on a platform on the left-hand side.

In the main land-service variant the Flak 28 mount was set on a rotating ring on a twin-axled towed chassis. In the naval mount the rotating ring was attached to a round base plate fixed to the deck. Elevation was -6°/+90° and training was theoretically 360°, although it was limited in practice by the position of the mount aboard ship. Horizontal range was 9,500m and effective ceiling 6,200m.

High-explosive tracer rounds with self-destruct were used against aerial targets. They also had a impact fuse. The tracer ignited 300m from the muzzle and if the shell failed to hit the target, the self-destruct detonated it after 10.5 seconds. The guns used fixed 40 x 311R ammunition with a 0.955kg warhead. The propellant charge was 0.303kg of Str PC/38N. The entire round weighed 2.1kg (some sources say 2.06kg), and it was 447mm long (projectile 184mm long).

Top right: The damaged heavy cruiser *Admiral Hipper* in dry dock in Kiel. A Flak 28 Bofors gun with a shield can be seen atop 'C' turret.

Right: Bofors gun with a shield installed on the superstructure of *Prinz Eugen*. *(NARA)*

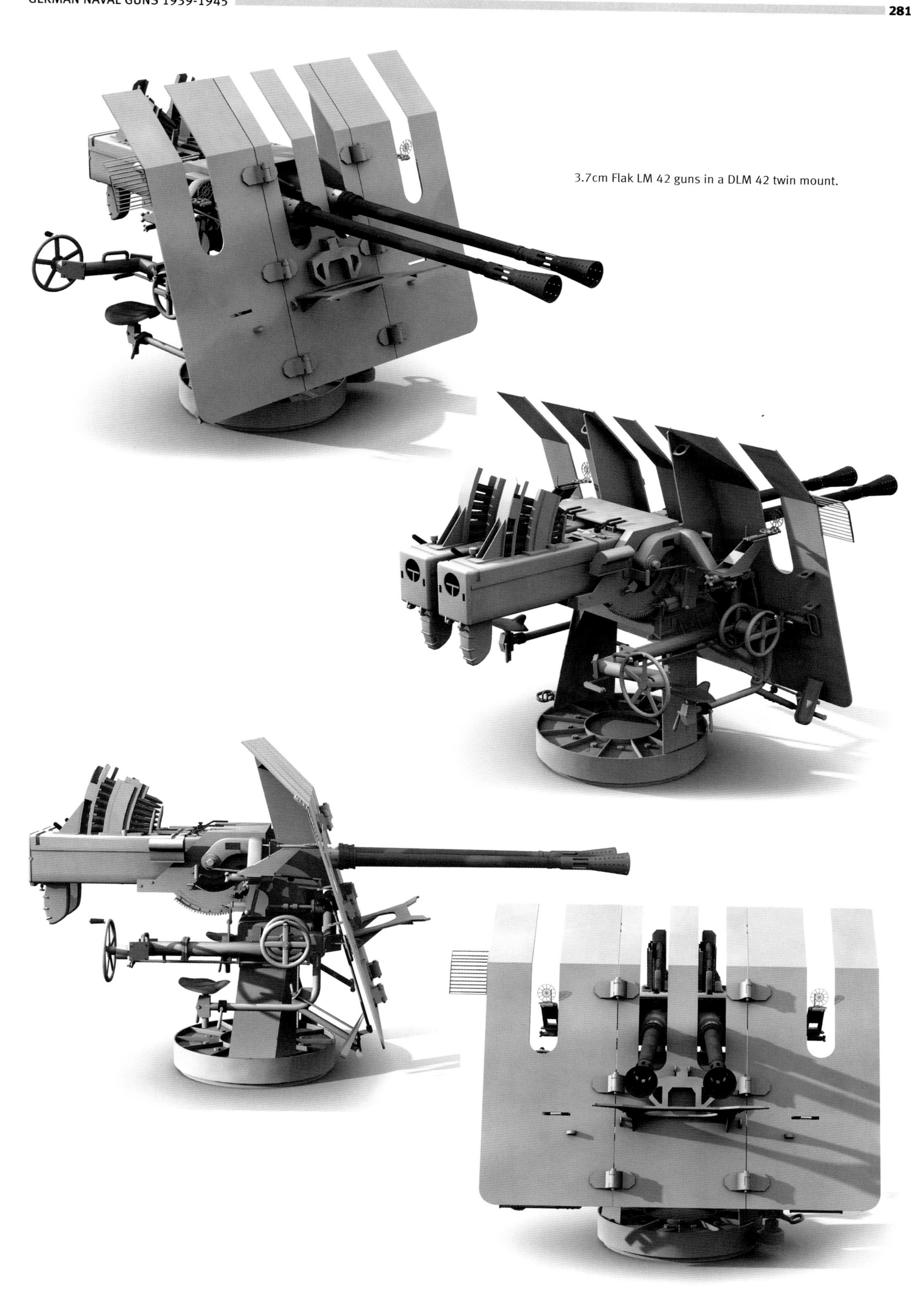

3.7cm Flak LM 42 guns in a DLM 42 twin mount.

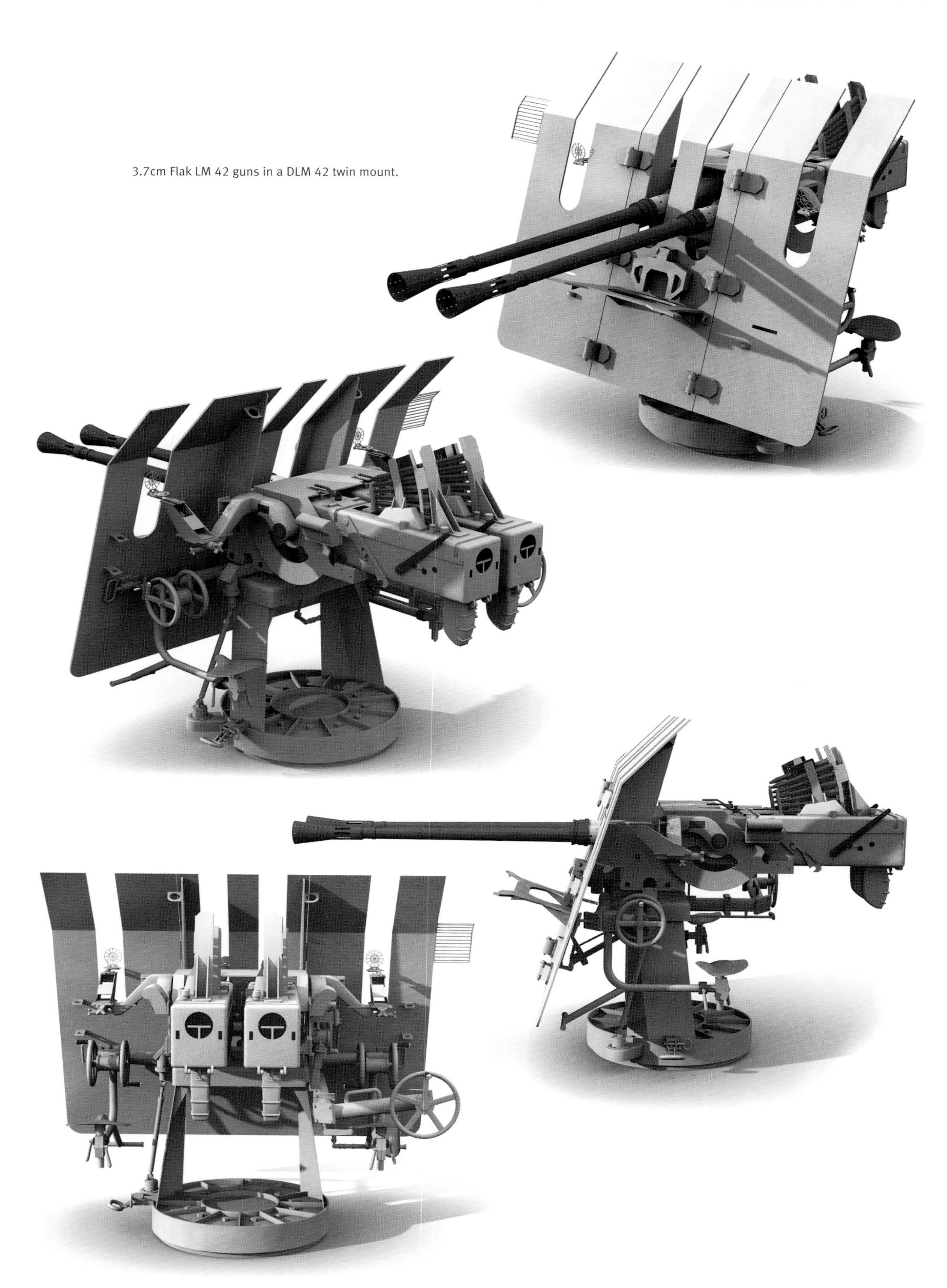

3.7cm Flak LM 42 guns in a DLM 42 twin mount.

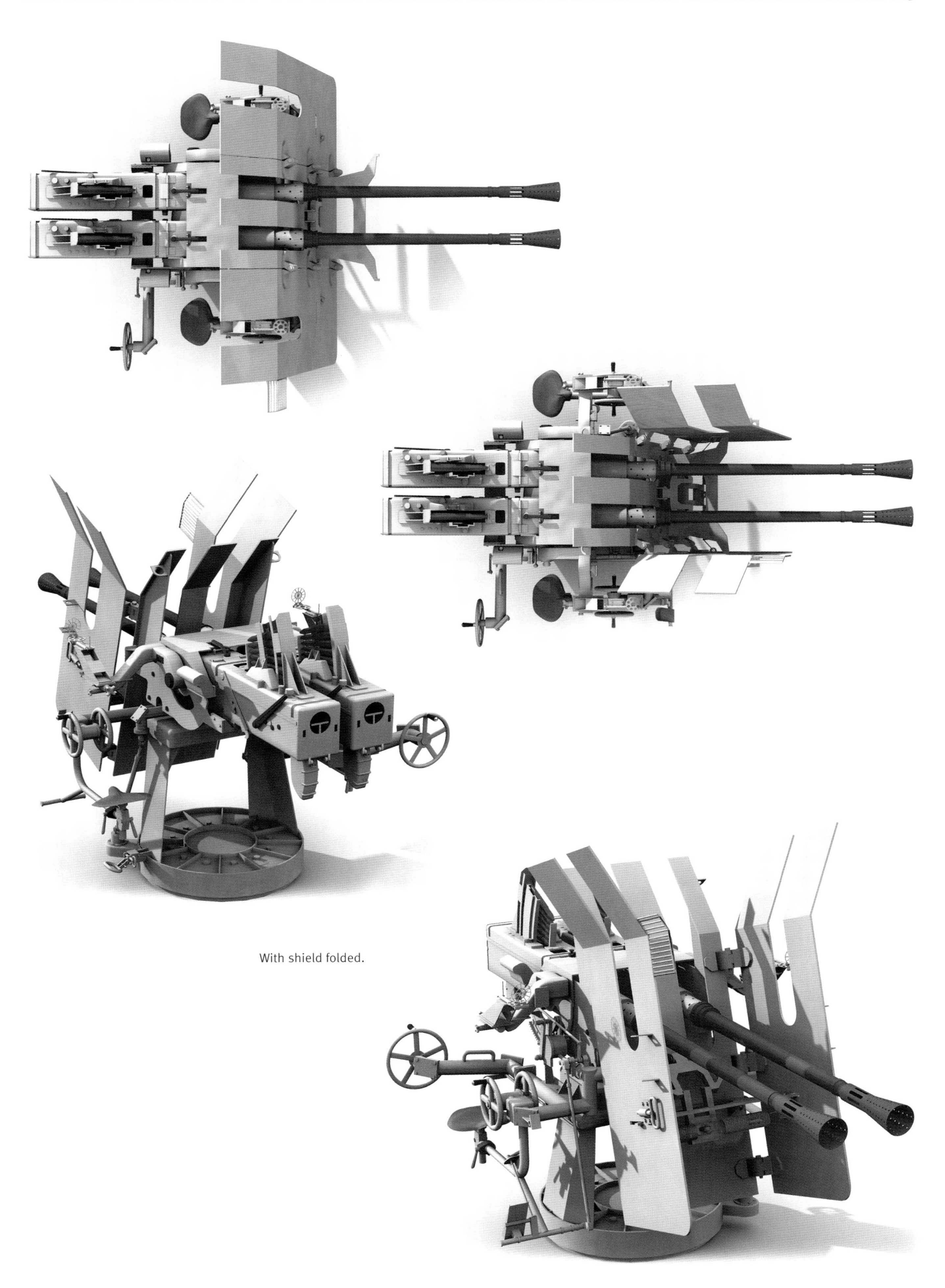

With shield folded.

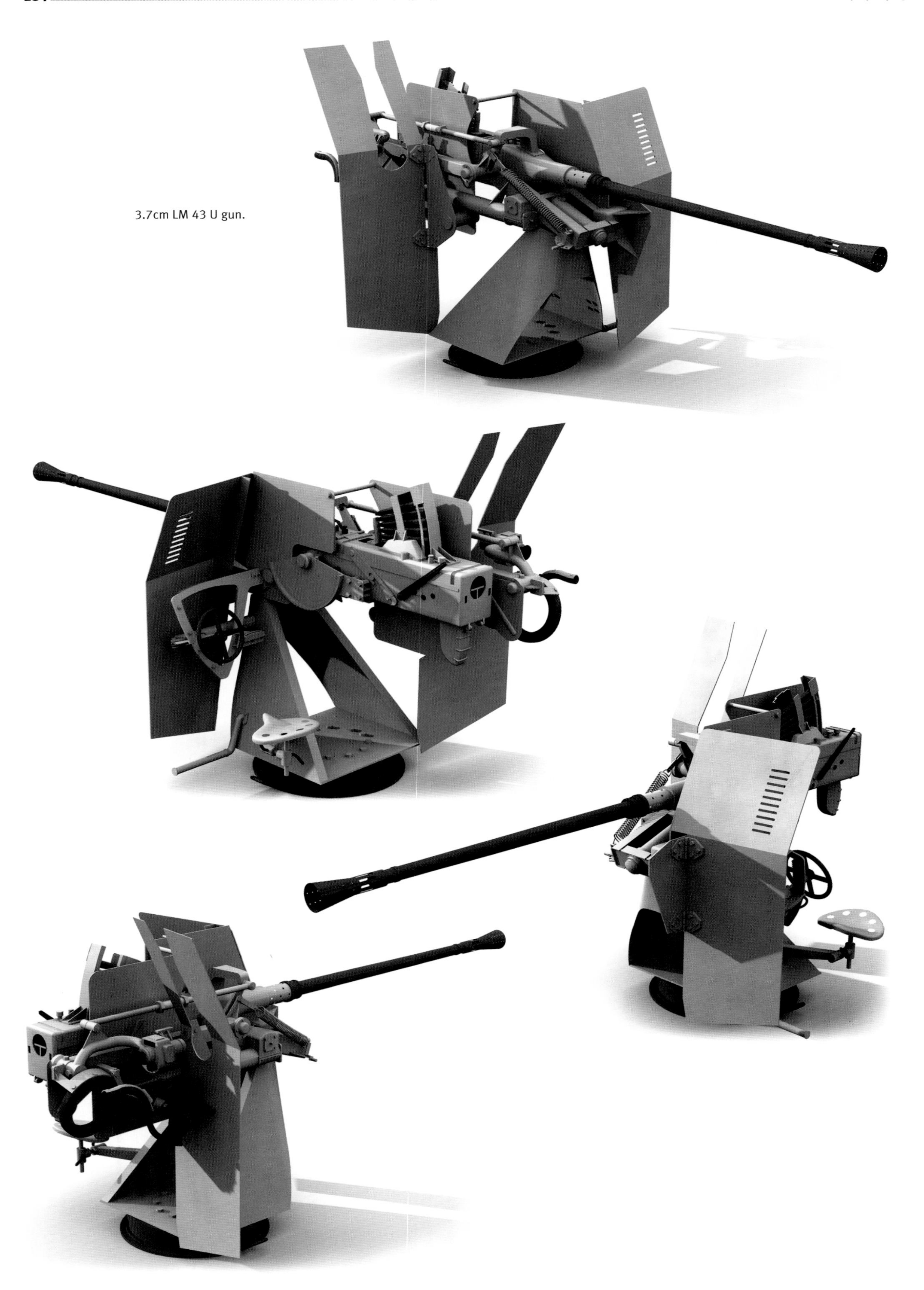

3.7cm LM 43 U gun.

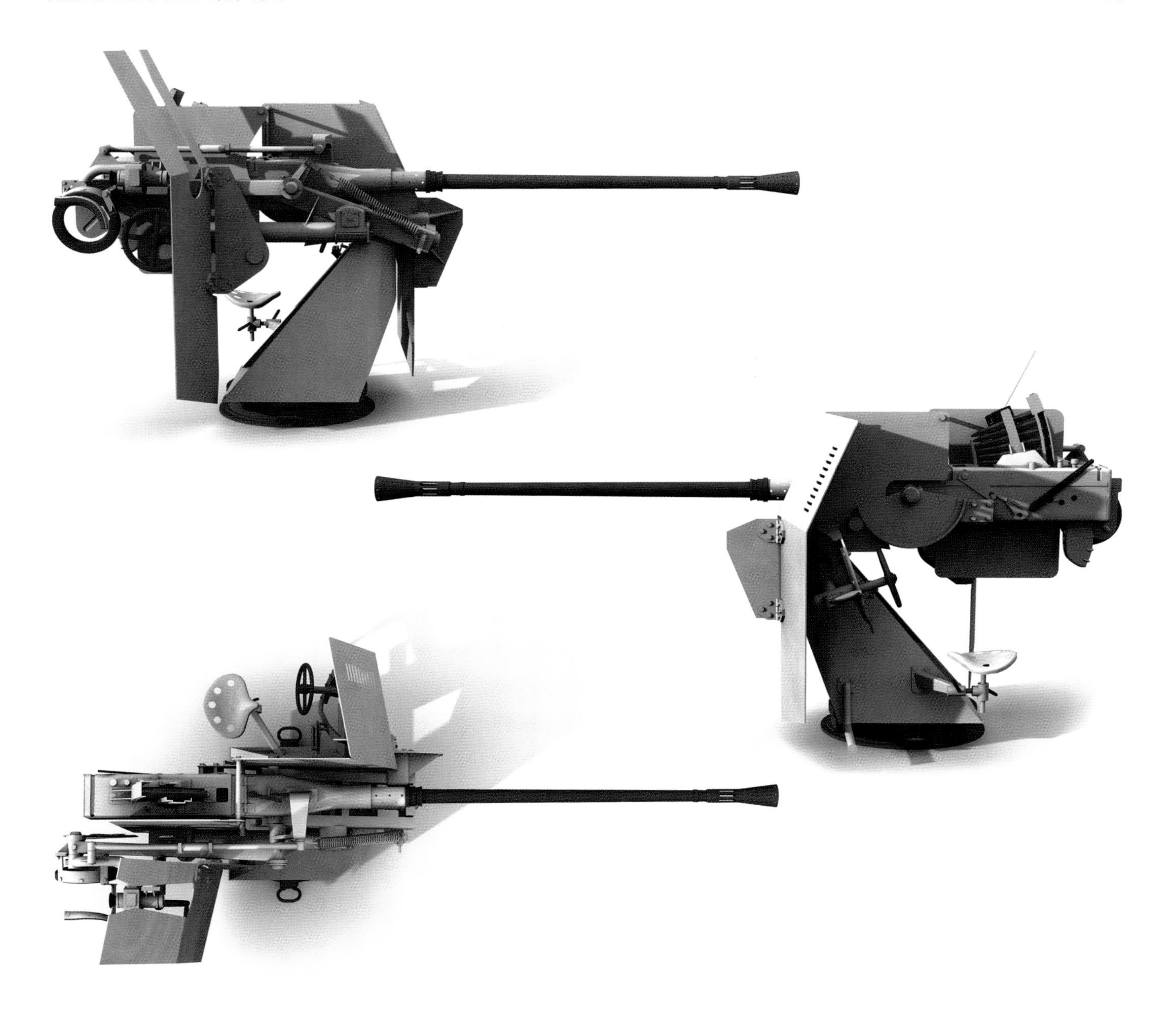

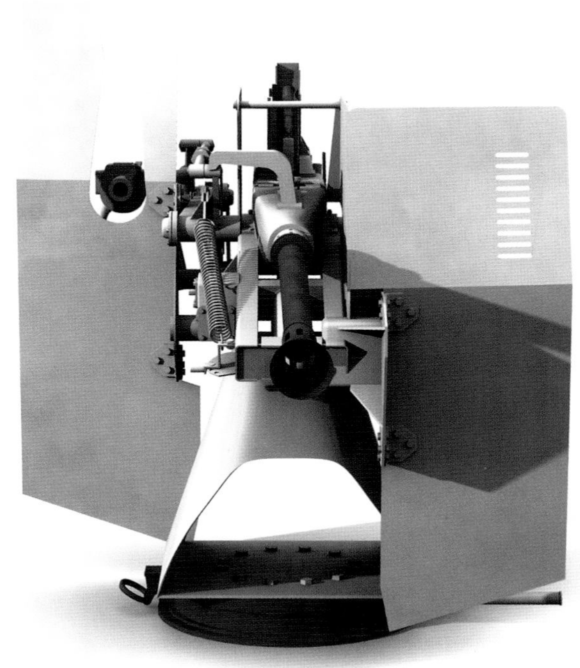

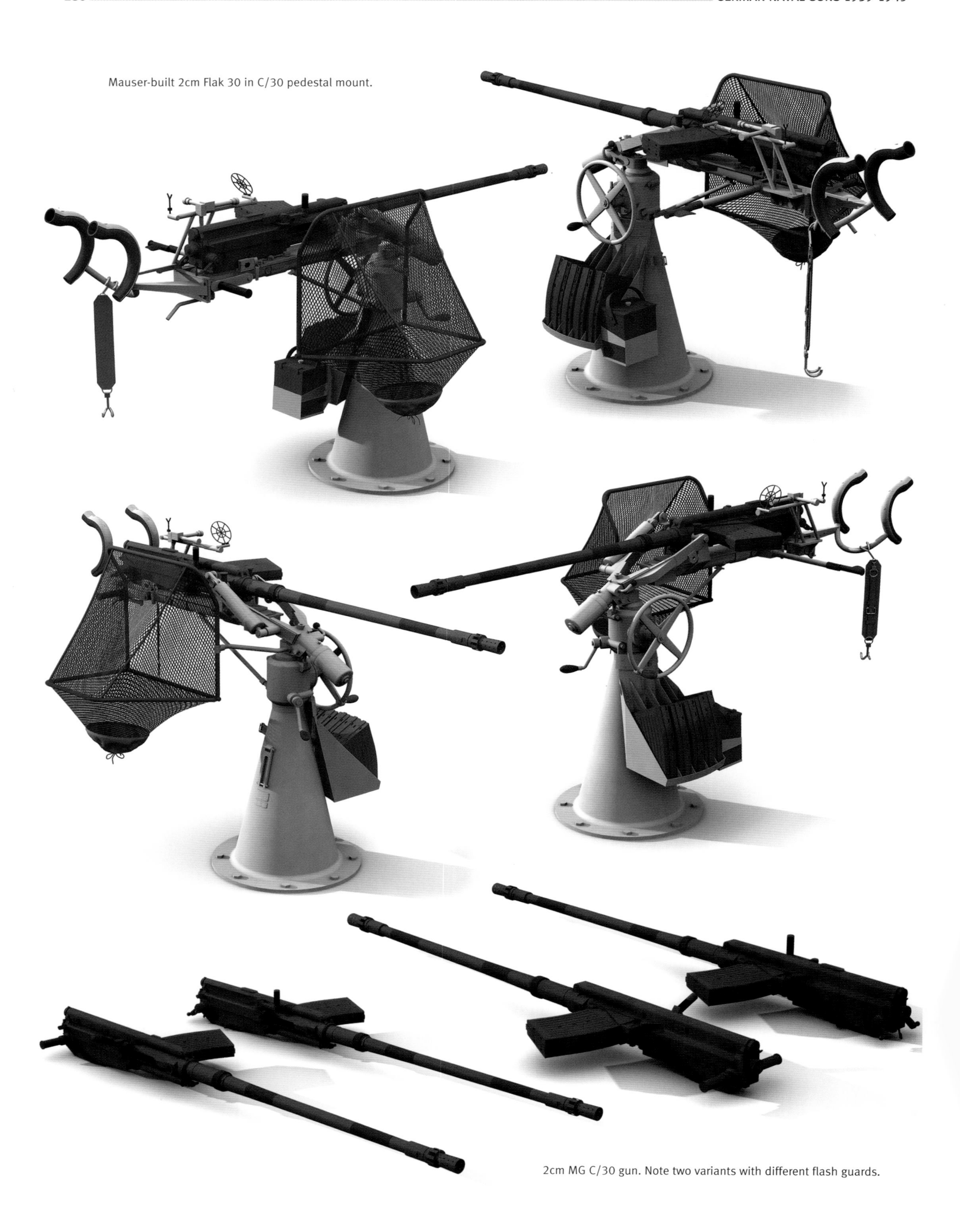

Mauser-built 2cm Flak 30 in C/30 pedestal mount.

2cm MG C/30 gun. Note two variants with different flash guards.

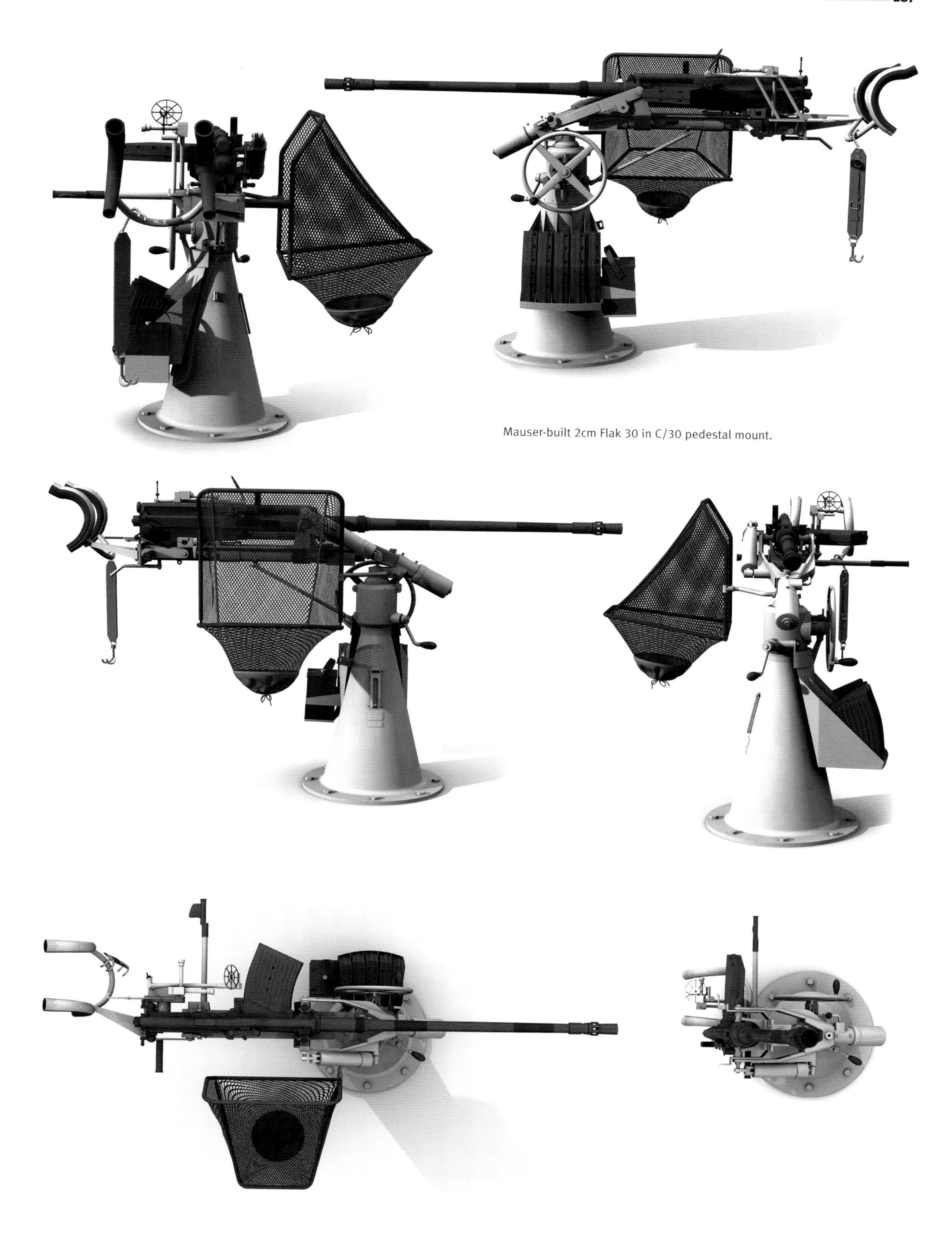

Mauser-built 2cm Flak 30 in C/30 pedestal mount.

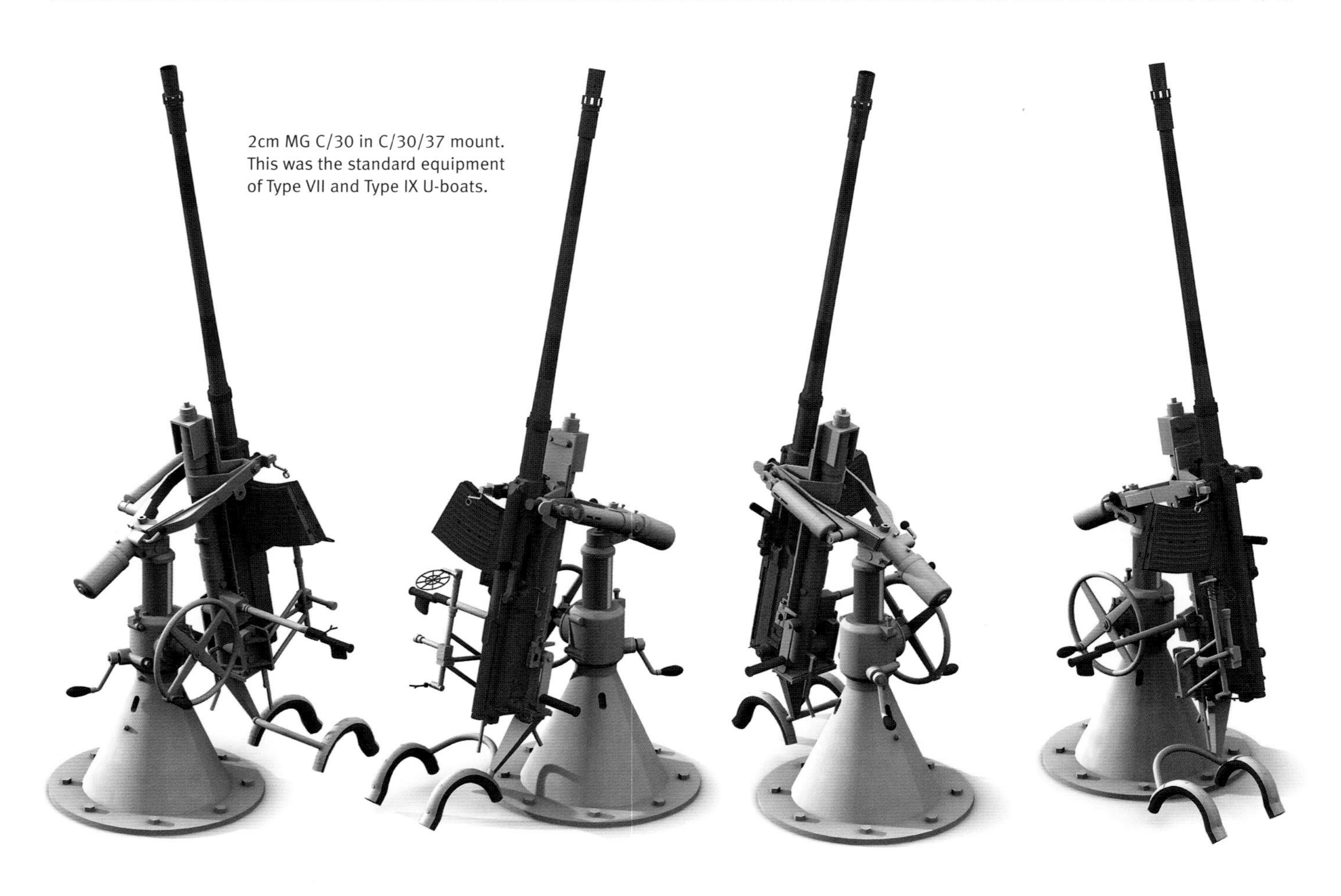

2cm MG C/30 in C/30/37 mount. This was the standard equipment of Type VII and Type IX U-boats.

2cm MG C/30 gun in C/30/37 mount.

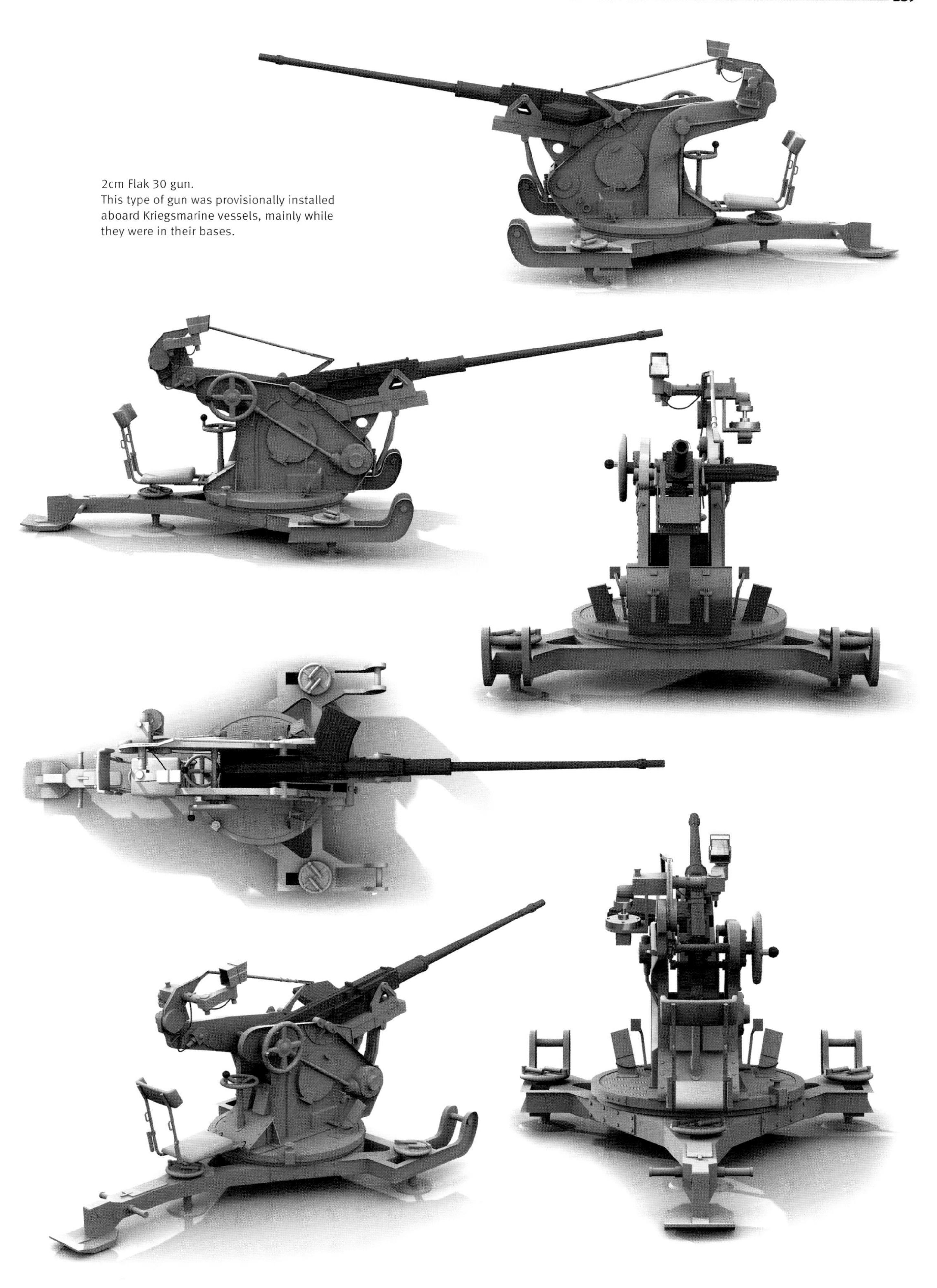

2cm Flak 30 gun.
This type of gun was provisionally installed aboard Kriegsmarine vessels, mainly while they were in their bases.

2cm C/38 gun in C/30 mount.

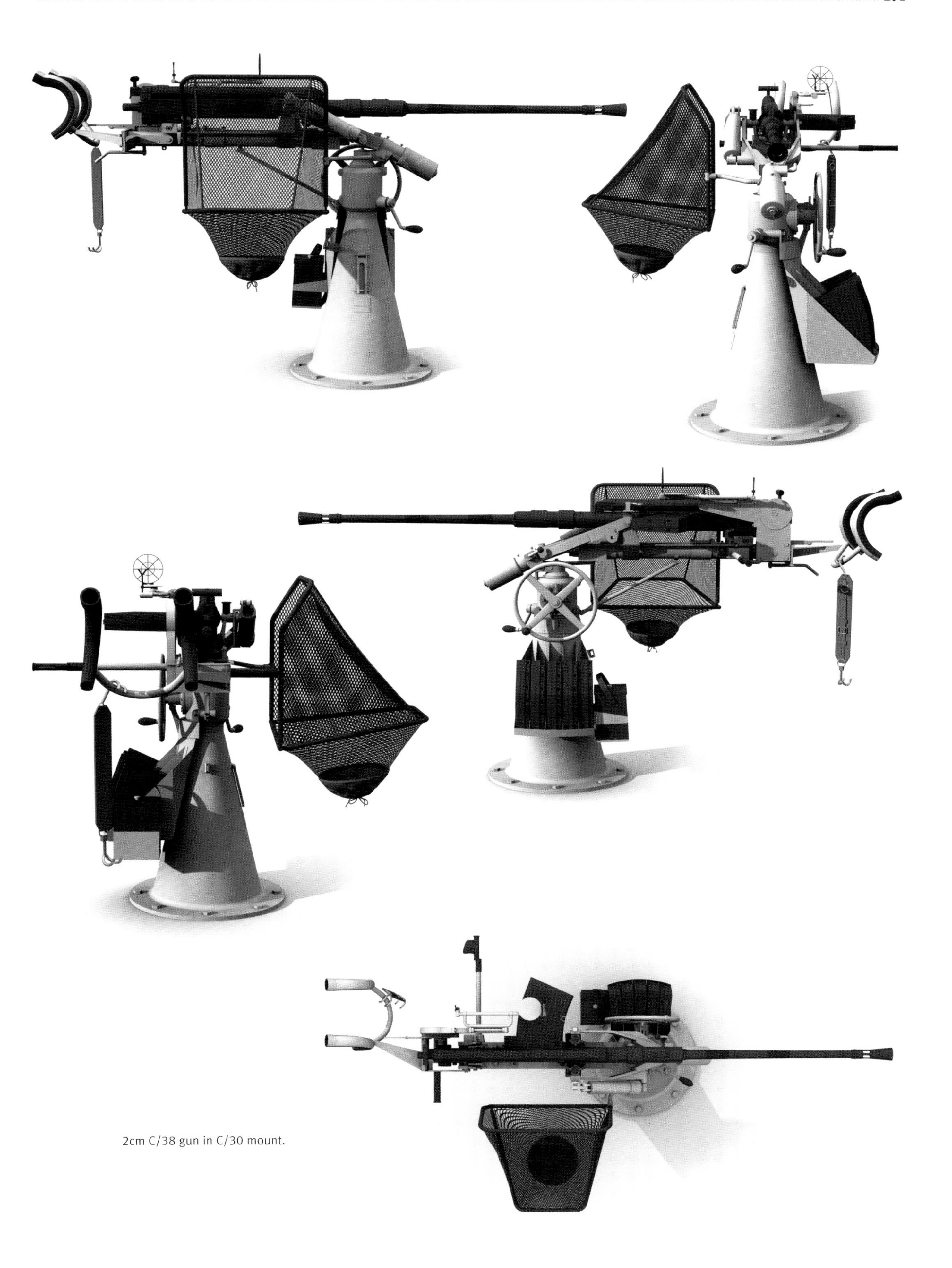

2cm C/38 gun in C/30 mount.

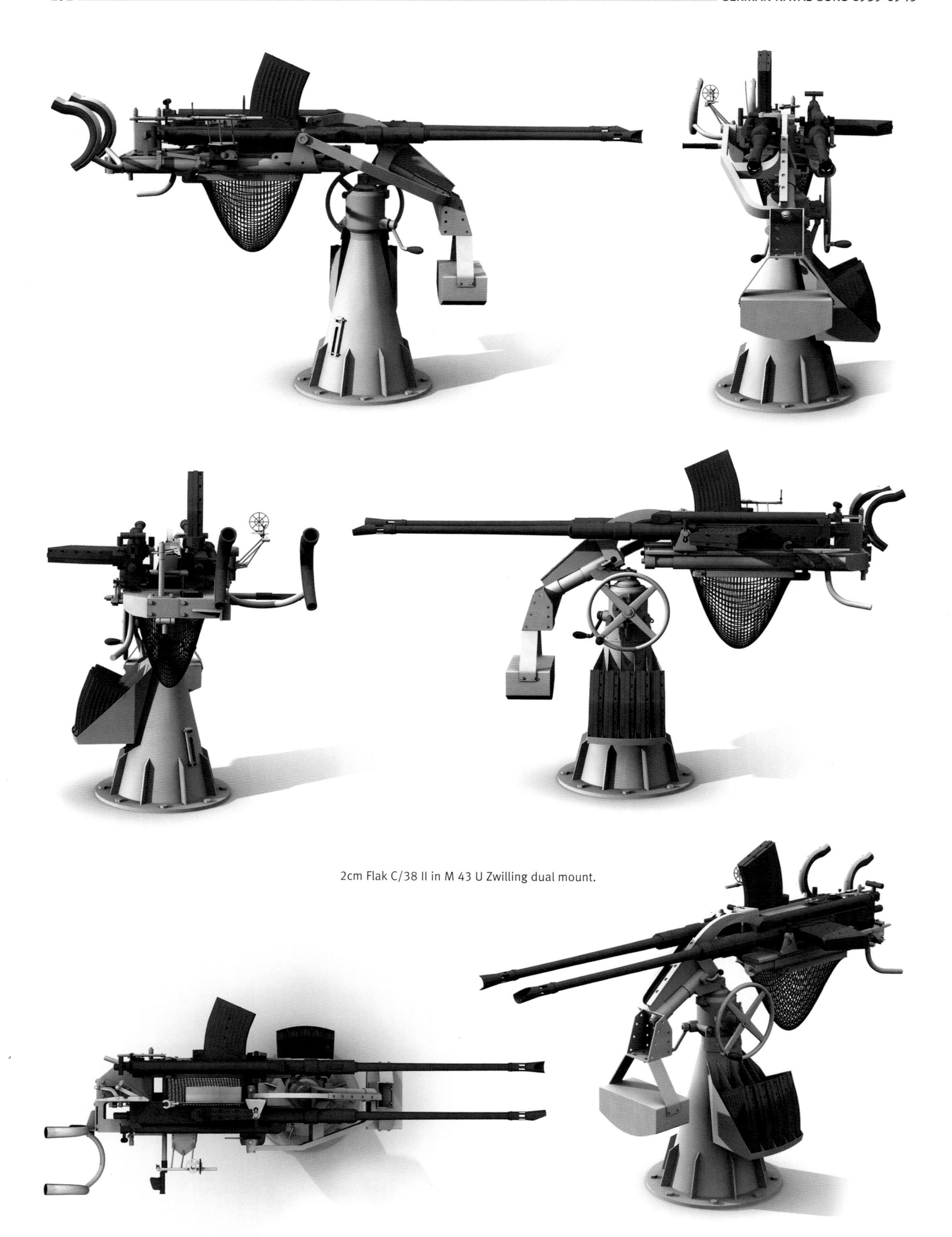

2cm Flak C/38 II in M 43 U Zwilling dual mount.

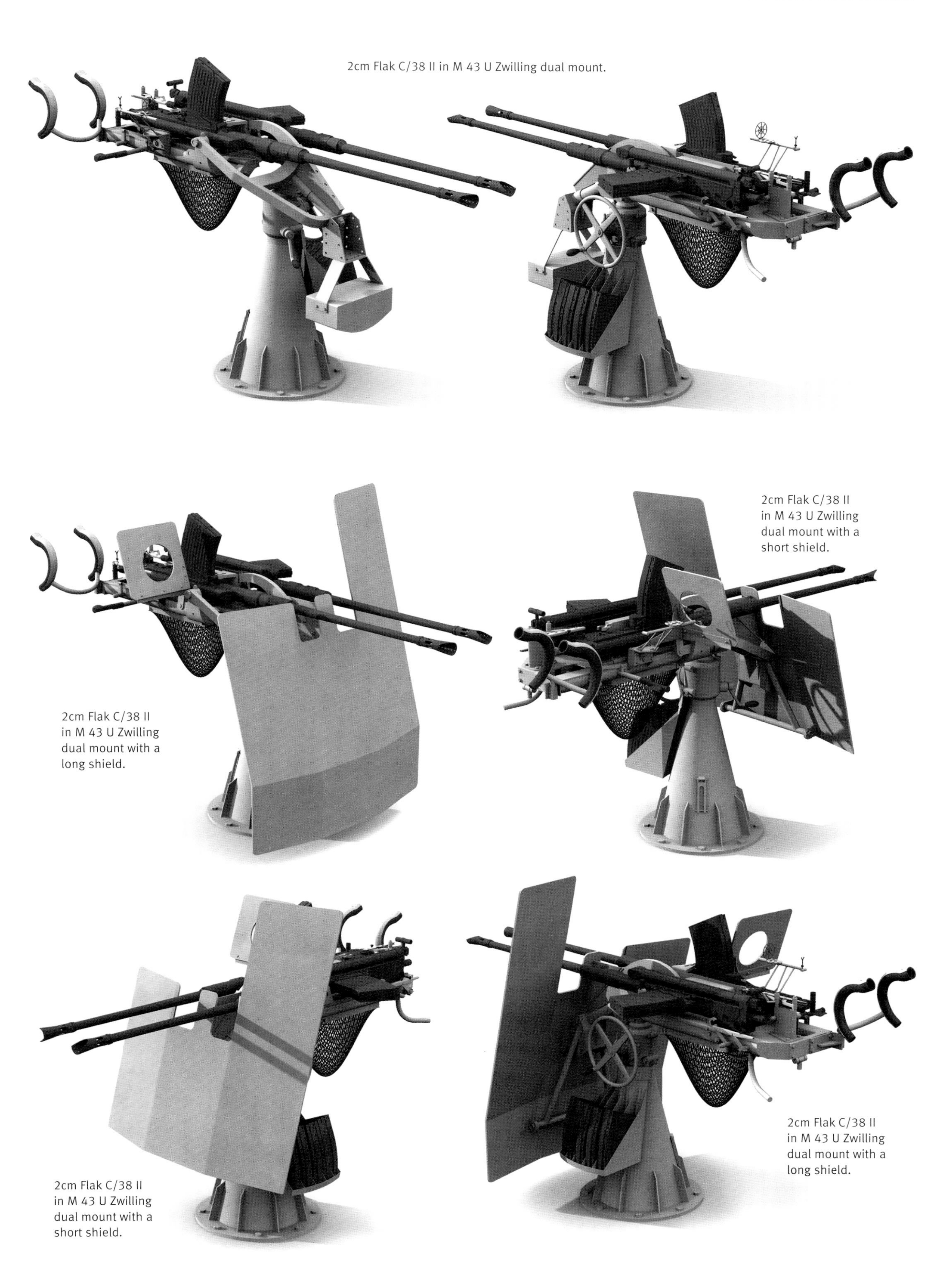

2cm Flak C/38 II in M 43 U Zwilling dual mount.

2cm Flak C/38 II in M 43 U Zwilling dual mount with a short shield.

2cm Flak C/38 II in M 43 U Zwilling dual mount with a long shield.

2cm Flak C/38 II in M 43 U Zwilling dual mount with a long shield.

2cm Flak C/38 II in M 43 U Zwilling dual mount with a short shield.

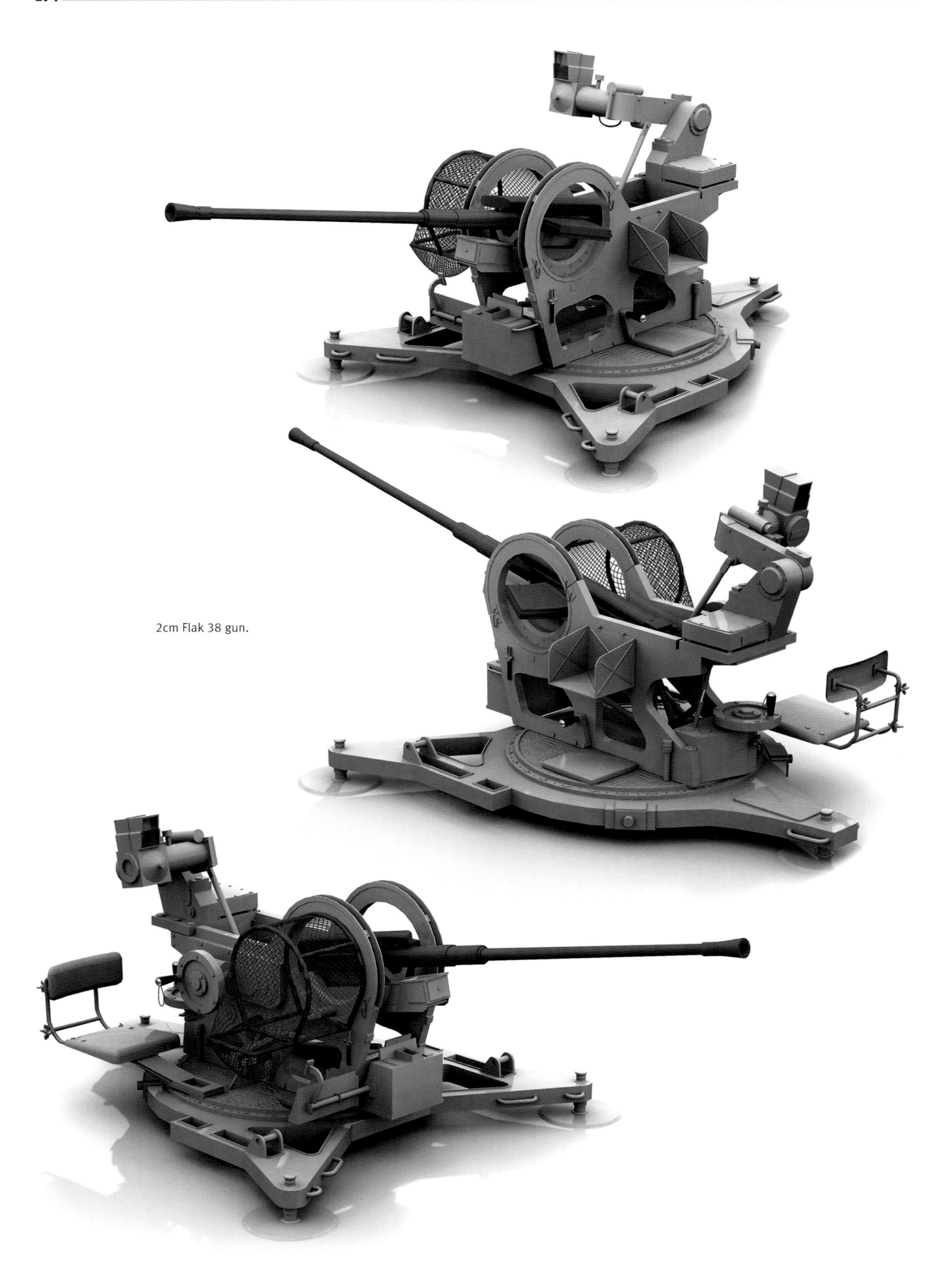

2cm Flak 38 gun.

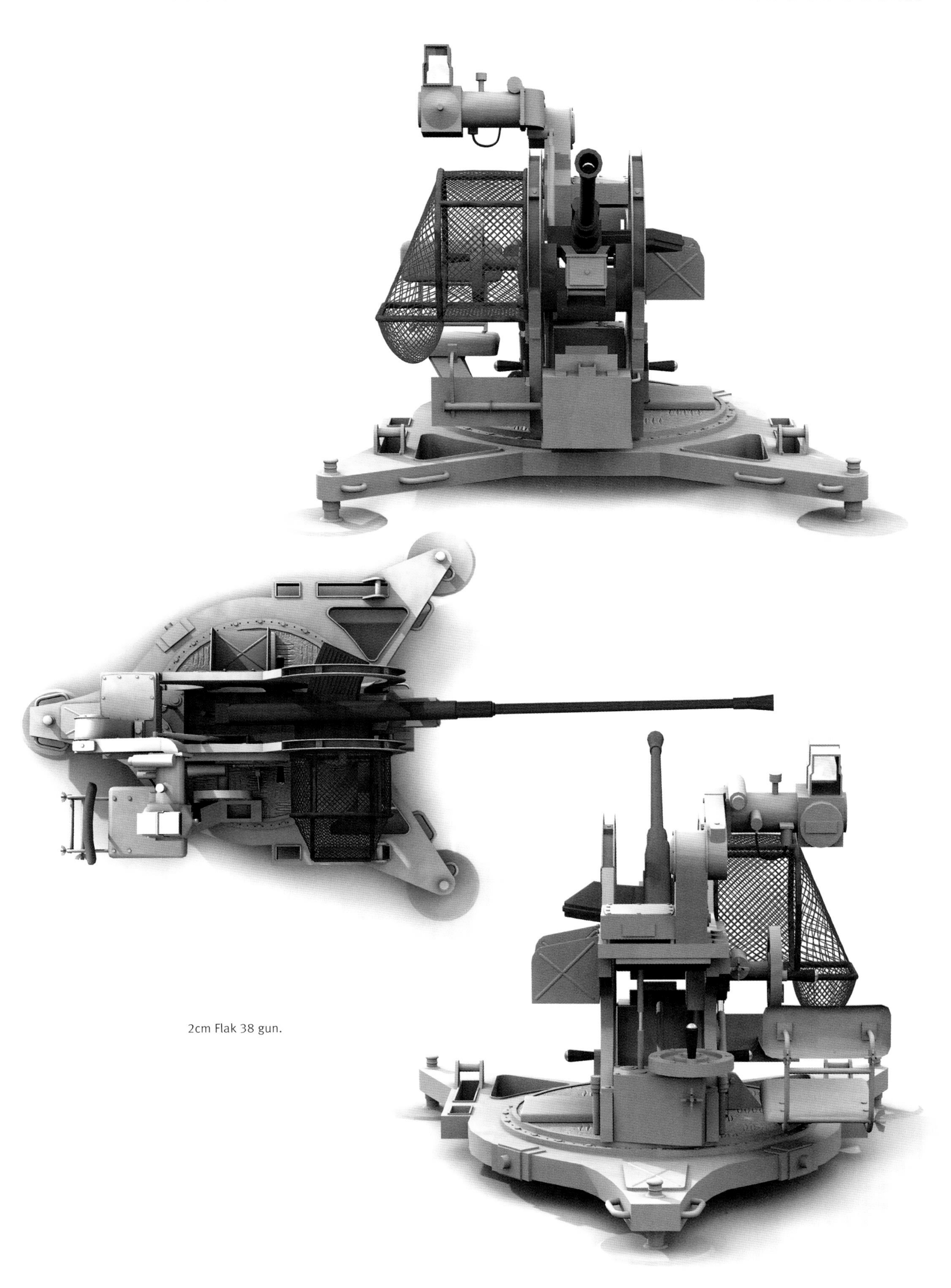

2cm Flak 38 gun.

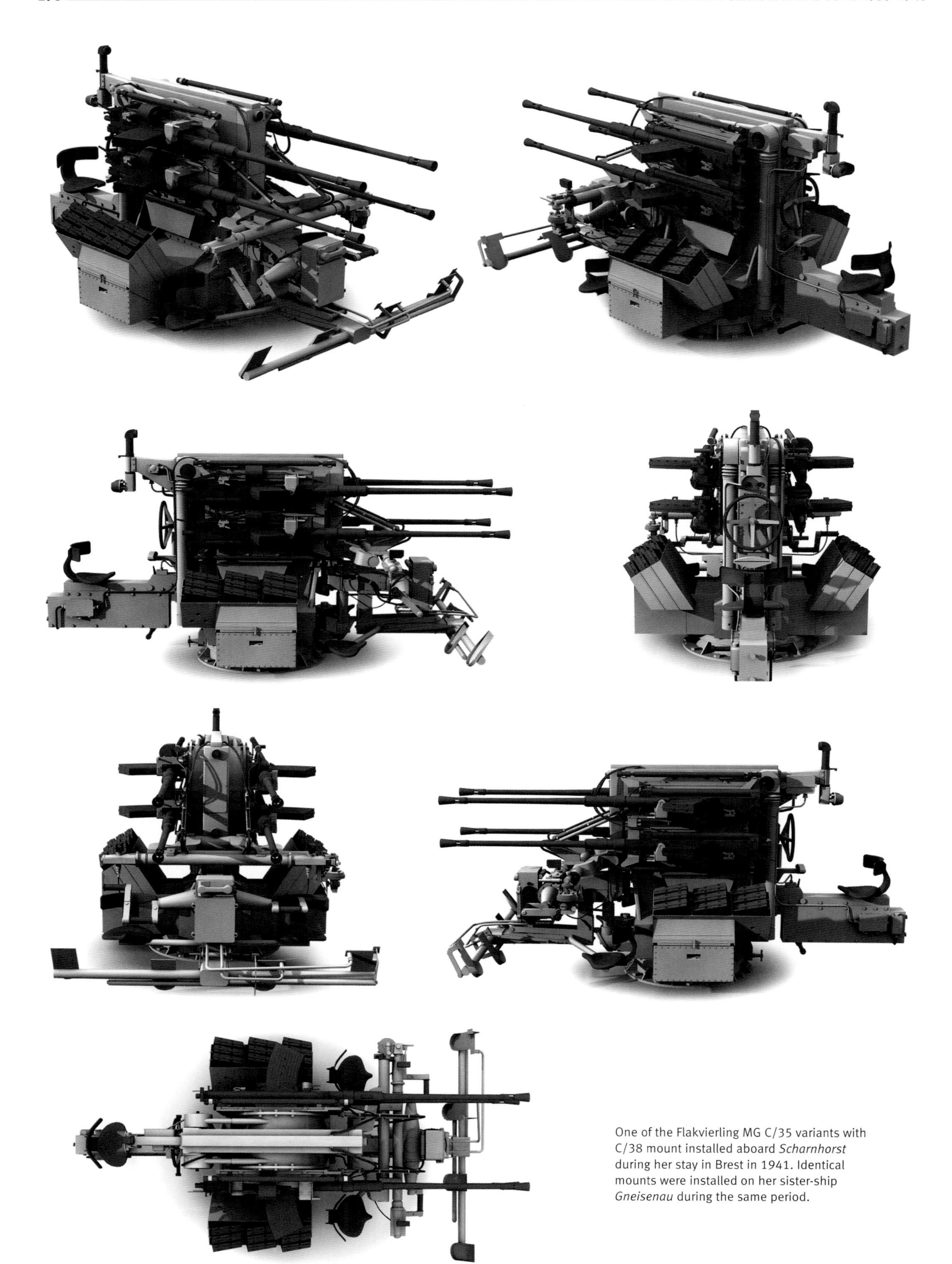

One of the Flakvierling MG C/35 variants with C/38 mount installed aboard *Scharnhorst* during her stay in Brest in 1941. Identical mounts were installed on her sister-ship *Gneisenau* during the same period.

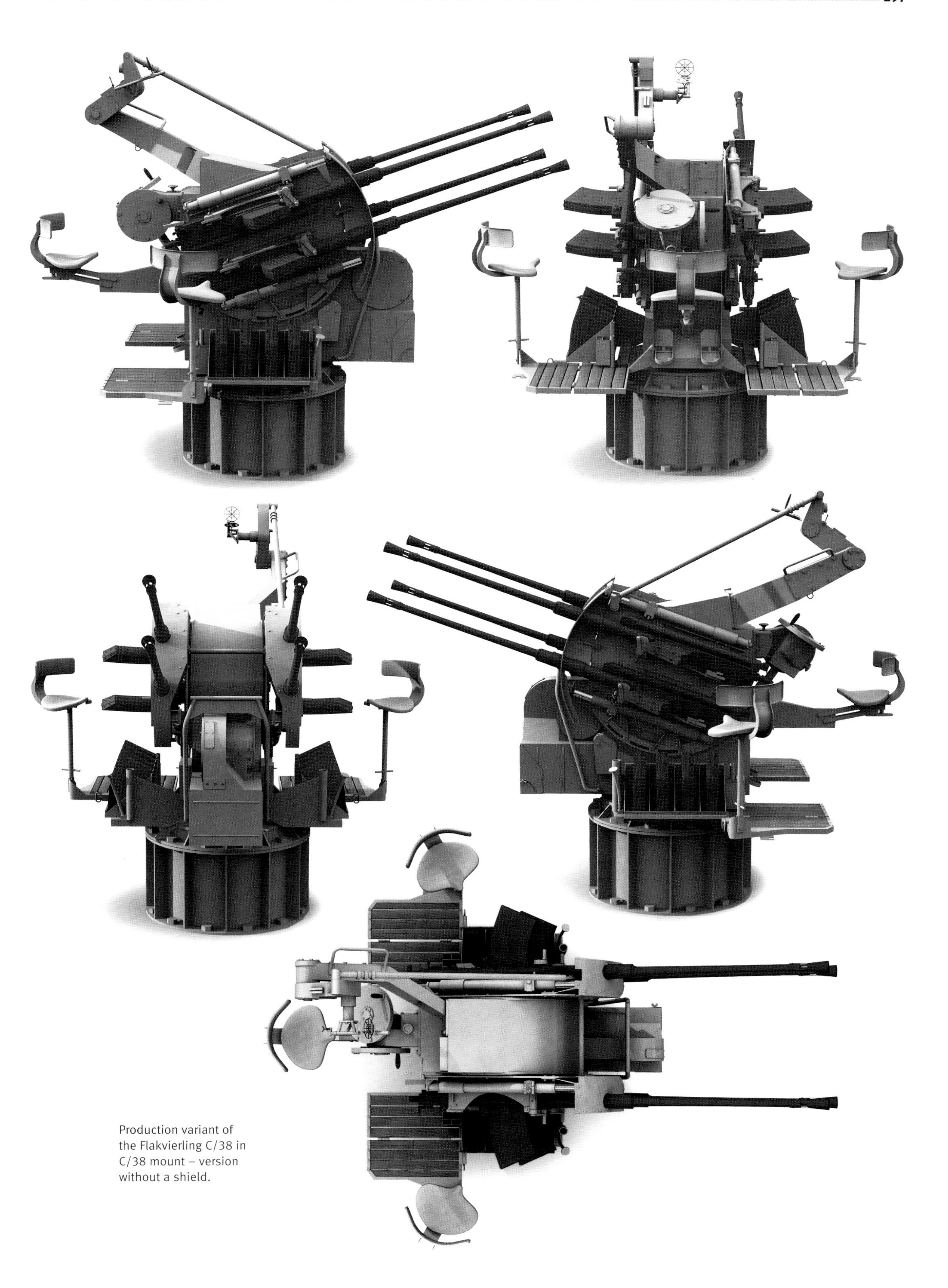

Production variant of the Flakvierling C/38 in C/38 mount – version without a shield.

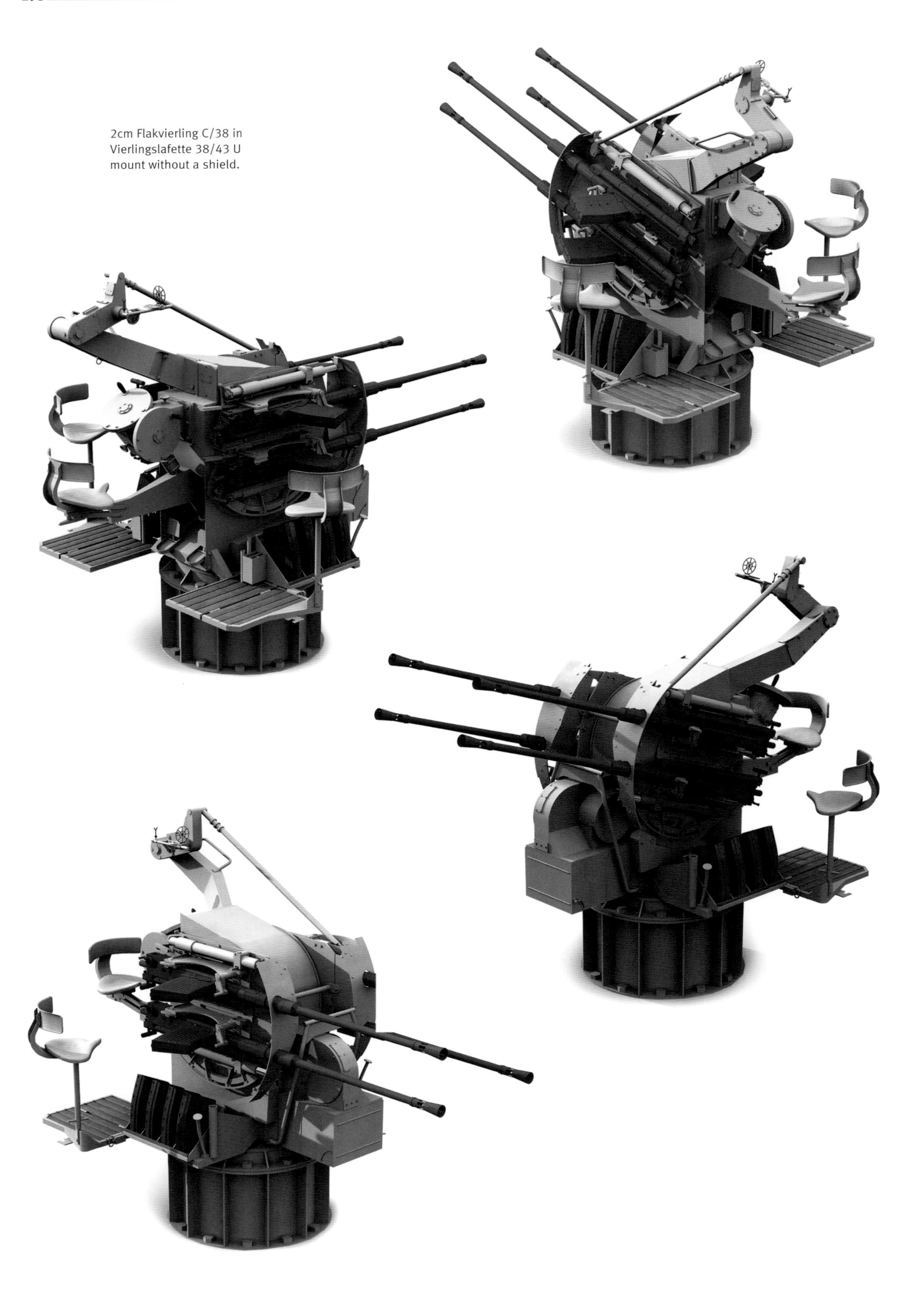

2cm Flakvierling C/38 in Vierlingslafette 38/43 U mount without a shield.

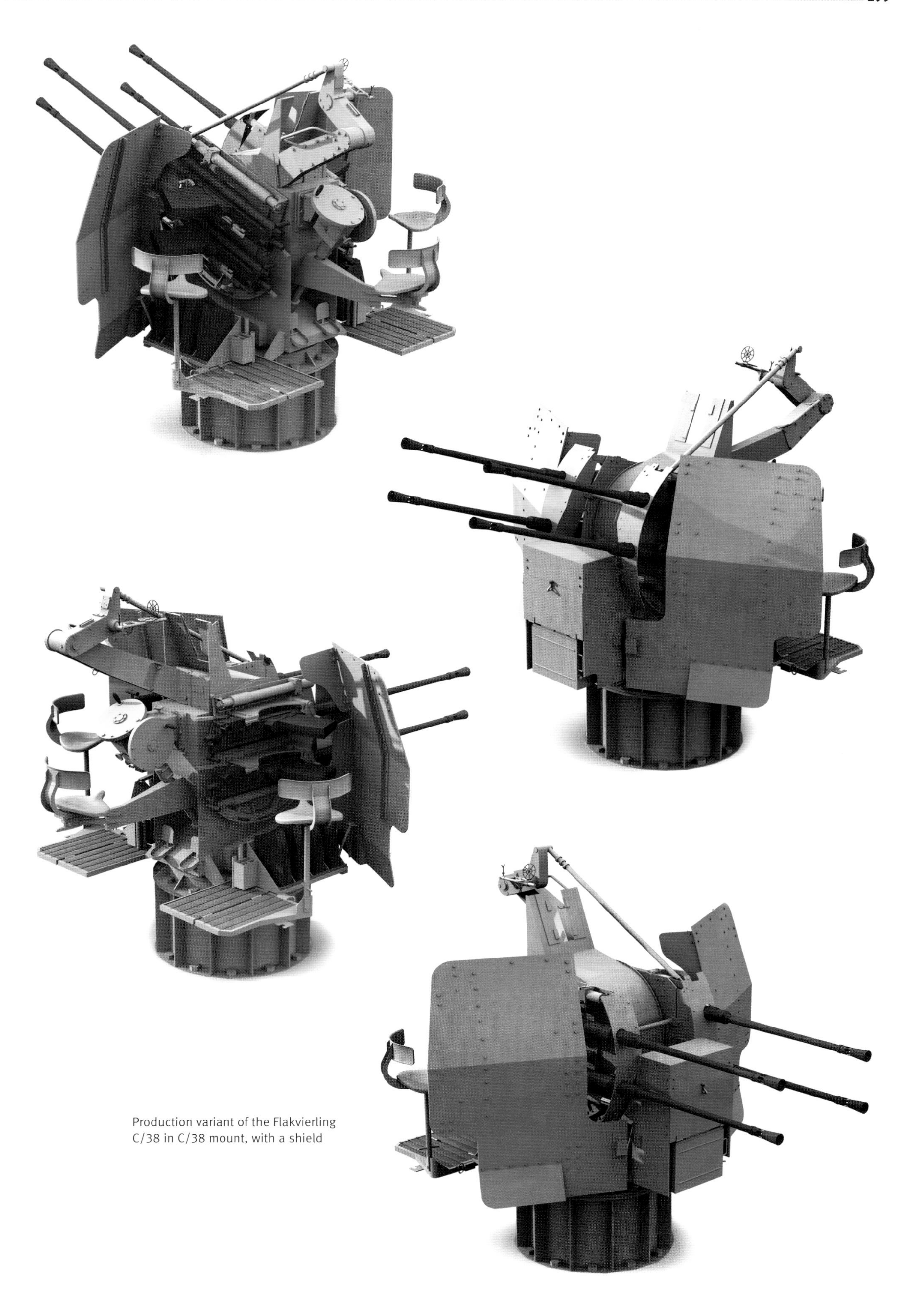

Production variant of the Flakvierling C/38 in C/38 mount, with a shield

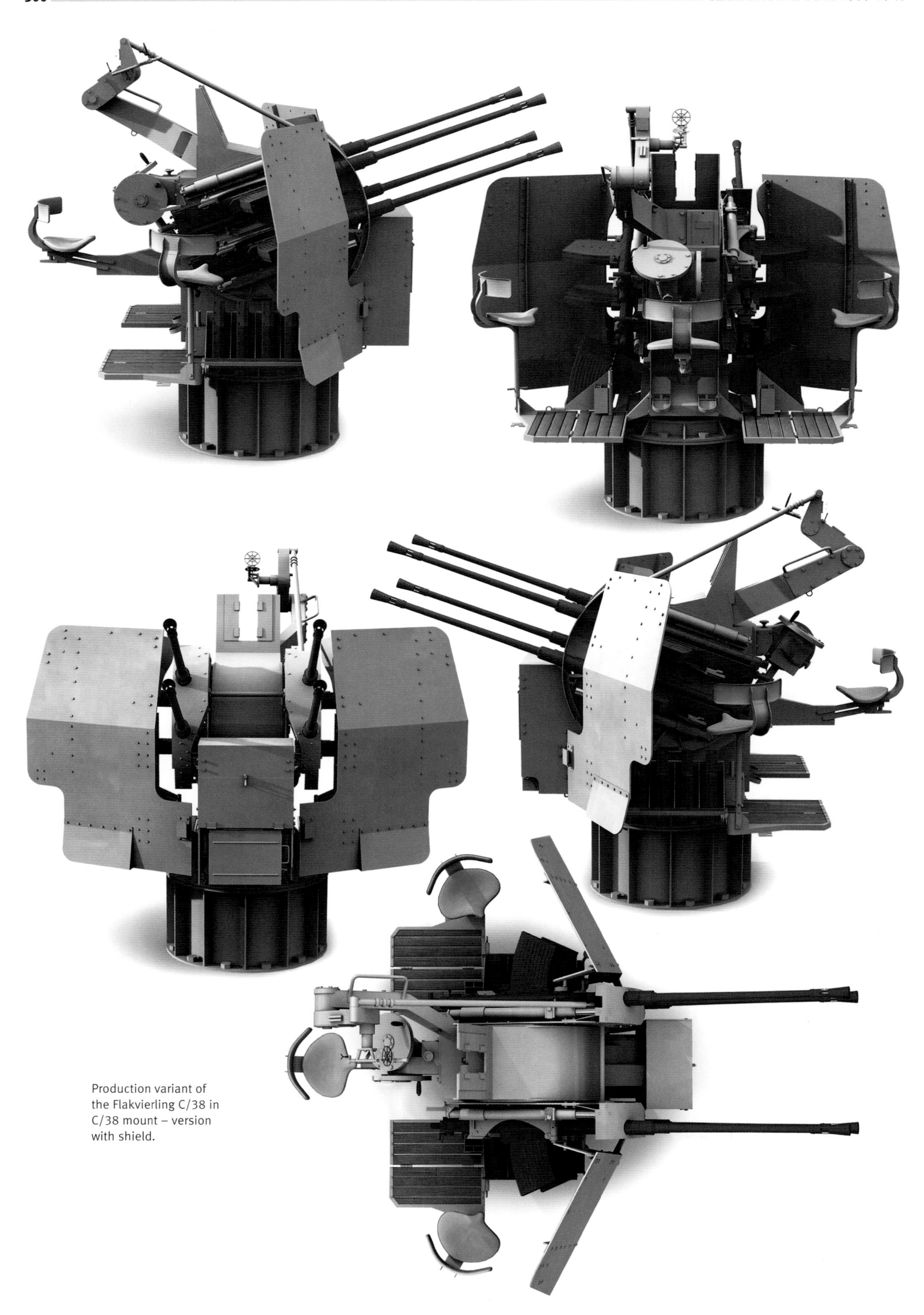

Production variant of the Flakvierling C/38 in C/38 mount – version with shield.

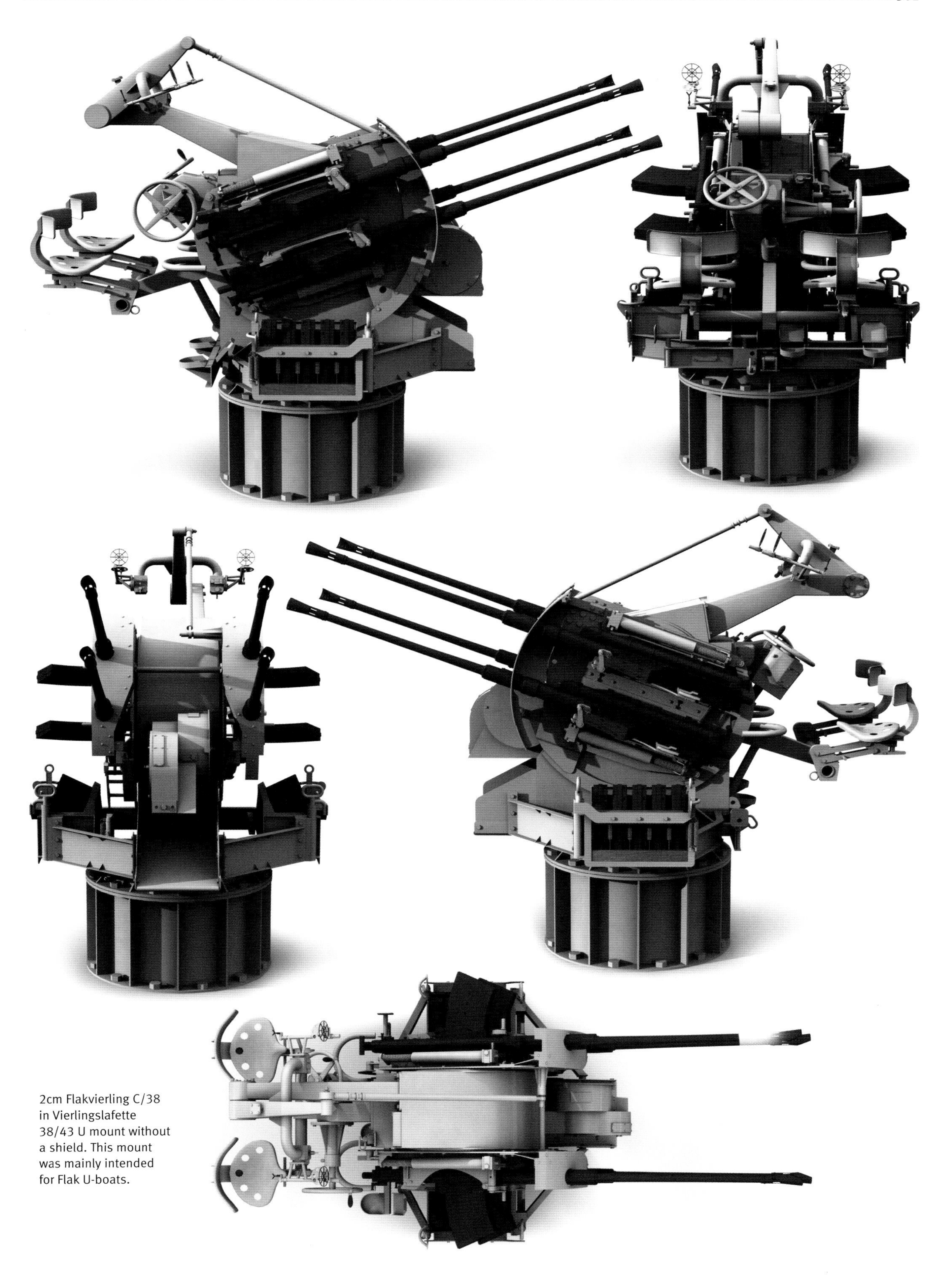

2cm Flakvierling C/38 in Vierlingslafette 38/43 U mount without a shield. This mount was mainly intended for Flak U-boats.

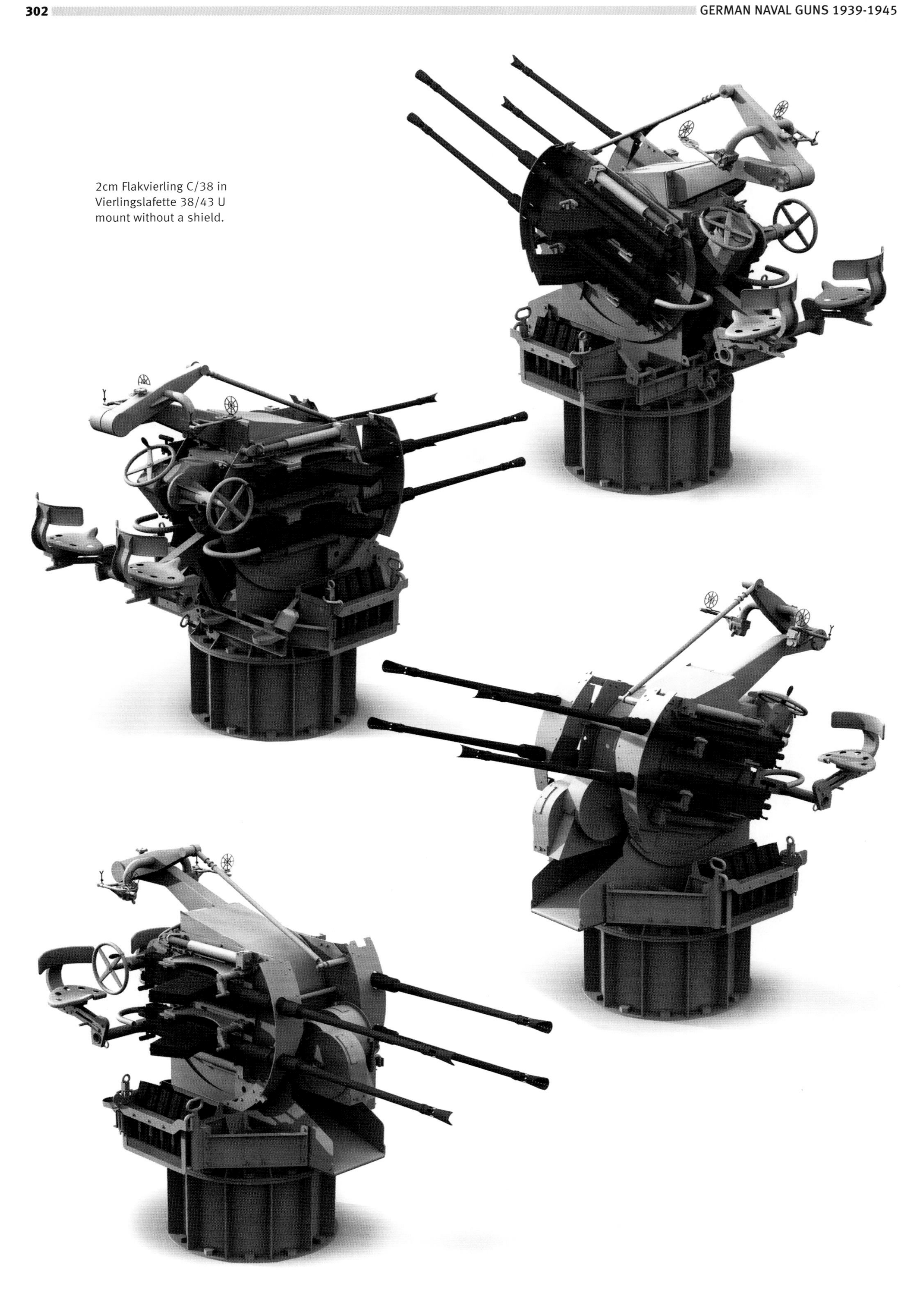

2cm Flakvierling C/38 in Vierlingslafette 38/43 U mount without a shield.

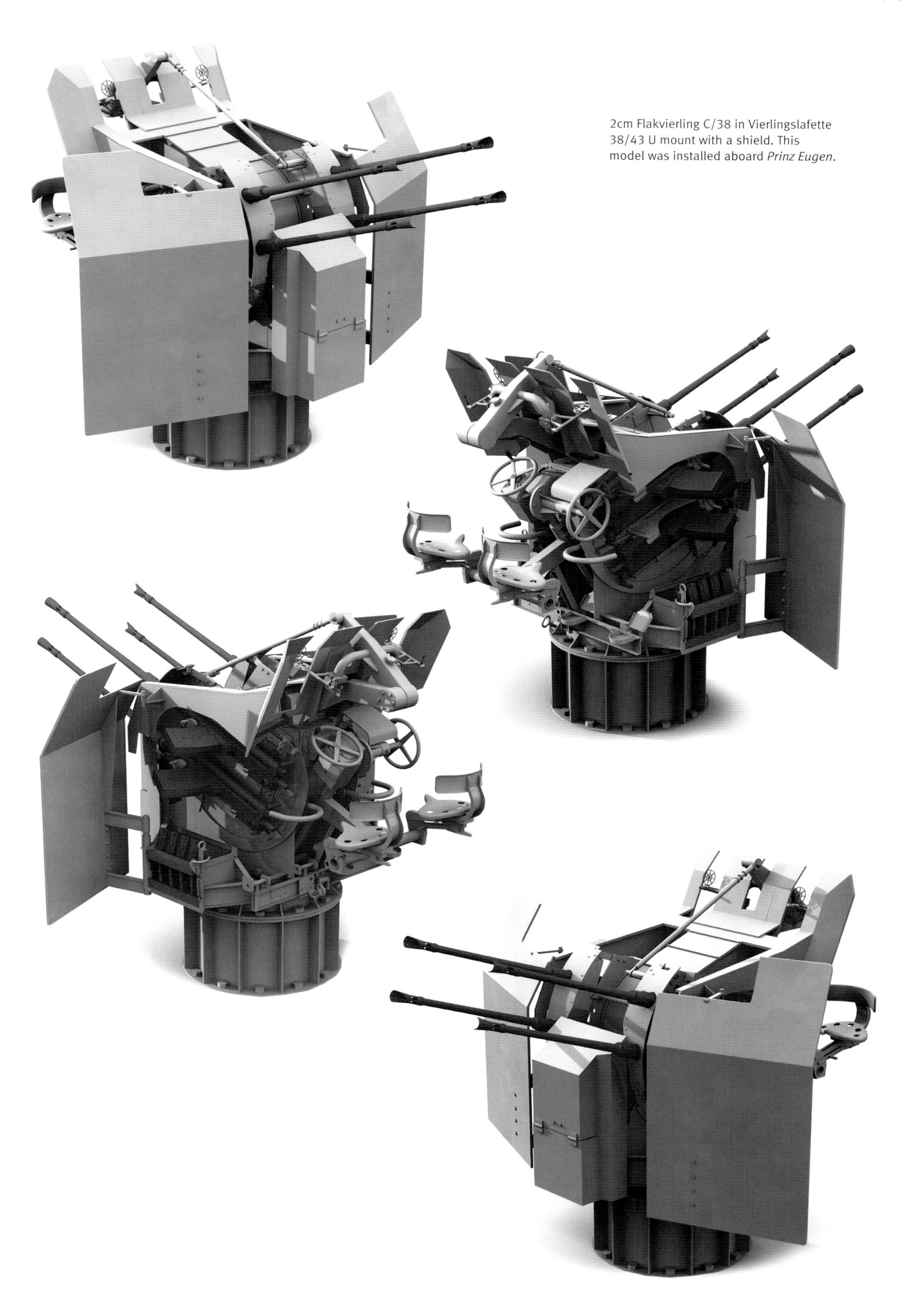

2cm Flakvierling C/38 in Vierlingslafette 38/43 U mount with a shield. This model was installed aboard *Prinz Eugen*.

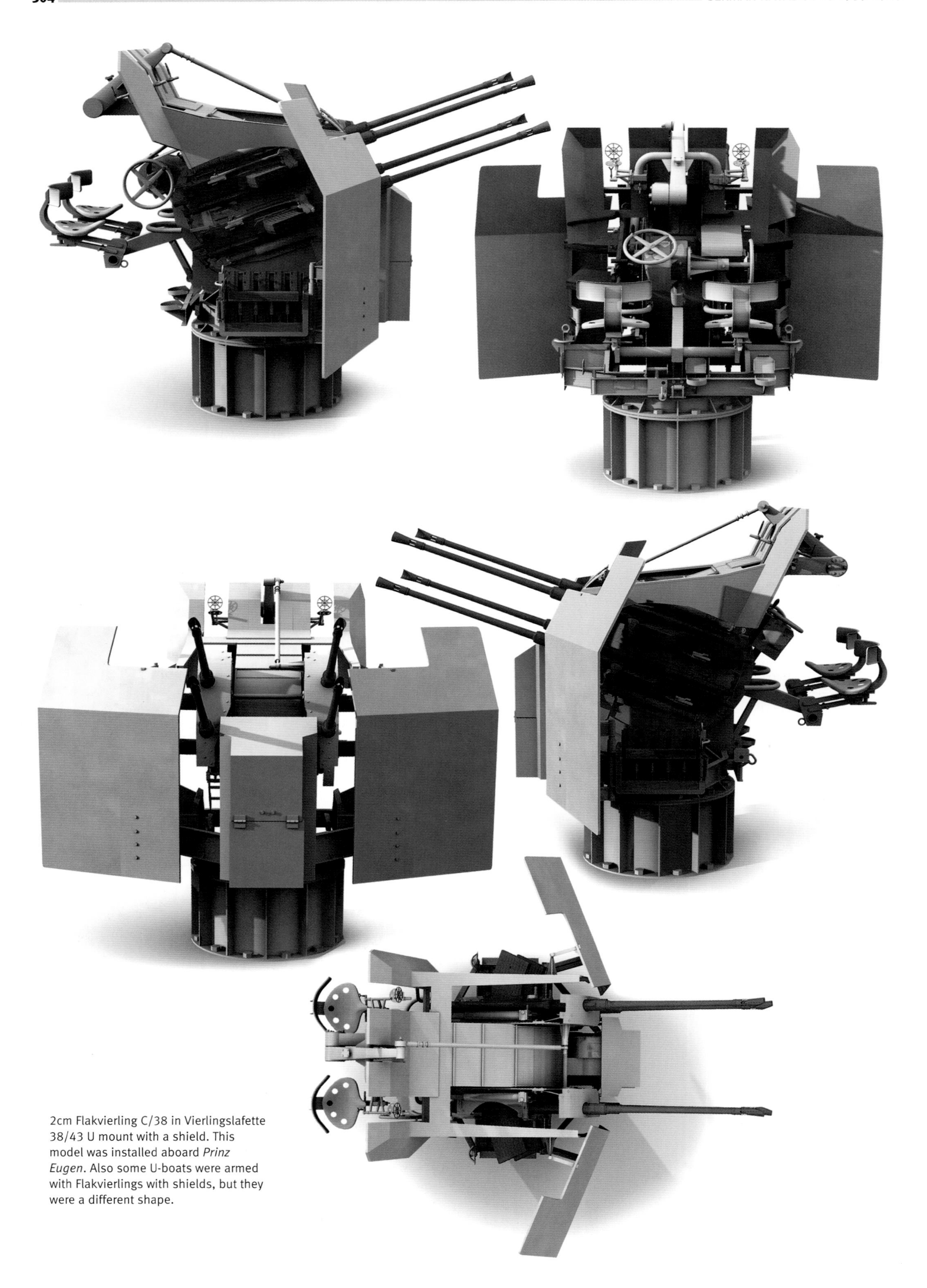

2cm Flakvierling C/38 in Vierlingslafette 38/43 U mount with a shield. This model was installed aboard *Prinz Eugen*. Also some U-boats were armed with Flakvierlings with shields, but they were a different shape.

17

3.7cm GUNS

Just like 20mm cannon, 37mm anti-aircraft guns were installed aboard almost every Kriegsmarine warship. The Germans developed numerous versions of the weapon to suit particular service applications. Most used the same barrel design, and the others had only minor modifications to it. The gun mount was the most frequently changed element. The history of their development is presented in chronological order, allowing the reader to accurately follow the evolution of 37mm guns and their mounts. Unfortunately space prohibits inclusion of the prototype models, only a few examples of which were built. I believe that at some time in the future a separate monograph on these designs will be published.

Analysis of documents and photographs permits accurate identification of the types of 37mm anti-aircraft guns[1] and their mounts fitted to U-boat conning towers between 1939 and 1945. The commonest types were:

(a) 3.7cm SK/C30U gun on Ubts. L C 30 mount.
(b) 3.7cm SK C/30U gun on Ubts. L C 39 mount.
(c) 3.7cm M 42U gun on LM 42U mount.
(d) 3.7cm M 42U gun on LM 43U mount.
(e) 3.7cm M 42U mount on DLM 43U mount.
(f) 3.7-cm Flak Zwilling M 42U on LM 42U mount.

1 Including the 3cm Flak M 44 on the LM 44U mount for Type XXI U-boats

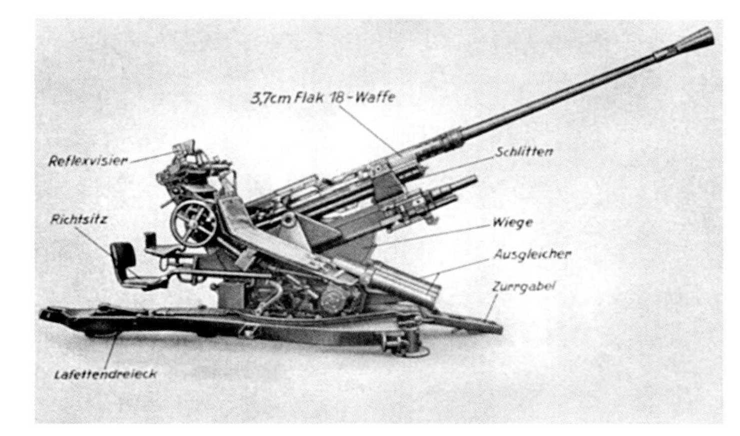

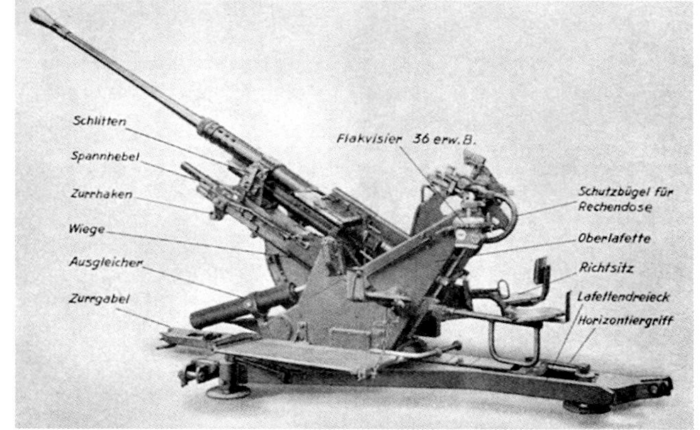

Below: The prototype 3.7cm Flak 37 land anti-aircraft gun. A naval weapon was derived from this model. *(M Skwiot collection)*

3.7cm Flak 36 and Flak 37 guns

In 1936, improved versions of the Flak 18 gun – the Flak 36 and Flak 37 – were put into production. They worked on the short recoil principle. After a round was fired, the breech opened, the bolt slid back, the empty casing was ejected, the returning bolt chambered another round and the breech closed again. The gun fired shells with a self-destruct mechanism and had a range of 3,600-4,200m. When firing armour-piercing shells without the self-destruct feature its range was greater, extending up to 8,000m. Ammunition was supplied in six-round strips loaded from the left, spent cases being ejected from the right-hand side of the gun. In the final stages of the war, this type of gun was installed aboard small transport barges and other Kriegsmarine auxiliary vessels, but it is difficult to be sure exactly what types of vessel received them and when. There was a war going on, and difficulties in manufacturing and supply meant that some naval vessels were equipped with the land-service version of the gun, particularly when the Germans were in retreat.

Operating principle of the gun

The monobloc barrel had rifling of increasing right-hand pitch. The end of the barrel was threaded on the outside so that a flash guard could be fitted. There was a bayonet joint at the base of the barrel to fit it into the breech ring and attach the slide. Inside the slide was a cylindrical bolt with a perpendicular charging handle, which moved along a horizontal slit in the right side of the receiver. This slit was curved, so that as the bolt approached the chamber it rotated anti-clockwise (seen from the rear), and at that moment the lugs on the face of the breech meshed with those on the barrel extension. After firing, the whole assembly (barrel with extension, bolt and control mechanism) recoiled together inside the receiver. After travelling 43mm, the base of the charging handle encountered the curve in the guiding slit which forced the bolt to rotate anti-

Above: The first naval 37mm guns were developed in the mid-1920s. The photograph shows a 3.7cm SK C/30 gun in a triaxially-stabilised C/30 mount – this version was put into production in 1930. The first ships to carry them were the 'K' class light cruisers and *Deutschland* class 'pocket battleships'. The photograph shows the gun aboard the cruiser *Königsberg*. *(A Jarski collection)*

Above: The land version of the 37mm gun was widely used by Wehrmacht and Luftwaffe units. The photograph shows such gun manned by its crew. *(CAW collection)*

Above: In 1934 3.7cm SK C/30 guns on Dopp. L C/30 mounts were introduced. The photographs shows the midships of the 'pocket battleship' *Admiral Scheer*. *(A Jarski collection)*

Below: Two photographs of 3.7cm SK C/30 guns aboard *Scharnhorst*. *(A Jarski collection)*

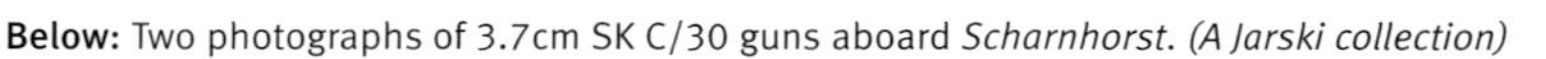

Left: Crew of a 3.7cm SK C/30 gun at action stations aboard *Gneisenau*. *(S Breyer collection)*

clockwise, disengaging the barrel. As recoil continued the control mechanism, via a cam, moved an arm which pushed the bolt further back. Meanwhile the barrel, slide and control mechanism halted their movement after 200mm and were then pushed back to their original position by the recuperating spring. The empty case was removed from the chamber by the extractor on the recoiling bolt, and it was then struck by the ejector pin and thrown out to the right. The spring of the firing pin inside the bolt was automatically compressed just after unlocking. If the gunner lifted his foot from the firing pedal, the bolt would stop once it reached the end stopper at the base of the receiver, held in place by a sear. As the barrel assembly moved

Below: *Scharnhorst* class battleships carried eight 3.7cm SK C/30 guns. A gun of this type installed aboard *Gneisenau* can be seen in the foreground of this photograph. *(CAW collection)*

Above: The destroyer *Erich Koellner* (*Z 13*). A 3.7cm SK C/30 in Dopp. L C/30 mount can be seen on the after funnel platform.

Above: *Admiral Scheer* with 3.7cm SK C/30 guns in Dopp. L C/30 mounts installed – among others – on both sides of the conning tower. *(S Breyer collection)*

Weights of gun components

Gun:	272kg
Barrel (without flash guard):	66.8kg
Flash guard:	4.5kg
Recoil assembly:	137.7kg
Bolt:	10.2kg
Ammunition strip (empty):	2.72kg
Ammunition strip container (empty):	7.8kg

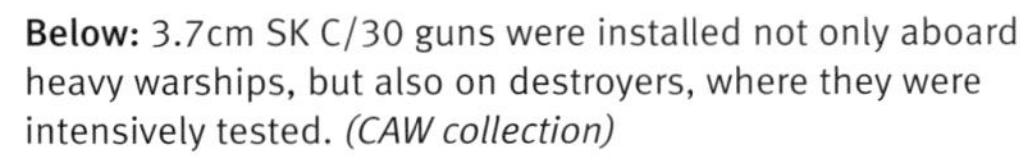

Below: 3.7cm SK C/30 guns were installed not only aboard heavy warships, but also on destroyers, where they were intensively tested. *(CAW collection)*

3.7cm Flak 18 and Flak 36 guns

Calibre:	37mm
Overall length (with flash guard):	3,626mm
(without flash guard):	3,301mm
Length bore:	2,112.2mm
Length chamber:	215mm
Volume chamber:	0.273 dm^3*
Space between shell without tracer) and end of barrel:	38mm
Length rifling:	1,826.4mm
Length between beginning of rifling and rear edge of barrel:	285.8mm
Grooves:	20 (0.55mm x 8.81mm)
Initial rifling twist:	59.95 cal. 3°
End rifling twist:	35.91 cal. 5°
Rate of fire (theoretical):	160rpm
(practical):	80rpm

* Measured from the bottom of the tracer to the bottom of the case

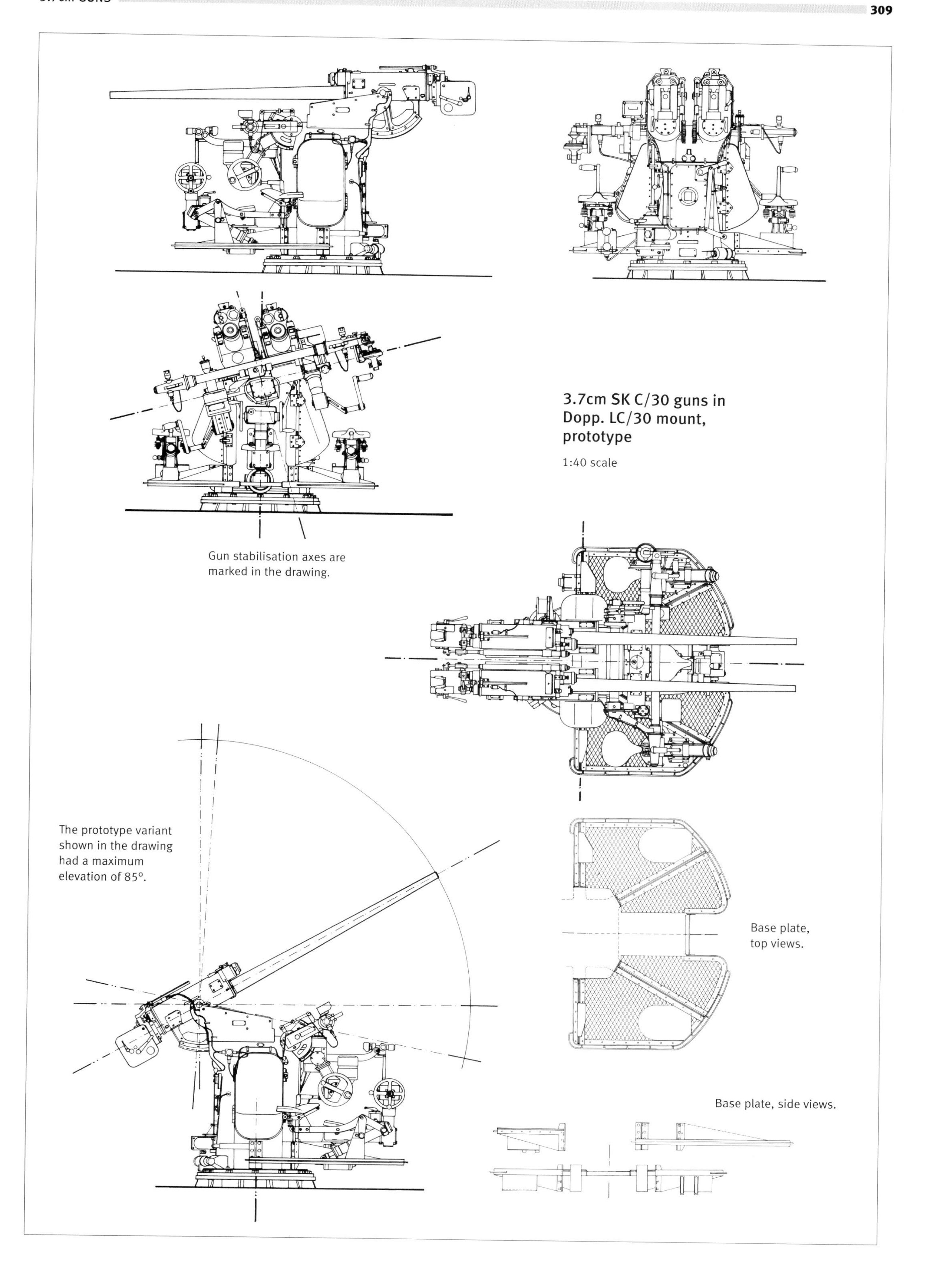
3.7cm SK C/30 guns in Dopp. LC/30 mount, prototype
1:40 scale
Gun stabilisation axes are marked in the drawing.
The prototype variant shown in the drawing had a maximum elevation of 85°.
Base plate, top views.
Base plate, side views.

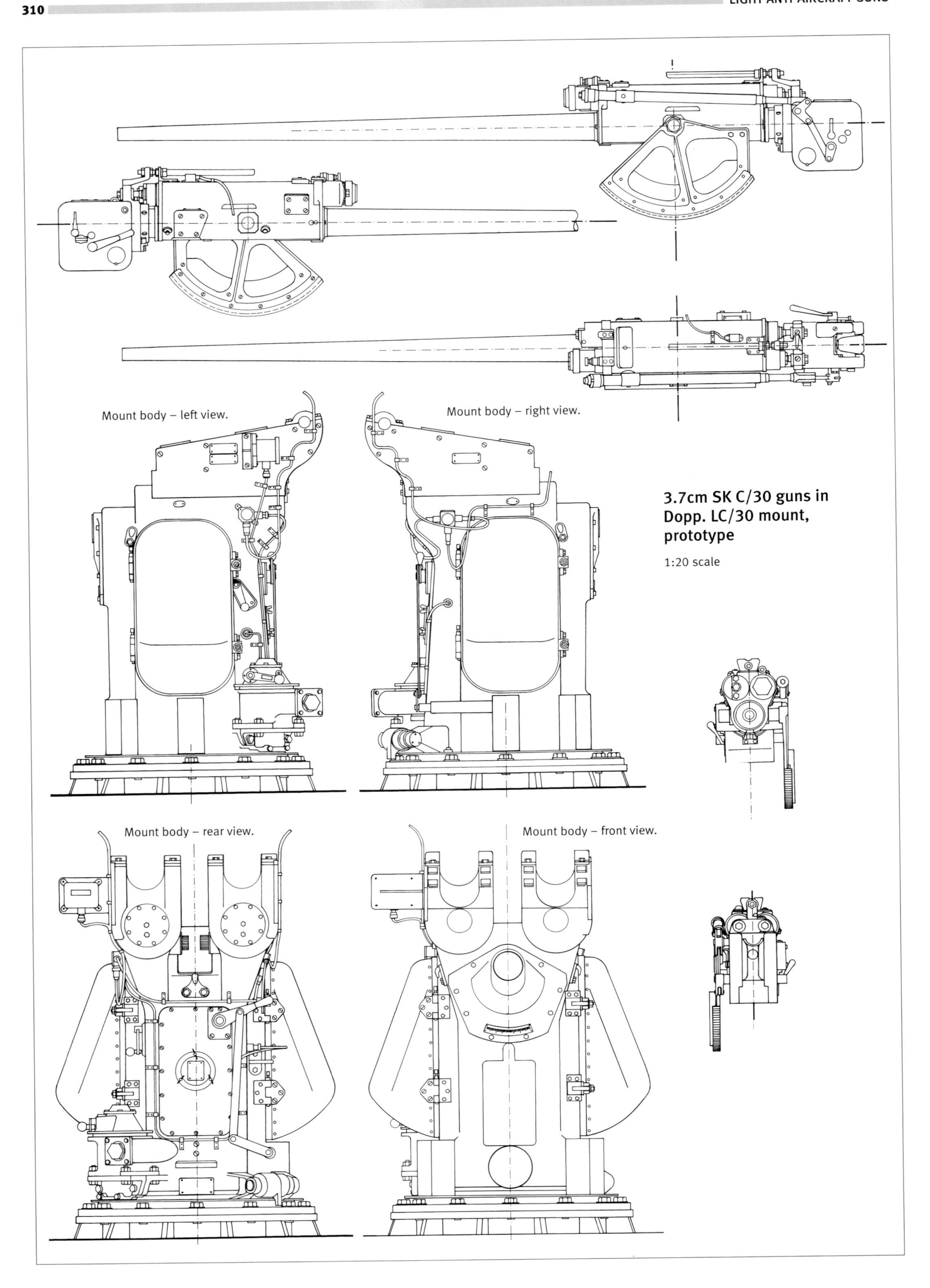

3.7cm SK C/30 guns in Dopp. LC/30 mount, prototype

1:20 scale

Mechanisms of the prototype 3.7cm SK C/30 guns in Dopp. LC/30 mount

Detailed drawings of elevation and training gears.

1:20 scale

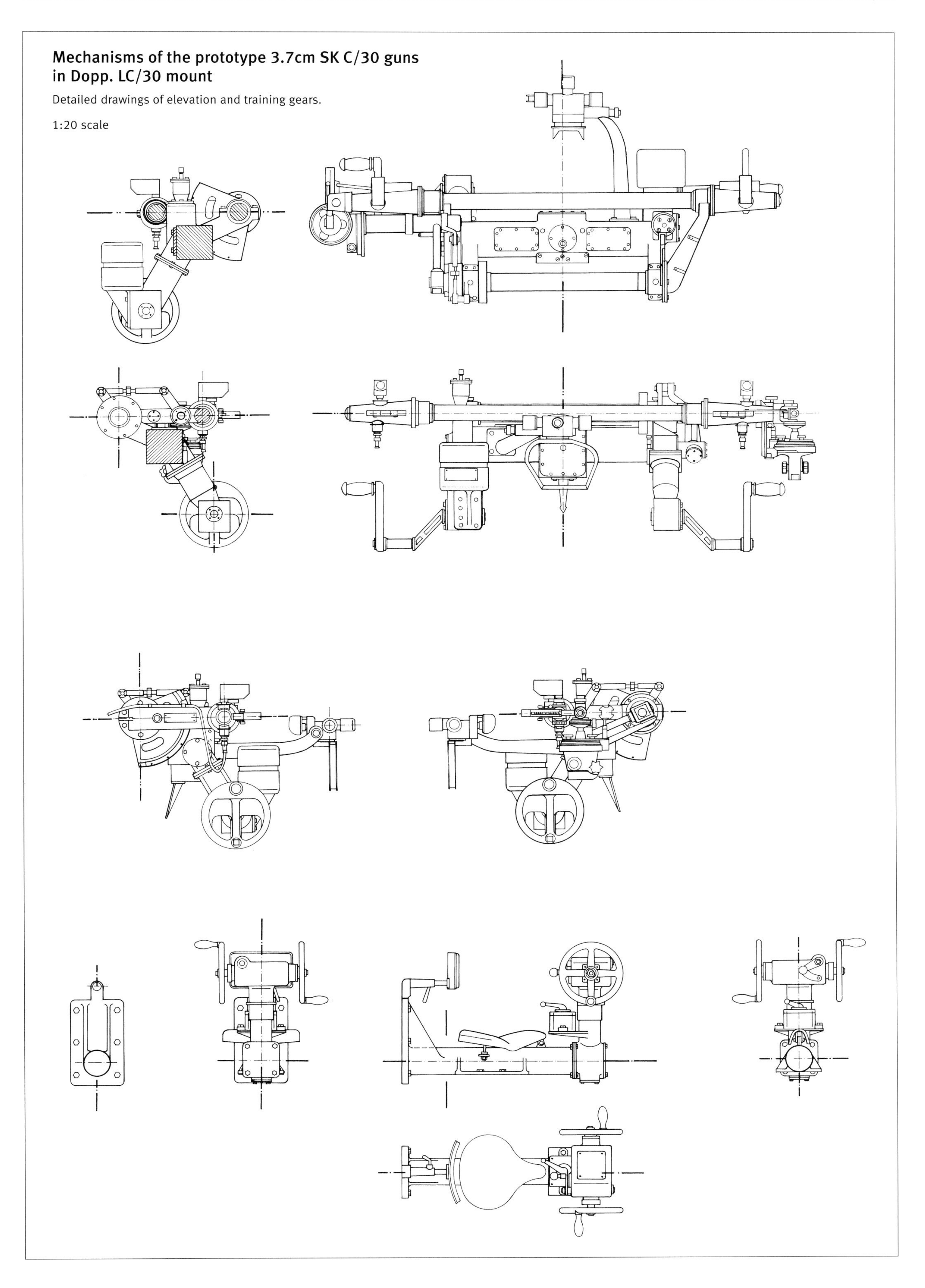

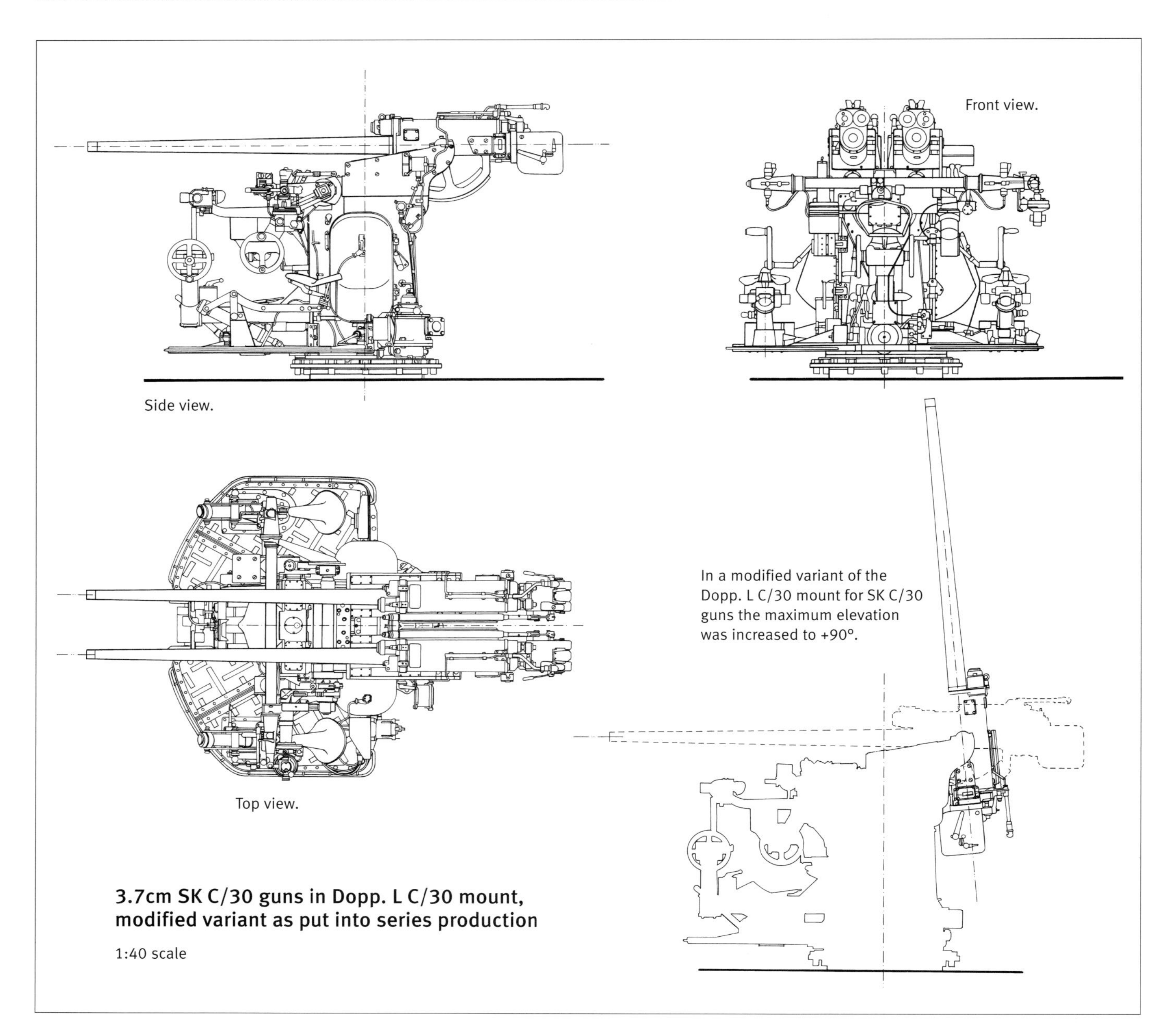

3.7cm SK C/30 guns in Dopp. L C/30 mount, modified variant as put into series production

1:40 scale

Right: 3.7cm SK C/30 guns in Dopp. L C/30 mount.

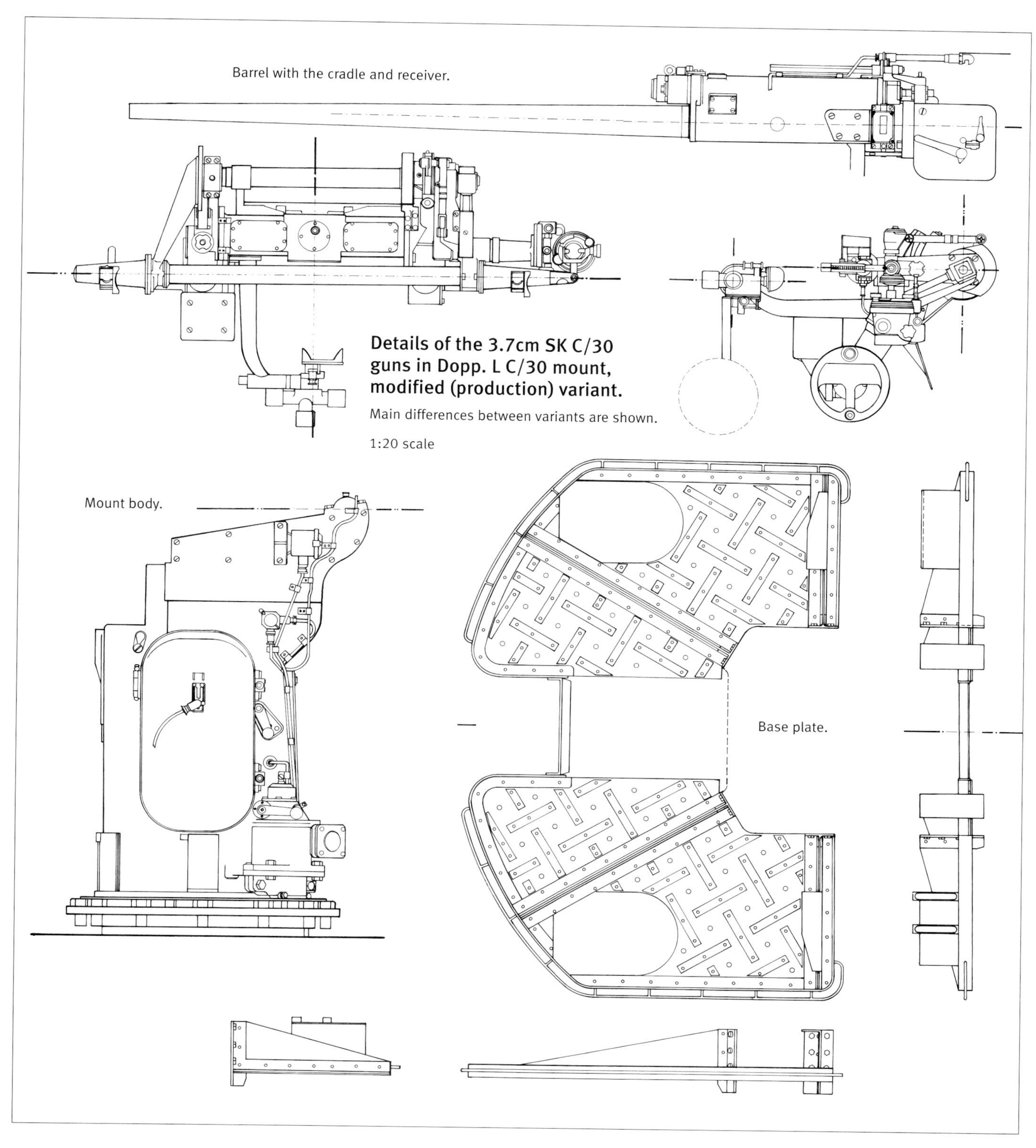

Details of the 3.7cm SK C/30 guns in Dopp. L C/30 mount, modified (production) variant.

Main differences between variants are shown.

1:20 scale

forward again it activated the ammunition feed. An ammunition strip, lying on a plate to the left, moved to the right, pushing another round into the path of the bolt. Pressing the trigger sent the bolt forward, driven by the spring of the recoil mechanism on the right of the gun, chambering the round and firing it. After firing the last round in a strip, the bolt automatically stopped in the rearmost position. The safety mechanism was fitted to the lower left-hand side of the receiver. It had two positions: 'Sicher' (Safe) and 'Feuer' (Fire).

Mount

The 3.7cm Flak 18 was originally fitted on the Model 18 mount, which had a cruciform base to which wheels could be attached for transport. The pedestal with the gun was fixed to this base. The gunner's seat was on the left-hand side of the mount, with the training and elevation handwheels. All of these elements were attached to the base of the sight. The gun's centre of gravity was located forward of the cradle's axis, so two counterbalance springs were installed on each side, with a third to compensate for the other two at high angles of elevation. The later Model 36 mount had a flat triangular base on three legs. The gunner's position was relocated to the right side of the pedestal, while a small platform for the loader to stand on was on the left. Instead of three counterbalance springs the new mount had only two

Right: Modified version of the 3.7cm SK C/30 in Dopp. L C/30 mount installed aboard *Admiral Hipper*. A censor has obscured new gun sights and elevation gear. *(CAW collection)*

Right: *Tirpitz* in a Norwegian fjord. A twin anti-aircraft gun – the production variant of the 3.7cm SK C/30 in Dopp. L C/30 mount – is seen in the foreground of the photograph. *(A Jarski collection)*

Below: Crew of improved 3.7cm SK C/30 guns in Dopp. L C/30 mount at action stations. *(CAW collection)*

telescoping spring assemblies at the front, connected to the cradle below the barrel.

II. 3.7cm SK C/30 gun

Development of 37mm guns for the Reichsmarine began in the mid-1920s. The first studies were carried out by Krupp and Rheinmetall, using the Flak 18 gun as a basis. Before the Flak 36 was developed, naval vessels used an improved variant of the Flak 18, designated the 3.7cm SK C/30, installed on a biaxially-stabilised single mount. In 1934 an 8mm-thick shield as introduced for this mount, but it reduced maximum elevation from +90° to + 80°. The first of these guns were fitted aboard the light cruiser *Nürnberg*, and smaller warships such as torpedo boats and the Type 35 minesweepers. The same type of gun was also used on U-boats, as the C/30 U, on unshielded C/39 mounts. However, operational

Left: Destroyers of this class had their 37mm guns installed on the after funnel platform. *(CAW collection)*

Left: Crew of 3.7cm SK C/30 guns in Dopp. L C/30 mounts aboard a German destroyer at action stations. *(CAW collection)*

Below: German destroyers with 3.7cm SK C/30 guns in Dopp. L C/30 mounts. *(CAW collection)*

service revealed that the combat effectiveness of this weapon was low: its practical rate of fire was only ninety rounds per minute, while that of the Flak 36 was 120 rounds per minute. The speed of traverse was also too slow, and although the theoretical effective ceiling of the gun was 6,500m, in practice it turned out to be only 2,000m! This inferior performance – far worse than expected – and information about successful foreign designs caused the Germans to begin work on improving the gun.

At this point we need to mention the triaxially-stabilised mount, invented by an engineer named Waninger in 1911 for a 105mm gun. This would be a feature of the new version of the SK C/30 cannon. The design of a twin 3.7cm SK C/30 gun on the triax-

Above: Torpedo boats were armed with one Dopp. L C/30 mount with 3.7cm SK C/30 guns installed aft. *(CAW collection)*

ially-stabilised Dopp. L C/30 mount was ready by 1930. Training, elevation and stabilisation were each controlled by a separate gunner. The gun had a semi-automatic breech, firing fixed ammunition loaded individually by hand. The stabilisation gear could be controlled either manually by two handwheels or mechanically by a gyroscope. The first trial series of twenty mounts were manufactured in 1930, and they were installed aboard the 'pocket battleship' *Deutschland* and the newly-built light cruisers. Before the weapons could fully reveal its drawbacks, it had been accepted as the standard naval light anti-aircraft gun.

The production version of the gun was installed either in single mounts (the biaxially-stabilised L C/30) or twin mounts (the triaxially-stabilised Dopp. L C/30). The mounts were entirely open – there was no protection for the crew either from splinters or the weather, although there were canvas covers for the guns and sights. The lack of crew protection lead to heavy casualties in action, and later in the war shields were fitted aboard some vessels, but they are only rarely seen in photographs. One good example of this is the light cruiser *Nürnberg*: a photograph taken in 1944 shows two shields on a 37mm gun mount, a larger one at the front for the gunners and a smaller one at the rear for the loaders. Occasionally, low shields were fitted to the front of the mount aboard destroyers. The first guns to be produced armed newly-built ships: it was not until production had stabilised and increased that they were retro-fitted to older vessels.[1] Due to high demand, the guns were not only built at the Rheinmetall plant, but also by other companies such as Krupp and Henschel.

The mount

The box-shaped body of the mount rotated around the pedestal fixed to the deck. The training limiters, traversing engine gear, the electric motor in the gyroscope and the two-part platform for the loaders were

1 Apart from German ships, this type of gun was also installed aboard the Spanish cruiser *Canarias*.

Right: 3.7cm SK C/30 guns in Dopp. L C/30 mounts were very popular and installed aboard most Kriegsmarine warships, including auxiliary vessels. *(A Jarski collection)*

The 3.7cm SK C/30 gun

Calibre:	37mm
Weight of gun:	243kg
Overall length:	3,074mm
Length bore:	2,960mm
Length chamber:	357mm
Volume chamber:	0.5dm³
Length rifling	2,554mm
Grooves:	16 (0.55mm x 4.76mm)
Weight projectile:	0.748kg
Propellant charge:	0.365kg of RP C/32
Muzzle velocity:	1,000mps
Working pressure:	2,950kgf/cm²
Approximate service life:	7,500 effective rounds
Maximum range:	8,500m at 35.7°
Maximum ceiling:	6,800m at 85°
Tracer range:	4,800m
Rate of fire (theoretical):	80rpm
(practical):	30rpm
Depression/elevation:	–10°/+80°

attached to the bottom of the body. Adjustable seats for the gunners were attached to the sides. The elevation gunlayer was on the right, and the training layer on the left. At the right rear of the mount was a box with a telephone for communication with the fire-control centre. Between the layers, at the centre of the mount, was the stabilisation layer's position, fixed to the front plate of the mount, with a seat, control wheels and the switch for the gyroscope engine. Above this, in the upper part of the body, was the central axis of the stabilisation system and two parallel gun cradles on articulated joints. A rectangular base frame was attached to the forward end of the central axis, supporting the gears and control wheels for the gunlayers, the balancing weight, transversal barrel support with the telescopic sights and lead calculator, and a forward-pointing fixed arm with the stability control sight and a spirit level for rough calculations. The maximum tilt of the stabilised parts was 19.5° to either side. The guns' rear-mounted pivots allowed elevation of -10°/+85°. Both gun cradles were of identical design, one mirroring the layout of the other.

The breech mechanism was fitted on the side of the receiver. A spring-loaded recuperator and hydraulic recoil brake were mounted over the barrel. The uppermost element of the gun was the recoil travel measurement bar – the correct recoil travel was 335mm. If a rapid change of aim was required, the training control wheel could be uncoupled, the mount quickly traversed and the drive then recoupled. When in harbour or in stormy weather, the mount could be secured to the deck by a special frame fitted over the receivers of the guns, while the barrels and sights were protected by metal covers. Each mount had a crew of eight: two gunlayers, the stabilisation operator, two loaders, two ammunition carriers and the commander.

The guns installed had very long barrels – up to 83 calibres in length – and semi-automatic vertically-sliding breech blocks. Rounds were individually hand-loaded, while breech-locking and extraction/ejection of spent cases was automatic. The 0.748kg shell reached a muzzle velocity of 1,000mps, which gave a maximum ceiling of 6,800m and a horizontal range of 8,500m. The practical rate of fire was determined in practice by the efficiency of the crew, a well-trained section being able to achieve thirty rounds per minute per barrel. The twin Dopp. L C/30 mount was manually trained and elevated. Elevation speed was 3°/sec and training speed 4°/sec. The guns fired fixed 162mm-long 37 x 381R 0.748kg shells, of which 0.365kg was the Fp 02 explosive charge. The complete round weighed 2.1kg and was 516mm long, the case containing 0.97kg of RPC/32 propellant. The shells used C/30 and C/34 nose fuses and could also be fitted with C/34 tracers (12 seconds burn time).

The cradle weighed 152.2kg, the mount 2,162kg, optical instruments 87kg and electrical equipment 630kg, the complete weight of a gun position being 3,670kg.

Above: 3.7cm SK C/30 guns in Dopp. L C/30 mounts on the after funnel platform. *(CAW collection)*

Below: Crew of a 3.7cm SK C/30 gun in Dopp. L C/30 mount at action stations aboard an auxiliary warship. Note the helmets attached to the outside. *(CAW collection)*

Right: Maintenance of 3.7cm SK C/30 guns in Dopp. L C/30 mount. *(CAW collection)*

Below: A 3.7cm SK C/30 in Dopp. L C/30 mount installed on the after part of a ship. Details of the gun can be seen clearly. *(CAW collection)*

Left: Installation of this type of gun was quite simple – its pedestal was bolted down to the deck. The photograph shows a moment of loading a 3.7cm SK C/30 gun in Dopp. L C/30 mount aboard an auxiliary vessel. *(CAW collection)*

Left: Gun crew at action stations. *(CAW collection)*

Above and left: Kriegsmarine auxiliary ships carried 3.7cm SK C/30 guns in Dopp. L C/30 mounts installed on specially-reinforced platforms. *(Both photos CAW collection)*

The aircraft carrier *Graf Zeppelin*

Graf Zeppelin was armed with twenty-two 3.7cm SK C/30 anti-aircraft guns in twin triaxially-stabilised Dopp. L C/30 mounts. They were laid out as follows: one on a forecastle platform, six on sponsoned platforms on the port side, three on the starboard side and one on the starboard side of the superstructure, just forward of the funnel. According to the ship's artillery specification dated 6 May 1940,[1] she was to carry 44,000 high-explosive shells and star shell for her 37mm guns – i.e. 2,000 rounds per barrel – the total weight of that ammunition being 131.2 tonnes.

Battleships

The first guns of this type to be produced were installed aboard the *Deutschland* class 'pocket battleships'. The first of the class to receive them was *Deutschland* herself, during her stay at the Marinewerft yard at Wilhelmshaven from December 1934 to January 1935. She received eight 3.7cm SK C/30 guns in twin Dopp. L C/30 mounts. The layout became the standard one for the class: two forward on a platform in front of the forward superstructure, and two on the superstructure aft, either side of the after rangefinder. She kept this number of guns until May 1944. After that, whilst in the shipyard at Gotenhafen (Polish Gydnia) in late August – early September 1944, the four mounts were replaced with 4cm Flak 28 Bofors guns. The second of class, *Admiral Scheer*, received her eight 3.7cm SK C/30 guns in 1935 which remained aboard until November 1944 when they were replaced with Flak 28s. The final 'pocket battleship', *Admiral Graf Spee*, had her eight 37mm guns from her commissioning until she was scuttled in December 1939. All three ships originally carried 2,000 rounds per gun, though the former two had that increased to 6,000 rounds per gun when operating in Norwegian waters.

The medium anti-aircraft batteries of the battleships *Scharnhorst* and *Gneisenau* were identical and each consisted of sixteen guns in eight Dopp. L C/30 mounts. Four mounts were located on the lower superstructure deck ('Aufbaudeck'), abaft of 'B' turret. Two more were fitted below the admiral's bridge, on the same level as the 7m rangefinder, another two abreast the after fire control station, on the superstructure deck, and the final pair just forward of 'C' turret on the lower superstructure deck. The ships carried between 8,000 and 24,000 rounds of 37mm ammunition, but never less than 60 per cent of maximum magazine capacity.

Heavy cruisers

Each of the *Admiral Hipper* class heavy cruisers as well as the *Prinz Eugen* carried twelve 3.7cm SK C/30 guns in Dopp. L C/30 mounts when commissioned. Two of these were either side of the forward superstructure, and the remaining four on the after superstructure, forward of 'C' turret. Both surviving cruisers had these guns until the autumn of 1944, when they were removed and replaced with 4cm Flak 28 Bofors. Each ship carried 1,200 rounds of ammunition per barrel.

Light cruisers

The situation was different for the 'K' class cruisers, as these ships had no 37mm guns when first commissioned. They only received them during overhauls in 1935-6, when each ship was armed with eight 3.7cm SK C/30s in four Dopp. L C/30 mounts. Two mounts were on the main deck on either side, just abreast the central section of the forward superstructure, and the

1 BA-MZA W-04/10 669.

Below: A 3.7cm SK C/30 gun in Ubts. L C/39 mount. Designed mainly for submarines, this was also sometimes used on surface vessels. *(CAW collection)*

Above and below: A 3.7cm SK C/30 gun in Ubts. L C/39 mount installed aboard an auxiliary vessel. *(Both photos CAW collection)*

Left: The 3.7cm SK C/30 gun in Ubts. L C/39 mount was designed for Type IX U-boats, but here it can be seen aboard a Type XIV boat, one of the so-called 'milch cows'. *(CAW collection)*

Left: A 3.7cm SK C/30 gun in Ubts. L C/39 mount aboard *U 103* – a Type IX B U-boat. *(CAW collection)*

other two were on both sides of the funnel on the superstructure deck. During the war, it was planned to increase the number of such guns aboard the *Köln* to ten but, just as with the plan to replace the original guns with the new M 42 model on LM 43 mounts, this was never done. Normally each of these ships carried 1,200 rounds of 37mm ammunition per barrel.

The cruisers *Leipzig* and *Nürnberg* had the same number of 37mm guns as the 'K' class. On the former ship, two mounts were positioned either side of the forward superstructure (abreast the forward rangefinder) and the other two were either side of the catapult. Aboard the latter, the first pair were in the same place, but the second pair were mounted on the after superstructure between the catapult and the after rangefinder. The available information on the cruiser Emden states that in 1944 she was armed with two 3.7cm SK C/30 guns on MPL C/30U single pedestal mounts. The armament upgrade programme called for fitting at least nine 37mm guns aboard this ship, but this was never done.

Destroyers and torpedo boats

Type 1936 destroyers usually had four 3.7cm SK C/30 guns on twin L C/30 mounts, installed on a platform near the after funnel. They carried 2,000 rounds of ammunition per barrel.

Right, and opposite, lower: Another example of a 3.7cm SK C/30 gun installed in Ubts. L C/39 mount on a small Kriegsmarine auxiliary vessel. *(Both photos CAW collection)*

Above: An example of a shield installed on 3.7cm guns in Ubts. L C/39 mounts. This photograph shows a non-standard shield which also gave the gun crew protection from the sides. *(CAW collection)*

S-boats ('Schnellboote')

Depending on their class and when they were in service, S-boats could carry a gun of this type in a single C/34 mount, but owing to the scarcity of reliable sources it is difficult to precisely identify the types and numbers of guns installed on individual vessels of this type.

U-boats

The greatest number of modifications to the basic design of the 3.7cm SK C/30 gun were made to weapons installed aboard submarines. This subject was brought up for the first time in 1939 when OKM (Oberkommando der Marine, Naval High Command) ordered Rheinmetall to design a light 37mm anti-

Right: A 3.7cm SK C/30 gun in a single Ubts. L C/39 mount complemented the gunnery outfit of a Type IX U-boat. *(CAW collection)*

Below, left: Another example of a shield installed on 3.7cm guns in Ubts. L C/39 mounts. This is a typical version which provided only frontal protection. *(CAW collection)*

Below, right: A 3.7cm SK C/30 U gun in a Ubts. L C/39 mount installed aboard a Type IX U-boat. Note the conditions in which the gun had to be operated. *(CAW collection)*

Left: Another example of a shield used on a 3.7cm SK C/30 U gun in a Ubts. L C/39 mount installed aboard a destroyer. *(CAW collection)*

aircraft automatic cannon based on the SK C/30 design that would meet the needs of the submarine service. It should be noted that the performance of the existing 37mm gun on the C/30 and later the C/39 mounts was considered very good, apart from the rate of fire being too low. The first years of combat operations had shown that it was necessary to upgrade U-boats' anti-aircraft defences. This was a continuing process, beginning in 1941, to improve protection from the increasing threat of enemy aircraft. The early 3.7cm SK C/30U guns were installed aboard Type IX U-boats (variants A-D/42) on single Ubts. L C/30 mounts, and it was also intended to arm the Type XA, XB and later U-boat types with them. These guns were also planned to be fitted to early U-boat types – mainly the Type VII C boats – but this required alteration of the conning tower. In 1942, OKM ordered that lighter 2cm anti-aircraft guns were to be mounted on a additional platform on the conning tower, known as a 'Wintergarten' ('Bandstand'), and further development of submarine anti-aircraft armament and extending the conning tower to accommodate it continued in parallel. But there were some problems. Initially, the focus was on mounting more anti-aircraft guns on the boats' deck and conning towers, which adversely affected submerged manoeuvrability. In order to eliminate this problem in future designs of U-boat, it was decided to develop powerful anti-aircraft armament housed in streamlined turrets integrated into the structure of the conning tower. This

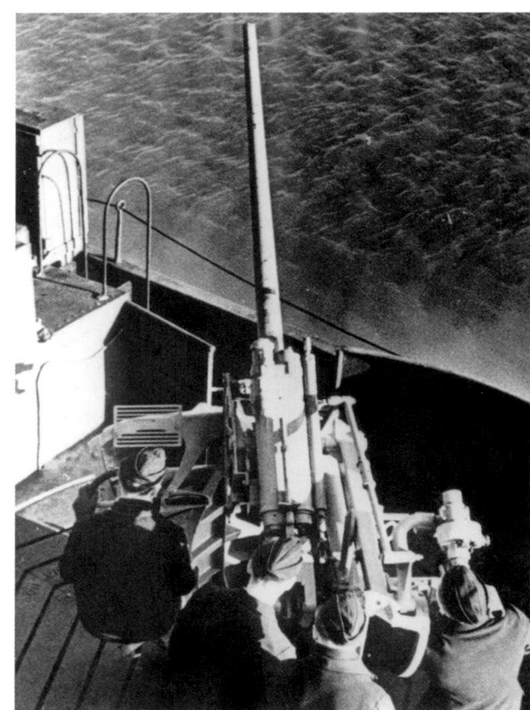

Above, left: Crew of a 3.7cm SK C/30 U gun in a Ubts. L C/39 mount aboard an auxiliary Kriegsmarine vessel. A Type VII C U-boat can be seen in the background. *(CAW collection)*

Above right and right: Two photographs showing examples of 3.7cm SK C/30 U guns in Ubts. L C/39 mounts used on auxiliary surface vessels. *(All photos CAW collection)*

was to be the specially-designed 3cm Flak M 44 gun in the LM 44 mount, but series production never began before the end of the war, only some prototype models being tested in early 1945.

As to the further development of the 3.7cm SK C/30 gun, the design of the new gun and mount was not completed by Rheinmetall until 1944. It was designated Flak M 42 and was supposed to be installed in a number of different types of mount. The parallel development of new submarine conning tower designs resulted in several different structures. The first was the Brückenumbau V, equipped with an additional anti-aircraft platform forward to accommodate either twin 20mm Zwilling guns or a 3.7cm Flak M 42 on a pedestal mount. Among the boats so equipped were *U 345* and *U 362*. The second was the Brückenumbau VI, with an additional position for a 3.7cm Flak M 42 on an open platform in front of the bridge. The first boats to have this were *U 673* and *U 973*. The third, Brückenumbau VII, had platforms both fore and aft, with a 2cm Zwilling and a 3.7cm Flak M 42. This was installed aboard *U 676*.

The next attempt to upgrade U-boats' anti-aircraft defences came in May 1943. It was decided to convert seven submarines into specialised anti-aircraft vessels ('Flak Unterseeboot'). The boats selected for this conversion were *U 211*, *U 256*, *U 263*, *U 271*, *U 441*, *U 621* and *U 953*. They were to be fitted with an augmented anti-aircraft armament consisting of two 2cm Flakvierling 38/43U mounts with shields and a single 3.7cm SK C/30 on a C/39 pedestal mount. They were intended to escort other submarines crossing the Bay of Biscay and defend them from Allied air attacks. A wooden mock-up of the installation was installed on the first of the boats selected for conversion – the Type VII C *U 441* – and then replaced with the real thing. However, sea trials proved that the first anti-aircraft submarine, already re-christened *U Flak 1*, failed to meet expectations and on 11 November 1943 the other conversions were cancelled.

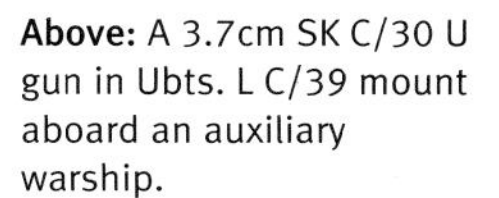

Above: A 3.7cm SK C/30 U gun in Ubts. L C/39 mount aboard an auxiliary warship.

The first 3.7cm Flak M 42 guns on LM 43 mounts were installed on four U-boats in October 1943. The twin version, the 3.7cm Zwilling, was introduced in late 1944 – the first boat to receive it was *U 870*. However, problems with supply meant that the plan of replacing all the 2cm Flakvierling mounts in the U-boat fleet with the 3.7cm Zwilling could not be accomplished, and in the spring of 1944 approximately 20 per cent of boats still had 20mm guns aboard.

Ammunition for anti-aircraft guns aboard U-boats was carried in watertight containers near the guns as well as within the boat. It was found that gun shields were often lost on patrol and crews frequently removed them as a result, which also cut down the drag they caused when running submerged.

III. 3.7cm SK C/30 U

Specifically designed for use aboard U-boats, this gun was installed on two types of pedestal mount, the Ubts. C/30 and the Ubts. C/39. The former was fitted to the first classes of U-boat built, whilst the latter – a biaxially-stabilised pedestal mount – proved to be a

Left: Another example of 3.7cm SK C/30 U gun in Ubts. L C/39 mount used on auxiliary surface vessels. *(All photos CAW collection)*

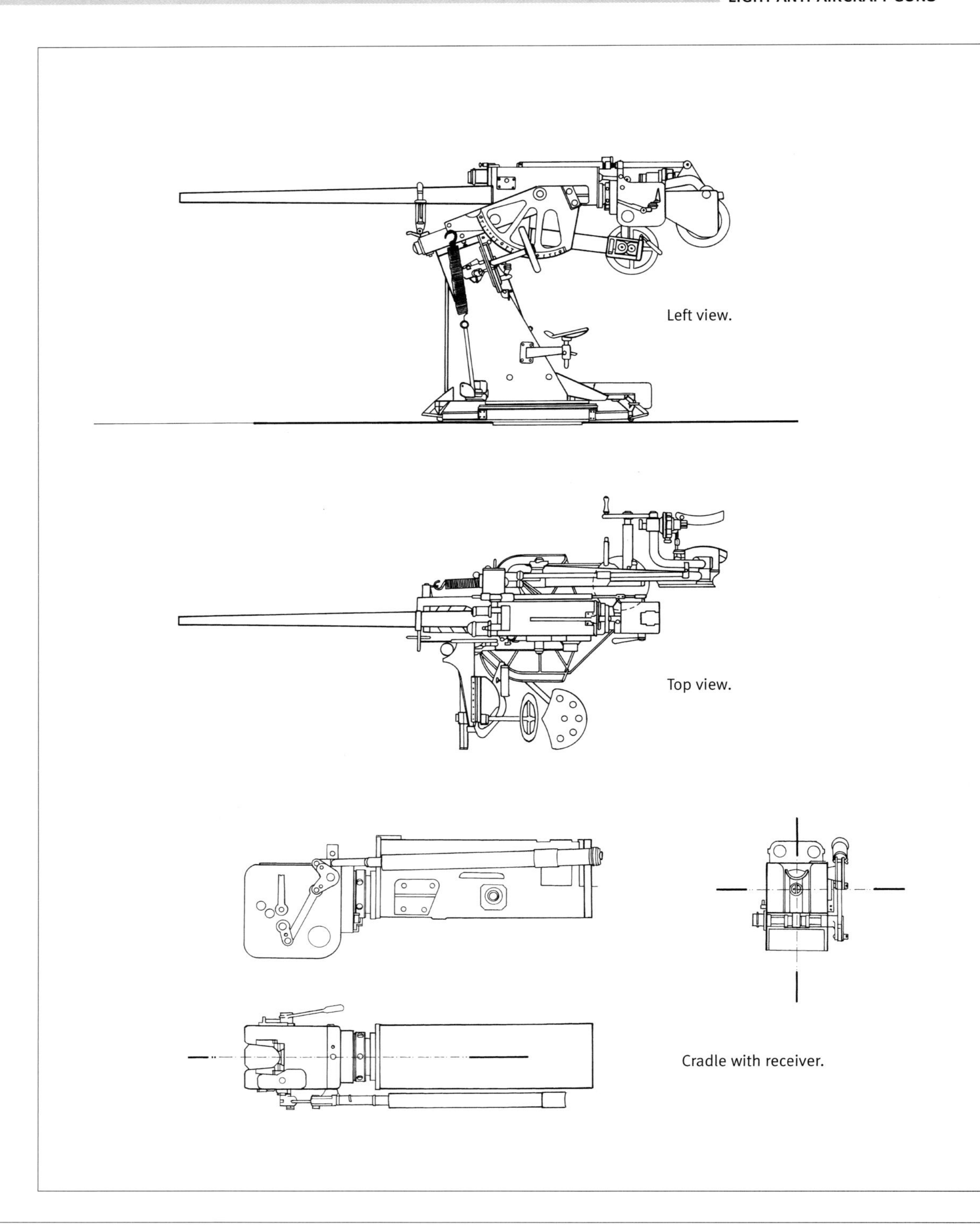
Left view.
Top view.
Cradle with receiver.

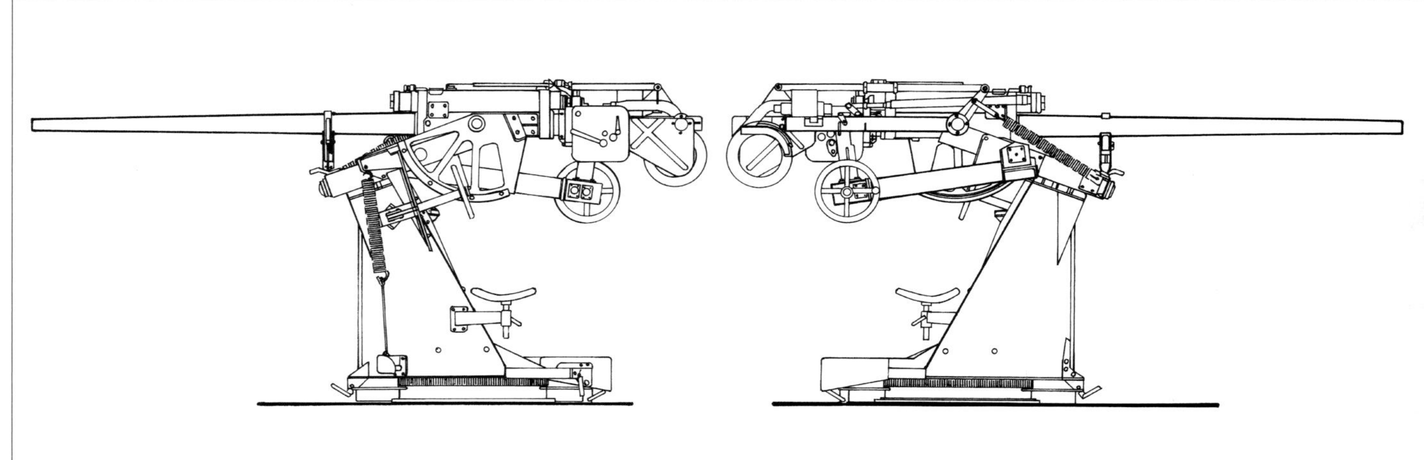

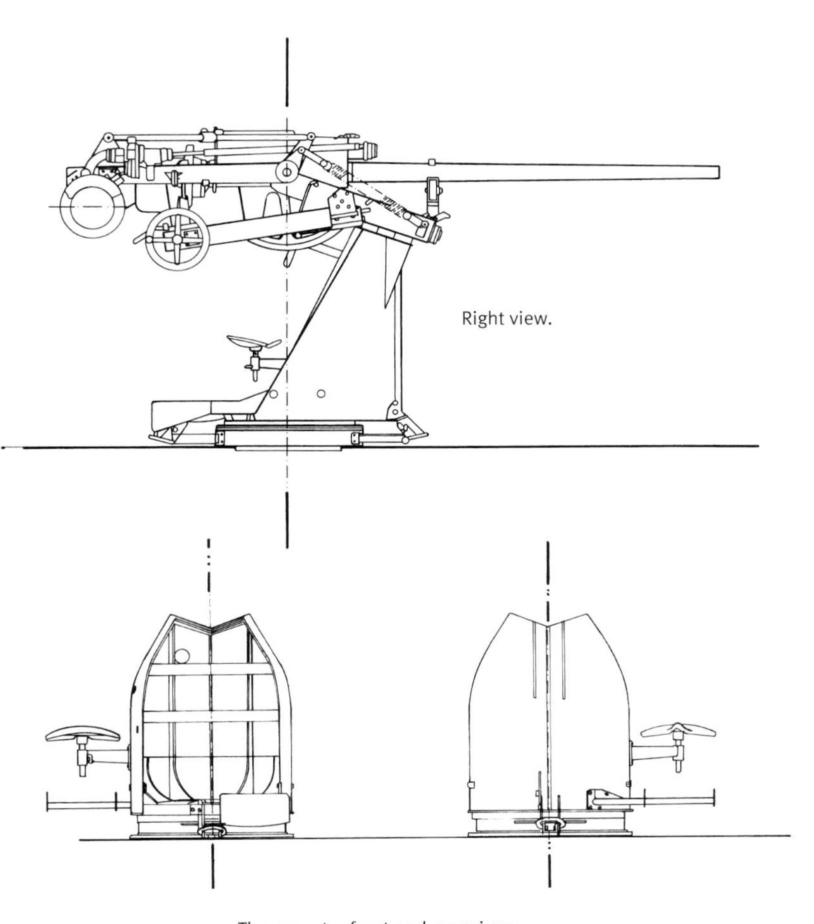

The mount – front and rear views.

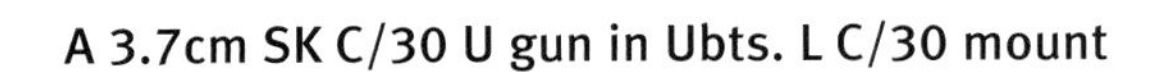

A 3.7cm SK C/30 U gun in Ubts. L C/30 mount

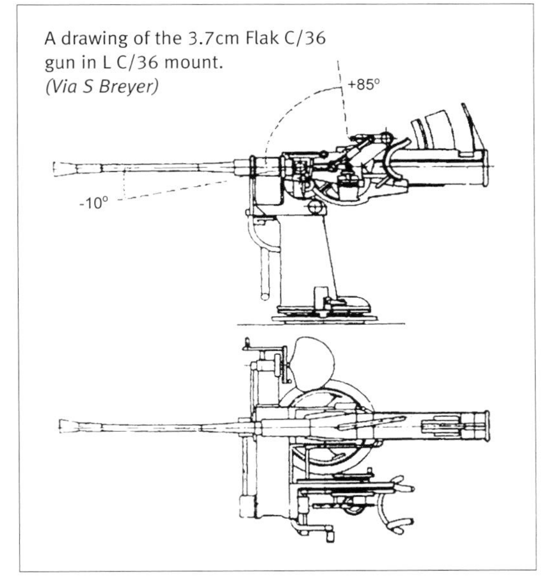

A drawing of the 3.7cm Flak C/36 gun in L C/36 mount. *(Via S Breyer)*

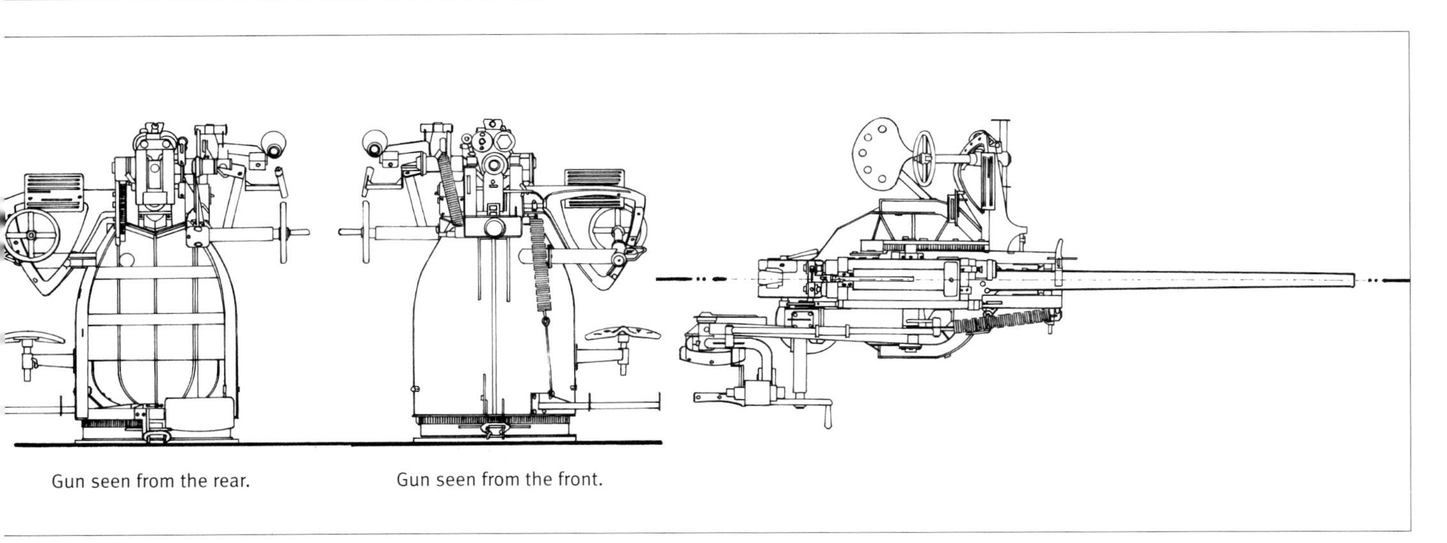

Gun seen from the rear.

Gun seen from the front.

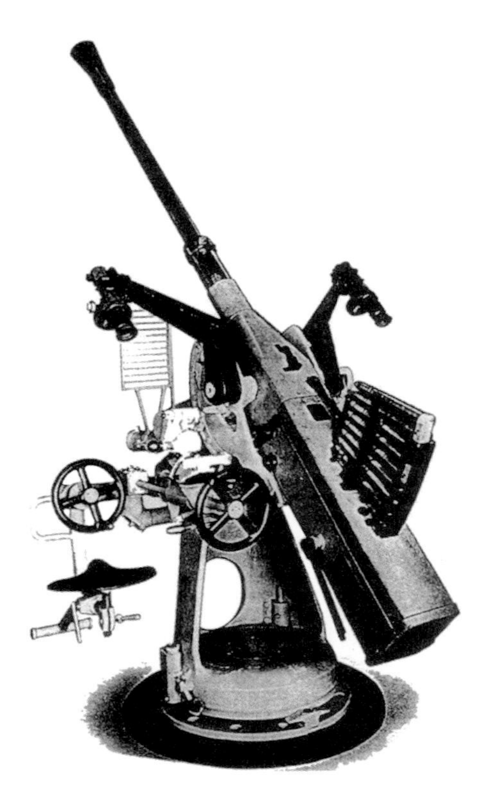

Above: Prototype 3.7cm Flak C/36 gun in C/36 mount. *(S Breyer collection)*

Below and right: Two views of a 3.7cm SK C/30 U gun in Ubts. L C/39 mount installed aboard an auxiliary surface vessel. *(Both photos CAW collection)*

Left: In case of small auxiliary ships the 3.7cm SK C/30 U gun in Ubts. L C/39 mount was the main armament – as was the case with the boat shown here – the gun is installed on her forecastle. *(CAW collection)*

rather disappointing modification of the original model. The early battles with Allied convoys had shown that the gun's rate of fire was insufficient, and also that the rates of training and elevation were too slow. Therefore the C/30 U was soon replaced by the newer 3.7cm Flak M 42. The C/39 mount, which was fitted aboard most Type IX U-boats was also intended to arm the U-Flak boats (i.e. *U 441*). Furthermore, several dozen mounts removed from U-boats were used to arm auxiliary vessels.

IV. 3.7cm Flak M 42

This was an improved variant of the earlier 3.7cm SK C/30 developed by Rheinmetall, which was approved

Below: Prototype 3.7cm Flak M 42 made by Rheinmetall. *(M Skwiot collection)*

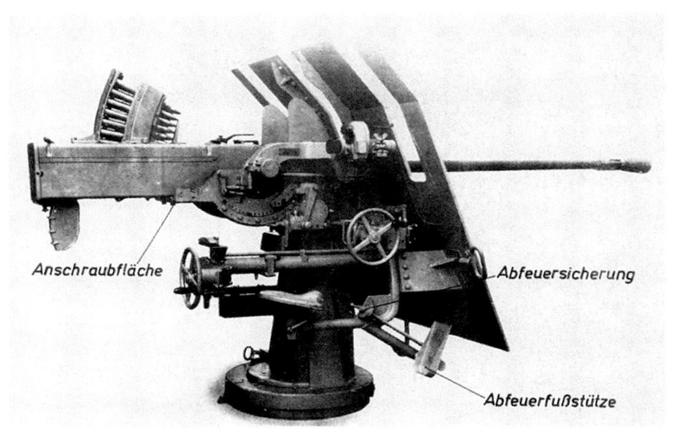

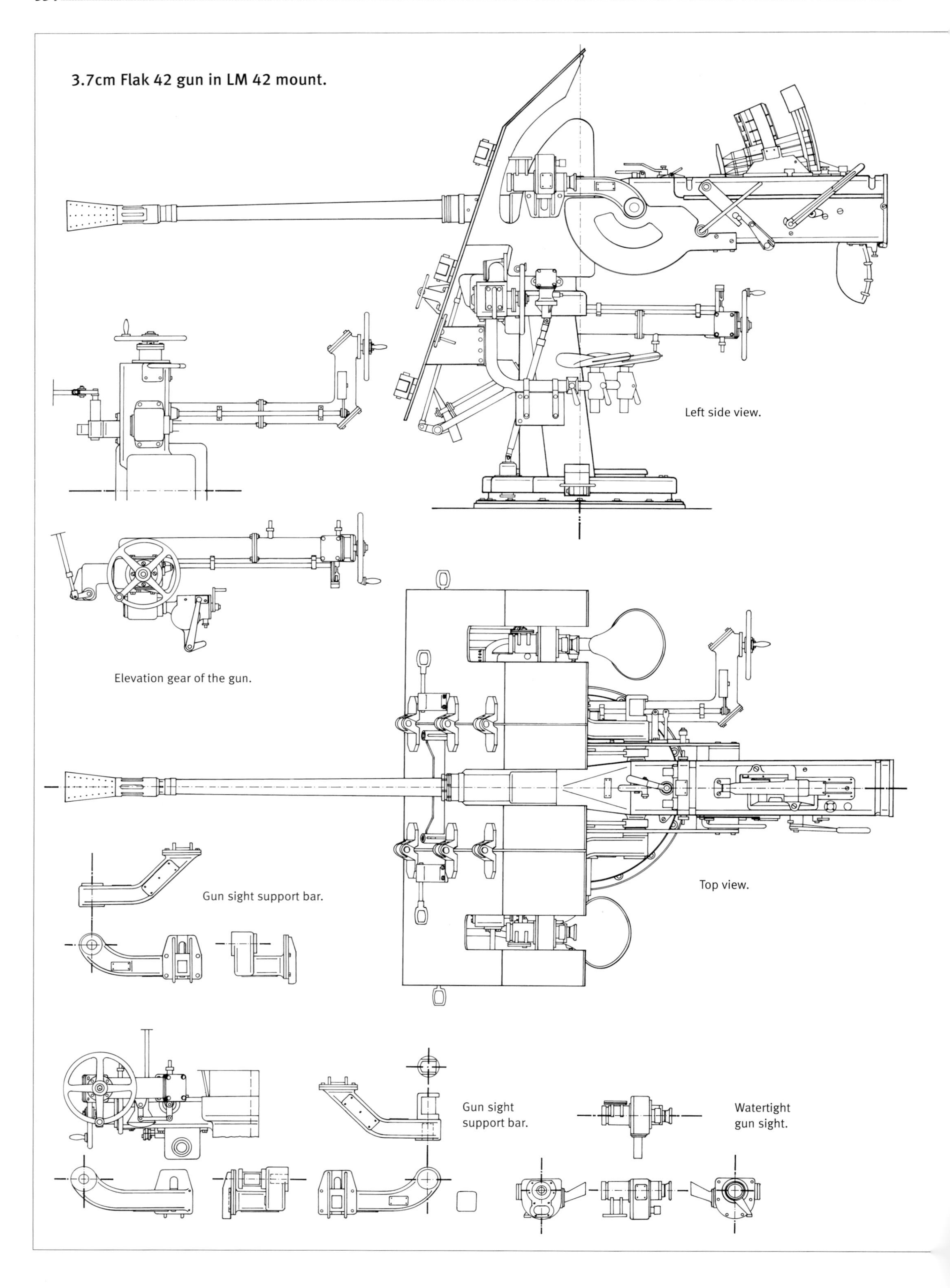

3.7cm Flak 42 gun in LM 42 mount.

Left side view.

Elevation gear of the gun.

Top view.

Gun sight support bar.

Gun sight support bar.

Watertight gun sight.

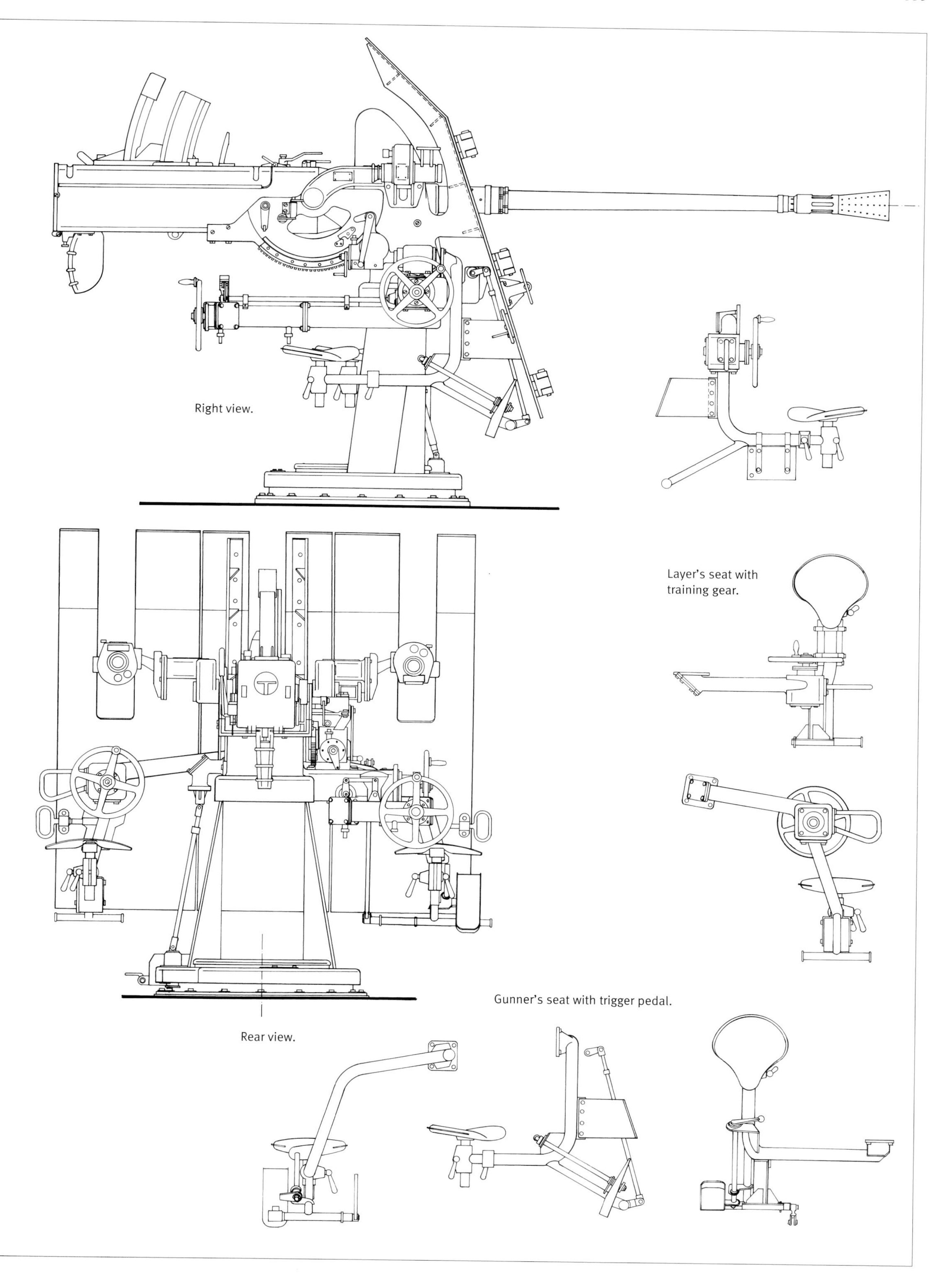
Right view.

Layer's seat with training gear.

Gunner's seat with trigger pedal.

Rear view.

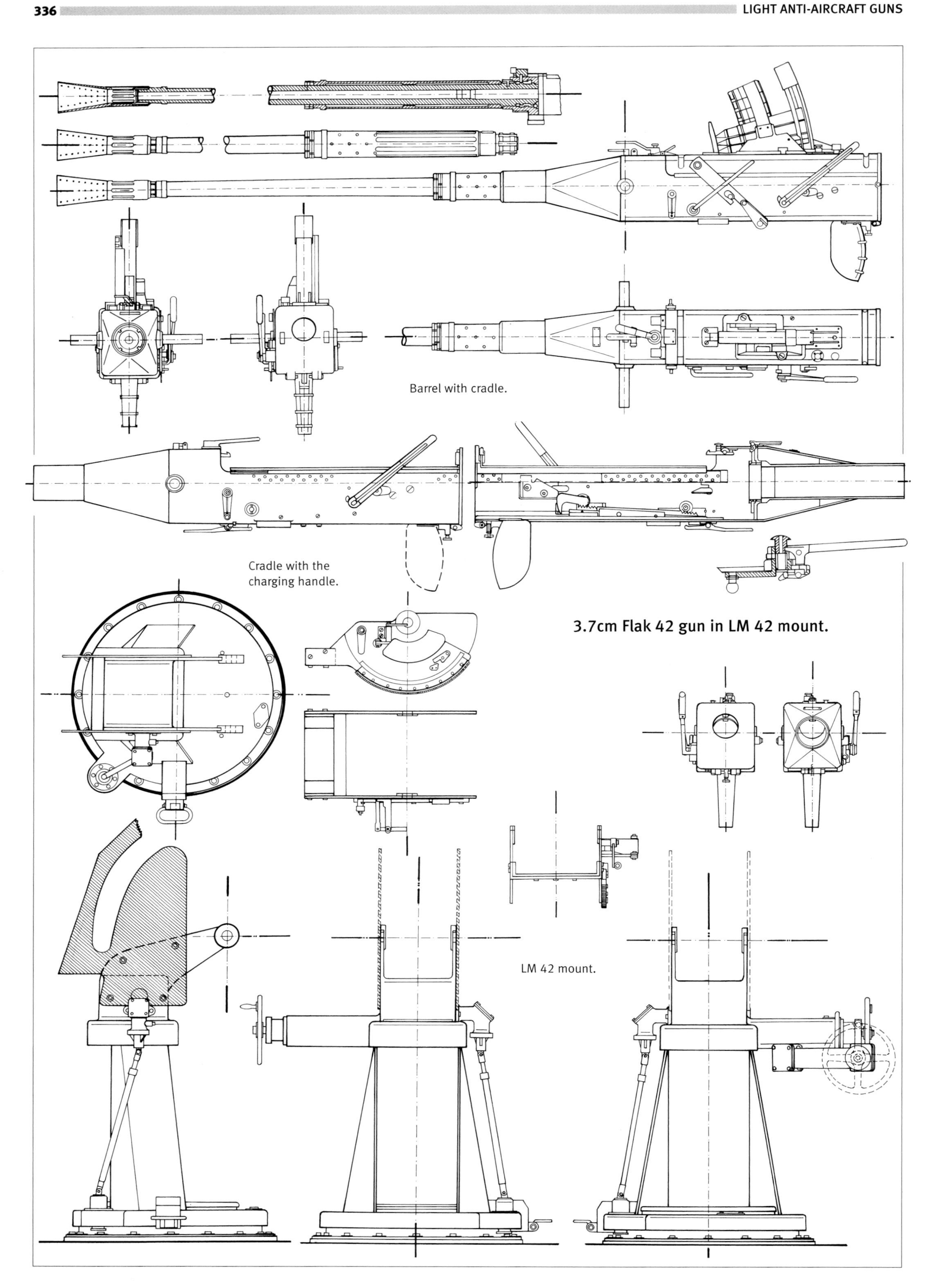

Barrel with cradle.

Cradle with the charging handle.

LM 42 mount.

Left: Preserved and restored 3.7cm Flak M 42 gun in LM 42 mount installed on the conning tower structure of *U 505* displayed in a museum in Chicago, USA.

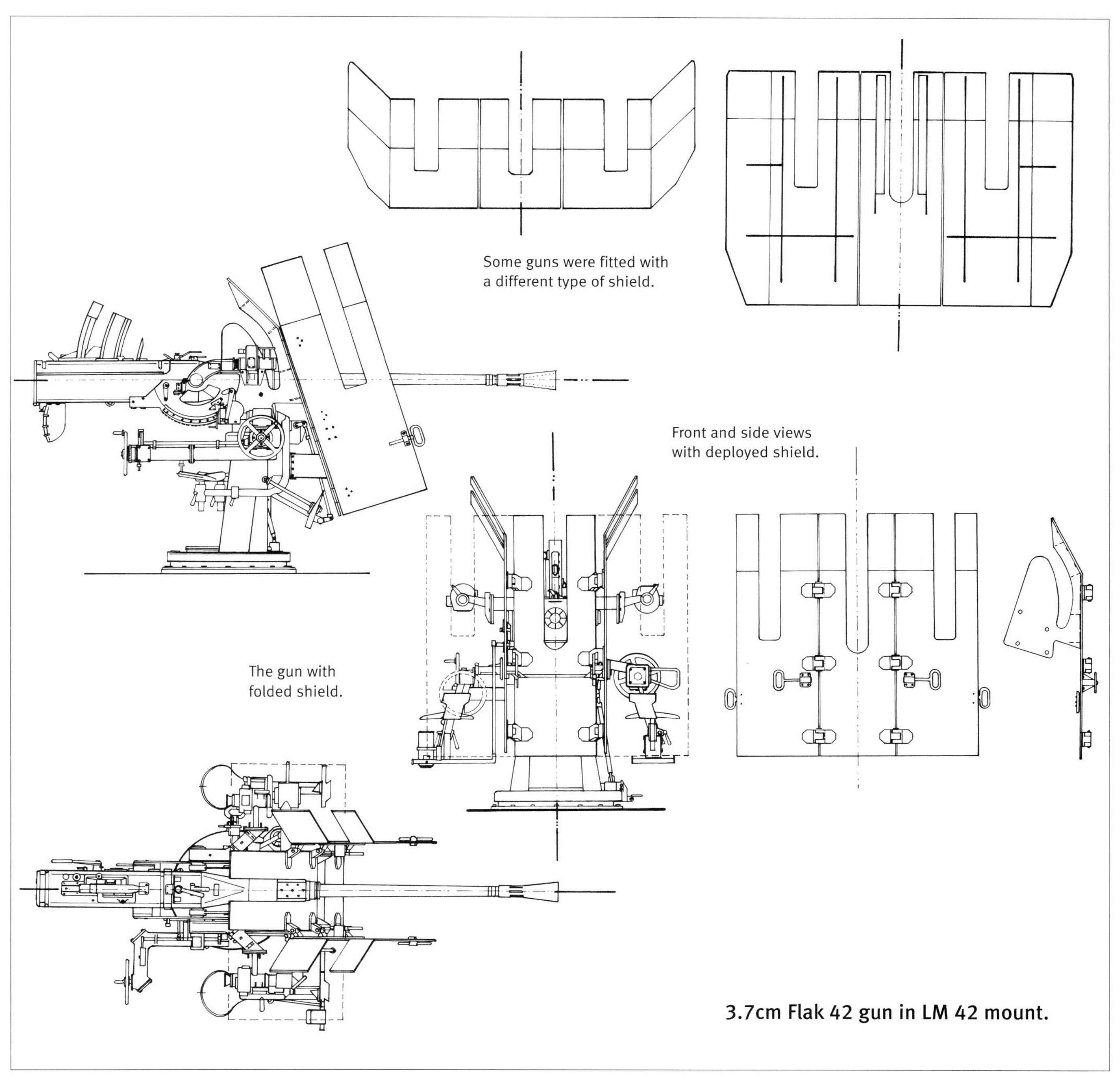

3.7cm Flak 42 gun in LM 42 mount.

Above: The 3.7cm Flak 42 gun with its LM 42 mount was designed as anti-aircraft armament for Type VII and Type IX U-boats.

Right: In the programme codenamed 'Barbara', which called for upgrade of anti-aircraft defences of Kriegsmarine destroyers and was approved in 1944, obsolete 3.7cm SK C/30 guns in Dopp. LC/30 mounts were replaced with new 3.7cm Flak M 42 guns in LM 42 mounts. *(NARA)*

Below: View of a cradle with a lifted receiver cover of the prototype version. *(Via M Skwiot)*

Bottom: Rear view of the cradle and receiver of a 3.7cm Flak M 42 gun. *(Via M Skwiot)*

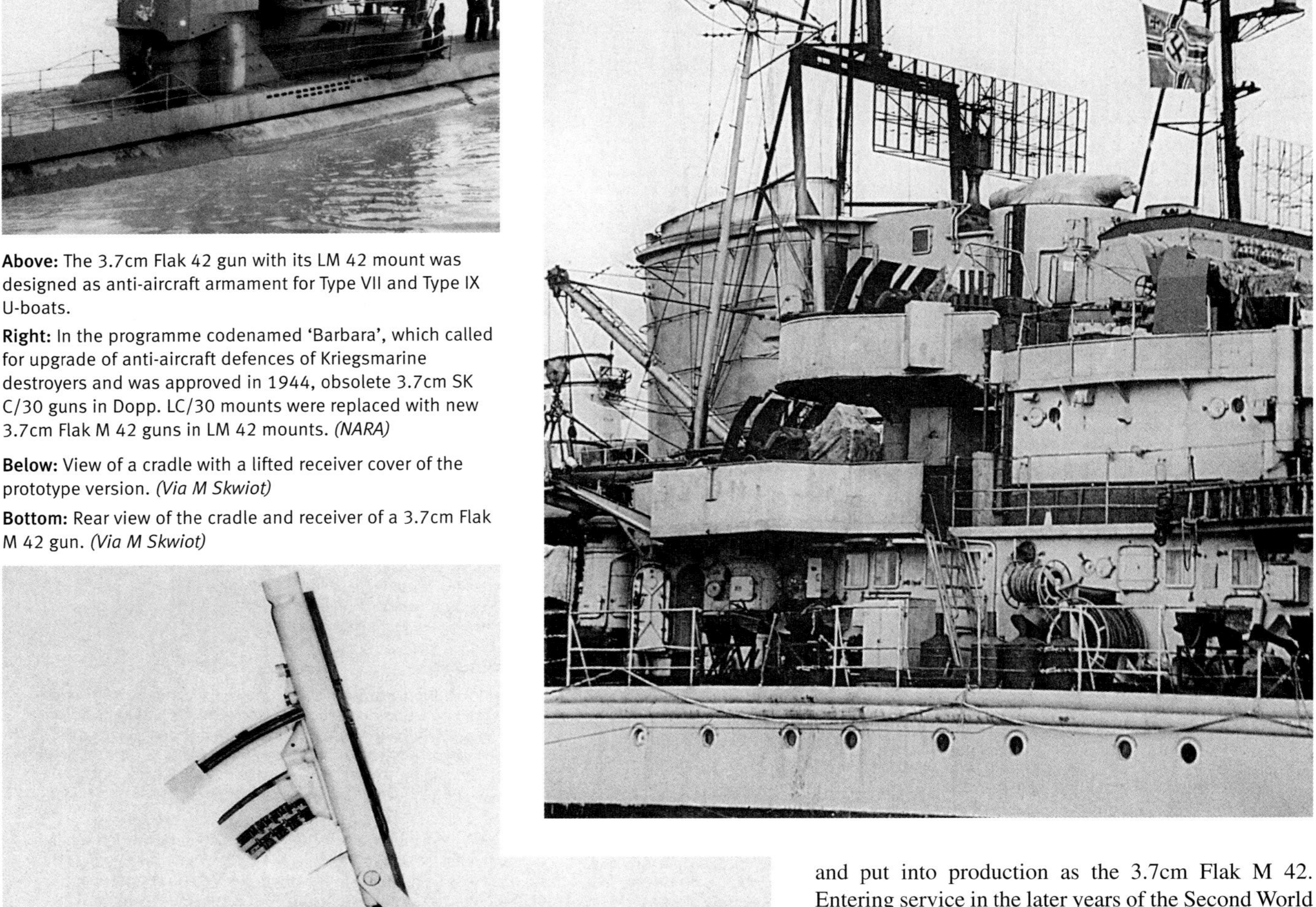

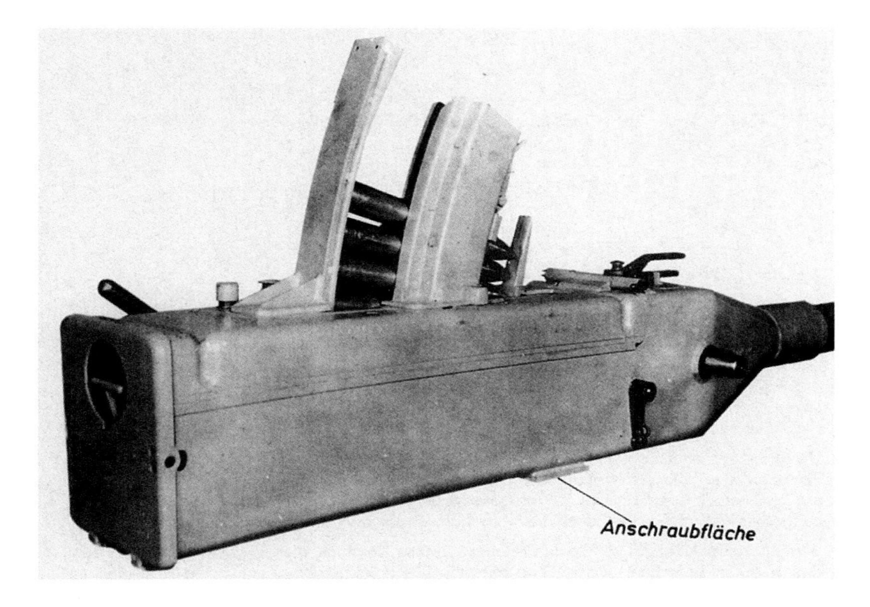

and put into production as the 3.7cm Flak M 42. Entering service in the later years of the Second World War, it initially – from the autumn of 1943 – armed U-boats, but with the start of the 'Barbara' programme in 1944 it was fitted aboard destroyers, minesweepers, patrol boats and auxiliary vessels such as ferries, barges etc.

The Flak M 42 was a fully-automatic recoil-operated cannon. The complete gun consisted of four main assemblies: the barrel, the receiver and bolt, the cradle and the cradle cover with the ammunition guide rails.

Description of the gun and its working principle

The monobloc barrel was cylindrical for the first third of its length, tapering thereafter, with a conical flash guard screwed to the muzzle. The barrel was attached to the breech ring by a double-threaded bayonet joint, allowing for rapid replacement. The rear part of the barrel was installed in a guiding sleeve which was connected to the opening of the cradle. Holes were drilled in the sleeve to help the barrel cool. The barrel was rifled with sixteen right-hand grooves, at a constant angle of 7°.

The base of the breech was box-shaped and fixed to the barrel, recoiling with the barrel within the internal guides of the cradle. Four parallel recoil mechanisms were fitted in the rear corners of this structure. There were two hydraulic recoil buffers at upper left and

lower right, and two spring-loaded recuperators at lower left and upper right. The levers of these elements were fixed to the front wall of the cradle, creating a mechanism that controlled the distance and speed of recoil of the breech and barrel. Inside the receiver, just behind the opening of the chamber, was a unique tilting breech assembly. Its rear end was mounted on a transversal axis, which tilted the front end up and down slightly thus opening and closing the breech. This tilting movement was controlled by a spring-and-arm mechanism which synchronised it with the recoiling of the breech ring. The striker was incorporated into the breech face, its spring being compressed when the breech moved down, simultaneously depressing the ejector arm. The other end of that arm, hooked into the extractor rim, extracted the empty case from the chamber which then fell down and out through the ejection port. The ammunition feed was on the left-hand side of the receiver. Its main components were the drive spring, gears and a sprocket chain with two pins. To ensure the chain moved at the correct speed, a planetary gear, which increased the speed of the spring threefold, was used. Of course, this system was synchronised with the movement of the breech block assembly. However, before the first shot the ammunition feed spring had to be cocked manually, with a handle on the left-hand side of the cradle.

The cradle was a metal box fitted on the transverse pivots of the mount. It also acted as the receiver. The conical forward part incorporated the pipe of the barrel slide with the guides for the breech ring fixed to the sides behind it. The cocking mechanism for the ammunition-feed spring was installed on the lower part of the cradle, its handle protruding to the left. There were two levers at the front of the top plate of the box-like structure. The first was the barrel quick-release, while the second, after pushing the locking handle, unlocked the recoil mechanism assembly, allowing the entire breech assembly to be removed from the cradle. Of course, these levers could only be operated when the breech was open.

The cradle cover was hinged at the front. Once the

Above: A close-up view of a 3.7cm Flak M 42 gun in DLM 42 mount aboard *U 190* (Type IX C/40). The photograph was taken just after Germany's surrender in May 1945. *(NARA)*

Below: A non-standard installation of a 3.7cm Flak M 42 gun in LM 42 mount on a special platform forward of the U-boat's tower. The gun's shield is folded.

Above: 3.7cm Flak M 42 guns in DLM 42 mount with its shield folded, installed on a platform aboard *U 889* photographed after Germany's surrender. *(NARA)*

Below: A front view of 3.7cm Flak M 42 guns in DLM 42 mount with folded shield on a U-boat's platform.

rear was opened it could be raised to allow easy access to the internal components. The ammunition guide bars were incorporated into that cover. The right-hand bar, equipped with spring latches, ensured that the shells could only move downwards. If a round had to be removed the latches could be disengaged by pressing a lever outside the right-hand guide bar. Below the guide bars was a mechanism delivering the rounds to the tray below. The cartridges were clipped in sets of five with metal strips. After loading the clip the strips were removed and thrown away to the left. Just behind the guide bars were two buttons. Before the first shot – after the loading mechanism's spring had been compressed – the loader pushed the forward button, staring the loading mechanism. The top part of the chain, travelling forward, caught the rim of a cartridge in the tray and chambered it. During this process the rim engaged with the upper part of the extractor. Its lower part was pivoting to the rear, unlocking the breech face from its lower position. The breech, pushed by a spring, lifted upwards, closing the chamber. The weapon was now ready to fire. The gunner pressed the trigger pedal and opened automatic fire, the length of burst controlled by how long he kept the pedal depressed. To cease fire in an emergency, pushing the rear button on the cradle cover would automatically disengage the ammunition feed.

Mounts

The 3.7cm Flak M 42 used several types of mount. The first guns were installed aboard Kriegsmarine warships on the Flaklafette C/36, but this very soon proved unsatisfactory and was quickly replaced by the newer Ubts. LC/39. Another mount, mainly intended for submarine use, was the 3.7cm U-Bootslafette C/39. This had triaxial stabilisation and a waterproof DOK 2 x 40° optical sight. The range of elevation was -10°/+90°, and it had 360° training. Another mount, the Flaklafette LM 42, was of similar design and was

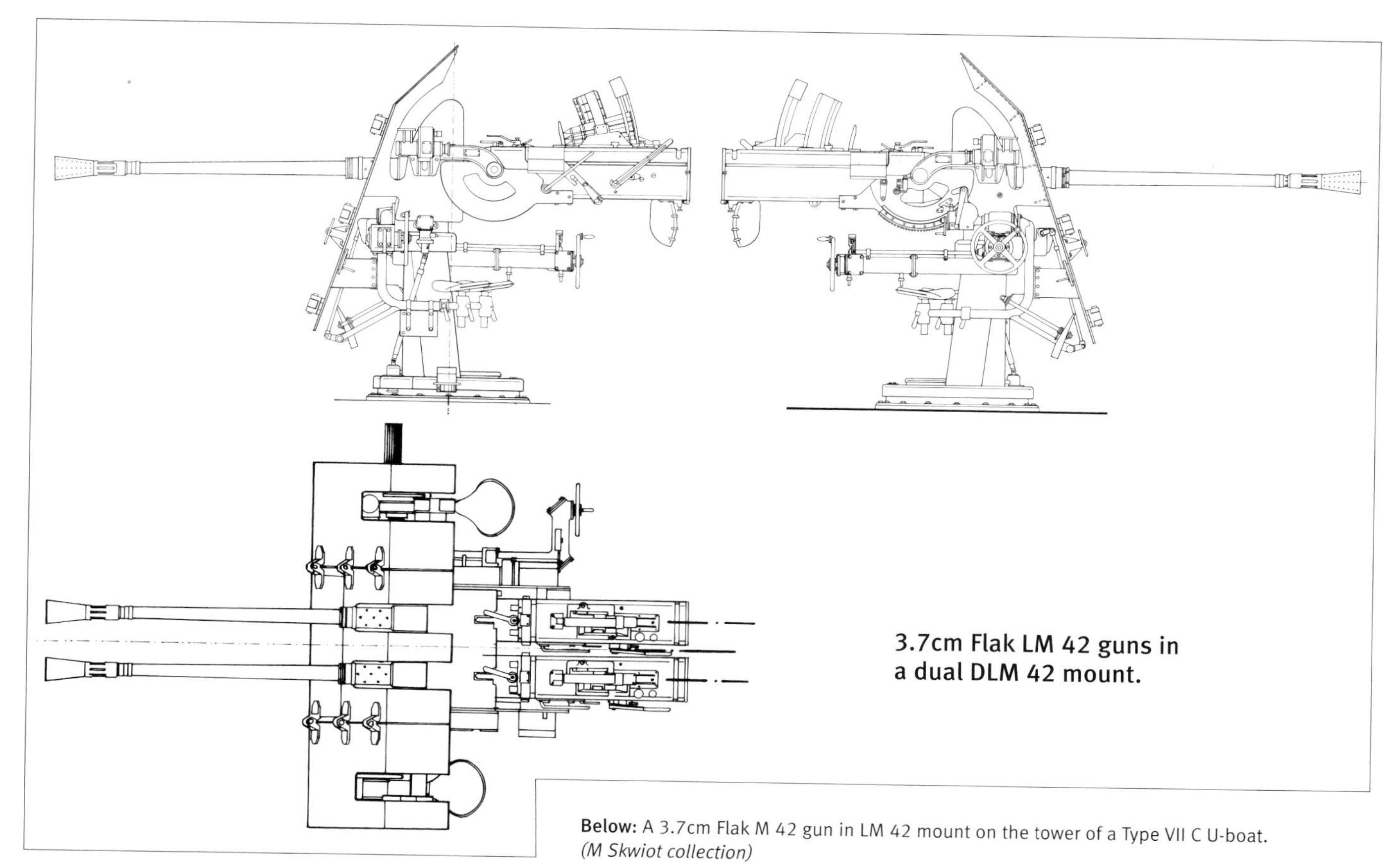

3.7cm Flak LM 42 guns in a dual DLM 42 mount.

Below: A 3.7cm Flak M 42 gun in LM 42 mount on the tower of a Type VII C U-boat. *(M Skwiot collection)*

The 3.7cm Flak M 42 gun

Calibre:	37mm
Weight of gun:	300kg
Overall length:	n/a
Length bore:	2,560mm
Length chamber:	357mm
Volume chamber:	0.5dm^3
Length rifling	2,267mm
Grooves:	16 (0.55mm x 4.76mm)
Weight projectile:	0.61kg
Propellant charge:	0.51kg of RP C/38n
Muzzle velocity:	N/A
Mine-shell:*	925mps
HE shell:	850mps
AP shell:	815mps
Working pressure:	2,950kgf/cm^2
Approximate service life:	7,000 effective rounds
Maximum range:	8,500m at 35.7°
Maximum ceiling:	6,800m at 85°
Tracer range:	4,800m
Rate of fire (theoretical):	160-180rpm
(practical):	60rpm
Depression/elevation:	–10°/+85° (-10°/+90°**)

* German: 'Minengeschoß', special type of explosive shell with walls thinner than standard high-explosive shell or 'Sprenggeschoß' (translator's note).

** According to other sources.

developed specifically for the 3.7cm Flak M 42. In this mount the gun had three crew – a training layer sitting on the left, an elevation layer on the right and a stabilisation operator standing behind them. A fourth man, the loader, stood behind the gun to one side. The mount was equipped with the DOK 2 x 40° sight as well as an additional 5 x 10° telescopic sight for engaging surface targets. The complete mount with shield weighed 1,350kg and training and elevation

Right: Type VII C/41U-boats after Germany's surrender. Anti-aircraft guns can be seen on the after conning tower platforms – in the foreground an LM 42 U, in the background an LM 43 U. Those were standard guns used on this class of submarines. *(M Skwiot collection)*

were the same as for the Ubts. L C/39. The axis of the cradle was 1,250mm above the deck.

Further improvements resulted in the Flaklafette LM 43, again specifically developed for the 3.7cm Flak M 42. This mount had only one gunlayer's station, but like the previous designs had the DOK 2 x 40° sight and also a ring sight. The mount and shield weighed 1,350kg and the cradle was 1,300mm above the deck.

The twin mount based on the LM 42 design was the Doppellafette LM 42, in which the guns were mounted side by side. The equipment, training and elevation and crew were identical to the other mounts, apart from the addition of a second loader. The complete mount weighed 1,750kg and the cradle was 1,500mm above the deck.

All these mounts had a slit in the front of the pedestal allowing unimpeded ejection of spent cases at the maximum elevation of 90°. The stabilisation gear was incorporated in the lower part of the mount, with the control wheel at the right rear. The stabilisation operator stood behind the gun. The waterproof DOK 2 x 40° optical sights were on a support fixed to the base of the mount. Beside the right-hand sight support was

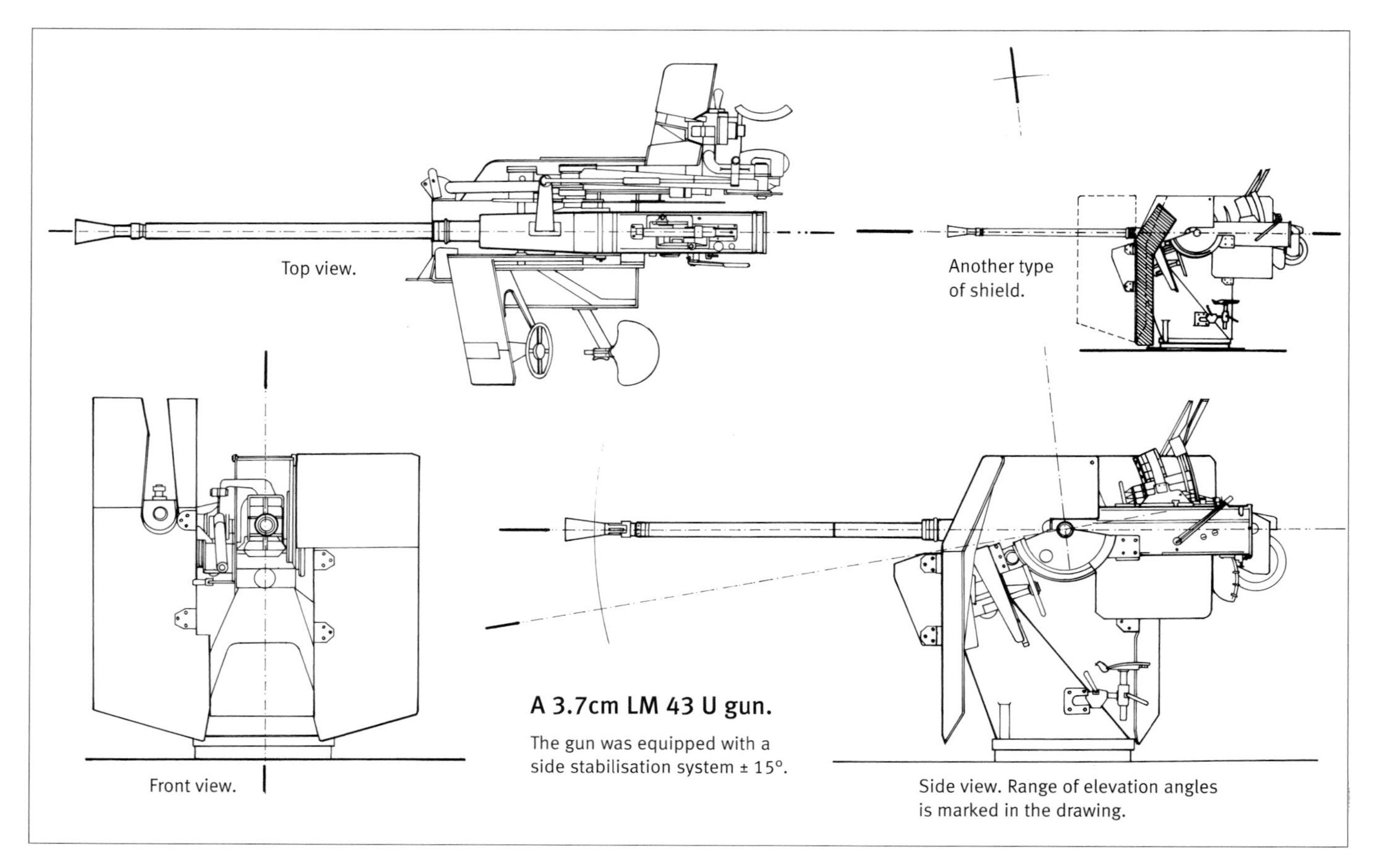

A 3.7cm LM 43 U gun.

The gun was equipped with a side stabilisation system ± 15°.

Side view. Range of elevation angles is marked in the drawing.

Above: *U 1009*, a Type VII C/41 boat, with a 3.7cm Flak M 42 gun in a single LM 43 mount returns to base after Germany's surrender. *(NARA)*

a push rod connected via the axis of the cradle to the trigger mechanism. Next to the gunlayers' control wheels were handgrips to help them keep their correct position in their seats in rough seas.

U-boat guns were fitted with flat hinged shields that could be folded forward parallel to the barrel. The shield was mounted on special cantilevers and two longitudinal support plates. Surface-vessel mounts had more complex-shaped shields similar to the one used on the Flakvierling 38, which did not fold away, but this feature was only necessary aboard submarines to reduce drag when running submerged.

Destroyers – the 'Barbara' programme

The other type of warship to use large numbers of 3.7cm M 42 guns were destroyers. A programme – codenamed 'Barbara' – to augment the anti-aircraft armament of Kriegsmarine warships in the face of the ever-increasing threat of Allied air power was approved in November 1944. This was made possible by the introduction of new guns which were more effective than those previously operated by the Kriegsmarine. These new guns also had splinter-proof shields which the 3.7cm SK C/30 guns on Dopp. L C/30 mounts had not had. In the case Type 1934/1934A destroyers the programme called for the removal of No. 3 main gun, which not only allowed more anti-aircraft guns to be fitted but also reduced the total weight of the ship. But the main focus of the programme was the replacement of 3.7cm SK C/30 guns on Dopp. L C/30 mounts with new 3.7cm Flak M 42a either in twin DLM 42 or single LM 43 mounts. Note that in order to provide the additional gunners the increased number of weapons required, some of the engine-room crew were retrained. The ships' 20mm guns were also replaced with new types, but this will be discussed below.

V. The 3.7cm Flak M 43 Gerät 341

This was developed from the land-service 3.7cm Flak 36 introduced into Wehrmacht service in 1943. The naval version was installed on the triaxially-stabilised LM 42 twin mounts. One advantage of this design was a significant increase in the automation of the firing process, thus increasing the rate of fire. The ammunition was loaded in eight-round magazines.

The 3.7cm Flak M 43 Gerät 341(Rheinmetall)

Calibre:	37mm
Total weight:	2,780kg
Length bore (L/57):	2,112.2mm
Weight projectile:	0.672kg
Weight explosive charge:	0.062kg
Propellant charge:	0.51kg
Muzzle velocity:	872mps
Maximum range:	6,600m
Maximum ceiling:	4,800m
Tracer range:	4,800m
Rate of fire:	180rpm

18

2cm U-BOAT TURRETS

The history of the development of these guns and their mounts is quite complicated. As was discussed above the previous attempt to increase the anti-aircraft firepower of U-boats had merely resulted in increasing the number of anti-aircraft gun positions aboard them. However, fitting more guns and the platforms to accommodate them on the boats' superstructure reduced their underwater manoeuvrability, a problem exacerbated by the shields fitted to some of the guns. This not only affected their submerged speed but also made them noisier. This, coupled with the improvements in enemy detection equipment, made the boats easier for the enemy to locate. There were two solutions to this problem. The first was the temporary expedient of removing the shields from the guns, which could be done immediately, while the second would apply to the new types of U-boat being designed – the installation of anti-

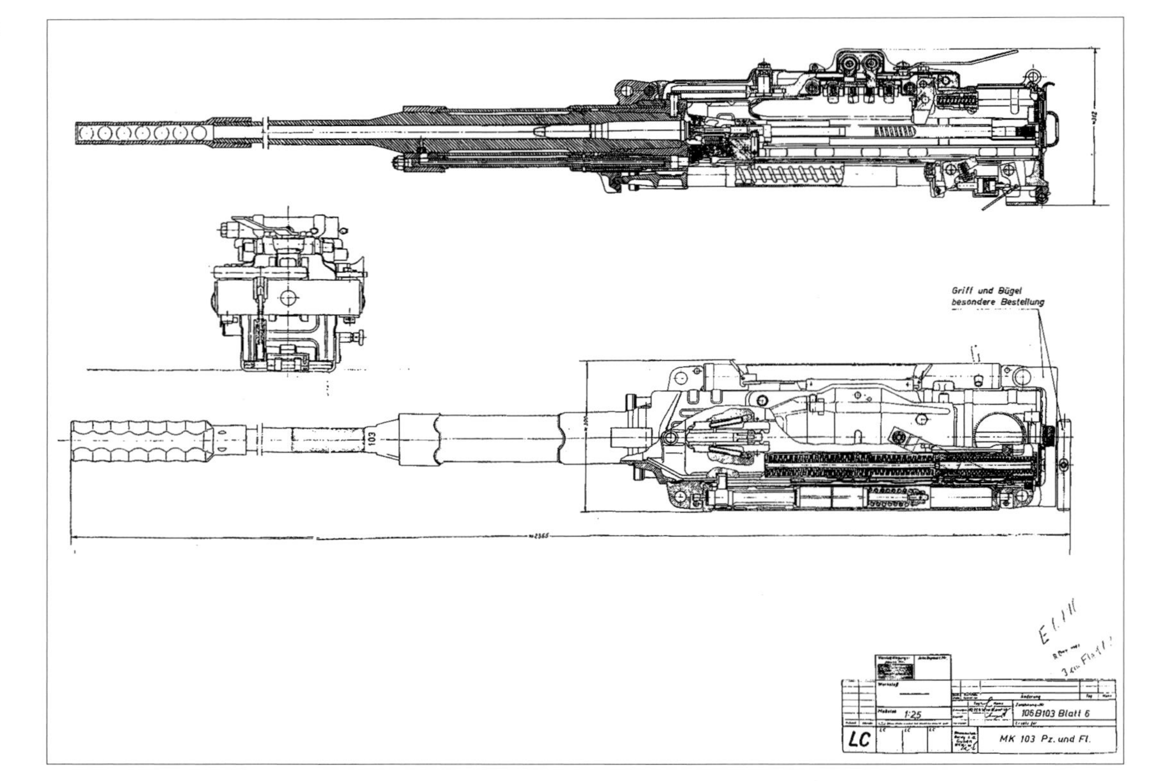

Right: Design drawings of a MK 103 Pz. und Fl. cannon designed for Type XXI U-boats.

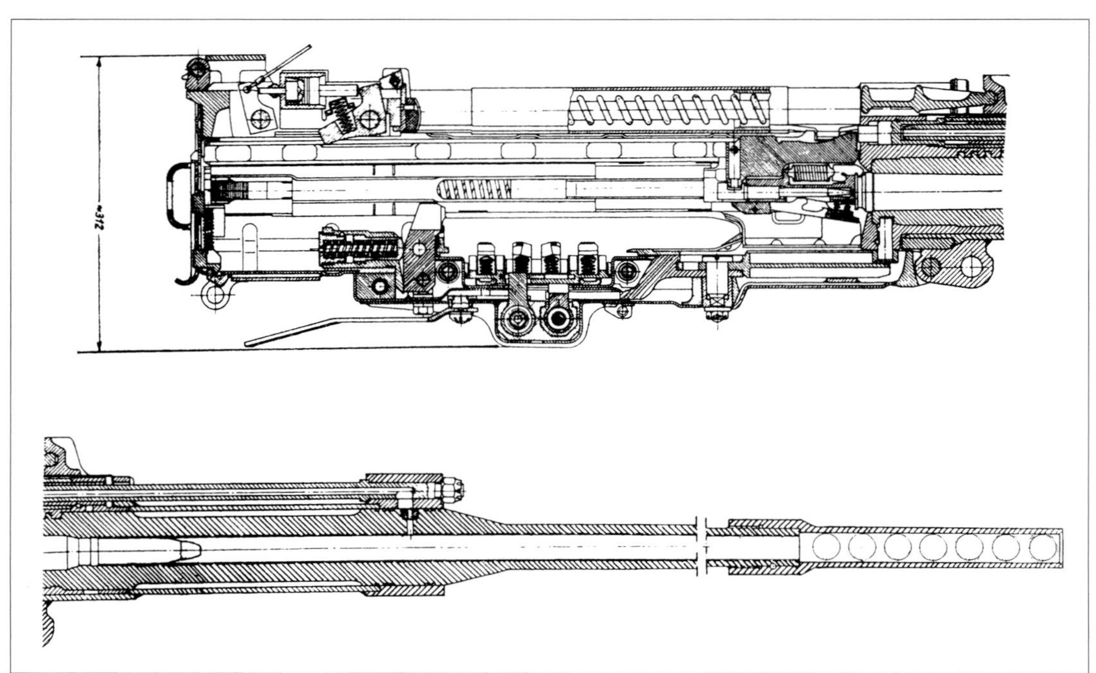

Right: Design drawings of a MK 103 Pz. und Fl. cannon designed for Type XXI U-boats.

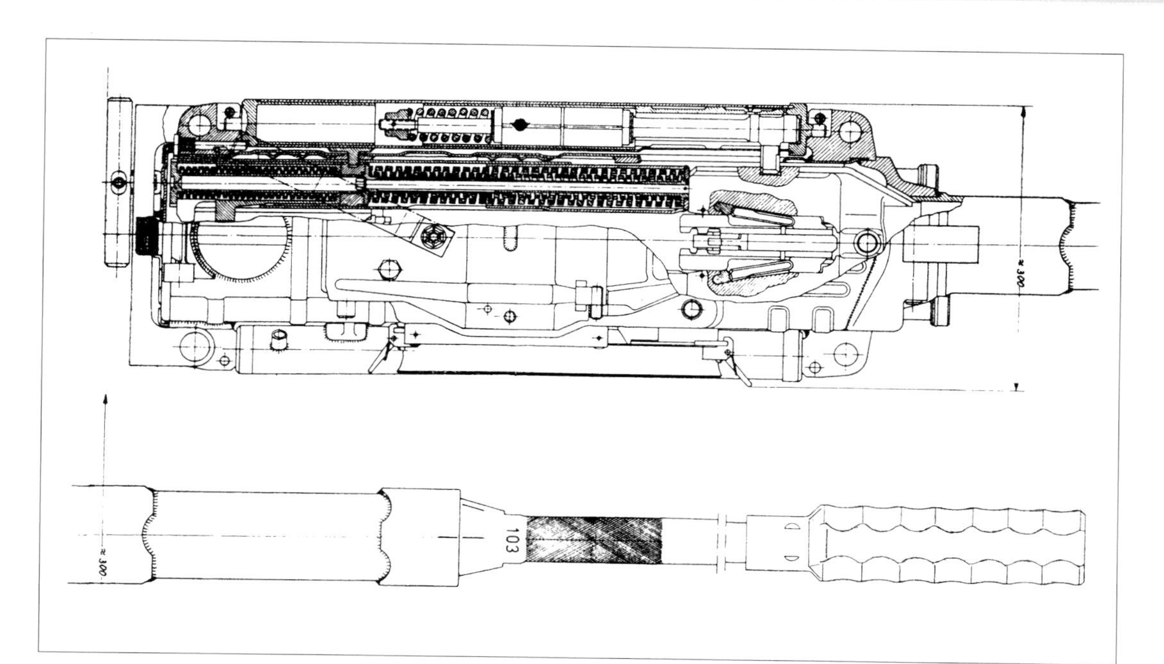

Left: Design drawings of a MK 103 Pz. und Fl. cannon designed for Type XXI U-boats.

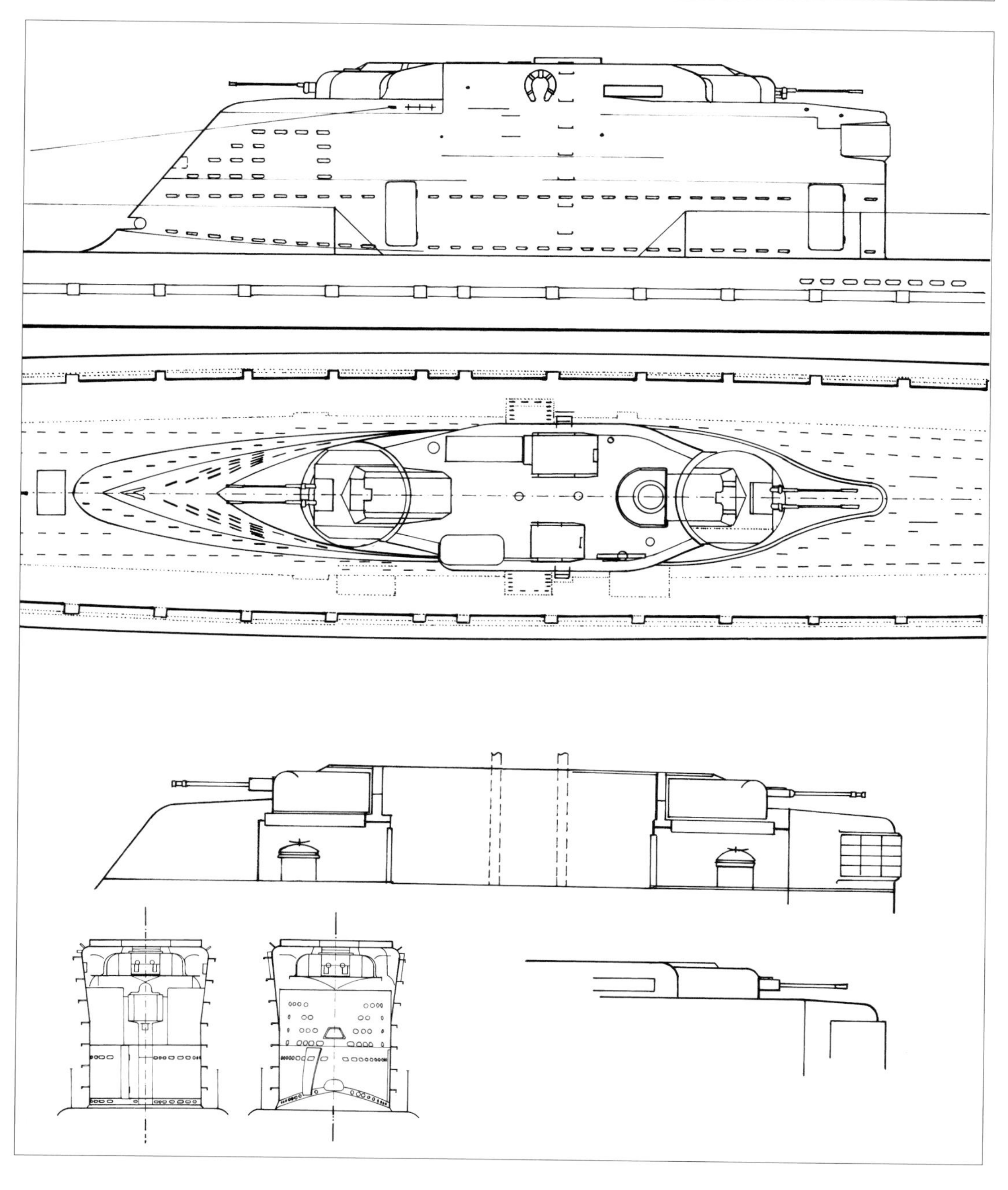

Left: Drawings of the conning tower of a Type XXI U-boat with 30mm gun turrets clearly visible.

aircraft armament in streamlined turrets integrated into the conning tower.

The initial version of the twin 20mm turret was specifically developed by Rheinmetall and Mauser for the Type XXI U-boat. The design was then handed over to the the Zbrojovka plant in Brno in occupied Czechoslovakia for further development. The Moravian plant was expected to develop a version armed with 30mm guns, designated the Br 300.[1] Work commenced under German supervision in 1940, but the Czech engineers delayed the project to such an extent that it never got beyond the design stage before the end of the war, and the turrets were never built. The few Type XXI U-boats to be completed therefore had to be armed with lighter 2cm Flak 38 guns.

Above: Prototype 3cm Flak M103/38 gun in 2cm Flak 38 mount. *(Via M Skwiot)*

1 The 3cm Flak M 44 anti-aircraft gun mounted in twin Br 300 in single-axis gun turrets was intended as an armament for Type XXI and Type XVIII U-boats.

Right: Type XXI U-boats after Germany's surrender in a British port. A turret armed with 20mm cannon can be seen in the foreground, in the centre of the photograph. *(MMW)*

Right: *U 3017* photographed in the British Vickers shipyard at Barrow-in-Furness on 29 August 1945. The boat already displays a British hull number, N 41. *(Via A Jarski)*

19

2cm GUNS

The development of automatic anti-aircraft guns took off in the second half of the 1920s, precipitated by the rapid development of combat aircraft. At that time the greatest aerial threat to warships was from low- and medium-level attacks, which required guns with high rates of fire to counter them. In 1928 the Reichsmarine issued a request for proposals for such weapons to the armaments manufacturers. In the same year Rheinmetall developed such a weapon for land service, designated the 2cm MG C/28. This was soon followed by another model, the 2cm MG C/30, which was put into production at the Mauser plant. This design was further developed by the Swiss Solothurn company and was accepted by the Reichsmarine. This was a fully-automatic cannon specifically designed to engage aerial targets, operated by short recoil and with a sliding breech block. Ammunition was fed from twenty-round magazines attached to the side, and there were high-explosive, tracer, blank and drill rounds available for this gun. The theoretical rate of fire was 300 rounds per minute. The gun was mounted on a special triaxial pedestal mount, the C/30, and had a crew of six. In 1934 the land-service version entered production, with the naval version following later the same year. The 218 guns of the first order were installed on almost every Reichsmarine vessel: eight to ten guns on each

Below: 2cm MG C/30 in C/30 pedestal mount.

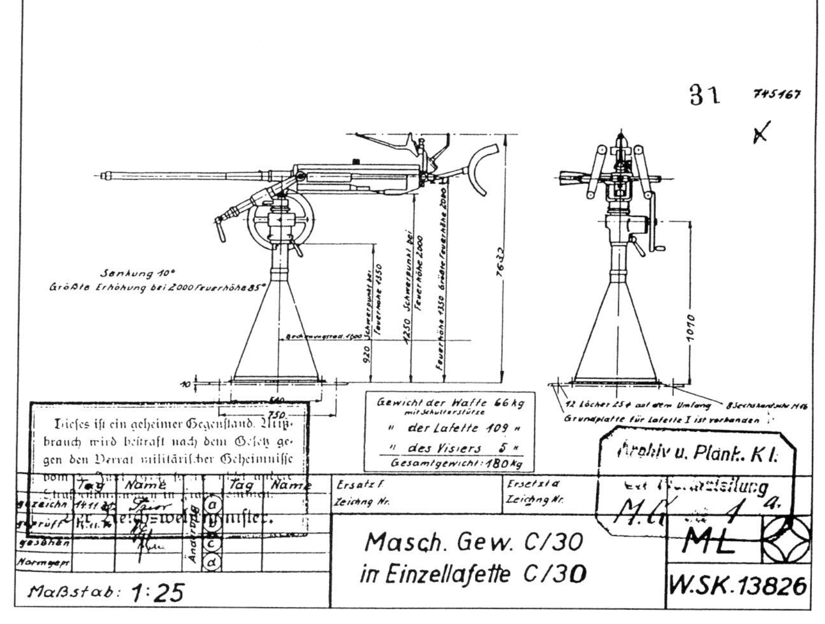

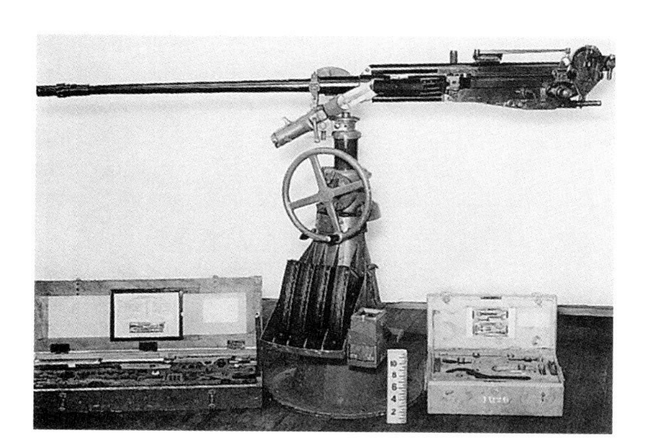

Above, left: Predecessor of the MG C/30 gun – the 2cm MK ST 52 with the No 1 barrel. *(M Skwiot collection)*

Left: The first vessels to receive the 2cm MG C/30 guns in C/27/30 mounts after they had been put into production were the Type II U-boats – like the Type II D *U 137* shown in this photograph. *(M Skwiot collection)*

Right: Imperfections in the early MG C/30 guns forced the designers to introduce modifications. The photograph shows one of the first guns adapted for naval conditions, designated MK ST 5. *(CAW collection)*

Deutschland class 'pocket battleship, six to eight guns on the light cruisers, four on each destroyer and two on each torpedo boat and minesweeper. Additionally, some U-boats mounted single guns of this type.

During the Spanish Civil War, the gun's performance was found to be quite good, apart from one significant drawback – an insufficient rate of fire, theoretically 280 rounds per minute. Mauser-Werke was therefore instructed to redesign the Flak 30 to achieve a higher rate of fire, but still using the same ammunition. The prototype of the new model was designated the 2cm Flak 38 and entered Army service in 1939. A specialised variant for mountain and airborne forces was also developed. In early 1940 these were followed by a new naval light anti-aircraft gun on the SL ('Sockellafette', pedestal mount) C/30 mount. It had a higher rate of fire, which was helped by being fed from twenty- or forty-round magazines. Just like other Kriegsmarine light anti-aircraft guns at this time, it did not originally have a shield – these

Right: 2cm Flak C/38 guns in dual C/30/37 mounts installed on the after platform of *U 889*'s conning tower (Type IX C/40) photographed after the surrender on 25 May 1945. Installation of two guns in a mount required adding a counterweight which can be seen in front of the pedestal. *(NHC)*

were not added until later. In 1944 a new LM 44 twin mount with a shield entered service aboard Kriegsmarine vessels.

The most effective solution developed by the German designers was installing four guns in a single mount. This was known as the 2cm Flakvierling 38 and had a theoretical rate of fire of 4 x 150 rounds per minute. The first versions, on a variety of mounts, were introduced in 1940, and the Flakvierling became known as one of the best anti-aircraft weapons of the Second World War. A drawback with the early versions, however, was that they had no shields for the crew, leaving them vulnerable to aircraft machine-gun and cannon fire. Only later were shield fitted to some mounts on vehicles and aboard ships. Another weak point were the twenty-round magazines, which could be emptied by seven seconds' firing. This enforced pauses between bursts from individual barrels as the magazine were changed. There were attempts to remedy this using belt-fed ammunition, but this never entered operational service.

Finally, several models of 20mm gun which were developed by the Germans but never put into production should be mentioned:

(a) The first was the 2cm Flak 40, a further development of the MG C/35 designed by Rheinmetall. It was gas-operated and belt-fed. Its planned theoretical rate of fire was 530 rounds per minute, and the gun weighed 45kg.

(b) The Gerät 240 – a further development of the 2cm KwK 38 tank gun designed by Rheinmetall. It was a highly automated gas-operated gun. It was supposed to be belt-fed, allowing it to reach a theoretical rate of fire of 900 rounds per minute. It weighed 50kg.

(c) The Salwenmaschinenkan 2cm SMK 18, V1, an eight-barrel automatic gun developed by Rheinmetall.

Above and below: Installation of four guns in a single mount turned out to be an outstanding solution. The photograph shows a 2cm Flakvierling 38 with a theoretical rate of fire of 4 x 150 rounds per minute. The first such guns were developed for the Luftwaffe, and then for the Wehrmacht. The upper photo shows a 2cm Flakvierling on a Sonderanhänger 52 trailer for the Luftwaffe; the lower – an identical gun installed on a Famo 18 t (SdKfz 9) tractor. *(CAW*

Above: When the Type IX U-boats entered service their standard anti-aircraft armament consisted of a 2cm MG C/30 gun in a C/30/37 mount on the conning tower platform (foreground) and a 3.7cm SK C/30 gun in a Ubts. C/39 mount on the deck aft (background). *(CAW collection)*

Left: A 2cm MG C/30 in a C/30/37 mount aboard *U 58* (Type II C). A magazine container can be seen by the side of it. *(CAW collection)*

Below: A 2cm Flakvierling C/38 in a C/38 mount (in the foreground) aboard a German destroyer. *(CAW collection)*

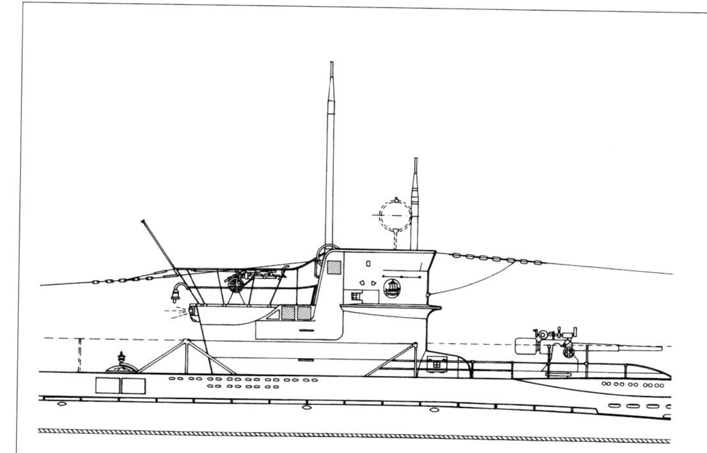

U 83 with a standard anti-aircraft armament – a 2cm MG C/30 gun in a C/30/37 mount.

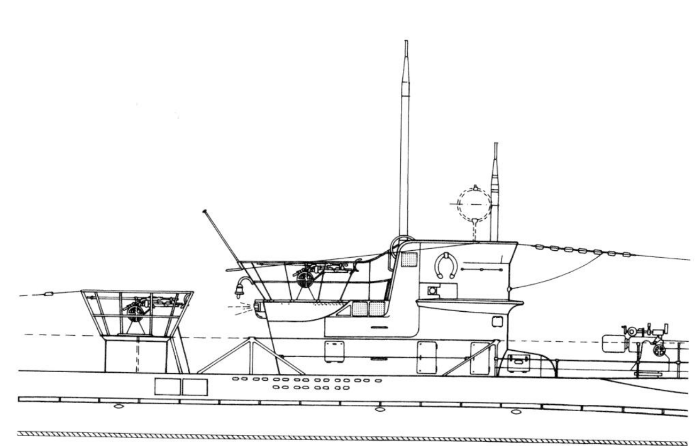

U 84 (Type VII B) with an additional free-standing platform for a 2cm MG C/30 gun in a C/30/37 mount installed abaft the conning tower.

The anti-aircraft armament of *U 1105* (Type VII C/41) consisted of a single 3.7cm LM 42 gun and two 2cm C/38 guns in a C/30/37 Zwilling mount.

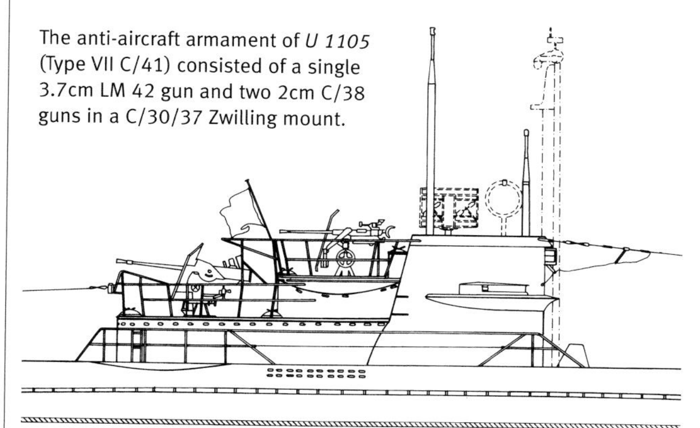

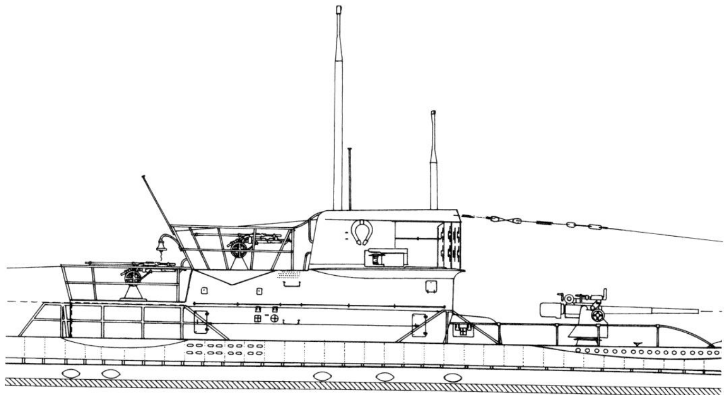

U 237 (Type VII C) with new 2cm C/38 guns in C/30/37 mounts installed on platforms behind the conning tower. An experimental FMG 41G (gU) Seetakt (FuMO 29) radar can be seen at the front of the conning tower.

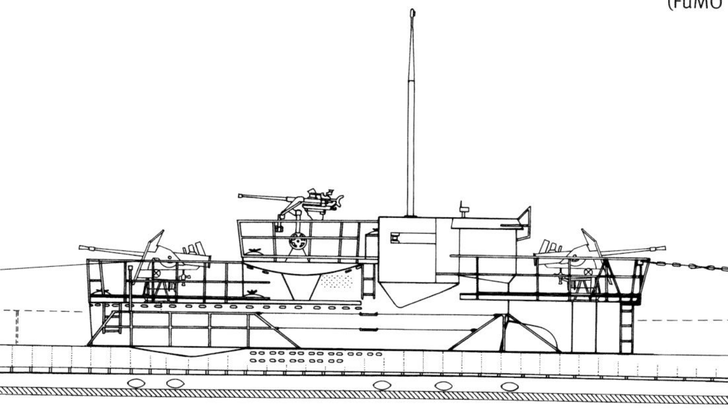

Some U-boats, before the tower structure replacements, were equipped with additional platforms for extra anti-aircraft guns. This can be seen on *U 673*, which carried 3.7cm M 42 U in LM 42 U mount in fore and after positions and a dual 2cm C/38 gun (Zwilling).

Two sets of 2cm Flak C/38 guns in C/38/ 43U mounts were planned for the new U-boat type intended to provide anti-aircraft protection for standard U-boats leaving bases and returning to them. *U 441* armed in such a way was temporarily renamed *U Flak 1*.

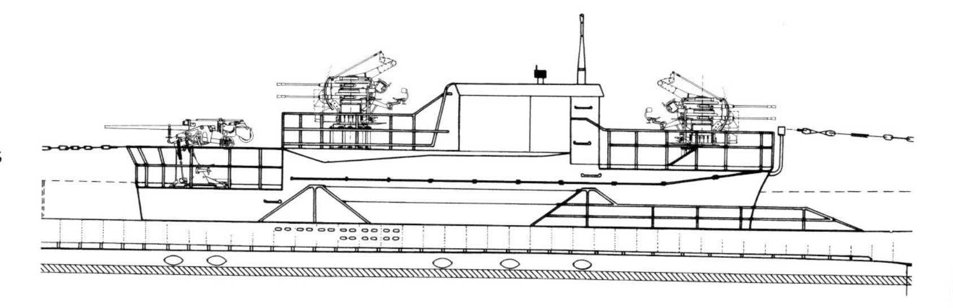

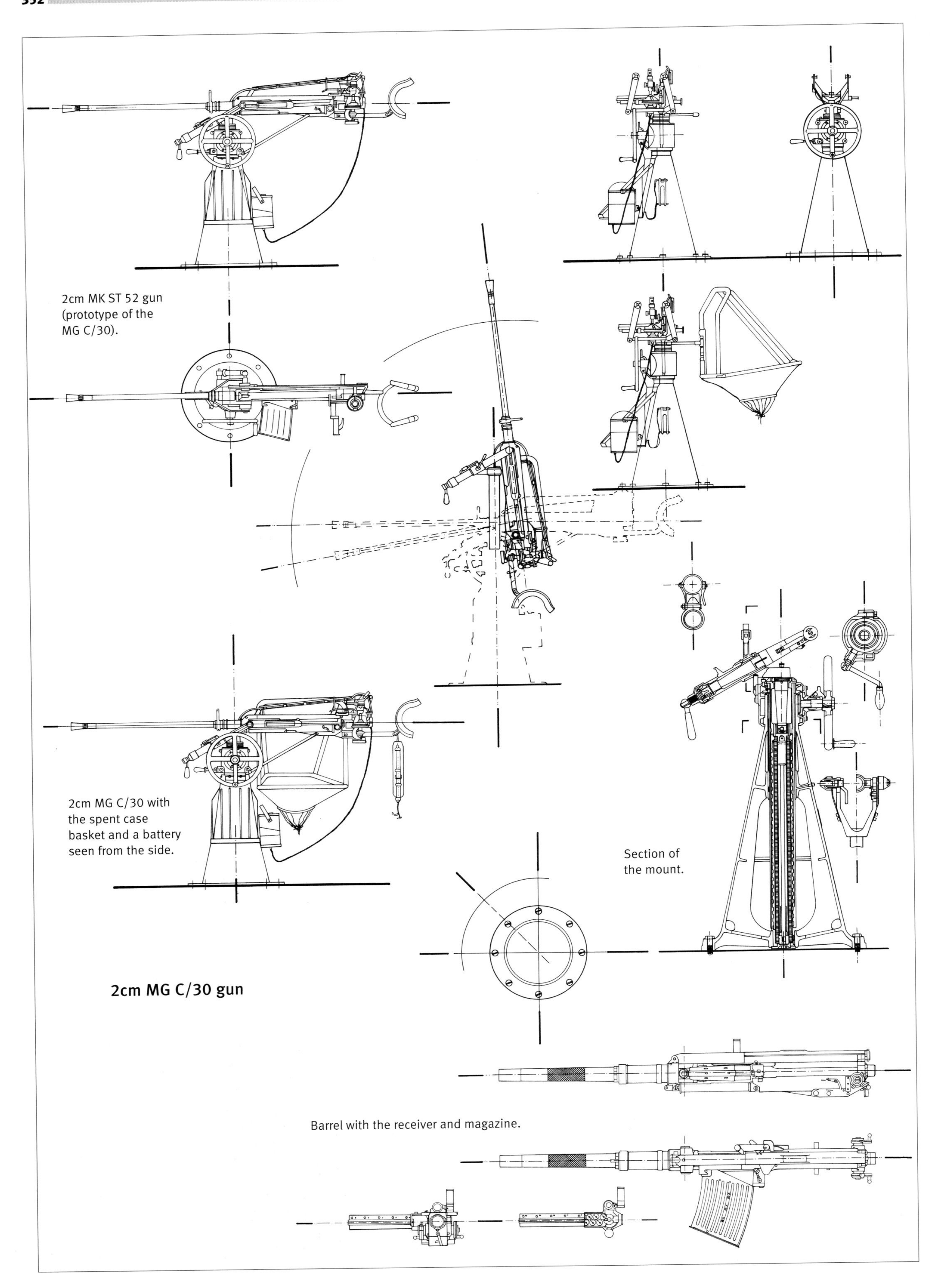

2cm MK ST 52 gun (prototype of the MG C/30).

2cm MG C/30 with the spent case basket and a battery seen from the side.

Section of the mount.

2cm MG C/30 gun

Barrel with the receiver and magazine.

It was recoil-operated and each barrel was fed from a twenty-round clip. The rate of fire was 8 x 80 rounds per ten-round clips. Weight was 450kg.

Photographic evidence for the mounts for 2cm Flakvierling 38 guns is quite scarce. The most important land and naval variants put into production were:

(a) 2cm Vierlingslafette Flak 38 – a biaxial anti-aircraft mount with a single layer's station, developed by Rheinmetall. In most cases used in fixed positions, but sometimes carried on a special trailer or mounted on a self-propelled chassis.

(b) 2cm Vierlingslafette Flak 38/43F – triaxial mount for warships, equipped with its own radar.

(c) 2cm Sockellafette 38 – a pedestal mount for individual or twin Flak 38 guns, although a quadruple version was also designed.

(d) 2cm Behelslafette – a so-called 'provisional' mount introduced shortly before the end of the war, with a simplified structure made of readily-available ersatz materials.

(e) 2cm Drehnkranzlafette 41 – a rotating-ring mount originally intended for a single Flak 38 gun, later also

Left: During the initial phase of the war the default anti-aircraft armament of a Type VII U-boat consisted of a 2cm MG C/30 gun in a C/30/37 mount on the after bridge platform. *(Both photos CAW collection)*

converted for a quadruple version. Small numbers of such mounts were built and installed aboard the Schnellboote.

(f) 2cm Flakvierling auf St IV – a quadruple mount installed on the chassis of the PzKpfw IV tank; two versions existed. The first was the so-called 'Möbelwagen' (German: furniture van), with hinged rectangular armour plates around the gun which were lowered for firing. The other was the 'Wirbelwind' ('Whirlwind') with a rotating turret.

Naval Flakvierling 38s were installed on three types of mount. The first was the 2cm Flak C/30,[1] in a quadruple 2cm Vierlingslafette C/35 mount. The prototype built by Mauser and Rheinmetall had a large shield at the front, but the modified version adopted for service by the Kriegsmarine lacked the shield. The mount was equipped with a Flakvisier 35 sight. The second and most common type was the 2cm Flak 38 in the 2cm Vierlingslafette 38. This quadruple mount was developed from a triaxially-stabilised naval mount and had two gunlayers' positions. The sight used was the Flakvisier 40. The mount had a crew of seven and was 1,500mm above the deck. Early models had no shields, these only being added later aboard ship. In the final stages of the war the designers experimented with a FuMO Rettin gunnery radar installed between the barrels. The third version was the 2-cm Flak C/38 in the 2cm Vierlingslafette 38/43U mount.[2] This quadruple mount was a further development by Rheinmetall of a triaxially-stabilised mount used for both anti-surface and anti-aircraft fire. Only a small number were built and they were mostly installed aboard submarines. It had two layers' stations, two ring sights and a crew of six. The cradle axis was 1,200mm above the deck.

Apart from guns specifically designed for naval service, the anti-aircraft defences of Kriegsmarine vessels were often provisionally boosted by shipping

Above: Another Type VII U-boat with a 2cm MG C/30 gun in a C/30/37 mount on the after bridge platform. *(CAW collection)*

1 This version is mentioned by Siegfried Breyer in his publication 'Leichte und Mittlere Artillerie auf Deutschen Kriegsschiffen', *Marine Arsenal*, Sonderheft band 18. Podzun-Pallas-Verlag.

2 A version equipped with a shield and intended for Kriegsmarine surface vessels was supposed to be designated C/43.

Above: Apart from submarines, small surface vessels were also armed with 2cm MG C/30 guns in C/30/37 mounts.

Below, and opposite, bottom: While U-boats were in service their anti-aircraft armament was constantly upgraded. An example can be seen here: left photograph shows a 2cm C/38 gun while the right and bottom ones show the 'old' model of 2cm MG C/30 in C/30/37 mount on the bridge platform. *(CAW collection)*

Right: Conning tower of a Type VII C/41 U-boat still with an early set of anti-aircraft armament, composed of single 20mm guns. It was possible though to install a Flakvierling on the pedestal seen behind the officer who is speaking. The single guns in turn were soon replaced with twin mounts (Zwilling). *(Via Author)*

Right: A 2cm MG C/30 gun in C/30/37 mount installed on a platform aboard a Type VII U-boat. *(CAW collection)*

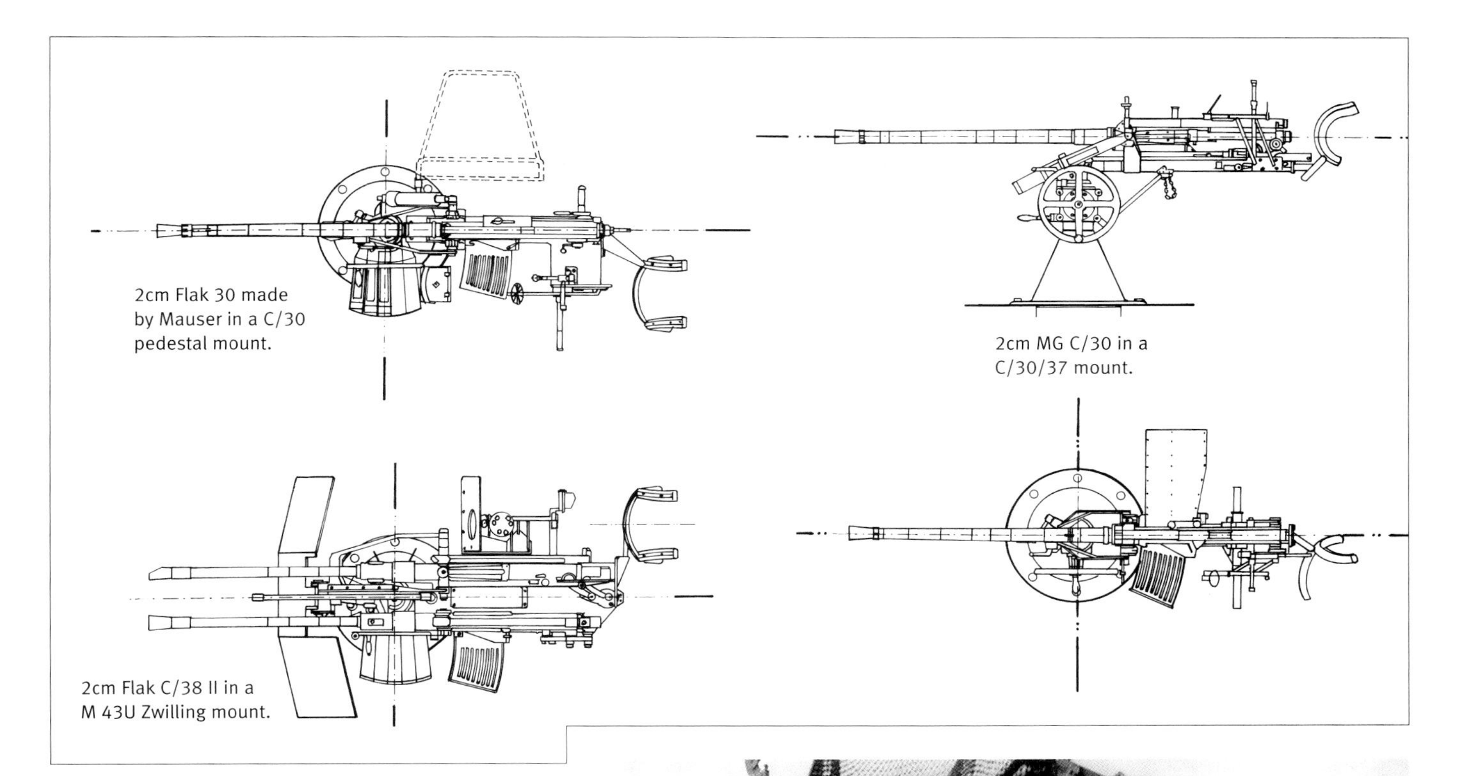

2cm Flak 30 made by Mauser in a C/30 pedestal mount.

2cm MG C/30 in a C/30/37 mount.

2cm Flak C/38 II in a M 43U Zwilling mount.

guns on land-service mounts. The most common of these were the Flak 30 and the Flak 38. The 2cm Flak 30 was the official designation of the 2cm MK ST 5 autocannon designed by the Swiss Solothurn company and adopted by the German Army and the Luftwaffe (for its ground units).

Analysis of documents and photographs allows us to clearly identify the types of 20mm anti-aircraft guns and their mounts aboard Kriegsmarine surface vessels between 1939 and 1945. The commonest types included:

(a) 2cm MG C/30L gun on SL 30L mount.
(b) 2cm MG C/30 gun on Ubts. L C/39 mount.

Above: An C/30 mount at maximum elevation with a 2cm MG C/30 gun. *(CAW collection)*

Left: MG C/30 (ST 5) gun photographed aboard a Kriegsmarine auxiliary ship with an early type of C/27/30 (?) mount. *(CAW collection)*

(c) 2cm Flak 29 gun on SL 40 mount.
(d) 2cm Flak 30 mount on Flak 30 mount.
(e) 2cm Flak 38 gun on LC/39 mount.
(f) 2cm Flak 38 gun on Flak 38 mount.
(g) 2cm Flak Vierling MG C/35 gun on C/38 mount.
(h) 2cm Flak Vierling C/38 gun on C/38 mount.

Aboard U-boats, the commonest types were:

(a) 2cm MG C/30 gun on LC/30 mount.
(b) 2cm MG C/30 gun on LC/30/37 mount.
(c) 2cm Flak C/38 gun on LC/30/37 mount
(d) 2cm Flak Zwilling C/38 II gun on M 43U mount
(e) 2cm Flak Vierling C/38/43 gun on M 43U mount.

I. 2cm MG C/30 L gun

Adopted in 1931 by the Reichswehr for its anti-aircraft units, this gun was recoil-operated with a sliding breech block. Thanks to its high muzzle velocity of 900mps its ballistic performance was very good. Horizontal range was 4,800m and effective ceiling 3,700m. However, it ultimately proved unsatisfactory, although it was use for a time aboard Reichsmarine vessels.

The barrel and cradle were installed on an SL 30 L pedestal mount. The gun was mounted in a mechanical cradle with a chain cocking mechanism and fed from a 100-round[1] T 100-C/30 drum magazine attached from below. The method of loading ammunition into this magazine was quite unorthodox: firstly, an empty magazine was attached to the gun, then the end of an ammunition belt was pushed inside and after

1 Actually it could only accommodate ninety-eight rounds.

This page and opposite: Various views of a 2cm MG C/30 gun in C/30 mount installed aboard a Raumboot and ready to fire. *(All photos CAW collection)*

being attached to the central axis fastenings, it was wound inside with a crank. This cumbersome and time-consuming process was enforced by the weight of the ammunition, and was one of the reasons production of this weapon was terminated. When under attack from a formation of fast-moving aircraft, such a reloading procedure would be far too slow.

Like most designs of gun, the MG C/30 L had its strengths and weaknesses. The latter included the training and elevating procedures – these were entirely down to the strength of the gunner, who elevated the weapon by leaning on the shoulder supports at the rear of the gun and training it by walking around the wooden grating laid around the pedestal. The gun was equipped with ring-and-aperture iron sights. As previously mentioned, some of these guns did arm some smaller Reichsmarine vessels, but it was not successful and was soon replaced by the newer MG C/30.

II. 2cm MG C/30

The history of the development of the MG C/30 has already been described, so here we will concentrate on its design and operating principle. This 'Maschinengewehr' consisted of seven main assemblies: the barrel with breech ring, the breech block, the receiver, the recoil mechanism, the cover of the recoil mechanism, the base of the receiver and the magazine.

The monobloc barrel was attached to the breech ring by a bayonet joint, and the muzzle was threaded so a sleeve and flash guard could be screwed on. The rifling was uniform with eight right-hand 1 in 36 grooves. Inside the receiver was the bolt, sliding horizontally along the axis of the gun, with a handle on

top. On the left-hand side of the receiver was the ammunition feed port, and the ejection port was on the right. Underneath was a lever for locking the bolt and stopping the barrel in the rearward position.

The bolt was a hollow cylinder with the striker and main spring inside it, and the extractor was fitted to the inner face of the forward part of the bolt. The chamber was a rigid structure ensuring that the position and recoil movement of the barrel and bolt were correct. Behind the cylindrical forward section of the barrel sleeve were the holes for the cradle pivot, and behind those on the left was a rectangular opening with a locking device for attaching the magazine and on the right the ejection port. The barrel recoil cylinder was attached to the lower forward part of the receiver and on top of it was a cover containing the recoil mechanism of the bolt.

The barrel recoil mechanism was a cylinder with

Below and right: 2cm MG C/30 in C/30 mount with a basket for empty cases attached as installed aboard Kriegsmarine warships. *(CAW collection)*

Above and below: During the later phase of the war most anti-aircraft guns were equipped with shields protecting their crews from splinters and fire from attacking aircraft. Photographs on this and the adjacent page show a curved shield for a 2cm MG C/30 gun in C/30 mount. *(CAW collection)*

Above and below: Further examples of late-war curved shields for 2cm MG C/30 guns in C/30 mounts. *(CAW collection)*

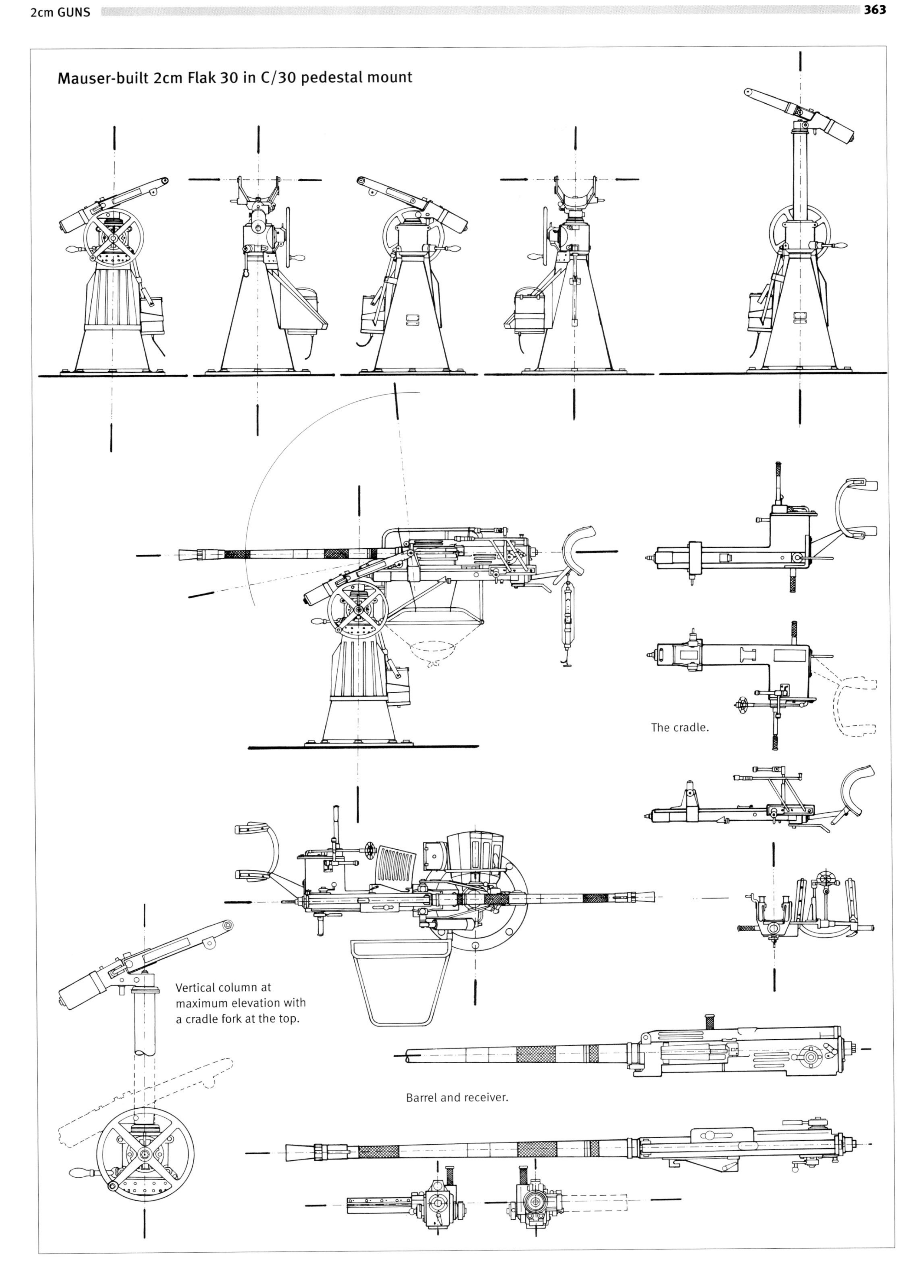

The cradle.

Vertical column at maximum elevation with a cradle fork at the top.

Barrel and receiver.

Right: Two 2cm SK C/30 guns in C/30 mounts installed on a platform between the funnels of a German destroyer.

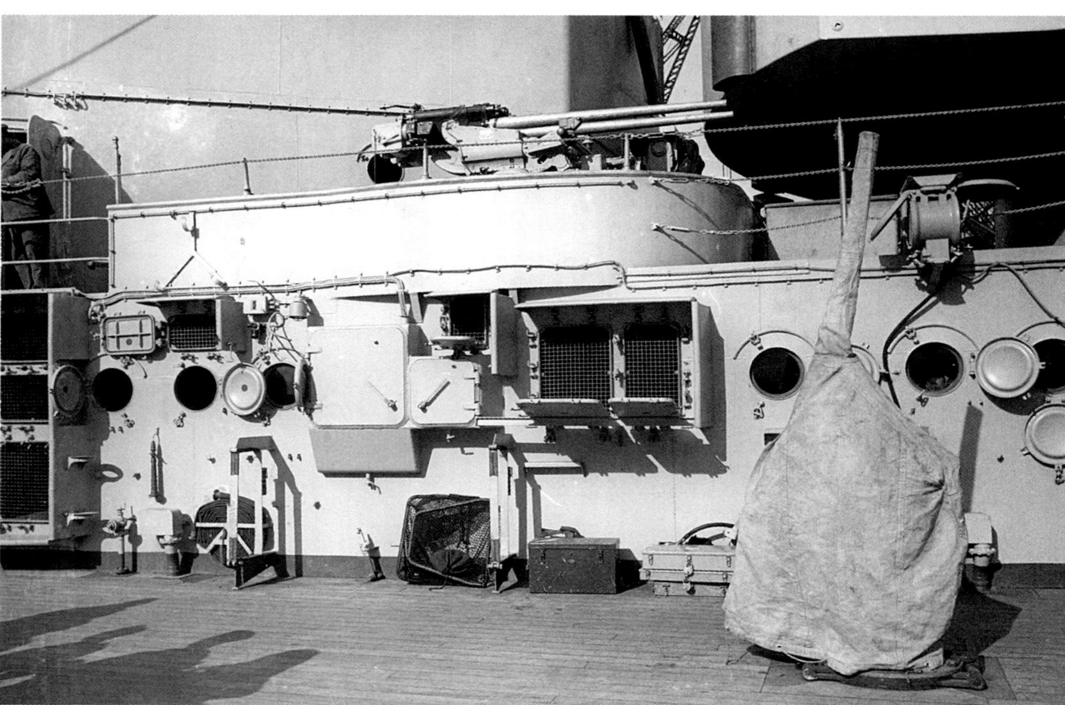

Right: Aboard *Bismarck* prior to Operation 'Rheinübung'. A 2cm SK C/30 gun tightly covered with canvas can be seen in the right. *(S Breyer collection)*

Below and opposite: 2cm MG C/30 in C/30 mounts with baskets for empty cases attached as installed aboard Kriegsmarine warships. *(CAW collection)*

dual springs and a tube sliding inside. The tube had an upward-pointing arm. After firing, the barrel recoiled and pushed against that arm, compressing the springs, which arrested the recoil and returned the barrel to its original position. The receiver cover containing the bolt recoil mechanism was a cylinder containing a slider with a protruding arm. There was also a thinner guide sleeve to which spiral springs were attached. When the bolt recoiled it would catch the arm and compress the springs, which would halt it and return it to its original position.

The base of the receiver was a fixed element forming its rear wall, with the bolt stop in the centre. There were two sleeve mounts on the sides connected to rotating trigger handles. The right-hand one was for

single shots, the left for automatic fire. The trigger assembly was in the lower part of the base. The gun used metal box magazines with a spring inside and a plate feeding rounds into the chamber.

Working principle

At rest, when the gun was not loaded, the breech was closed with the bolt locked in the forward position (up against the barrel). The gun was prepared for firing by sharply pulling the bolt handle backwards. For the first 21mm of movement, the breech ring and barrel travelled back with the bolt. Then the assemblies disengaged and after 30mm the barrel assembly was stopped by the lock of the lever system. The bolt continued to move, until its front end had passed beyond the ammunition feed port and it locked with the trigger mechanism. The recoil springs were resisting this movement with a force of up to 75kgf, so it was advisable to charge the gun at the maximum angle of elevation. The gun fired when the gunner, gripping the firing handles at the base, twisted one of them.

A half-turn of the right firing handle lowered the sear long enough to release the bolt, and the sear was then automatically returned by its spring to the upper position. The bolt, pushed by the upper recoil spring, travelled forward, chambering a round and – just before reaching the chamber – engaged the breech ring mechanism which released the barrel and breech ring. Then the lower recoil mechanism pushed the whole assembly forward, closed the breech and – in the final part of the movement – hit the rear end of the striker. After firing a round the whole moving assembly recoiled back. The barrel unlocked from the bolt, which continued to recoil, extracting the spent case from the chamber which was then removed by the ejector. The bolt reached the end stop and was held by the sear. Another round could only be fired by twisting the right-hand firing handle again.

A half-turn of the left firing handle lowered the sear and held it down until the gunner released the handle. The unrestricted movement of the bolt fired a continuous burst until the gunner released the handle or the magazine was empty. After the last round was fired the ammunition feed plate released the magazine locking lever and simultaneously tripped the latch that stopped the bolt travelling forward, thus alerting the crew that the magazine needed to be changed.

The 2cm MG C/30 gun

Overall length:	2,300mm
Length barrel:	1,300mm
Volume barrel:	0.434dm^3
Length bore:	1,159.4mm
Length chamber:	140.6mm
Volume chamber:	0.07dm^3
Volume combustion chamber:	0.048dm3
Grooves:	8 (0.35mm x 5.35mm)
Width rifling lands:	2.5mm
Depression/elevation:	–10°/+85°
Distance between cradle axis and base:	1,369-1,996mm
Diameter crew area:	1,500mm

The C/30 mount

The base of the mount was a conical pedestal with a vertical guiding sleeve, fixed to the deck or base plate by eight bolts. The handwheel controlling the eleva-

Below and opposite: 2cm MG C/30 in C/30 mounts with baskets for empty cases attached as installed aboard Kriegsmarine warships. *(CAW collection)*

Weights of the 2cm MG C/30 gun

Gun with sights and support:	90kg
Gun only:	61kg
Moving parts:	34kg
Barrel:	18kg
Mount (modernised version):	c. 260kg (c. 350kg)
Gun equipment box:	43kg
Mount equipment box:	22kg

tion gear was on the upper part of the pedestal, beside which was a lever to lock the current elevation setting. To assist elevation, two spring counter-weights were fitted between the guiding sleeve and the vertical axis. An intermediate oblique axis, to facilitate aiming at higher angles of elevation, particularly on a rolling deck, was installed on the rotating head of the vertical axis. On the lower end of this was a locking screw with a handle, and on the upper end a fork with a horizontal axis. There was also a hinged fastening for securing the base of the barrel in the horizontal position. A rack for five magazines was fitted to the pedestal. The gunner trained the weapon manually, leaning into two curved shoulder rests fixed to the rear of the receiver. In order to facilitate control of the gun a back strap was often used, which held the gunner's body close to the rests. The inner surfaces of the rests were padded with rubber. Guns with factory numbers up to 138 were mostly fitted with ring sights, while later guns had telescopic sights. These required fitting the appropriate mounts for them and extending the firing handles. A special basket for catching spent cases was attached to the right-hand side of the gun.

Ballistic properties of the 2cm MG C/30 gun

Muzzle velocity:	835mps
Maximum gas pressure:	2,900kgf/cm^2
Gas pressure at muzzle:	760kgf/cm^2
Maximum range:	4,400m
Maximum ceiling:	3,200m
Rate of fire:	c. 300rpm

Ammunition

Weight complete round:	0.32kg
Weight projectile:	0.134kg
Weight propellant charge:	0.038kg
Weight case:	0.148kg

The 2cm MG C/30 gun

Calibre:	20mm
Weight of gun:	57.5kg
Overall length:	2,300mm
Length barrel:	1,300mm
Length bore:	1,159.4mm
Length chamber:	121.5mm
Volume chamber:	0.048dm^3
Grooves:	8 (0.325mm x 5.2mm)
Weight projectile:	0.12kg
Propellant charge:	0.415kg of NzRP
Muzzle velocity:	835mps
Working pressure:	2,800kgf/cm^2
Approximate service life:	20,000 effective rounds
Maximum range:	4,800m
Maximum ceiling:	3,700m
Tracer range:	4,800m
Rate of fire (theoretical):	280rpm
(practical):	120rpm
Depression/elevation:	−11°/+85°

Weights of the 2cm MG C/30 gun

Barrel:	18kg
Gun and mount:	420kg
Gun without optical instruments:	828kg
Optical instruments and drill equipment:	96.6kg
Shield:	500kg
Complete gun:	2,150kg

Dopp. C/37 twin mount

Just before the outbreak of war, the C/37 triaxially-stabilised twin mount for MG C/30 guns was developed. Unusually, the guns were mounted one above the other. Training was manual, while stabilisation and elevation were mechanical. However, initial trials aboard one of the Type 1936A destroyers were unsuccessful and the design was not put into production.

Ubootslafette C/30 mount

The first submarine mount was developed for the Type II A and Type II B U-boats. The 2cm MG C/30 guns were installed on C/30 pedestal mounts. The mount stood on a cylindrical base, which served as a watertight container for the gun. As with standard C/30 mounts, the gunner trained and elevated the gun by his own movements. It took thirty-two seconds to get the gun into action after surfacing and slightly longer, forty seconds, to pack it away before the boat dived. In most cases this mount was installed forward of the

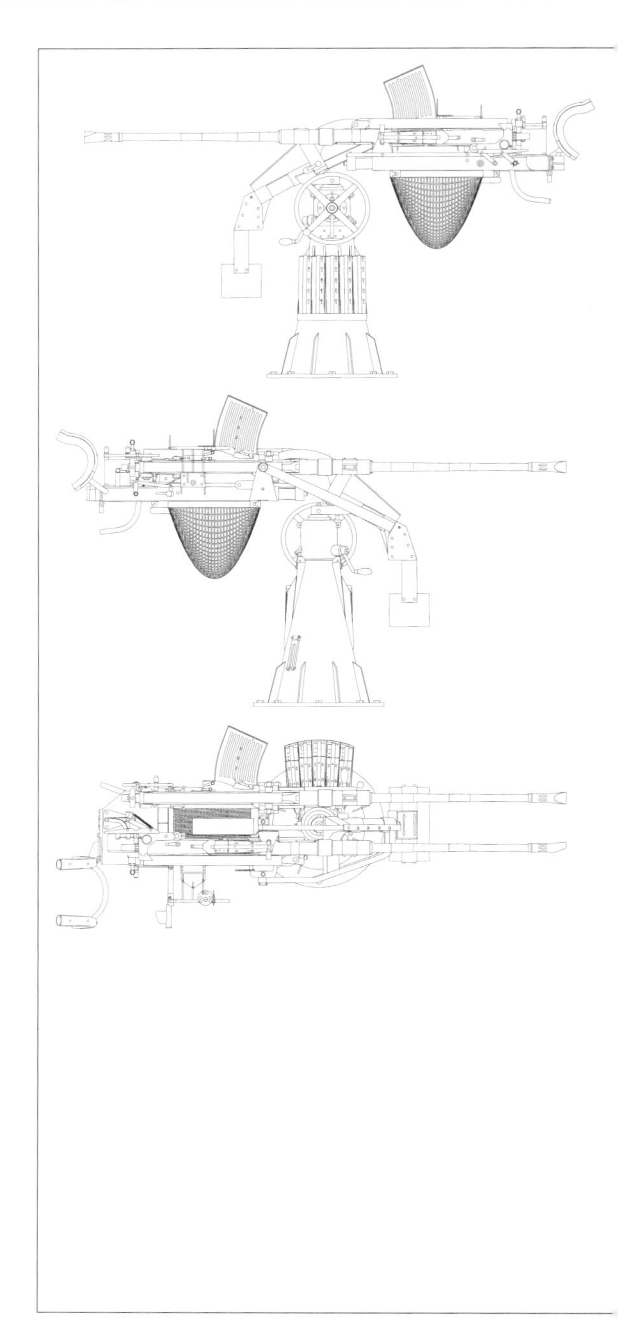

conning tower on Type II A (e.g. *U 1* and *U 6*), Type II B (*U 24*) and Type II D (*U 145*) boats.

Submarine mounts

The most extensive changes to the design of the 2cm MG C/30 gun and the C/30 pedestal mount were introduced for the submarine service. The first alterations were made in early 1940 aboard Type VII C U-boats. The rear part of the bridge was widened and a 2cm MG C/30 installed there, but this soon proved inadequate. Due to frequent defects and insufficient firepower, in 1942 OKM ordered that it be replaced by a twin MG 151 and a 20mm gun in a 'Wintergarten'. This also proved unsatisfactory and was later removed. As mentioned previously, new designs of conning tower were developed to accommodate U-boats' increased anti-aircraft armament. In this period three types of tower ('Brückenumbau') were used:

(a) Brückenumbau II – introduced in November 1942 and first installed on *U 193* (Type IX C/40) and *U 237*

Opposite: 2cm Flak C/38 II gun in dual M 43 U Zwilling mount on the bridge of *U 172* – a Type IX U-boat. *(M Skwiot collection)*

Above: *U 1165* (Type VII C/41) photographed after Germany's surrender, alongside ORP *Krakowiak*. The guns have been removed, only the mounts and shields remaining. *(MMW)*

Right: 2cm Flak Zwilling C/38 guns in M 43 mounts with shields on the forecastle of the light cruiser *Nürnberg*, photographed in late 1944 in the Baltic. *(M Skwiot collection)*

Below: Some 2cm MG C/30 guns were installed in watertight containers (Versenktopf) which also acted as a base for the Ubootslafette C/30 mount. The photograph shows a container with the gun inside installed forward of the conning tower aboard *U 145* (Type II D). *(M Skwiot collection)*

Above and below: Type II U-boats of the Weddigen flotilla and their tender *Saar* moored at their base in Kiel before the war. It can be seen that only some of the Type II boats were fitted with C/30 gun containers. This weapon was difficult to operate and eventually their use was discontinued. *(M Skwiot collection, upper, W Markowski collection, lower).*

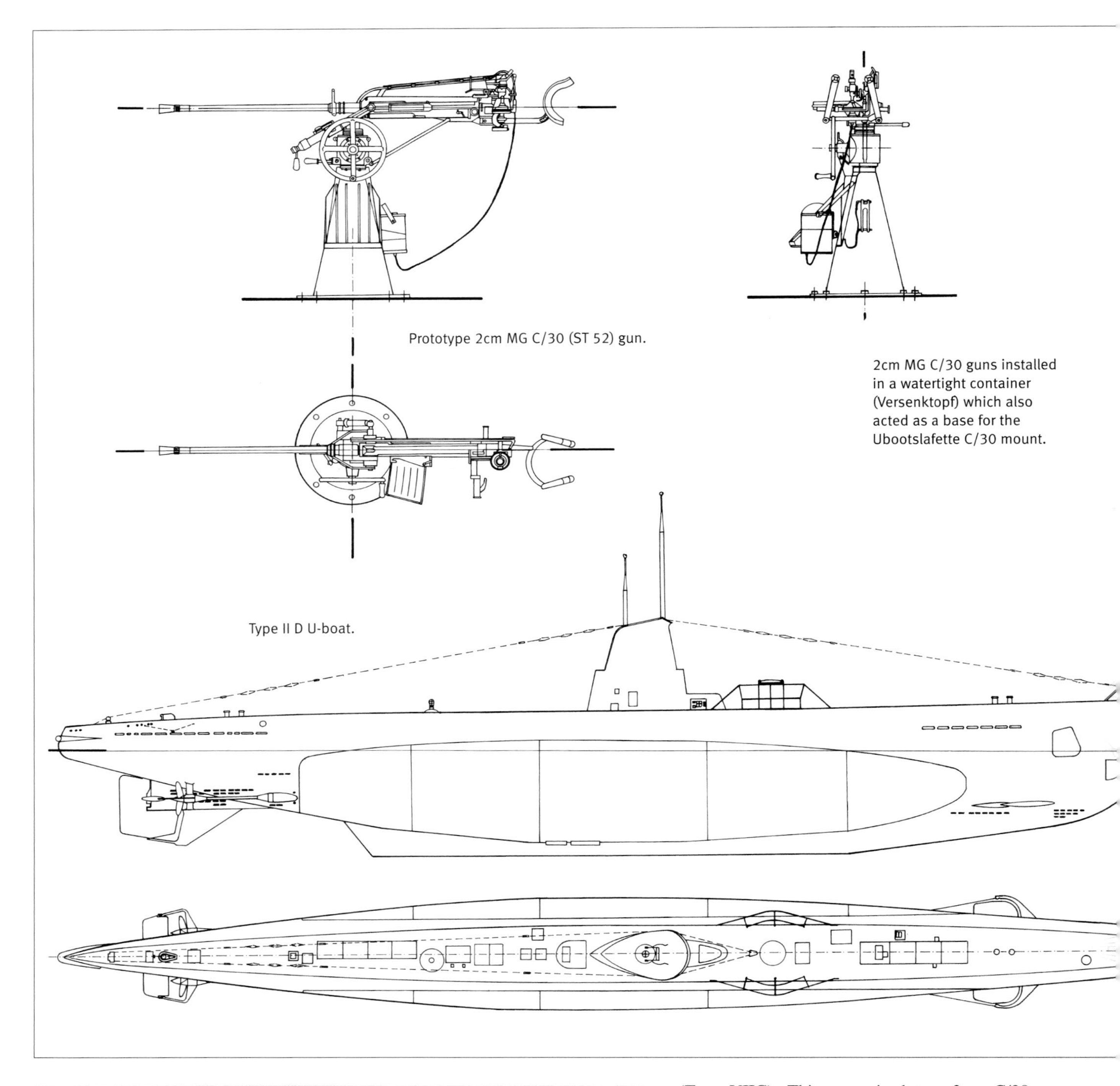

Prototype 2cm MG C/30 (ST 52) gun.

2cm MG C/30 guns installed in a watertight container (Versenktopf) which also acted as a base for the Ubootslafette C/30 mount.

Type II D U-boat.

(Type VIIC). This comprised two 2cm C/38 guns fitted to the bridge deck and a platform at the back of the tower. This was considered a temporary expedient and was removed when new twin and quadruple 20mm guns, as well as 3.7cm Flak M 42 guns, became available.

(b) Brückenumbau III – a version with two 2cm C/38 guns installed on an enlarged bridge deck. This was principally used on Type VIID U-boats.

(c) Brückenumbau IV – a version with two twin 2cm C/38 guns on the enlarged bridge deck and either a 2cm Flak Vierling C/38 or a 3.7cm Flak M 42 on the after platform.

The first submarines to carry the 2cm Flak Vierling C/38 were the Type VIIC boats *U 564* and *U 758*. The guns were installed in May 1943. Unfortunately

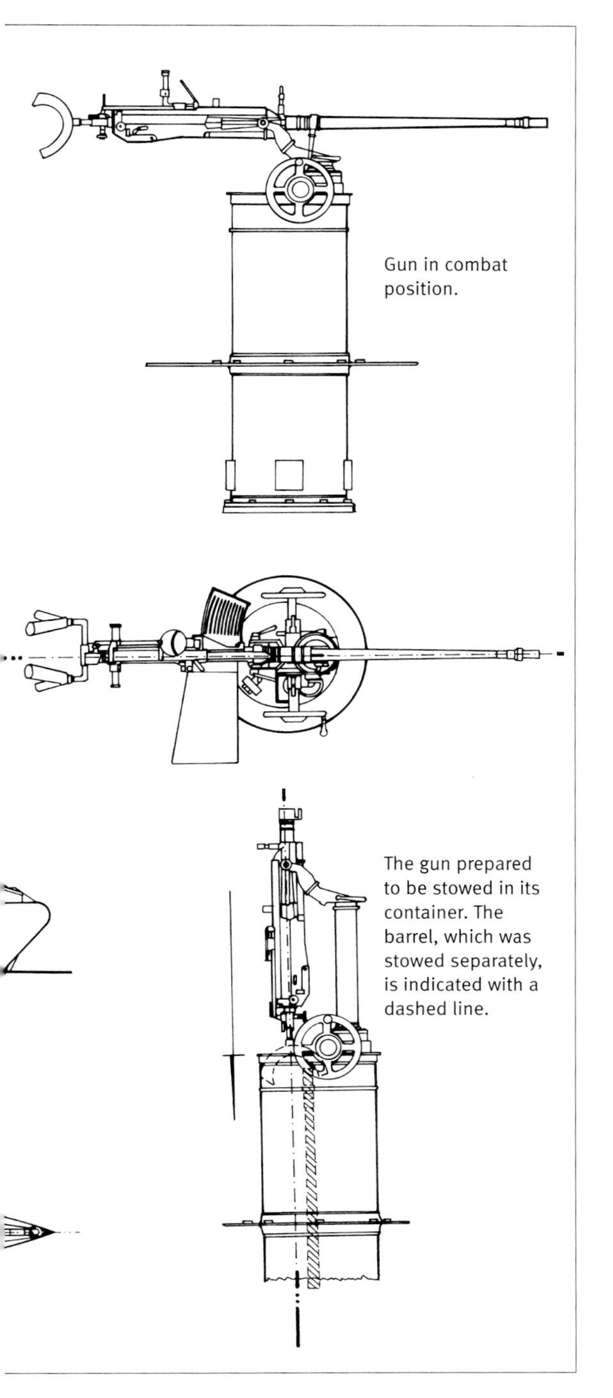

Gun in combat position.

The gun prepared to be stowed in its container. The barrel, which was stowed separately, is indicated with a dashed line.

Above: *U 142* (Type II D) with a 2cm C/30 gun in a container clearly in view. *(W Markowski collection)*

Left: Another Type II U-boat, most probably *U 3*, with a 2cm C/30 gun in a watertight container. *(M Skwiot collection)*

Opposite: One more Type II boat – *U 9* (Type II B) with a 2cm C/30 gun in a container clearly in view. *(M Skwiot collection)*

production of 20mm guns for U-boats did not begin as scheduled, and thus the re-arming of the U-boats was delayed. In order to get around the directive of 14 June 1943 forbidding U-boats without at least minimal anti-aircraft armament from leaving port, 2cm MG C/30 guns on C/30 pedestal mounts were 'temporarily' fitted, along with other lighter anti-aircraft weapons.

III. The 2cm Flak 30 gun

A further development of the MG C/30, the 2cm Flak 30 was designed by Mauser in 1934. It was adopted by the Reichsmarine that same year, and by the Luftwaffe and Wehrmacht a year later. The Flak 30 mount was designed to be carried on a special trailer that could be towed by most German military vehicles. Early models were equipped with Flakvisier 35

Below: Prototype of a land-service 2cm Flak 30 gun. *(Via M Skwiot)*

Above: While German warships were based in Brest their armament was complemented with land models of the 2cm Flak 30 gun. The photograph shows the heavy cruiser *Admiral Hipper* with such a gun atop 'B' turret. *(M Skwiot collection)*

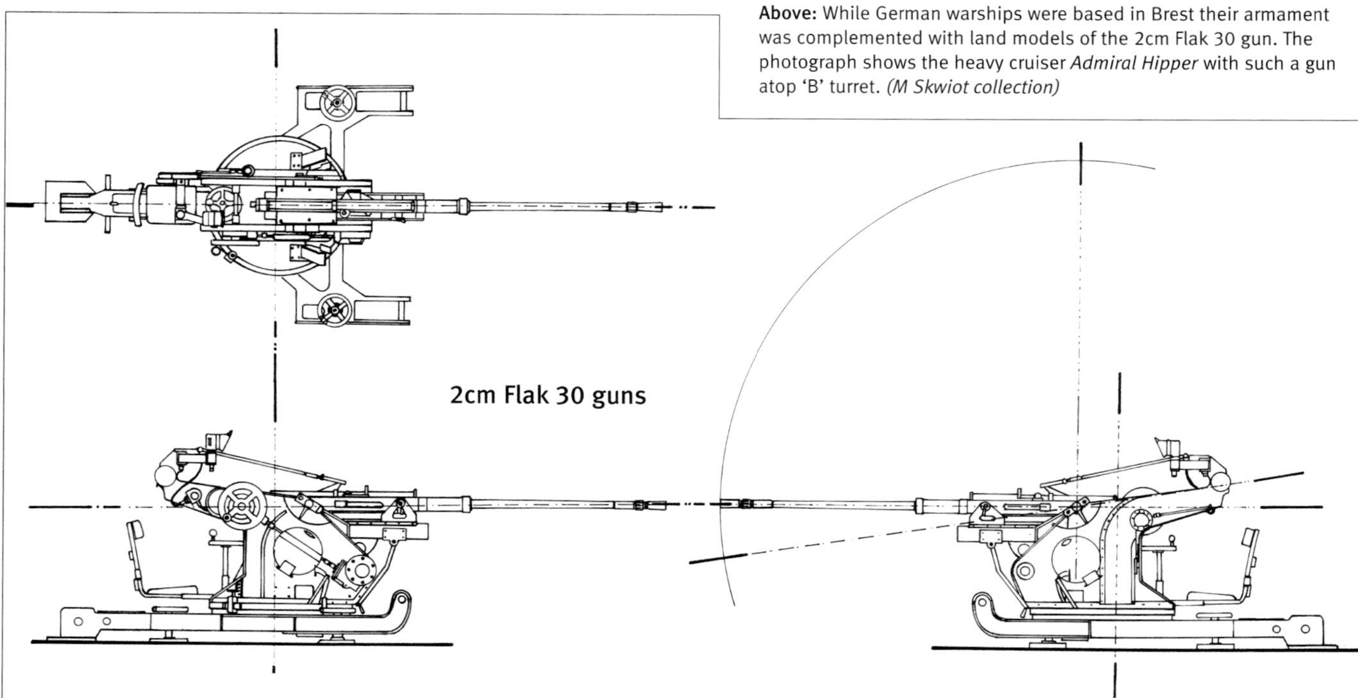

sights, replaced in 1941 by the newer Linealvisier 21. Finally these were themselves replaced by the Schwebekreisvisier 20. The gun itself was eventually superseded by the 2cm Flak 38.

The gun was recoil-operated. When a round was fired the barrel and bolt recoiled together until the shell left the muzzle. Then the breech was unlocked and the barrel stopped, while the bolt kept moving, extracting and ejecting the spent case. Then the compressed recuperator spring pushed it back forward. Unless stopped by the sear, the bolt chambered another round, locked the breech and continued forward with the barrel until the next round was fired. Just like the MG C/30 the Flak 30 consisted of seven main assemblies, with the first two – the barrel with breech ring and flash guard, and the bolt – formed the

Left: 2cm Flak 30 gun set up on the promenade in the Dutch town of Scheveningen. *(A Jarski collection)*

Below: Fully-manned 2cm Flak 30 land-type gun during drills. The gun is mounted on a barge. This weapon was quite portable which made it very popular and it was used in various applications – as proved by this photograph. *(A Jarski collection)*

Right: 2cm Flak 30 gun position seen firing. Such anti-aircraft artillery positions were densely deployed around German bases and anchorages in Norway. *(CAW collection)*

Right: 2cm Flak 30 guns were also installed on auxiliary Kriegsmarine vessels, like this ship escorting a coastal convoy. *(CAW collection)*

Left: Another 2cm Flak 30 gun position. *(CAW collection)*

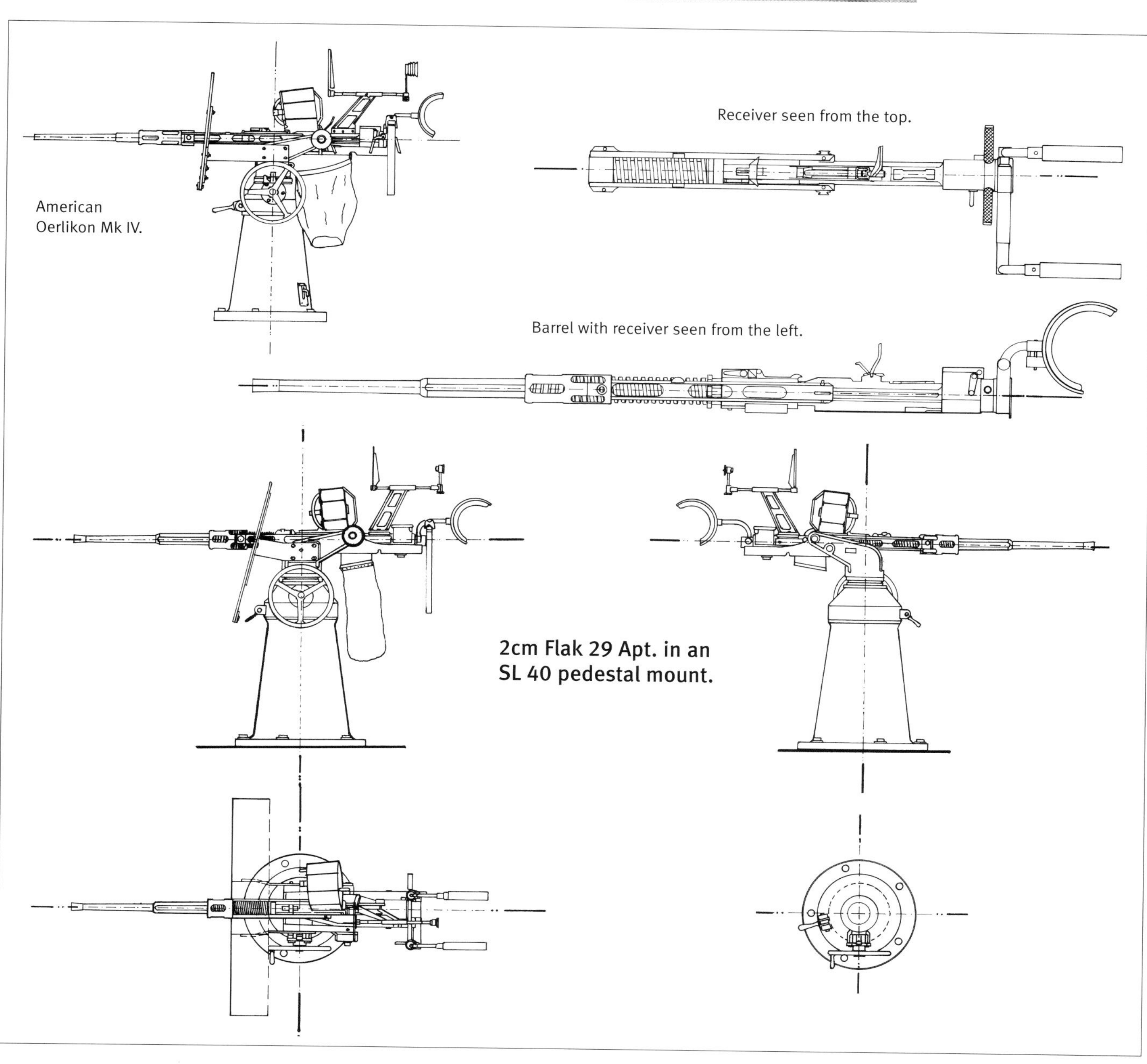

2cm Flak 29 Apt. in an SL 40 pedestal mount.

Right: 2cm Flak 29 Apt. in an SL 40 pedestal mount. It was a licence-built design of the Swiss company Oerlikon. *(CAW collection)*

so-called moving assembly. All the other parts – the barrel recoil mechanism, the cover with the bolt recoil mechanism and charging gear, the receiver, the receiver base and the magazine – were fixed.

The barrel was identical to that of the MG C/30, and could be fitted with two types of flash deflector. The first had an inner diameter of 41mm and the second of 35mm. The first type was used when greater friction was observed when firing – this could happen with factory-fresh guns or at lower temperatures. The second type provided more effective muzzle-braking and was used on more freely-working guns.

The breech ring, bolt and recoil mechanism were also the same as on the MG C/30, with one difference:

Below: 2cm Flak 29 Apt. gun in an SL 40 pedestal mount as installed aboard Kriegsmarine auxiliary vessels. *(CAW collection)*

there was no charging handle. This role was fulfilled by a mechanism with a vertical handle installed on top of the receiver.[1]

Because a new type of mount which was quite low had been developed, the trigger mechanism was changed. The gunner now sat behind the gun on the rotating mount, with his feet on two trigger pedals, the right one for single shots and the left for automatic fire. The gun was fed from standard twenty-round Magazin 30 magazines.

The mount

The Flak 30 mount developed for army units could be carried on the special single-axle Sonderanhänger 51 trailer, or installed in fixed positions or on vehicles. In a very few cases it was installed aboard ships. The mount consisted of the base, the body and the cradle. The base was a rigid flat triangular frame supported on three legs, the height of which could be adjusted to level the gun, assisted by a built-in spirit level. The socket for the mount's pivot was surrounded by a toothed ring.

A circular plate on six ball-bearings was mounted loosely over the base on the main vertical axis. Two vertical plates attached to this circular element were the main structural components of the body of the mount. The bearings for the cradle pivot were at the top of these plates at the front, and the training gear handwheel was at the rear, between the two plates. The elevation gear was on the right. An extension of the left-hand plate, angled to the rear, was the mount for the sight. It was connected by an articulated joint and push rod to the arm of the cradle, thus ensuring it was always parallel to the barrel. The rearmost element of the mount was the gunner's seat, which was adjustable to suit the height of the gunner.

The cradle consisted of a box, two side girder plates with pivots and a toothed arc. Beside the right pivot there was a scaled arc allowing the angle of elevation to be read off. The slider, which held the

The 2cm Flak 30 gun

Calibre:	20mm
Weight of gun with mount:	450kg (770kg with carriage)
Length (with mount):	4,080mm
Width (with mount):	1,810mm
Height (with mount):	1,600mm
Length gun:	2,300mm
Length barrel:	1,300mm
Pitch of rifling:	720mm
Grooves:	8
Muzzle velocity:	900mps
Average recoil distance:	33mm
Maximum recoil distance:	44mm
Maximum range:	4,400mm
Maximum ceiling – without self-destruct:	3,200m
with self-destruct:	2,000m
Rate of fire (theoretical):	280rpm
(practical):	100-120rpm
Training arc:	360°
Depression/elevation:	−12°/+90°

Above: 2cm Flak 29 Apt. gun in an SL 40 pedestal mount (right). On the left there is a 2cm MG C/30 gun with the pedestal at maximum elevation. *(CAW collection)*

Left: 2cm Flak 29 Apt. gun in an SL 40 pedestal mount as installed aboard Kriegsmarine auxiliary vessels. *(CAW collection)*

1 Such a mechanism had been used previously on 2cm MK ST5 and ST 52 designs.

Flakvisier 35 and Linealvisier 21 anti-aircraft sights

	Flakvisier 35	*Linealvisier 21*
Target speed:	25-435km/h	38-540km/h
Target altitude:	200-2,000m	330-1,650m
Range:	2,950m	1,600m

forward part of the receiver with side bolts, was mounted on rails riveted to the box, inside which there was an oil-filled recoil brake coupled to the slider. The cradle pivots were located beyond the gun's centre of gravity, so two spring counterweights were fitted below the cradle. Both the elevation and training gears were fitted with locking latches. There were also appropriate fastenings to secure the mount for transport.

The C/30 pedestal mount

In this type of mount a vertical column, the height of which could be raised or lowered by a handwheel, was fixed to a conical base. It took 29-30 turns of the handwheel to move the column from its lowest to its highest position. A latch on the side allowed it to be locked at the desired height. At the top of the column, the fork of the cradle was mounted loosely on a pivot, allowing it to rotate. Deflecting the cradle axis from the default position allowed the gunner to keep the gun level while the ship was rolling. Magazines were stored in a rack fixed to the base, beside which was a rod for locking the gun in the horizontal position at cruising stations. Some mounts were also fitted with a battery to power the Flakvisier Z sight.

The sights and shoulder rests for the gunner were offset some 35cm to the left of the gun's axis of rotation, as were the gunner's handgrips, and to facilitate his control of the mount there was a back strap. In order to balance the weight difference between the breech and cradle and the barrel, a spring counterweight was fitted on the right-hand side of the gun. A basket for spent cases was also on the right side, the lower frame of which was designed to fold away for cruising stations.

The C/30 pedestal mount

Weight of gun and mount:	420kg
Range:	4,800m
Ceiling:	3,800m
Rate of fire (theoretical):	280-300rpm
(practical):	120rpm
Training arc:	360°
Depression/elevation:	-11°/+85°

Ammunition for 2cm Flak 30 and Flak 38 guns

The guns used four main categories of ammunition: combat ('Kriegsmunition'), training ('Übungsmunition'), blank ('Platzmunition') and drill ('Exerziermunition').

(a) 2cm armour-piercing round with tracer ('Panzergranate L'spur') – weight 148g, painted black with a red, yellow or white band. Supplied to combat units in airtight boxes of 100.

(b) 2cm high-explosive round with tracer ('Sprenggranate L'spur'), self-destruct and sensitive impact fuse – weight 132g, for anti-aircraft use, painted yellow with red, yellow or white bands. Supplied to combat units in airtight boxes of 100.

(c) Training round – without explosive warhead or fuse, painted grey, either with tracer (yellow band) or without.

(d) Blank round – with wooden projectile. A special smoothbore barrel was fitted to the gun when firing this ammunition. Its base ensured the gun operated in the same way as with combat ammunition, but at the muzzle there was a special device that shattered the wooden projectiles.

(e) Drill round – for loading drills. A single solid piece made of aluminium.

IV. 2cm Flak 29 and Flak 29 Apt. guns

These guns, on the SL 40 pedestal mount, were specifically intended for light warships, and therefore the mount had to be triaxially stabilised. The first axis was the axis of rotation, the second of elevation and the third ran across the base of the cradle's fork parallel to the barrel, enabling the gunner to keep the gun quite stable. The design was modelled after the Oerlikon system. The only minor difference between the Flak 29 and the Flak 29 Apt. was that the latter did not have a funnel-shaped muzzle. The gun was controlled by the gunner's movements – he rested his back against bar supports and had two handgrips. Twisting the left grip opened automatic fire and a

Below: Prototype quadruple anti-aircraft gun developed by Mauser and designated Flakvierling MG C/35. *(Via M Skwiot)*

Above: Prototype of the 2cm Flakvierling MG C/35 with C/38 guns and a shield, designed by Rheinmetall. *(Via M Skwiot)*

trigger next to the gun was used for single shots. The SL 40 mount consisted of two main assemblies: the fixed conical base and an upright cylindrical column with the cradle mounted on top of it. The column could be raised or lowered with a special wheel to facilitate aiming at various angles of elevation. The head of the base with this handwheel was free to move on the axle allowing the operator to follow the gunner's movements. The gun had a ring-and-aperture sight and was fed from a sixty-round drum magazine attached to the top left-hand side of the breech. Spent cases were ejected to the right into a bag hung there to catch them. The theoretical rate of fire was 560-600 rounds per minute but this was lower in practice owing to the need to replace the magazine. The training arc was 360° and depression/elevation was -8°/+100°. The stabilisation system allowed for ± 15° movement. Range was 4,400m and ceiling 2,700m.

V. 2cm MG C/35 and 2cm Flakvierling 38 guns

The development in the 1930s of multi-barrel anti-aircraft guns for British warships (pompoms) and later American designs (the quadruple 1.1in Mark 1/1 guns) encouraged German designers to develop similar weapons. Initially a quadruple 2cm MG C/35 on the C/38 mount was developed by Mauser, but production was then taken over by Rheinmetall and – during the war – by other armaments manufacturers. The gun proved very effective in its early years of service, but as the enemy introduced faster and better-protected aircraft, its combat utility declined. The gun was used aboard Kriegsmarine vessels.[1] The first (unofficial) designation of the gun was C/35, derived from the Flakvisier 35 sight taken from the 2cm MG C/30.

The weapon consisted of four 2cm Flak C/30 guns installed in pairs on either side of the mount. Between the body of the mount and the base there was a fork-shaped spar fixed to that base. The longitudinal axes of the guns were installed on the ends of that spar. A U-shaped bar was mounted on that axis, and the body with guns was fixed to it. The guns were fed from twenty-round magazines attached to the outer sides. Spent cases were ejected inwards into a metal funnel and fell into metal boxes beneath it. The stabilisation operator seated behind the guns used his handwheels to keep the guns level. He could compensate for up to 15° of motion on either side. The layers' seats, gun drive and sights were attached to the lower parts of the frame. The guns' centre of gravity was forward of the mount's pivots, so two cast-iron weights and two moving counterweights were installed at the rear.

The further development of this gun proceeded along two paths. The first has been described by S Breyer: an improved version with Flak 38 guns and shields for the crew was built. The other was the installation of the Flakvisier 40 sight (designed for the C/38 gun), with its designation consequently changing to 2cm Flak C/38 auf Vierlingslafette C/38. Analysis of photographs confirms that this was a new model of the gun. One further version was also developed, intended exclusively for submarines.[2] This was designated the Vierlingslafette C/38/43U and had folding protective shields.

Finally, it should be noted that during the final stages of the war, the Telefunken company designed the 'Rettin' gunnery radar specifically for these quadruple guns and for the new 30mm cannon, derived from the 'Pauke S' airborne radar. Only a few test models of naval mounts with this radar were ever built, however. The antenna was located between the barrels.

VI. The 2cm Flak 38 gun

Just like its predecessors the 2cm Flak 38 was a fully-automatic gun principally intended for use against aircraft but capable of engaging surface targets as well. Operating on the short recoil principle, it had a higher theoretical rate of fire than earlier designs, between 420 and 480 rounds per minute. It used twenty-round box magazines and consisted of six main assemblies. The first of these was the barrel with muzzle brake and bolt-locking sleeve. The monobloc barrel was 1,300mm long with the chamber (but excluding the muzzle brake) and was rifled with eight right-handed grooves with a pitch of 720mm. The diameter of the bore was 20.00 + 0.10mm and the diameter of the grooves was 20.70 + 0.10mm. The barrel was connected to the locking sleeve by a bayonet joint on the outer surface of its rear end. The locking sleeve recoiled with the barrel along the guides in the receiver, with the rear end of the assembly resting against the recoil spring. On the inside of the sleeve, just behind the barrel, there was another bayonet joint with which a piston indexed. In the middle of the barrel were two knurled sections to help when gripping it when changing the barrel. A special wrench, the Schlussel 2cm K 38, was used to change barrels – it was kept attached to the flat part of the base of the barrel.

1 Siegfried Breyer in his publication 'Leichte und Mittlere Artillerie auf Deutschen Kriegsschiffen' – *Marine Arsenal* No 18, states that this model was also used on U-boats. He also mentions that the battleship *Tirpitz* had eight such guns aboard in 1944, but while studying photographs taken in this period I could see no guns of this type.

2 In fact in wartime it was also installed aboard surface ships, one example being the *Prinz Eugen*. Photographs taken in 1945 show this mount on board.

Right and below: Quadruple 2cm MG C/35 gun in C/38 mount designed by Mauser photographed aboard the training battleship *Schleswig-Holstein* while the ship bombarded the Westerplatte in the first days of September 1939. The first such guns were tested in combat conditions in Poland. *(Via S Breyer)*

The breech was an all-new multi-piece design. The main elements were the bolt and the guide tube – connected with two inner tubes: connecting and worm. This enabled not only the reciprocating movement of the entire assembly, but also the twisting movement of the bolt which was equipped with a bayonet joint mating with the joint on the locking sleeve. Behind the joint were two rollers which travelled along the elliptical edges of the locking sleeve and guide tube, forcing the bolt to rotate. A case extractor was fitted to the right side of the bolt and the ejector to the left (spent cases were ejected to the right). The longitudinal guide tube was empty inside and moved along specially-shaped guide bars, top and bottom: it could only move reciprocally. The upper guide bar had a pin for the bolt's recoil mechanism and the lower bar had one for the trigger mechanism. The protruding front edges of the bars acted as movement limiters for the bolt rollers. Inside the guide tube at the rear was a loose inertial tube. When the locked bolt stopped in its foremost position, this tube, by inertia, shifted forward slightly, driving the striker into the percussion cap of the cartridge.

The cylindrical barrel guide was screwed down to the receiver at the front. A sliding sleeve was inserted in it, from the front, and the latch that prevented the barrel from twisting was located behind it (from the top). Further inside was a flat friction spring that halted the recoiling barrel. Further to the rear was a locking sleeve connected to the barrel. Its bottom lug fitted into a longitudinal slit, preventing the sleeve from twisting as the bolt was locked. The control ring

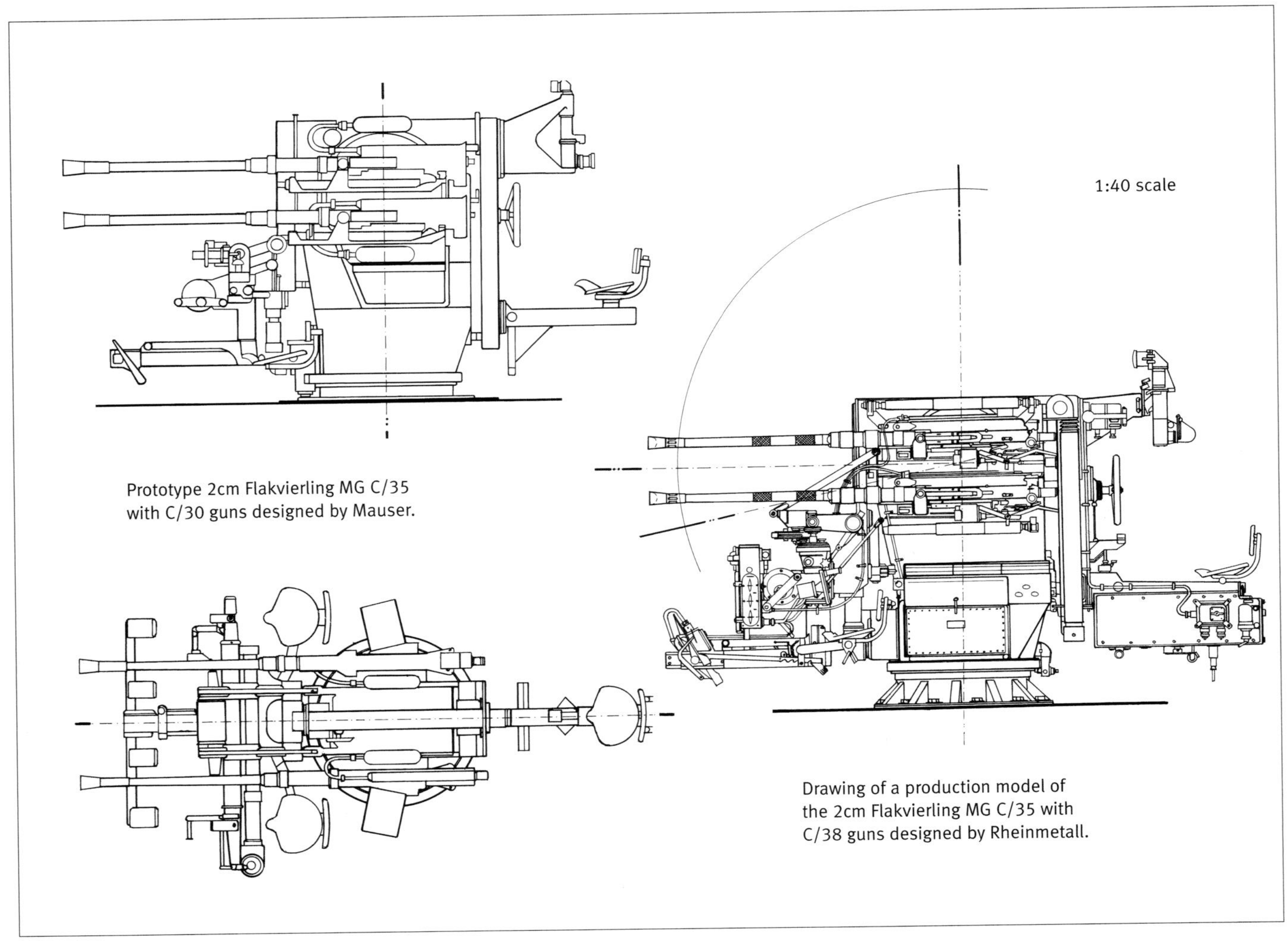

Prototype 2cm Flakvierling MG C/35 with C/30 guns designed by Mauser.

Drawing of a production model of the 2cm Flakvierling MG C/35 with C/38 guns designed by Rheinmetall.

Left: A production Flakvierling MG C/35 with land-type Flak 30 guns installed aboard *Prinz Eugen* while she stayed in Brest in 1941.
(M Skwiot collection)

was mounted behind the locking sleeve. The recoiling bolt's rollers encountered this and forced the breech to unlock with a twisting motion. In the middle of the receiver was the ammunition feed port (left) with the magazine locking mechanism and the ejection port (right) which could be protected by a special anti-dust cover. The fire-selection switch was on the left rear of the receiver: it had two letters on it – E for 'Eninzelfeuer' (single shots), and D for 'Dauerfeuer' (automatic fire).

The top cover of the receiver played two roles. Firstly it acted as a guide for the upper bar of the bolt, and secondly it housed the bolt's recoil spring together with the spring and chain with the head of the cocking mechanism. Both springs were separated by a guiding tube. A chain coming out of the rear, between the rollers, ended in a grip. As with the previous 20mm guns, the cover was hinged across the top, allowing the rear section to be unlatched and lifted up for easy access to the interior of the receiver.

The base of the receiver was fixed to the bottom plate with a transverse bolt. A specially-shaped pin simultaneously connected the rear part of the gun with its mount. The latch of the trigger mechanism was installed in the lower part of that base, connected by a system of levers to the rotating firing handle on the

Below: A production Flakvierling MG C/35 with land-type Flak 30 guns installed aboard a 'K' class light cruiser.
(CAW collection)

outside of the gun, on the right. In front of it was the safety catch, which could be switched between two positions, forward marked F for 'Feuer' (Fire) and back marked S for 'Sicher' (Safe). The rear stop for the bolt was screwed down to the rear face of the receiver. The Flak 38 used the curved Magazin 38 or sometimes the Magazin 32. The older Magazin 30 could be used, but this was not recommended as it lacked the later versions' additional internal guides, which could lead to the weapon jamming due to its higher rate of fire. All types of magazine had numbered holes in their upper surface, allowing the crew to monitor the expenditure of ammunition.

At rest, the closed bolt was in its foremost position. Before the first shot the handle of the cocking chain had to be pulled sharply to the rear. This unlocked the bolt connected to the end of the chain and pulled it back until it engaged with the trigger mechanism, and also compressed the bolt spring. When the handle was released, another internal spring moved the head of the chain back to its forward position. The gun was ready to fire when a magazine was attached and the safety switched to 'F'. All the gunner then had to do was select the firing mode – single shot or automatic fire.

Mount design

Just like that of the Flak 30, the mount of the Flak 38 consisted of three main assemblies: the base with the rotating ring, the main body and the gun cradle. The triangular base had three adjustable legs and a spirit level by the left leg. The hole in the centre of the base acted as a mounting for the rotating ring which was the bottom part of the main body. The gunlayer's seat

was fixed to a plate installed on that ring, on the right. The foot stirrups were at the front. Holes were drilled around the plate to install training stops, to restrict the arc of fire to a particular zone.

The box-shaped body of the mount was attached to the rotating base by four bolts. Its main components were the side plates, which had a ring-type mounting for the cradle at the top. Attachment points for a shield were at the front. A box with a battery for the lighting system was suspended from the front plate. The drive for the trigger mechanism and the elevation gear were on the left. Elevation was driven manually

Above, below and opposite: A production Flakvierling MG C/35 with land-type Flak 30 guns as installed aboard Kriegsmarine auxiliary warships. *(CAW collection)*

Opposite, bottom: A production Flakvierling MG C/35 with land-type Flak 38 guns installed on barge *AFP 27* in the Black Sea, 1944. After the gun sight was replaced with a Flakvisier C40 model and the gun model was changed, the whole setup was redesignated the 2cm Flak C 38 auf Vierlingslafette C/38. *(CAW collection)*

Left: *Prinz Eugen* with a 2cm Flakvierling C/38 in a triaxially-stabilised Vierlingslafette C/38 mount on 'B' turret. *(M Skwiot collection)*

Right: A production Flakvierling MG C/35 with land-type Flak 30 guns as installed aboard Kriegsmarine auxiliary warships. *(CAW collection)*

Left: One of the few photographs of a 2cm Flak C/38 in Vierlingslafette C/38 with a shield. This weapon was installed aboard a landing craft, most probably during transport. *(CAW collection)*

Above: The *Graf Zeppelin* was equipped with seven Flakvierling MG C/35 sets of the Mauser design. They were installed on platforms on both sides of the aircraft carrier. The photographs show the sets installed on the ship. The guns differed from the production models in several details, including different magazine connecting locations. *(Archives of S Breyer)*

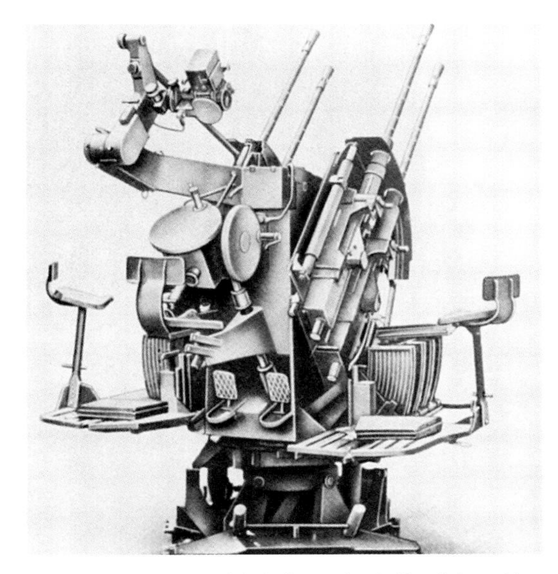

Above: Prototype 2cm Flakvierling 38 in Vierlingslafette C/38 mount. *(Via M Skwiot)*

Above: 2cm Flakvierling C/38 installed on a railway flatcar. This weapon was very effective and in widespread use throughout the German services. *(CAW collection)*

Above: 2cm Flakvierling C/38 (on the right) installed in a triaxially-stabilised Vierlingslafette C/38 mount aboard a German destroyer.

Left: 2cm Flakvierling C/38 (in the background) installed in a triaxially-stabilised Vierlingslafette C/38 mount aboard a German torpedo boat. The mount is equipped with a shield. *(CAW collection)*

Weights of the 2cm Flak 38 gun

Gun with barrel and muzzle brake:	56kg
Gun without barrel:	37.8kg
Barrel with muzzle brake:	18.2kg
Recoiling part:	24.2kg
Barrel with muzzle brake:	18.2kg
Locking sleeve:	2.25kg
Bolt:	3kg
Sleeve of bolt recoil spring:	0.75kg
Gun with sliding cradle:	80kg
Complete gun:	56kg
Full 20-round magazine:	9.5kg
Cradle slide:	12.2kg
Recoil brake (moving parts):	2.3kg

Left: The light cruiser *Nürnberg* with a Flakvierling C/38 installed atop 'B' turret. Baltic Sea, 1944-5. *(M Skwiot collection)*

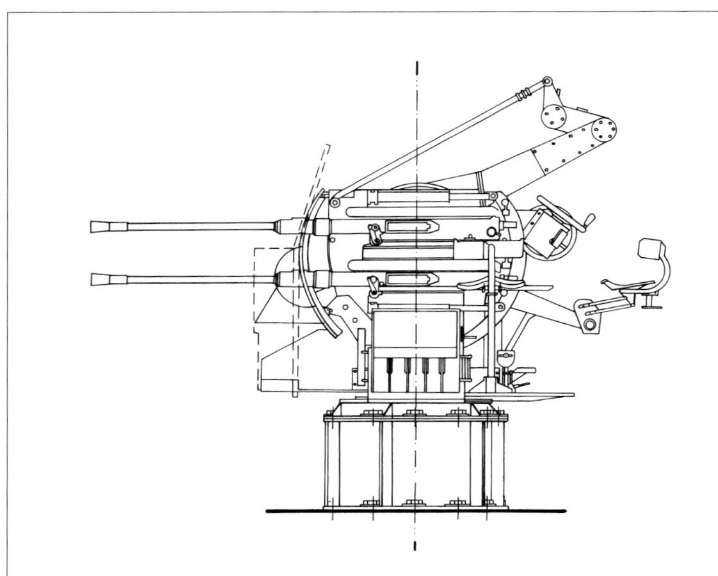

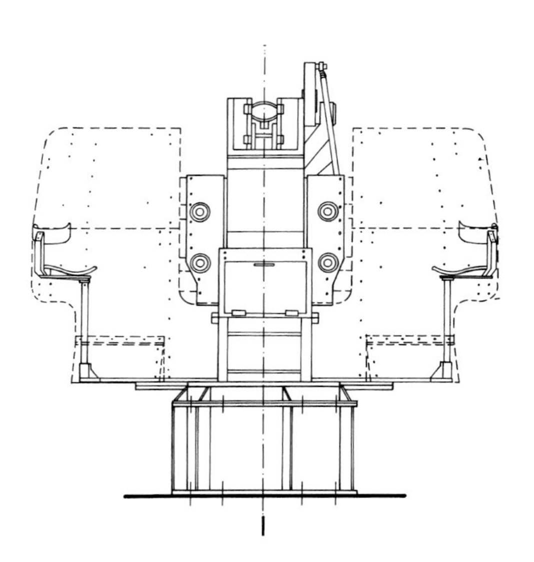

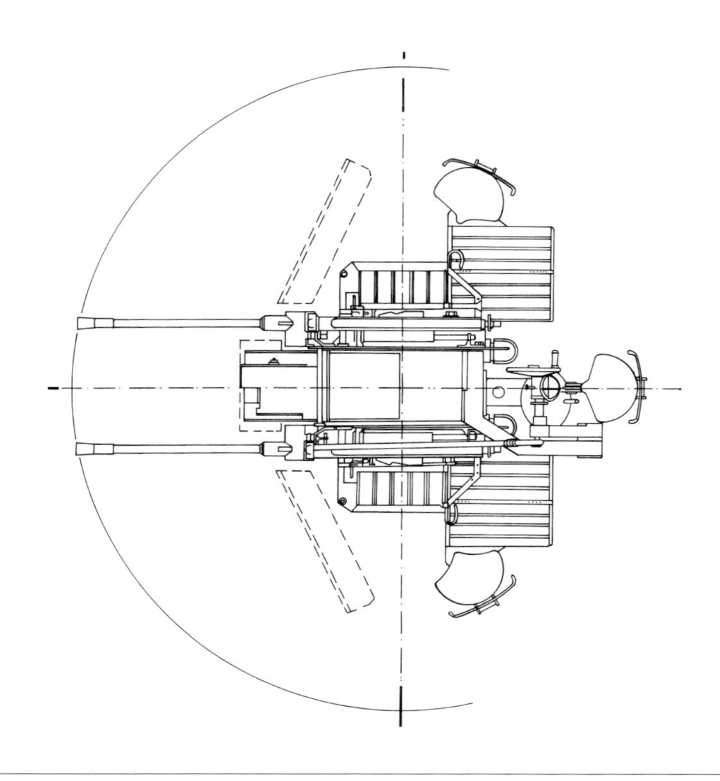

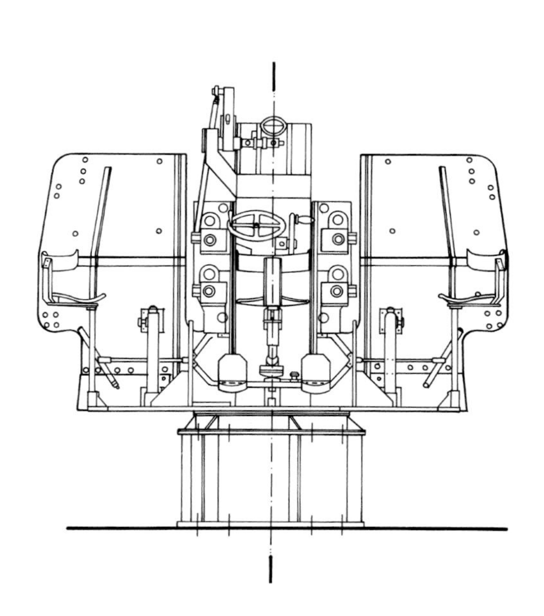

by a handwheel connected to a cog on the right pivot of the cradle. Training was controlled by a horizontal handwheel on the lower rear body plate. The top plate supported the moving gunsight base.

The sight base was connected to the cradle with push rods, which ensured that the sight remained parallel to the barrel. A rack for spare magazines was attached to the left side of the body. Between the side plates there was a spring counterbalance for the body. A latch on the front plate could lock both the training of the mount and the movement of the cradle.

The sliding cradle of the gun was mounted above the body of the mount, on two guide rails. The forward pivots of the slide attached it to the gun using the holes drilled in front of the magazine port and the rear fork connected it to the axis of the rear plate of the receiver. Inside it was a recoil brake connected to the sliding cradle. Two rings, acting as the cradle's

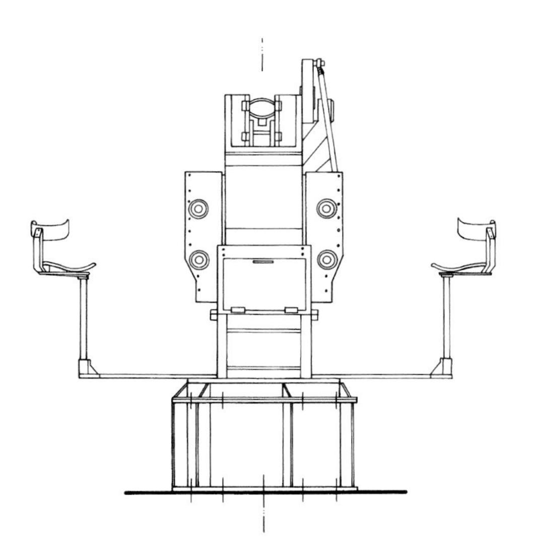

Above: One of the prototype Flakvierling C/38 sets installed in Vierlingslafette 38/43 U mount. This version was slightly modified and adopted for serial production to be installed aboard Type VII C/41 and Type IX U-boats. *(NARA)*

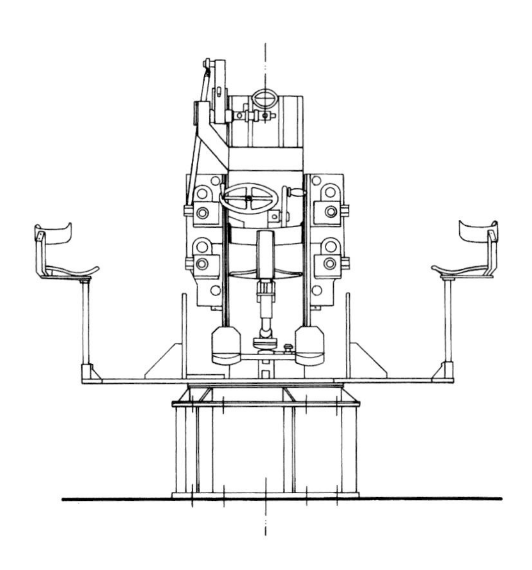

2cm Flakvierling C/38 in a triaxially-stabilised Vierlingslafette C/38.

This is a version without a protective shield.

The 2cm Flak 38 gun

Length with barrel and muzzle brake:	2,252mm
Length without barrel:	1,257.5mm
Distance between front of muzzle brake and centre of cradle's axial holes:	1,490mm
Distance between the centre of cradle's axial holes and the end of the bolt stopper:	762.5mm
Width (without magazine):	193.5mm
Height:	207.5mm
Length barrel – without muzzle brake:	1,300mm
– with muzzle brake:	1,451mm
External diameter barrel – maximum:	68mm
– minimum:	42mm
Volume barrel:	0.434dm^3
Length bore:	1,159.4mm
Length chamber:	140.6mm
Volume chamber:	0.07dm^3
Volume combustion chamber:	0.048dm^3
Pitch of rifling:	720mm
Grooves:	8 (0.35mm x 0.35mm)
Width lands:	2.5mm
Length bolt recoil spring:	970 ± 10mm
Length barrel recoil spring:	163 ± 1mm
Height of cone of bolt stopping disc spring:	4mm
Length disc spring assembly:	130mm

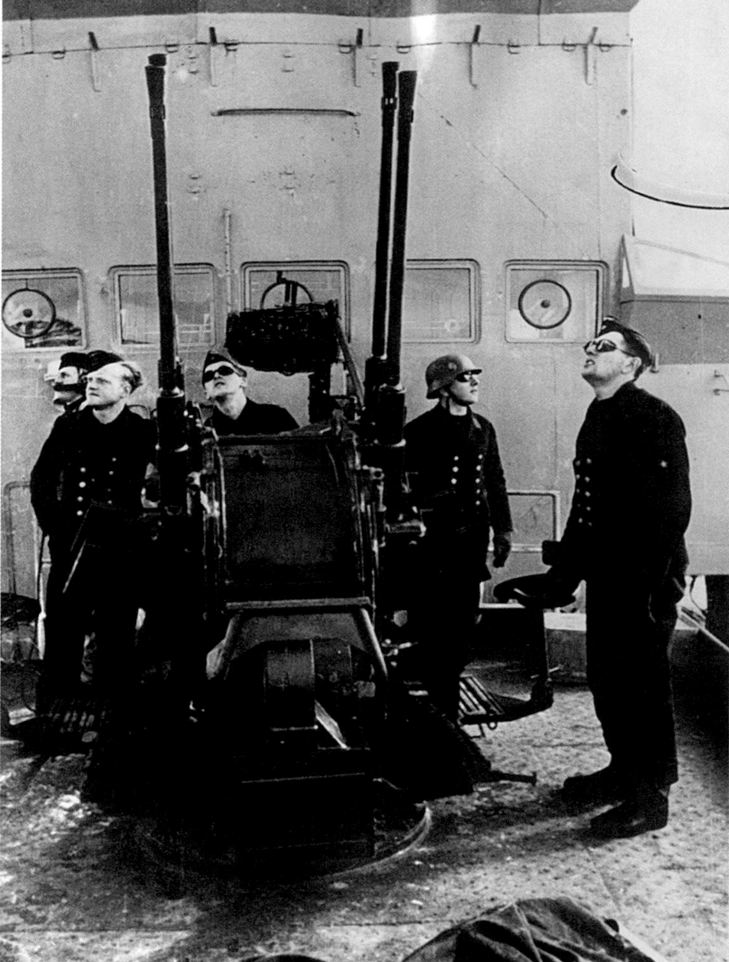

Above, left and below: 2cm Flakvierling C/38 in a triaxially-stabilised Vierlingslafette C/38 as installed aboard German ships. *(CAW collection)*

Above: 2cm Flakvierling C/38 in a Vierlingslafette 38/43 U mount installed on the platform aboard *U 869*, seen from the front. Ceremony of hoisting colours aboard the boat at the AG Weser shipyard in Bremen, 26 January 1944. *(M Skwiot collection)*

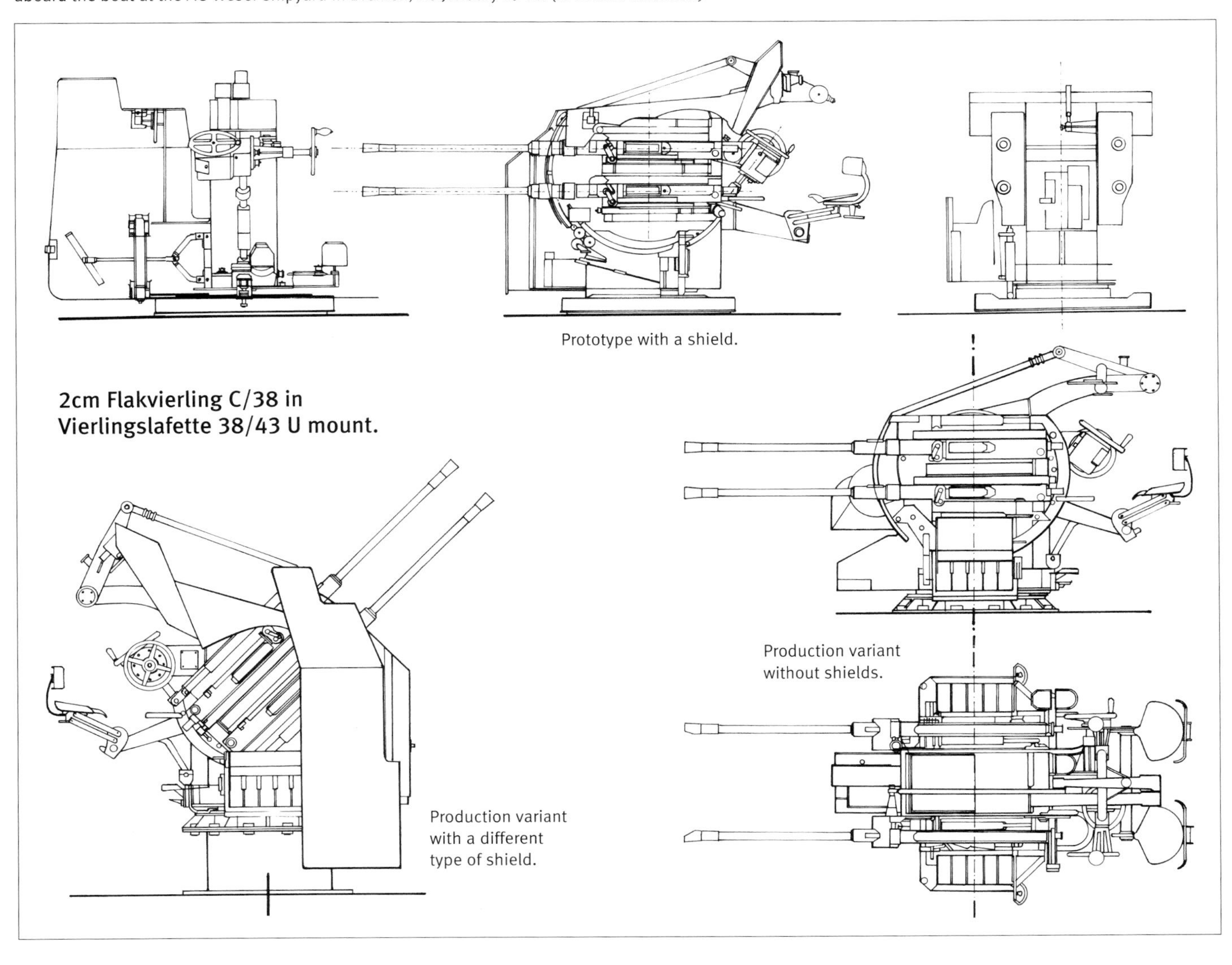

Above: Two 2cm Flakvierling C/38 sets in Vierlingslafette 38/43 U mounts installed on platforms aboard *U 441* (*U Flak 1*). *(M Skwiot collection)*

Left: Another view of the 2cm Flakvierling C/38 in a Vierlingslafette 38/43 U mount aboard *U 869* on 26 January 1944. *(M Skwiot collection)*

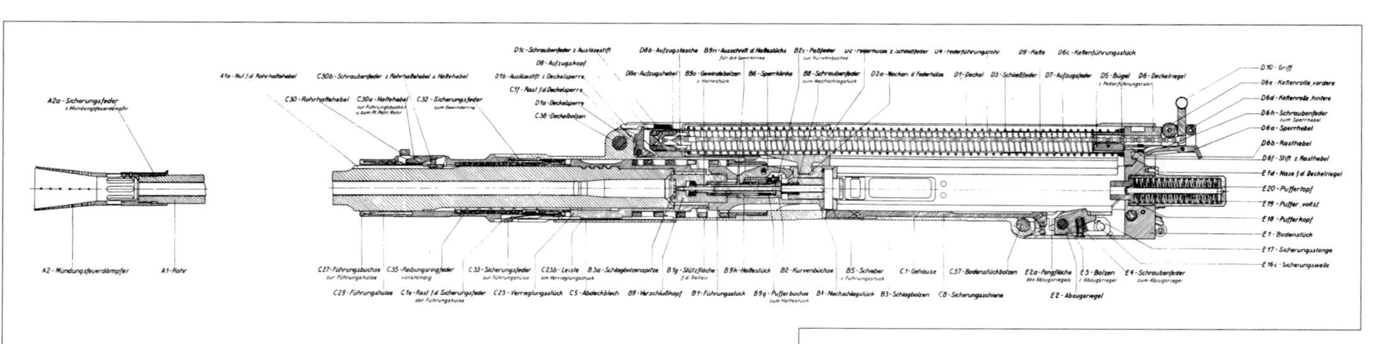

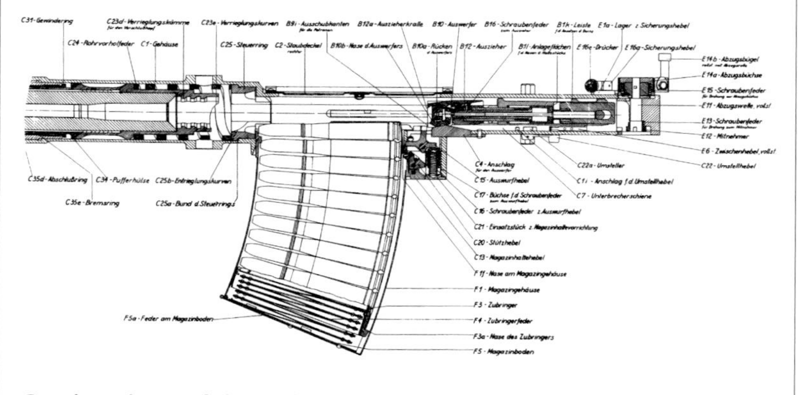

Section views of the Flak 38 gun.

Right: Prototype land gun Flak 38. *(Via M Skwiot)*

The 2cm Flakvierling C/38/43

Length barrel:	1,300mm
Rate of fire (theoretical):	1,800rpm

The 2cm Flak C/38 gun

Calibre:	20mm
Length bore (L/65):	1,300mm
Weight projectile:	0.115kg
Explosive charge:	0.0062kg
Propellant charge:	0.0039kg
Muzzle velocity:	835mps
Range:	4,800m
Ceiling:	3,700m

Ballistic performance of the 2cm Flak 38 gun

Weight of shells:	115g	148g
Muzzle velocity:	900mps	830mps
Maximum gas pressure:	3,200kgf/cm^2	3,200 kgf/cm^2
Muzzle gas pressure:	400-500 kgf/cm^2	400-500 kgf/cm^2
Range:	4,800m	4,800m
Ceiling:	3,800m	3,800m
Rate of fire (theoretical):	420-450rpm	180-450rpm

Below and left: Crew of a 2cm Flakvierling C/38 in Vierlingslafette 38/43 U mount. During the later phase of the war such mounts received two types of shields – one is shown in the photographs to the side and below. *(CAW collection)*

Above, left: The *Bismarck*, when leaving for her first (and only) combat mission in May 1941 was equipped with the land variant of Flak 38 guns. In the photograph a gun of this type can be seen below the after fire control position, next to the liferafts. *(M Skwiot collection)*

Left: Anti-aircraft defence of key objectives – in this case a bridge – in many cases depended on 2cm Flak 38 guns due to their portability. *(CAW collection)*

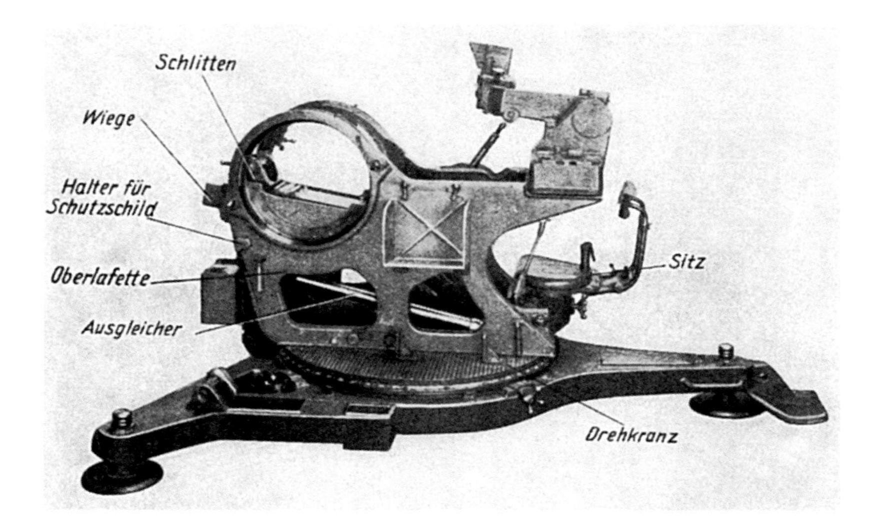

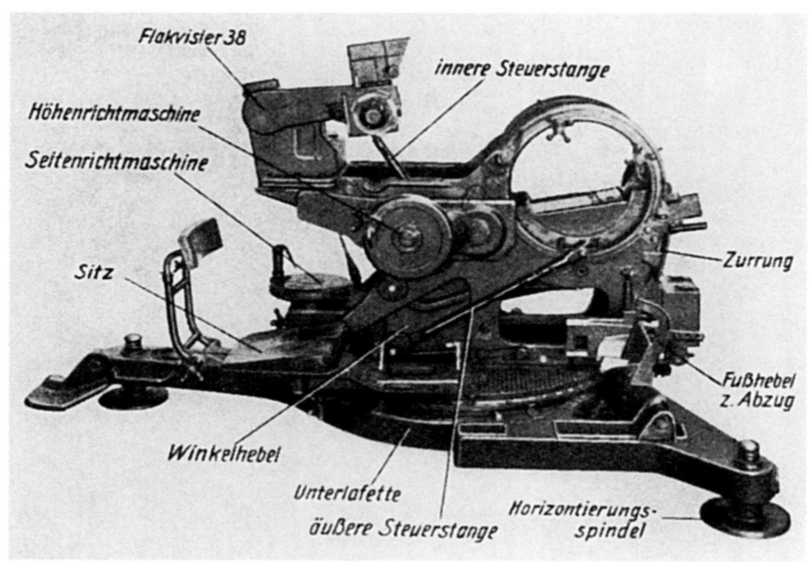

Above: Mount for the 2cm Flak 38.

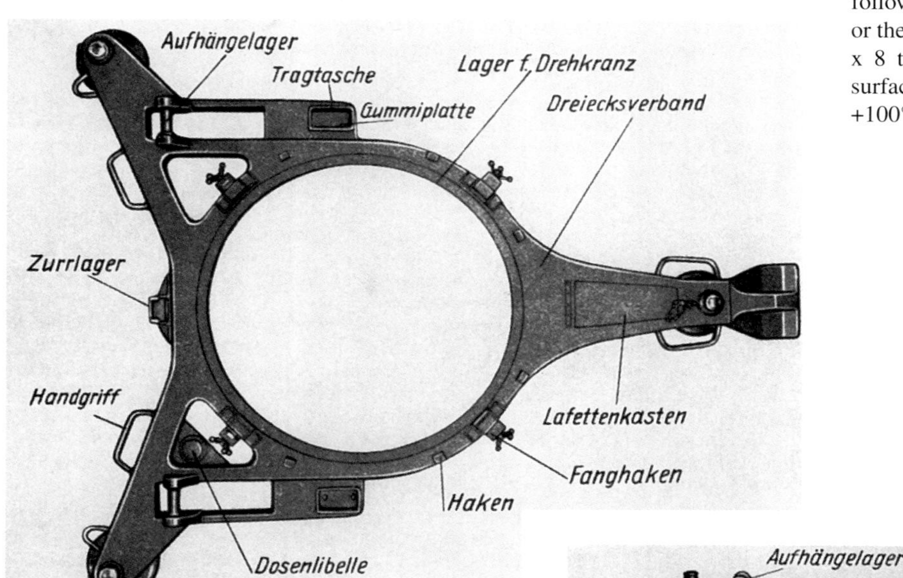

Above and right: Base plate of the 2cm Flak 38 mount.

bearings, were bolted to the side plates of the mount body. A basket for spent cases was attached to the right side, next to the cradle.

VII. The 2cm Flak 38 gun

This model entered service aboard Kriegsmarine warships in 1940. It was an improved variant of the earlier 2cm C/30 and used the SL C/30 pedestal mount. It had a higher practical rate of fire than its predecessor thanks to the use of forty-round magazines, although the twenty-round clips could be used as well. Shields were not fitted until the final stage of the war. In 1944 a twin LM mount with a shield was introduced.

VIII. The 2cm Flakvierling gun

This weapon's design and ballistic performance were identical to the Flak 38 except for one feature. Due to the layout of the mount the right-hand pair of guns had their magazines attached to the right with spent cases being ejected to the left.

Vierlingslafette C/38 naval mount

This was a pedestal mount with a ring cradle, which could be used both in fixed positions and aboard ship. The rotating body of the mount was installed over the base. It was made up of two side plates connected by the bottom plate. Each slide plate carried a pair of guns on parallel sliders, mounted on a ring cradle. Two platforms with seats for the loaders were fitted to the lower part of the body on each side. At the rear, behind the side plates, was the gunner's position with an adjustable seat, two handwheels for elevation and training and two trigger pedals, each of which fired a pair of guns diagonally opposite each other on the mount. This allowed one pair of guns to be fired while the magazines of the other two were being replaced. At the top of the unit was the gunsight base, which was attached to the cradle. This carried one of the following types of sight: Flakvisier 40, Linealvisier 21 or the stabilised sight (Schwebekreisvisier) 30/38. A 3 x 8 telescopic sight could also be fitted to engage surface targets. The range of elevation was –10° to +100°

Above: Sd Kfz 10/4 self-propelled gun armed with a 2cm Flak 38. The vehicle belonged to the 4th Company, 48th Light Self-Propelled Anti-Aircraft Artillery Battalion assigned to the 8th Panzer Division. Eastern Front, 1941. *(CAW collection)*

Right: A coastal anti-aircraft artillery position with a 2cm Flak 38 gun. The crew is at full alert, ready to fire. *(CAW collection)*

Left: 2cm Flak 38 gun. The bands on the barrel most probably denote kills. *(CAW collection)*

Index

Page numbers in italics refer to illustrations. All ships are German unless otherwise specified.

A

Admiral Graf Spee *9*, 32, *40*, *44*, 45, *46–7*, *49*, *55*, *120*, 121, *122*, 126, *138*, 206, *227–8*, 258, 262, 321, *plan* 35, *plan* 124
Admiral Hipper *10*, *16*, *60–2*, *65*, *85–6*, *88–9*, 91, 209, *214*, 271, *280*, *314*, *374*
class 22, *87*, 87–91, *92*, 271, 321
see also *Blücher*, *Lützow*, *Prinz Eugen*, *Seydlitz*
Admiral Scheer *6*, *9*, *17*, 32, *41–3*, 45, *45*, *55–6*, *119*, 121, *122–3*, 125–6, *138*, 206, 258, 262, 273, *308*, 321, *plan* 35, *plan* 124
Akagi (Japan) 129
Algérie class (France) 85
Ariadne 96
Atlantik (tug) *14*
Austria 270–1

B

barbettes *22–3*, *23*, 31, 40, 44, *52*, *58*, *62*, *74*, 83, 91, 108, 118, 132, 135
Bayern *21*
Behncke, Admiral 32
Bismarck 13, *14*, 15, 17, 19–32, *20–2*, *24*, 31, *49–54*, 88, *133–4*, 133–61, *136–7*, *140–2*, 205, 209, *213*, 213–14, *393*, *plan* 131, *plan* 135, *plate* 135, *table* 22
Blücher *88–90*
Bremse 176
Breslau *68*
Britain 270, 381
naval treaty with Germany 13
Bruno Heinemann 161

C

camouflage *27*, *71*, *86*, *89*
coastal defence guns 7, 19, 84, 95, 129, 132, 136, 174
see also land artillery

D

'D' battleship 7, 73, 77, 126
Danzig 19
Derfflinger *67*
destroyers *see* 1934B class destroyers, Z class destroyers
Deutschland *2*, *6–8*, *11*, 13, 15, 32–3, *34*, *36–9*, 40, *42*, 44–5, *46–7*, *55–7*, 77, 79, *119–20*, 126, *128*, *138*, 205–6, 216, *225–6*, 258, 262, *plan* 7, *tables* 42
class 7, 13, 17, 80, 119–26, *121*, 127, 265, 273, 321, 347–8, *plan* 33
ammunition 44, *45*, 119, 125, *table* 34
see also Admiral Graf Spee, *Admiral Scheer*
Dunkerque (France) 85
class 15, 73, 77

E

Emden 96, *96*, 96–102, *97–8*, *100*, 103, *219*, 265
ammunition 99, *table* 99
Erich Koellner *308*
Ersatz Hannover see Bismarck
Ersatz Preussen see Deutschland
Ersatz Schleswig Holstein 13, 15, 17, 29–31, 97, *100–2*
see also Tirpitz

F

fire control *24*, *26*, *64*, 182, 185
floatplanes *41*, *78–9*
France 15, 19, 31, 77
Friedrich Eckholdt *181*
FuMO gunnery radar 354

G

Gneisenau *12–13*, 19, 31, *49*, *57–8*, 77, 79, *80–2*, 83, *126–8*, 127–30, 132, 135, *138–40*, 209, 262, *307*, 321, *plan* 124, *plan* 135, *plate* 132
Graf Zeppelin 129, *129*, *142*, 321, *387*
Grille 176
guns
names and designations 18, 99, 125–6, 174
2cm 268, 327, 347–95
C/38 *290–1*, *355*, *plate* 351
Flak 28 267–8
Flak 29 358, 380–1
Flak 29 Apt *378–9*, 380–1, *plan* 377, *plate* 379
Flak 30 *289*, 348, 357–8, *374*, 374–80, *375–7*, *379*, *plate* 357, *plate* 374, *plate* 379
ammunition 380
Flak 38 *66*, 268, *294–5*, 346, 357–8, 380, 394, *394–5*, *table* 388
Flak 40 349
Flak C/30 381
Flak C/38 *292–3*, 354, *369*, *386*, *388*, *plate* 357, *plate* 388–9
Flakvierling 18, *26*, 273, 300–1, 394, *394*
Flakvierling 28 381
Flakvierling 30 354
Flakvierling 38 *53–4*, *66*, *72*, 224, 268, 348, 349, 353–4
Flak 38/43F 353
Flakvierling C/38 *297–9*, *302–4*, *350*, *358*, *387–9*, *392–4*, *plan* 391, *plan* 392, *plate* 351, *table* 392
Flakvierling MG/35 *296*
Flakvierling MG C/35 358, *380–7*, *plate* 382
Gebirgsflak 18 268
Gebirgsflak 38 268
Gerät 240 349
MG 151 368
MG C/28 347
MG C/30 268, *286*, *288*, 347, 348, *348*, *350*, *353–6*, 357, 358, *358*, 359, *359*, 360, *360–2*, *364*, 364–76, *365*, 366, *370–1*, 381, *plate* 351–*plate* 352, *plate* 357, *plate* 363, *plate* 366, *plate* 368
MG C/35 381, *382–3*, *plate* 382
MG C/30 L 268, 357–8, 369
MK ST 52 *347*, *plate* 347
SMK 18 VI 349, 353
ST 4 268
ST 52 268
2.8cm *66*
Flak 30 *65*, 268, 357
3cm 346, *plate* 345
Flak M 44 *346*
Flak M103/38 *346*
3.7cm 119, 321, 324
Flak 18 267, 305
Flak 28 321

Flak 36 267, 271, 307, *plate* 308
Flak 37 267, 271, 305, *306*, 307, *plate* 308
Flak 42 328, 339–40, *340*
Flak 43/M 267
Flak C/36 *332*, *plate* 331
Flak LM 42 *281–2*
Flak M 42 *246–8*, 267, 333–43, *337–9*, 343, *343*, *plate* 341, *plates* 334–7
Flak M 43 Gerät 341 343, *plate* 343
Flaklafette LM 42 342
Flaklafette LM 43 342
Flakzwilling M 42U 305
LM 42 *plate* 351
LM 43 U *342*, *plate* 342
M 42 343
M 42U 305
SK C/30 *215*, *236–41*, 267, *268*, *273*, *305–6*, *307*, *308*, 314, *314*, 315, 317, *318–20*, 321, *321–3*, 324, *324–5*, *326–7*, 326–7, 333, 343, *plan* 309–13, *plate* 317
SK C/30 U *242–5*, 305, 314, *326*, 327, *327–8*, *332*, 333, *333*, *plan* 330–1
4cm
Flak 28 *66*, *230–5*, 267, *267–9*, 269–304, *270–5*, 280, 321, *plate* 276–8
prototype Aktiebolaget Bofors *plate* 269
Flak 38 268
LM 43 U *284–5*
5.7cm
L55 M/24 269
L57 M/99B 269
7.5cm 185
Flak L/60 185
8.8cm 119, 185, 188, 205, 216–64, 216–67
Bofors 185, 187
Flak 16 188
Flak 18 185, 188
KM41 (Ubts Flak L C/31) 250
L/35 265
L/45 *228–9*, 265, *265–6*
SK C/25 205, 262, 264
SK C/30 *158*, *216*, *218–23*, 224, 249–59, 249–66, *plate* 217, *table* 224, *table* 251
SK C/30U 249
SK C/31 205, 216, 219, *225–8*, 258, *259–61*, 262, *262–3*, 264, *table* 258, *tables* 219
SK C/32 262, 264, *table* 264
SK C/32 L 76 *187*, 258, *259*
SK C/35 *159*, 249, *249*, *252–8*, *plate* 249–50, *table* 253
SK C/35 U 250
10.5cm *24*, 185–215, 250, 258, 262
SK C/23 nT 213
SK C/28
SK C/28 MPL 60 189, 204, *table* 205
SK C/28 Ubts KL/45 *205*
SK C/31 *106*, *205*, *208–9*, *212*, *215*, *plan* 206, *plan* 210–*plan* 211
SK C/32 *149–52*, *160*, 188, *198–203*, *plate* 196, *plate* 197, *plate* 202, *table* 204
SK C/32 nS *189*, 189–97, *190–1*, *196–7*, 197–205, *plans* 192–5, *plates* 197, *table* 204
SK C/33 *154–5*, 205, 209, 213, *214–15*, *plan* 212, *plate* 207
SK C/33 nT 205
SK C/37 nS *187*
12.7cm *147*, 161, *167*
SK C/34 *146–8*, 175–84, *176–8*, 182–4, 183–4, *plan* 179. 182, *plate* 178, *table* 177, *table* 184
15cm 13, 103, 119, 126, 161, *168*
Bofors 28 L/156 118
SK C/25, *103*, 104–5, *105–6*, 108, 115, 117–26, *plan* 114, *plan* 116, *plan* 119, *plans* 103
SK C/28 119–26, *120*, *126*, 126–8, *128*, 129, 133–60, *138–40*
SK L/45 96–102, *100*, *plan* 101, *table* 96
Tbts KC/36 99, *99*, *143–4*, 161–74, *163–4*, *169–70*, *plan* 162, *plan* 166, *plan* 172, *plate* 163
19cm 85, 103
20.3cm 86, *87*, 95, *table* 87
SK C/34 85–95, *85–95*, *table* 91
28cm *12*, 13, 77, 119
SK C/28 32–72, *49–72*, *table* 32
SK C/34 *21*, *49*, *57*, 73–84, *74–7*, *80*, *table* 79
SK L/50 32
30cm 7
33cm 7, 13, 15, 77
35cm 7, 13, 15, 77
SK L/45 97, 99
38cm 7, *14*, 15, 77
SK C/34 20–32, *21–2*, 23, *23–30*, *49*, *table* 20
40cm
SK C/34 19, *19*, *table* 19
land-based 267–8
7.5cm 267
8cm 267
see also coastal defence guns, land artillery

H

'H' battleship 19
Hermann Schoemann 181
Hitler, Adolf 13, 15, 19, 31, 73

I

ice, effects of *10*, *183*, *194*, *254*

J

'J' battleship 19
Japan 188

K

'K' battleship 19
'K' class cruisers 96, 130, *187*, 205, 321, 324, *383*
see also Karlsruhe, *Köln*, *Königsberg*
Kaga (Japan) 129
Karlsruhe 68, 103, 108, *109–11*, 258
KFK auxiliaries *221–2*, *270*
Köln 67–9, 103–6, *104–5*, 108, *111–13*, *187*, *225*, 258, *259*, 262, *plan* 114
Königsberg 67, 96, 103, *107*, 108, *110*, *113*, 188, 258, 265, *265–6*, *plan* 114,
see also 'K' class, *Karlsrühe*, *Köln*
Kronstadt (USSR) 31

L

'L' battleship 19
'L' cruiser (*Hipper* class) 85–6
land artillery 254, *306*, 343, 348, 357, *383*, *plate* 344–5
see also coastal defence guns
Leberecht Maas class destroyers *180*

Leipzig *69–71*, *115*, *115–16*, 205, *259*, 264, 271, *272*, 324
Leopard *175*, 175–6
Linealvisier 21 sights *plate* 380
Luchs *175,* 175–6
Lützow (ex-*Deutschland*) *120*, 213, 273

M
'M' battleship 19
'M' class cruisers 258
mounts 121
  naming 18
  Behelslafette 353
  C/30 198, 204, *218*, *290–1*, *357–9*, *361–2*, *364–6*, 366–7, 380, *plate* 197, *plate* 217, *plate* 357, *plate* 363, *plate* 380
  C/30/37 *350*, *353–4*, *plate* 357
  C/31 205, 209, 213, 219–20, *table* 219
    C/31 gE *plate* 209
    C/31d *plate* 209
  C/32 189, *259*
  C/37 *157*, 209, 258
  C/38 *296–7*, *300–1*, *350*, 358, *382*
  C/38/43U *303*, *plate* 351
    DLM 42 *282–3*, *340*, 343, *plate* 341
  Dopp. C/37 368
  Dopp. L C/25 262
  Dopp. L C/30 *236–41*, *306*, *314–15*, 316–17, *317–20*, 321, 343, *plan* 309–13
  Dopp. L C/31 *153–6*, *186*, *205*, 207, *208*, 209, *225–8*, 258, *259–62*, 264, *plan* 206–7, *plate* 207, *plate* 262, *table* 262
  Dopp. L C/31d 209, *212*, 213, *214*, *plan* 211
  Dopp. L C/31gE *plate* 209–10
  Dopp. L C/32 262, *plate* 263, *table* 263
  Dopp. L C/37 213, *215*, *plan* 212, *plate* 213
  Dopp. L C/38 213–14, *plate* 215
  Doppellafette LM 42 342
  Drehnkranzlafette 41 353–4
  Flak 28 280
  Flak 30 358, 379–80
  Flak 38 *346*, 358, 384–5, *plate* 388–9
  Flak L C/30 *218*, *220–4*
  Flak LM 41 *table* 252
  Flaklafette C/36 340
  Flaklafette LM 42 240–1
  Flakvierling 38 343
  Flakvierling auf St IV 354
  'Handelbetrieb' 174
  L C/30 *305*, 324, 327, 358
  L C/32 258
  L C/34 326
  L C/36 *332*
  L C/39 327, 358
  L C/27/30 *347*
  L C/30/37 *288*, 358
  LM 42 *246–8*, *328*, *337–9*, 343, *plates* 334–7
  LM 43 343
  LM 42 U 305, *plate* 351
  LM 43 U 305
  M 42 324
  M 43 *370*
  M 43 U 358
  M 43 U Zwilling *292–3*, *369*, *plate* 357
  MPL C/13 *228–9*, 265, *265–6*, *table* 265
  MPL C/16 97, 99
  MPL C/28 80, 119, *120*, 121, *138*, 176, *table* 121
  MPL C/30 *149–51*, *216*, 249–51, *table* 204, *table* 258
  MPL C/32 *189–91*, *196*, *plans* 192–5
  MPL C/34 *146–7*, 175, 182, *tables* 183–4
  MPL C/35 127, *128*, *139*, *plan* 124
  MPL C/36 129
  MPL C/38 *175*
  MPL C/30 U 324
  MPL C/32 gE 205, *table* 204
  MPL C/36 U 151–2
  MPL C/37 gE *187*
  SK 31 219
  SK C/35 253, *table* 253
  SL 30 *268*
  SL 40 358, *379*, 380–1
  SL C/30 348, 394
  SL 30L 357
  Sockellaffete 38 353
  Tbts K C/36 99, *99*
  Tbts L C 36 *144*
  U-Bootslafette C/39 340
  Ubts C/30 *219–20*, 368
  Ubts C/35 *252–8*
  Ubts C/39 357
  Ubts L C/35 U 258, *table* 258
  Ubts L C/36 U 201, *202–3*, *plate* 202–3, *table* 205
  Ubts L C/30 305, 327, *plan* 330–1
  Ubts L C/32 U *199–201*, 204, *table* 204
  Ubts L C/35 249, *plate* 249–50
  Ubts L C/36 189
    Ubts L C/36 U *table* 204
  Ubts L C/39 *242–5*, 305, *321–8*, *332*, 340, 342
  Vierlingslafette C/38 *390*
  Vierlingslafette 38/43 U *302*, *304*, 354, *391–3*, *plan* 391
  Vierlingslafette C/35 354
  Vierlingslafette C/38 *387*, 394
  Vierlingslaffette 38/43 U *298–9*, *301*

N
'N' battleship 19
Narvik 19
1934B class destroyers *175*
Norway 19, *27*, 271, 273
Nürnberg *71–2*, 117–18, *186*, 205–6, *262–3*, 271, 316, 324, *370*, *388*, *plate* 117

O
'O' battlecruiser 31, *145*

P
'P' battlecruiser 31, *145*
Paul Jacobi (Ger) *179*
Poland 19, 271
PQ17 convoy *9*
Prinz Eugen (Ger) *10*, *90*, 214, *232–4*, 271–3, *274*, *278–80*, 321, *383*, *plate* 277
  AA guns *63*, *65–6*
  ammunition *215*
  turrets *63–6*, *93–4*, 272, 321, *plans* 92–3

Q
'Q' battlecruiser 31, *145*

R
radar 354, 381

Raeder, Grand Admiral 15, 31, 73, 85, 129, 271
rangefinders and sights *21*, 22, *24*, *25–6*, *49*, *62*, *74*, 87–8, 135, 182, *190*, 340–3, 354, 380, *383*, *plate* 164, *plate* 380

S

S-boats (Schnellboote) 326, 354
Scharnhorst *12*, 13, 19, *49*, *58–9*, *73–9*, 77, 79, 83–4, 126–8, 127, 129–30, 132, *132*, *138–40*, *198*, *208*, 209, 262, *296*, *306*, 321, *plan* 124, *plan* 135, *plate* 132, *table* 80
Schliesen 97, *100–1*
Sevastopol (USSR) 31
Seydlitz 85–6, 95, 213
Spain 45
  Civil War 206, 209, 268, 270, 348
Spearfish, HMS *39*
Studler, Lt-Col R R 270
Sweden 188, 205, 267, 269, 271

T

'T' torpedo boats 197
Tirpitz (Ger) *11*, *16–18*, 20–32, *24–30*, *49*, *53*, 54, *54*, 88, *133*, 133–5, 133–61, *134*, 135–6, *137*, 205, 209, 213, 214, *215*, *314*, *plan* 135, *plate* 135
Todt, Dr Fritz 31
turrets *11*, 13, 15, 20, *24*, 31, 79, 103, 129, 344–6, *plan* 28–9
  designations and markings *3*, *6*, 18, 29–31, 34, 45, *55–6*, *59–60*, *63–5*, *67–72*, *75*, 84, *105–7*, *110–12*, 113, 115, *116*, 118, *121–2*, 125, 132, 136, *167*
  Br 300 346
  C/36 *145–6*, 165–7, *plan* 165, *plate* 165
  C/38 *171*
  DrhL C/25 103–4, *104–5*, 108, 115, 130, *plan* 114, *table* 107
  DrhL C/28 *32*, 32–8, *33*, *57*, *117–18*, *plate* 117, *table* 38
  DrhL C/34 20–2, *49*, *52*, 79, *81*, 128, 130–2, 131–2, *133*, 133–5, *134*, *140–2*, *plan* 130–1, *plan* 135, *plate* 132, *table* 22, *table* 82, *table* 91
  DrhL C/38 167, *170*, 173–4, *174*, *plate* 173
  MPL C/36 turret *143–4*
  ventilation 62

U

U-boats 189, 249, 314, 326–7, 333
  Type II *371–3*, *plan* 372–3
  Type IX *199–200*, *288*, *323*, 327, 333, *350*
  Type VII *220*, *250*, *254–8*, *328*, *342*, *353–4*, *356*, 368, *370*, *plate* 351
    Type VII B 257
    Type VII C 327
  Type X 327
  Type XXI 346, *346*, *348*, *plate* 345
  U 3 373
  U 9 373
  U 69 256
  U 83 plate 351
  U 84 plate 351
  U 103 323
  U 142 273
  U 237 plate 351
  U 441 333, *plate* 351
  U 561 254
  U 564 372
  U 673 plate 351
  U 758 372
  U 889 348
  U 1009 343
  U 1105 plate 351
  U 1165 370
  U 3017 346
USA 22, 270
USSR 31, 185, 271
  Nazi-Soviet Pact 31

V

Versailles, Treaty of 7, 32, 96, 119, 161, 175, 185, 205, 267–8
  abrogation of 13, 15
Vickers 269

Z

'Z' class destroyers (Ger) *145*, 161, *161*, *161–74*, 167–4, 175–84, *181*
  Z 5 175–6
  Z 7 (*Herman Schoemann*) *181*
  Z 10 175–6
  Z 15 175–6
  Z 17 (*Friedrich Eckholdt*) *181*
  Z 21 (*Paul Jacobi*) *179*
  Z 25 172–3
  Z 32 174
  Z 34 168
  Z 35 176
  Z 36 176
  Z 37 174
  Z 38 171, 174
  Z 39 174
  Z 43 176
  Z 44 176
  Z 45 176